Pearson Education

Test Prep Series

For

AP® CHEMISTRY

MARIAN DeWANE
University of California–Los Angeles

THOMAS GREENBOWE
University of Oregon

To accompany:

CHEMISTRY: A MOLECULAR APPROACH
FIFTH EDITION
AP EDITION

NIVALDO J. TRO

Executive Courseware Portfolio Manager, General Chemistry: Terry Haugen

Courseware Portfolio Manager Assistant: Harry Misthos

Senior Product Manager: Elizabeth Bell

Managing Producer, Science: Kristen Flathman

Senior Content Producer, Science: Beth Sweeten

Production Management and Composition: SPi Global

Cover Designer: 17th Street Studios

Senior Procurement Specialist: Stacey Weinberger

6 2020

AP® is a trademark registered and/or owned by the College Board, which was not involved in the production of, and does not endorse, this product.

ISBN-10:   0-13-499566-X
ISBN-13: 978-0-13-499566-3

Marian DeWane taught AP Chemistry and AP Environmental Science in Boise, Idaho. She recently retired from high school teaching after thirty years but continues to teach for the University of California-Los Angeles. She has won numerous awards for her teaching including the Presidential Award for Science Teaching in 2009. She was involved as an editor and author of the AP Chemistry Special Focus Series for the College Board which included AP Chemistry Focus: Chemical Equilibrium, AP Chemistry Special Focus: Thermodynamics, AP Chemistry Focus: Acids and Bases, and the *AP Chemistry Guided Inquiry Activities for the Classroom* Curriculum Module. She authored two chapters and a lab in the *AP Chemistry Guided-Inquiry Experiments: Applying the Science Practices Laboratory Manual*. She has been a question writer for both the old and new AP exams and has been involved at the AP Chemistry Reading in several capacities including as a Reader, Table Leader, and Question Leader. Her current assignment has been on the International AP Exam. She has worked as a consultant for the College Board giving workshops, institutes, seminars, and lectures around the world on AP Chemistry. She has also presented at ACS and NSTA meetings on the teaching and learning of chemistry.

Thomas J. Greenbowe is currently a faculty member in the Department of Chemistry and Biochemistry at the University of Oregon. He is also a Morrill Professor of Chemistry Emeritus at Iowa State University. He served on the test development committee for AP Chemistry seven years, and has been involved in the AP Reading as a Reader, Table Leader, and Question Leader. He is also an AP Chemistry Consultant with ten years experience facilitating workshops and summer institutes for AP Chemistry teachers. He is the co-editor and co-chapter author of the *AP Chemistry Curriculum Module Guided Inquiry Activities for the Classroom* and a co-author on the *AP Chemistry Multi-Day Workshop Handbook and Resources*. His work with the Science Writing Heuristic and the Process Oriented Guided-Inquiry Learning (POGIL) Projects have contributed to our understanding of effective techniques for implementing guided-inquiry in the chemistry laboratory. For Pearson Education, he has worked on a project developing a series of interactive computer simulations and computer visualizations depicting chemical processes at the particulate nature of matter level of representation with John Gelder (retired), Oklahoma State University, and Michael Abraham (retired), University of Oklahoma. He is a co-editor of the University of Oregon chemistry education web site *chemdemos* https://chemdemos.uoregon.edu/ which is being up-graded to *Chemistry Interactive Demonstrations and Educational Resources* (CIDER) https://cider.uoregon.edu/ This web site provides access to resources for chemistry teachers.

Thomas Greenbowe served as Chair of the Division of Chemical Education of the American Chemical Society, General Chair of the 18th Biennial Conference on Chemical Education (Iowa State University), Chair of the 2009 Gordon Research Conference on Chemical Education Research and Practice, and Program Chair for the 26th Biennial Conference on Chemical Education (Oregon State University). He has served as Chair of the 1993 ACS General Chemistry Exam, Co-Chair of the 2014 ACS General Chemistry Conceptual Exam, and a member of the 2013 ACS Laboratory Practical Exam Committee.

Tom Greenbowe has received teaching awards from Iowa State University and awards from the American Chemical Society including the 2013 ACS Mid-West Section E. Ann Nalley Award for Volunteer Service, the 2014 James Flack Norris Award for Outstanding Achievement in the Teaching of Chemistry, the 2014 George C. Pimentel Award in Chemical Education, and was named a Fellow of the American Chemical Society in 2013.

This book is dedicated to my son Patrick. These months without you have been so hard. Every word I write is with you on my heart and I can continue to hear your encouraging words. You were dealt a tough hand, but you never gave up. You were a wonderful uncle and a steadfast and true friend to those who knew you. I still watch your favorite shows and can hear your laughter. You always stepped up to the plate when you needed to for family and friends. I was so moved by your desire to donate your organs to others so they could have another chance. You were and are a role model for all of us. You live on in others and especially in my heart. Jean-Patrick Russel DeWane 1983.02.17–2018.10.05.

Marian DeWane

Thank you to my family for all their patience and understanding during the time-frame of this project including working on vacations: My wife Lynette, children Ben and his wife Sue, Joel, Meagan, Kaitlyn and husband Eric, and my grandchildren Ephraim, Willem, Atticus, Lorelie, and Theodore. They all provided me the space and time to think and write when work needed to be done.

Thank you to my co-author, Marian, for all of her collaborations while this work was in progress. Her advice, wisdom, and friendship are much appreciated.

Thomas Greenbowe

Contents

The AP Chemistry Course

The AP Chemistry Curriculum and Exam address concepts in a first year college chemistry course. The focus of teaching and learning is covered in nine units and six science practices. Each unit is subdivided into topics, eduring understandings, learning objectives and points of essential knowledge to make up each Learning Objective. Under these, learning objectives identify what students should be able to know and be able to do to be successful on the exam. Each learning objective (LO) is also tied to a big idea of Scale, Proportion, and Quantity (SPQ), Structure and Properties (SAP), Transformations (TRA), or Energy (ENE). Specific guidelines, suggested skills and pacing guides, and sample syllabi for AP Chemistry are on the College Board website. The College Board now also provides Personal Progress Checks in each unit that can be used to check for understanding. The College Board recommends a minimum of 25% of the AP Chemistry course should be dedicated to laboratory activities. The AP Chemistry Exam will include questions assessing students' ability to design a laboratory experiment to answer a research question, to analyze data collected in a laboratory activity, and to explain how errors will influence the results.

Units of AP Chemistry

Units:

1. Atomic Structure and Properties
2. Molecular and Ionic Compound Structure and Properties
3. Intermolecular Forces and Properties
4. Chemical Reactions
5. Kinetics
6. Thermodynamics
7. Equilibrium
8. Acids and Bases
9. Applications of Thermodynamics

Six Science Practices (SP) of AP Chemistry

1. **Models and Representations:** Describe models and representations, including across scales.
   - Describe the components of and quantitative information from models and representations that illustrate particulate-level properties only.
   - Describe the components of and quantitative information from models and representation that illustrate both particulate-level and macroscopic-level properties.
2. **Question and Method:** Determine scientific questions and methods.
   - Identify a testable scientific question based on an observation, data, or a model.
   - Formulate a hypothesis or predict the results of an experiment.
   - Identify experimental procedures that are aligned to a scientific question (which may include a sketch of a lab setup).
   - Make observations or collect data from representations of laboratory setups or results, while attending to precision where appropriate.
   - Identify or describe potential sources of experimental error.
   - Explain how modifications to an experimental procedure will alter results.

3. **Representing Data and Phenomena:** Create representations or models of phenomena.
   - Represent chemical phenomena using appropriate graphing techniques, including correct scale and units.
   - Represent chemical substances or phenomena with appropriate diagrams or models.
   - Represent visually the relationship between the structures and interactions across multiple levels or scales (e.g., particulate to macroscopic).

4. **Model Analysis:** Analyze and interpret models and representations on a single scale or across multiple scales.
   - Explain chemical properties or phenomena (e.g., of atoms or molecules) using given chemical theories, models, and representations.
   - Explain whether a model is consistent with chemical theories.
   - Explain the connections between particulate-level and macroscopic properties of a substance using models and representations.
   - Explain the degree to which a model or representation describes the connection between particulate-level properties and macroscopic properties.

5. **Mathematical Routines:** Solve problems using mathematical relationships.
   - Identify quantities needed to solve a problem from given information (e.g.,text, mathematical expressions, graphs, or tables).
   - Identify an appropriate theory, definition, or mathematical relationship to solve a problem.
   - Explain the relationship between variables within an equation when one variable changes.
   - Identify information presented graphically to solve a problem.
   - Determine a balanced chemical equation for a given chemical phenomenon.
   - Calculate, estimate, or predict an unknown quantity from known quantities by selecting and following a logical computational pathway and attending to precision (e.g., performing dimensional analysis and attending to significant figures).

6. **Argumentation:** Develop an explanation or scientific argument.
   - Make a scientific claim.
   - Support a claim with evidence from experimental data.
   - Support a claim with evidence from representations or models at the particulate level, such as the structure of atoms and/or molecules.
   - Provide reasoning to justify a claim using chemical principles or laws, or using mathematical justification.
   - Provide reasoning to justify a claim using connections between particulate and macroscopic scales or levels.
   - Explain the connection between experimental results and chemical concepts, processes, or theories.
   - Explain how potential sources of experimental error may affect the experimental results.

Reasoning Processes: What students need to be able to do

1. **Define/Classify:** Characteristics, Traits
   - Define characteristics visually, verbally, numerically, or quantitatively.
   - Classify objects based on visual characteristics or properties, numerical characteristics or properties.
   - Identify relationships using characteristics or properties.

2. **Explain Comparisons:** Similarities, Differences, Contrasts, Juxtapositions
   - Explain a relationship visually, verbally, numerically, or quantitatively.
   - Identify similarities and/or differences.
   - Explain similarities and/or differences.
3. **Explain Cause and Effect:** Cause, Effect, Consequence, Factors
   - Identify the cause of an outcome or the result of a process.
   - Explain the cause of a phenomenon.
   - Explain the effect or consequence of one process or phenomenon on another.
   - Explain the changes in the output of a process based on changes in the input.

About this Correlation Guide for AP Chemistry for Tro's "Chemistry: A Molecular Approach"

The correlation guide at the end of this section will list the Learning Objectives of each Unit. Practically, the correlation guide helps you find this information in the Tro textbook.

Core content, vocabulary, and the learning objectives in each chapter are reviewed. The essential content and vocabulary are identified per section as they correspond to the chapter. Misconceptions students have indicated on previous exams are identified in these sections as well. Refer to the text for more examples and sample problems of each concept. End of chapter questions for additional practice on the concepts are listed in Additional Practice. Sample AP multiple-choice questions with answers associated with the material in the chapter are given at the end of the chapter. Two full sample AP Exams with both multiple-choice and free response questions with answers are given for practice at the end of the book.

- Learning Objectives addressed in the chapter are identified
- Important concepts and vocabulary to know are reviewed
- Good additional practice problems from the text are identified
- Sample AP Problems for each chapter are given
- Two full AP sample exams are included

AP Chemistry Laboratory Experiments

The College Board believes the laboratory portion of the AP Chemistry course will help students gain a better understanding of chemistry processes. At least six of the 16 recommended AP Chemistry laboratory experiments must be in a guided-inquiry format. Most college general chemistry laboratory courses included 10–12 laboratory experiments each semester or 7–9 experiments each quarter for a total of 20–24 experiments. Colleges want to know students have a college level laboratory experience in their AP Chemistry laboratory course. To earn laboratory credit, some institutions will have a chemistry professor review each student's AP Chemistry laboratory notebook.

The AP Chemistry Exam Format

The AP Chemistry Exam is a comprehensive assessment of the topics presented in a first year general chemistry college course for science and engineering majors. The exam is divided into two parts: Multiple-Choice and Free Response. Each section will account for fifty percent of the total score on the exam. When the overall scores are tallied and cut scores are determined, students deemed to be extremely well qualified will receive a mark of 5, the highest mark. Marks range from a 1 to 5. A table of marks and the recommendation associated with the mark is below. Depending on the institution the student attends for college, the institution will determine if they will give credit for the mark the student earned. This can be researched on the College Board website at apcentral.collegeboard.com.

AP Mark	Recommendation to Colleges
5	Extremely well qualified
4	Well qualified
3	Qualified
2	Possibly qualified
1	No recommendation

The exact score needed for each mark varies from year to year but in general a score of 80 will usually result in a 5, 70 in a 4, 55 in a 3, and 45 in a 2.

An Overview of AP Chemistry Exam

Section I Multiple-Choice Questions

The multiple-choice section will have sixty questions to be done in ninety (90) minutes. This means students have, on average, one and a half minutes (1 min 30 seconds) per question. Some questions will take longer than others to answer. Each question assesses a learning objective or a combination of learning objective and essential knowledge. Each question will have four choices. Every learning objective combines a Science Practice with content knowledge. The exam is scored using Rights Scoring, where no points are deducted for a wrong answer. This means the student should answer every problem even if they have to guess. The multiple-choice section will include chemistry problems requiring calculations. Since the AP exam is scored out of 100 points and 50 of those are from the Multiple Choice, each multiple choice question has a final value of 0.833 points.

Calculators are not allowed on Section 1. The numerical values in the multiple-choice section are purposely selected to facilitate easy calculations. This skill of doing simple calculations without the aid of a calculator needs to be practiced. For example, students should be able to obtain the log of 1,000, the square root of 36, and multiply and divide using scientific notation. Often students make errors with the placement of decimal points or putting the numerator in the denominator. Students need to solve every problem showing all of their work, not skipping steps, and including units with all answers even though they will only choose a letter answer. Skipping steps often leads to errors and results in choosing the wrong answer.

Other multiple-choice questions will assess students' conceptual understanding of chemistry. Both types of multiple-choice questions will involve data and/or models to analyze. Many questions will be grouped to one set of data or model.

The questions will vary in difficulty and there is no pattern of spacing them within the exam. The easiest question could be the last question. Students need to have a strategy to not end up getting stuck on a question. If the student does NOT know anything about the question, they should make their best guess. If the student knows something about the topic but is not sure or thinks it will take longer than a minute to do, the student should mark the question and come back to it later. If the student knows the topic, make sure they read the entire question and answer choices before answering. This way the student will make it through all the questions and will only go back to the ones they have a question on and CAN answer. The students will need to make sure they always put the answer to a question on the right question on the answer sheet. When working through the sample AP Chemistry Exam style questions, the student needs to practice being on pace by placing a time limit for answering the multiple-choice questions in Section I.

Strategies:

- Practice staying on a pace of 1 minute 30 seconds per question.
- Read the entire question.
- Practice mathematical routines without the use a calculator!
- If you do not know the answer, try to eliminate choices and then guess. If you need additional time, mark the question and come back to it but in the end answer every multiple-choice question.
- Make sure you put the answer to each question on the right line of the answer sheet.

If you have to erase, completely erase. Also, do not have stray marks on your answer sheet. The exam will include a Periodic Table, physical constants and important equations. These can be found on the AP website apcentral.collegeboard.org in the course description. The tables, equations, and information may change from year to year so it is always good to check each year for the current version. A copy of the SAME Periodic Table and equation tables used on the AP Chemistry Exam should be used all year long in the classroom and on class exams. This way the students are familiar with the values, arrangement of the equation pages, and the formulas. It is important for students to recognize different texts may use a slightly different formula than those used on the AP Chemistry Equation tables. For instance, there are different ways to write the specific heat equation; $q = m\Delta T C_P$, $q = m\Delta Ts$, and $q = m\Delta Tc$. On the AP Chemistry Exam Equation Pages $q = m\Delta Tc$ is used.

Strategy:

- Practice using the periodic table and equation pages used on the exam.

The multiple-choice section will include two types of questions; single questions and grouped questions. Grouped questions will be based on one set of data or diagrams and several questions asked relating to the data or the scenario. The grouped questions will not necessarily focus on one topic (i.e. stoichiometry, calorimetry) but will include questions from several different topics. Examples of both types of questions will be in the Sample Questions Section.

An Overview of Section II: Free Response Questions

The Free Response portion of the exam is divided into long and short questions. The long questions will be the first three questions worth ten (10) points each and the short will be the last four questions worth four (4) points each. Students should plan to spend no more than approximately twenty (20) minutes per long question and no more than approximately ten (10) minutes per short question. In this section of the exam, students are allowed to use the provided periodic table, equation pages, and a calculator. Most questions will involve more than one area of chemistry. Students will need to explain concepts to show an understanding of experimental design, to show how to apply mathematical concepts in the lab setting, and show how to apply one or more of the science practices.

There are restrictions on the type of calculator permitted to be used on Section II. Calculator restrictions can be checked on the College Board website apcentral.collegeboard.com by searching AP Chemistry calculator policies but in general calculators with QWERTY keyboards and ones with printing capabilities are not allowed. Students should use an accepted AP Chemistry approved calculator throughout the course and they should be familiar with the proper order of operations for their calculator. For example, students will need to know how to use their calculator to take a square root, how to do natural and common logs, antilogs, e^x, etc.

Overall within the Free Response section, there are five types of problems. There are two types of questions involving lab, two types of representation problems, and quantitative problems. Each type will be explained and examples given in the Sample Questions Section. During the AP Chemistry Exam Section II, the free response section, we recommend doing all the short questions (4–7) first and then doing the long questions in preferential order. Students should first quickly scan the long questions and then choose to answer the ones they feel they know the most about first. Students can then return to the other long questions when the ones they know best are answered. In other words, students do not need to answer each question in the order provided. Questions 1–3 are marked out 10 points each and the short questions 4–7, are marked out of 4 points each. The total points marked in the Free Response section of the exam are 46. The Free Response accounts for 50 points in the final score which means each mark is worth 1.086 points.

Regardless of the type of Free Response question, answers are expected to be in clear concise writing and in mathematical computations show clear work with units included. Students should not erase mistakes. Simply put a SINGLE line (~~SINGLE~~) through what they do not want the Reader to score. This should be emphasized in the classroom by the AP Chemistry teacher all year. It is helpful for the person who reads your exam if the final answers to mathematical problems are circled or boxed, but it is not required. It is also helpful if you identify what part of the question in multipart questions you are answering such as "c)". You do not need to rewrite or paraphrase the question as this wastes valuable time.

Strategies:

- Read all the questions quickly and then answer the ones you know best first.
- Do not erase but put a ~~SINGLE~~ line through incorrect information.
- Practice explaining concepts in clear concise writing.
- Practice providing evidence for each concept in three sentences or less.
- In mathematical problems include units and show all work. Box or circle final answers.
- Keep track of time spending no more than 20 minutes on each of questions 1–3 and 10 minutes on each of questions 3–7.

Summary

Section	Percentage	Time	Structure	Allowed to Use
Multiple-Choice	50%	90 minutes	60 Questions all with 4 choices; up to half grouped questions	Periodic Table and Equation Page
Free Response	50%	105 minutes	7 Questions; 3 long and 4 short; 5 types	Periodic Table, Equation Pages, and Calculator

How to Study

Begin studying for the AP Chemistry Exam at the very beginning of the school year. If you take the time each week to study and review, you will not need to cram at the end. This takes discipline and practice. Set aside the same time each week such as Monday night from 8–10 P.M. Have a space where you can focus and not do anything else. Turn off your phone and other devices. Do the study guides for the corresponding chapter(s) being covered in your course. Do the recommended problems at the end of each study guide chapter. Make a review sheet of the major concepts or add to one in progress if you are in the same unit, make new vocabulary flash cards if needed, and include the evidence to support concepts. Make review cards for each learning objective in the AP curriculum. Strategy: Have each L.O. on an index card and on the back make all your notes on the topic. Review your index cards each week. Review previous concepts, go through all your vocabulary flash cards, work through the section in this book corresponding to the topics being presented by your AP Chemistry teacher in class and do the sample AP questions on the topics being covered in class. Only attempt the AP Chemistry Practice Test A 2 months and Test B 1 month out from the exam. Each time, look at the questions missed and review daily those concepts prior to taking the AP Chemistry Exam.

General Hints

- All year long
  - Have a set aside time to study
  - Make vocabulary flash cards—there are apps you can put on your phone to study vocabulary. Review these cards WEEKLY!
  - Do the study guides and suggested problems for each chapter. Make concept maps linking learning objectives to the big ideas. Review these weekly.
  - Use data and models to practice explaining the concepts
  - Do practice AP problems
  - Two months before the exam take a sample AP Exam
  - Review all concepts addressed in the exam
  - One month before the exam take another Sample Exam
  - Review all concepts addressed in the exam
- Two weeks before the exam
  - Read over all your concept maps
  - Review all the learning objectives cards you have made
- The Night before the exam
  - Review your concept maps
  - Get a good nights rest
- Test Day
  - Have a good breakfast
  - Be early and have your proper identification
  - Take pencils for multiple-choice with number 2 lead (mechanical pencils are fine)
  - Take good erasers for multiple-choice so no stray marks are left
  - Take ball point pens (never felt tip—they will bleed through the paper)
  - Take a calculator with extra batteries or an extra calculator you know how to use

AP Chemistry Exam Style Sample Questions with Answers

The AP Chemistry Exams are secure examinations. Students do not have access to the exact questions on the exam until they take the exam. The questions on each of the AP Chemistry Exams vary from year to year. The questions in Section II, the "Free Response" or "Constructed Response" questions are posted online approximately two days after the exams is administered. By looking at past exam questions, the style and format of the questions combined with the learning objectives can provide a framework for the practice questions. Due to testing time limitations, the AP Chemistry Exam will not asses students understanding on every topic presented in class. Students should be prepared to answer questions on all topics corresponding to the information described in Essential Knowledge and Learning Objectives for the AP Chemistry course.

The multiple-choice questions are all linked to one learning objective or a combination of learning objectives and essential knowledge. The learning objectives are all listed at the end of this chapter. There are two types of questions:

- discrete items
- grouped questions

The Free Response sample questions are also linked to learning objectives and can include five types of questions.

- Lab I—includes writing a design for a lab procedure to answer a specific problem
- Lab II—includes analyzing provided laboratory data and drawing conclusions based on the evidence provided by the data
- Representation I—includes explaining how particle behavior at the microscopic or particulate level and then explaining how this observed at the macroscopic level
- Representation II—includes drawing diagrams to explain how particle behavior at the microscopic or particulate level and then explaining how this observed at the macroscopic level
- Quantitative—includes solving mathematical problems with work shown

Samples of the different styles of questions with their explanations and answers are in the next section.

Sample AP Chemistry Style Questions—Section I Multiple-Choice

For the following sample questions, the learning objectives and enduring understanding used in the question or grouped questions are indicated. The answers and explanations are at the end of the sample questions.

Question 1. The net dipole moment of three compounds with similar molar masses are listed in the table below

Substance	Net Dipole Moment (D)
X	0.1
Y	2.7
Z	3.9

The three substances are, in no particular order are acetonitrile (CH_3CN), acetaldehyde (CH_3COH), and propane ($CH_3CH_2CH_3$). If 0.250 mole of each substance is placed in a flask (with a piston at the top) at 228 K ($-45\,°C$) and the flask is slowly heated under a pressure of 1.00 atm, which substance will exhibit the highest boiling point? What factor is responsible for the high boiling point?

A) propane, due to having only weak intermolecular forces, London dispersion forces.

B) acetaldehyde, due to having strong intermolecular forces, hydrogen bonding.

C) acetonitrile, due to having medium intermolecular forces, dipole-dipole forces.

D) All three compounds will have about the same boiling point because all three have about the same molar mass and all three have London Dispersion Forces.

This question addresses the following unit, topic(s), enduring understanding, learning objective, big idea, essential knowledge, science practice, and learning objectives.

Unit	3. Intermolecular Forces and Properties
Topic(s)	3.1 Intermolecular Forces and 3.2 Properties of Solids
Big Idea	Structure and Properties (SAP)
Enduring Understanding	Intermolecular forces can explain the physical properties of a material.
Learning Objective(s)	SAP5.A Explain the relationship between the chemical structures of molecules and the relative strength of their intermolecular forces when— • The molecules are of the same chemical species. • The molecules are of two different chemical species. SAP5.B Explain the relationship among the macroscopic properties of a substance, the particulate-level structure of the substance, and the interactions between these particles.

Essential Knowledge SAP-5.A	–London dispersion forces (LDFs) are a result of the Coulombic interactions between temporary, fluctuating dipoles. LDFs are often the strongest net intermolecular force between large molecules.
	
	   a. Dispersion forces increase with increasing contact area between molecules and with the increasing polarizability of the molecules.
	
	   b. The polarizability of a molecule increases with increasing number of electrons in the molecule; and the size of the electron cloud. It is enhanced by the presence of pi bonding.
	
	   c. The term "LDFs" should not be used synonymously with the term "van der Waals forces."
	
	–The dipole moment of a polar molecule leads to additional interactions with other chemical species.
	
	   a. Dipole-induced dipole interactions are present between a polar and nonpolar molecule. These forces are always attractive. The strength of the forces increases the magnitude of the dipole of the polar molecule and the polarizability of the nonpolar molecule.
	
	   b. Dipole-dipole interactions are present between polar molecules. The interaction strength depends on the magnitude of the dipoles and their relative orientation. Interactions between polar molecules are typically greater than those between nonpolar molecules of comparable size because these interactions act in addition to LDFs.
	
	–The relative strength and orientation dependence of dipole-dipole and ion-dipole forces can be understood qualitatively by considering the sign of the partial charges responsible for the molecular dipole moment, and how these partial charges interact with an ion or with an adjacent dipole.
	–Hydrogen bonding is a strong type of intermolecular interaction that exists when hydrogen atoms covalently bonded to the highly electronegative atoms (N, O, and F) are attracted to the negative end of a dipole formed by the electronegative atom (N, O, F) in a different molecule, or a different part of the same molecule.
	–In large biomolecules, noncovalent interactions may occur between different molecules or between different regions of the same large biomolecule.

Essential Knowledge SAP-5.B	Many properties of liquids and solids are determined by the strengths of the types of intermolecular forces present. Because intermolecular interactions are broken when a substance vaporizes, the vapor pressure and boiling point are directly related to the strength of those interactions. Melting points also tend to correlate with interaction strength, but because the interactions are only rearranged, in melting, the relations can be more subtle.
Science Practice	6. Argumentation—E. Provide Reasoning to justify a claim using connections between particulate and macroscopic scales or levels.

Questions 2–6 refer to the following information

Half-reaction	$E°(V)$
$Cr^{3+}(aq) + 3e^- \rightarrow Cr(s)$	−0.74
$Ni^{2+}(aq) + 2e^- \rightarrow Ni(s)$	−0.23
$Ag^+(aq) + e^- \rightarrow Ag(s)$	+0.80

2. Which reaction will occur be favorable in the forward direction?

   A) $3Ni(s) + 2Cr^{3+}(aq) \rightarrow 3Ni^{2+}(aq) + 2Cr(s)$

   B) $2Ag(s) + Ni^{2+}(aq) \rightarrow 2Ag^+(aq) + Ni(s)$

   C) $Ni(s) + 2Ag^+(aq) \rightarrow Ni^{2+}(aq) + 2Ag(s)$

   D) $Cr^{3+}(aq) + 3Ag^+(aq) \rightarrow Cr(s) + 3Ag(s)$

An electrochemical cell is constructed using two compartments connected by salt bridge. In one compartment silver metal is placed in 1.0 M silver nitrate and in the second compartment nickel metal is placed in 1.0 M nickel(II) nitrate. Wires connect the metal electrodes to a voltmeter.

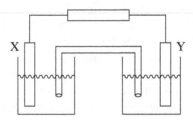

3. If the above electrochemical cell generates a positive emf, the anode is

   A) Ni

   B) Ag

   C) Ni^{2+}

   D) Ag^+

4. Calculate the cell potential of the above electrochemical cell.

   A) −1.03 V

   B) −0.57 V

   C) +0.57 V

   D) +1.03 V

5. If 0.010 M silver nitrate solution is used instead of 1.0 M for the cell described in question 3, how would this influence the emf of the cell?

   A) the cell voltage would increase

   B) the cell voltage would decrease

   C) the cell voltage would stay the same

   D) there is not sufficient information given to provide an answer

6. Select the statement describing the difference between a Ni-Ag voltaic cell and a Ni-Ag electrolytic cell

   A) In a voltaic cell, oxidation occurs at the anode. In an electrolytic cell, oxidation occurs at the cathode.

   B) An electrolytic cell generates energy without outside help. A voltaic cell needs a continuous input of energy.

   C) In a Ni-Ag electrolysis cell, silver cations in the aqueous solution migrate toward the cathode. In a voltaic cell, the cations migrate toward the cathode.

   D) In an electrolysis cell, a continuous input of current forces a non-spontaneous reaction to occur, while in a voltaic cell chemical reactions occur to generate energy.

Questions 2–6 addresses the following unit, big idea, enduring understanding, essential knowledge, science practice, and learning objectives.

Unit	9. Applications of Thermodynamics
Topic(s)	9.7 Galvanic (Voltaic) and Electrolytic Cells, 9.8 Cell Potential and Free Energy, and 9.9 Cell Potential Under Nonstandard Conditions
Big Idea	Energy (ENE)
Enduring Understanding	Electrical energy can be generated by chemical reactions.
Learning Objective(s)	ENE-6.A Explain the relationship between the physical components of an electrochemical cell and the overall operational principles of the cell. ENE-6.B Explain whether an electrochemical cell is thermodynamically favored based on its standard cell potential and the constituent half-reactions within the cell. ENE-6.C Explain the relationship between deviations from standard cell conditions and changes in cell potential.
Essential Knowledge ENE-6.A	–Each component of an electrochemical cell plays a specific role in the overall functioning of the cell. The operational characteristics of the cell can be described at both the macroscopic and particulate levels. –Galvanic, sometimes voltaic, cells involve a thermodynamically favored reaction, whereas electrolytic cells involve a thermodynamically unfavored reaction. Visual representations of galvanic and electrolytic cells are tools of analysis to identify where half-reactions occur and in what direction current flows. –For all electrochemical cells, oxidation occurs at the anode and reduction occurs at the cathode.

Essential Knowledge ENE-6.B	–Electrochemistry encompasses the study of redox reactions that occur within electrochemical cells. The reactions are either thermodynamically favored (resulting in positive voltage) or thermodynamically unfavored (resulting in a negative voltage and requiring an externally applied potential for the reaction to proceed). –The standard cell potential of electrochemical cells can be calculated by identifying the oxidation and reduction half-reactions and their respective standard potentials. $\Delta G°$ is proportional to the negative of the cell potential for the redox reaction from which it is constructed. Thus, a cell with a positive $E°$ involves a thermodynamically favored reaction, and a cell with a negative $E°$ involves a thermodynamically unfavored reaction. $\Delta G° = -nFE°$
Essential Knowledge ENE-6.C	–In a real system under nonstandard conditions, the cell potential will vary depending on the concentrations of the active species. The cell potential is a driving force toward equilibrium; the farther the reaction is from equilibrium, the greater the magnitude of the cell potential. –Equilibrium arguments such as Le Châtelier's principle do not apply to electrochemical systems because the systems are not in equilibrium. –The standard potential $E°$ corresponds to the standard conditions of $Q = 1$. As the system approaches equilibrium, the magnitude of the cell potential decreases, reaching zero at equilibrium (when $Q = K$). Deviations from standard conditions that take the cell further from equilibrium then $Q = 1$ will increase the magnitude of the cell potential relative to $E°$. Deviations from standard conditions that take the cell closer to equilibrium then $Q = 1$ will decrease the magnitude of the cell potential relative to $E°$. In concentration cells, the direction of spontaneous electron flow can be determined by considering the direction needed to reach equilibrium. –Algorithmic calculations using the Nernst equation are insufficient to demonstrate an understanding of electrochemical cells under nonstandard conditions. However, students should qualitatively understand the effects of concentration on cell potential and use conceptual reasoning, including the qualitative use of the Nernst equation: $E = E° - (RT/nF) \ln Q$ to solve problems.
Science Practice(s)	5. Mathematical Routines—F. Calculate, estimate, or predict an unknown quantity from known quantities by selecting and following a logical computational pathway and attending to precision (e.g., performing dimensional analysis and attending to significant figures). 5. Mathematical Routines—E. Determine a balanced chemical equation for a given chemical phenomenon. 5. Mathematical Routines—C. Explain the relationship between variables within an equation when one variable changes. 6. Argumentation—A. Make a claim.

Sample AP Chemistry Style Free Response or Constructed Response Questions

Long Question Sample (Lab II)

1. A student runs an experiment measuring the concentration of N_2O_5 several times after N_2O_5 dissolves in CCl_4 at 45 °C and obtains the following data for the decomposition reaction of N_2O_5.

$$2N_2O_5 \longrightarrow 4NO_2 + O_2$$

Time (sec)	$[N_2O_5]$ (M)
0.00	1.500
900.0	0.857
1800.0	0.489
2700.0	0.279
3600.0	0.160
4500.0	0.061
5000.0	?

The student plots a graph of concentration of N_2O_5 versus time.

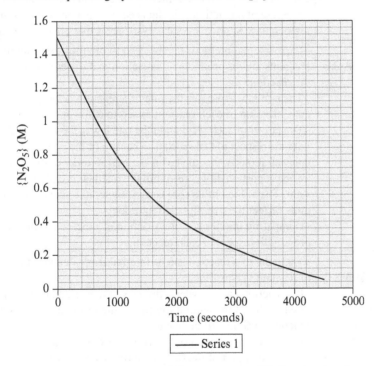

a) How is the average rate of disappearance of N_2O_5 related to the average rate of appearance of NO_2? Explain how to relate the rates of N_2O_5 and NO_2 to each other.

b) Calculate the average rate of appearance of NO_2 between the start of the reaction and 1,800.0 seconds.

c) Determine the order of this reaction.

d) Determine the rate constant for this reaction at 45 °C. Include units with your answer.

e) Determine or estimate the concentration of N_2O_5, in units of molarity, at 5,000.0 seconds.

This question addresses the following unit, big idea, enduring understanding, essential knowledge, science practice, and learning objectives.

Unit	5. Kinetics
Topic(s)	5.1 Reaction Rates, 5.2 Introduction to Rate Law, and 5.3 Concentration Changes Over Time
Big Idea	Transformations
Enduring Understanding	TRA-3 Some reactions happen quickly, while others happen more slowly and depend on reactant concentrations and temperature.
Learning Objective(s)	TRA-3.A Explain the relationship between the rate of a chemical reaction and experimental parameters. TRA-3.B Represent experimental data with a consistent rate law expression. TRA-3.C Identify the rate law expression of a chemical reaction using data that show how the concentrations of reaction species change over time.
Essential Knowledge TRA-3.A	–The kinetics of a chemical reaction is defined as the rate at which an amount of reactants is converted to products per unit of time. –The rates of change of reactant and product concentrations are determined by the stoichiometry in the balanced chemical equation. –The rate of a reaction is influenced by reactant concentrations, temperature, surface area, catalysts, and other environmental factors.
Essential Knowledge TRA-3.B	–Experimental methods can be used to monitor the amounts of reactants and/or products of a reaction and to determine the rate of the reaction. –The rate law expresses the rate of a reaction as proportional to the concentration of each reactant raised to a power. –The power of each reactant in the rate law is the order of the reaction with the respect to that reactant. The sum of the powers of the reactant concentrations in the rate law is the overall order of the reaction. –The proportionality constant in the rate law is called the rate constant. The value of this constant is temperature dependent and the units reflect the overall reaction order. –Comparing initial rates of a reaction is a method to determine the order with respect to each reactant.
Essential Knowledge TRA-3.C	–The order of a reaction can be inferred from a graph of concentration of reactant versus time. –If a reaction is first order with respect to a reactant being monitored, a plot of the natural log (ln) of the reactant concentration as a function of time will be linear. –If a reaction is second order with respect to a reactant being monitored, a plot of the reciprocal of the concentration of that reactant versus time will be linear. –The slopes of the concentration versus time data for zeroth, first, and second order reactions can be used to determine the rate constant for the reaction. Zeroth order: $[A]_t - [A]_o = -kt$ First order: $\ln[A]_t - \ln[A]_o = -kt$ Second order: $1/[A]_t - 1/[A]_o = kt$ –Half-life is a critical parameter for first order reactions because the half-life is constant and related to the rate constant for the reaction by the equation: $t_{1/2} = 0.693/k$ –Radioactive decay processes provide an important illustration of first order kinetics.

Science Practice(s)	4. Model Analysis—A. Explain chemical properties or phenomena using given chemical theories, models, and representations. 5. Mathematical Routines—C. Explain the relationship between variables within an equation when one variable changes. 5. Mathematical Routines—F. Calculate, estimate, or predict an unknown quantity from known quantities by selecting and following a logical computational pathway and attending to precision (e.g., performing dimensional analysis and attending to significant figures). 6. Argumentation—A. Make a claim.

2. Several students conduct a series of experiments in which the conductivity of a solution was monitored as a function of how much titrant (or titrator) was added to the analyte (or titrand) during an acid–base titration. The procedure called for the slow addition of 0.500 M KOH(*aq*) solution in a buret to 500.0 mL of 0.500 M acetic acid solution, $CH_3COOH(aq)$ in an Erlenmeyer flask.

Before collecting any data the students sketched graphs of how they thought electrical conductivity of the resultant solution would vary as base is added to the acid. The electrical conductance is shown in arbitrary units.

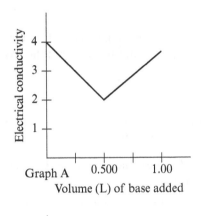

Graph A — Volume (L) of base added

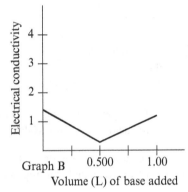

Graph B — Volume (L) of base added

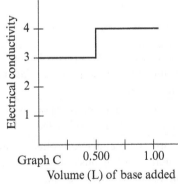

Graph C — Volume (L) of base added

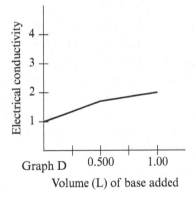

Graph D — Volume (L) of base added

a) Which graph best matches your expectation for Experiment #1? Explain why the electrical conductivity changed from the point when the titrant was first added to the point at which all of the acid reacted.

b) Write a balanced chemical equation representing the reaction of an aqueous acetic acid solution with an aqueous potassium hydroxide solution.

c) What volume of base was added to react with all of the acid?

d) Indicate the point on your graph (use the letter "P") just when all of the acid reacted with the base.

e) The diagram below on the left represents a small volume of the acetic acid solution at the particulate nature of matter level before any base is added. Water molecules have been omitted for clarity. The diagram is not to scale. In the circle on the right, make a similar particulate drawing representing the important species present just at the point where enough KOH is added to react with all of the acid in the circle on the left. Be sure to include any newly formed water molecules.

Initial

The point where all of the acid has reacted with the base.

Acetic acid   Acetate ion

f) Is the pH greater than, less than, or equal to 7 at the point in which all of the acid reacts with KOH? Justify your answer.

This question addresses the following big idea, enduring understanding, essential knowledge, science practice, and learning objectives.

Unit	8. Acids and Bases
Topic(s)	8.5 Acid–Base Titrations
Big Idea	Structure and Properties
Enduring Understanding	SAP-9 The chemistry of acids and bases involves reversible proton-transfer reactions, with equilibrium concentrations being related to the strength of the acids and bases involved.
Learning Objective(s)	SAP-9.E Explain results from the titration of a mono- or polyprotic acid or base solution, in relation to the properties of the solution and its components.
Essential Knowledge	–An acid–base reaction can be carried out under controlled conditions in a titration. A titration curve, plotting pH against the volume of titrant added, is useful for summarizing results from a titration. –At the equivalence point, the number of moles of titrant added is equal to the number of moles of analyte originally present. This relationship can be used to obtain the concentration of the analyte. This is the case of strong acids/bases and weak acids/bases. –For titrations of weak acids/bases, it is useful to consider the point half-way to the equivalence point, that is, the half-equivalence point. At this point, there are equal concentrations of each species in the conjugate acid/base pair, for example, for a weak acid $[HA] = [A-]$. Because pH = pKa when the conjugate acid and base have equal concentrations, the pKa can be determined from the pH at the half-equivalence point in a titration.

Science Practice(s)	1. Models and Representations—B. Describe the components of and quantitative information from models and representations that illustrate both particulate-level and macroscopic-level properties. 3. Representing Data and Phenomena—C. Represent visually the relationship between the structures and interactions across multiple levels or scales (e.g., particulate to macroscopic). 4. Model Analysis—A. Explain chemical properties or phenomena using given chemical theories, models, and representations. 4. Model Analysis—D. Explain the degree to which a model or representation describes the connection between particulate-level properties and macroscopic properties. 5. Mathematical Routines—E. Determine a balanced chemical equation for a given chemical phenomenon. 5. Mathematical Routines—D. Identify information presented graphically to solve a problem. 6. Argumentation—A. Make a claim. 6. Argumentation—B. Support a claim with evidence from experimental data.

3. Students perform an acid–base titration to standardize an HCl solution by placing 20.00 mL of HCl(*aq*) in an Erlenmeyer flask, then titrating with a known concentration of NaOH(*aq*). Two laboratory technicians have determined the concentration of a sodium hydroxide solution, NaOH(*aq*) to be 0.1482 M ± 0.0002 M. and the concentration of the HCl(*aq*) solution to be 0.2223 M ± 0.0002 M. The students have the following indicator color chart to consult.

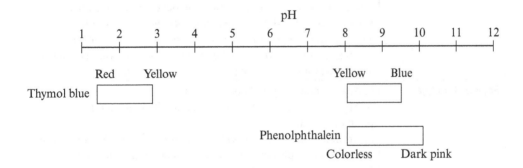

Student X adds a few drops of thymol blue indicator to the acid. Student X rinses a buret with water, then rinses a buret twice with 0.1482 M NaOH(*aq*) solution, before filling the buret with fresh 0.1482 M NaOH(*aq*). Student X performs a titration of the acid using the 0.1482 M NaOH solution and stops adding NaOH(*aq*) when the color of the solution in the Erlenmeyer flask just turns from red to orange. Student X records in his notebook the volume of NaOH(*aq*) required to neutralize the HCl(*aq*), then calculates the concentration of the HCl(*aq*) solution.

Student Y adds a few drops of phenolphthalein indicator to the acid. Student Y rinses a buret twice with water and does not allow most of the water to drain from the buret before filling the buret with 0.1482 M NaOH(*aq*). Student Y performs a titration of the acid using the NaOH solution and stops adding NaOH(*aq*) when the color of the solution in the Erlenmeyer flask just turns from colorless to faint pink. Student Y records in her notebook the volume of NaOH(*aq*) required to neutralize the HCl(*aq*), then calculates the concentration of the HCl(*aq*) solution.

a) Will the concentration of HCl(*aq*) reported by Student X be higher, lower, or about the same as the concentration of HCl(*aq*) reported by the technicians? Explain.

b) Will the concentration of HCl(*aq*) reported by Student Y be higher, lower, or about the same as the concentration of HCl(*aq*) reported by the technicians? Explain.

c) The term *error* indicates the numerical difference between a calculated (or measured) value and the true value. Errors can be classified as determinate (systematic), and indeterminate. Determinate errors can be further classified as *methodic*, *operative*, and *instrumental*. What type of error did Student X make? Explain. What type of error did Student Y make? Explain.

This question addresses the following big idea, enduring understanding, essential knowledge, science practice, and learning objectives.

Unit	4. Chemical Reactions
Topic(s)	4.6 Introduction to Titration
Big Idea	Scale, Proportion, and Quantity (SPQ)
Enduring Understanding	SPQ-4 When a substance changes into a new substance, or when its properties change, no mass is lost or gained.
Learning Objective(s)	SPQ-4.B Identify the equivalence point in a titration based on the amounts of titrant and analyte, assuming the titration reaction goes to completion.
Essential Knowledge SPQ-4.B	–Titrations may be used to determine the concentration of an analyte in solution. The titrant has a known concentration of a species that reacts specifically and quantitatively with the analyte. The equivalence point of the titration occurs when the analyte is totally consumed by the reacting species in the titrant. The equivalence point is often indicated by a change in a property (such as color) that occurs when the equivalence point is reached. This observable event is called the endpoint of the titration.
Science Practice	6. Argumentation—A. Make a claim. 6. Argumentation—B. Support a claim with evidence from experimental data. 6. Argumentation—D. Provide reasoning to justify a claim using chemical principles or laws, or mathematical justification. 6. Argumentation—G. Explain how potential sources of experimental error may affect the experimental results.

Answers

Section I Multiple-Choice

Answers: *1. C;   2. C;   3. A;   4. D;   5. B;   6. D*

1. The net dipole moment of three compounds with similar molar mass are listed in the table below

Substance	Net Dipole Moment (D)
X	0.1
Y	2.7
Z	3.9

The three substances are, in random listing, acetonitrile (CH_3CN), acetaldehyde (CH_3COH), and propane $(CH_3CH_2CH_3)$. If 0.250 mole of each substance is placed in a flask (with a piston at the top) at $-45\,°C$ and the flask is slowly heated under a pressure of 1.00 atm, which substance has the highest boiling point. What factor is responsible for the high boiling point.

A) propane, due to having only weak intermolecular forces, London Dispersion forces.

B) acetaldehyde, due to having strong intermolecular forces, hydrogen bonding.

C) acetonitrile, due to having medium intermolecular forces, dipole-dipole forces.

D) All three compounds will have about the same boiling point because all three have about the same molar mass and all three have London Dispersion Forces.

(A)	This option is incorrect. Propane is a nonpolar compound. Individual London dispersion forces are responsible for keeping propane molecules together as a liquid. London dispersion forces are weak IMFs. Propane has a net dipole moment of 0.1. Propane will have the lowest boiling point of the three compounds.
(B)	This option is incorrect. Acetaldehyde is a polar compound. Dipole-dipole forces are responsible for keeping acetaldehyde molecules together as a liquid. Dipole-dipole forces are moderate IMFs. Acetaldehyde has a net dipole moment of 2.7. Acetaldehyde does not have an "O—H" group. It does not have hydrogen bonding. Acetaldehyde will have the second highest boiling point of the three compounds.
(C)	This option is correct. Acetonitrile is a polar compound. Dipole-dipole forces are responsible for keeping acetaldehyde molecules together as a liquid. Dipole-dipole forces are moderate IMFs. Acetaldehyde has a net dipole moment of 3.1. The dipole-dipole IMF in acetonitrile is stronger compare to the dipole-dipole IMF in acetaldehyde. The difference in electronegativity value between the "C" and the "N" is larger compared to the difference in electronegativey between "C" and "O" in Acetaldehyde. Therefore the C—N is more polar compared to the C—O bond. Acetaldehyde will have highest boiling point of the three compounds.
(D)	This option is incorrect. These compounds do not have similar IMFs and therefore they do not have similar boiling points.

Questions 2–6 refer to the following information

Half-reaction	$E°(V)$
$Cr^{3+}(aq) + 3e^- \rightarrow Cr(s)$	-0.74
$Ni^{2+}(aq) + 2e^- \rightarrow Ni(s)$	-0.23
$Ag^+(aq) + e^- \rightarrow Ag(s)$	$+0.80$

2. Which reaction will occur be favorable in the forward direction?

    A) $3Ni(s) + 2Cr^{3+}(aq) \rightarrow 3Ni^{2+}(aq) + 2Cr(s)$

    B) $2Ag(s) + Ni^{2+}(aq) \rightarrow 2Ag^+(aq) + Ni(s)$

    C) $Ni(s) + 2Ag^+(aq) \rightarrow Ni^{2+}(aq) + 2Ag(s)$

    D) $Cr^{3+}(aq) + 3Ag^+(aq) \rightarrow Cr(s) + 3Ag(s)$

(A)	This option is incorrect. $E° = E°_{cathode} - E°_{anode} = -0.74\ V - (-0.23\ V) = -0.51\ V$ A negative $E°_{reaction}$ values indicates a non-favorable reaction.
(B)	This option is incorrect. $E° = E°_{cathode} - E°_{anode} = -0.23\ V - (+0.80\ V) = -1.03\ V$ A negative $E°_{reaction}$ values indicates a non-favorable reaction.
(C)	This option is correct. $E° = E°_{cathode} - E°_{anode} = +0.80\ V - (-0.23\ V) = +1.03\ V$ A positive $E°_{reaction}$ values indicates a favorable reaction.
(D)	This option is incorrect. The equation is not an oxidation-reduction equation since $Cr^{3+}(aq) + 3e^- \rightarrow Cr(s)$ is a reduction half-reaction and $3Ag^+(aq) + 3e^- \rightarrow 3Ag(s)$ is also a reduction half-reaction. An oxidation half-reaction is missing.

An electrochemical cell is constructed using two compartments connected by salt bridge. In one compartment silver metal is placed in 1.0 M silver nitrate and in the second compartment nickel metal is placed in 1.0 M nickel(II) nitrate. Wires connect the metal electrodes to a voltmeter.

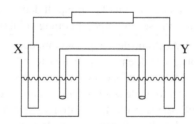

3. If the above electrochemical cell generates a positive emf, _____ is the anode.

    A) Ni

    B) Ag

    C) Ni^{2+}

    D) Ag^+

(A)	This option is correct. $Ni^{2+}(aq) + 2e^- \rightarrow Ni(s)$ $E° = -0.23$ V is a reduction half-reaction $Ag^+(aq) + e^- \rightarrow Ag(s)$ $E° = +0.80$ V is a reduction half-reaction Accordingly, Ni is the more active metal compared to Ag. Ni will serve as the anode and Ag will serve as the cathode. $Ni(s) \rightarrow Ni^{2+}(aq) + 2e^-$ oxidation occurs at the anode
(B)	This option is incorrect. $Ni^{2+}(aq) + 2e^- \rightarrow Ni(s)$ $E° = -0.23$ V is a reduction half-reaction $Ag^+(aq) + e^- \rightarrow Ag(s)$ $E° = +0.80$ V is a reduction half-reaction Accordingly, Ni is the more active metal compared to Ag. Ni will serve as the anode and Ag will serve as the cathode. $Ag^+(aq) + e^- \rightarrow Ag(s)$ reduction occurs at the cathode
(C)	This option is incorrect. The $Ni^{2+}(aq)$ metal cation in aqueous solution can not serve as the anode in part because it can not undergo oxidation (lose electrons).
(D)	This option is incorrect. The $Ag^+(aq)$ metal cation in aqueous solution can not serve as the anode in part because it can not undergo oxidation (lose electrons).

4. Calculate the cell potential of the above electrochemical cell.

   A) -1.03 V   B) -0.57 V   C) $+0.57$ V   D) $+1.03$ V

(A)	This option is incorrect. $E° = E°_{cathode} - E°_{anode} = -0.23$ V $- (+0.80$ V$) = -1.03$ V A negative $E°_{reaction}$ values indicates a thermodynamically unfavorable reaction.
(B)	This option is incorrect. Students often reverse which $E°$ value represents the cathode and anode. $E° = E°_{cathode} - E°_{anode} = -0.80$ V $- (-0.23$ V$) = -0.57$ V
(C)	This option is incorrect. Students often reverse which $E°$ value represents the cathode and anode. $E° = E°_{cathode} - E°_{anode} = 0.80$ V $- (0.23$ V$) = +0.57$ V
(D)	This option is correct. $E° = E°_{cathode} - E°_{anode} = +0.80$ V $- (-0.23$ V$) = \pm 1.03$ V

5. If 0.010 M silver nitrate solution is used instead of 1.0 M for the cell described in question 3, how would this influence the emf of the cell?

   A) the cell voltage would increase

   B) the cell voltage would decrease

   C) the cell voltage would stay the same

   D) there is not sufficient information given to provide an answer

(A)	This option is incorrect. For concentration cells, $E° = E°_{cathode} - E°_{anode} = +0.80$ V $- (-0.23$ V$) = +1.03$ V Reducing the Ag^+ concentrations will cause a shift to increase the Ag^+, a reactant, that will reduce the emf. Students often incorrectly reverse the values for $Q = [Ag^+]^2/Ni^{2+} = [0.010$ M$]^2/1.0$ M $= 0.00010$ Mathematically, $E_{cell} = E°_{cell} - (0.0592/n)\log Q = +1.03$ V $- (0.0592/2)(-4)$ The emf calculates to be greater than $+1.03$ V

(B)	This option is correct. $Ni(s) + 2Ag^+(aq) \rightleftharpoons Ni^{2+}(aq) + 2Ag(s)$ $E° = E°_{cathode} - E°_{anode} = +0.80\ V - (-0.23\ V) = +1.03\ V$ Reducing the Ag^+ concentrations will cause a shift to increase the Ag^+, a reactant, that will reduce the emf. Mathematically, $Q = [Ni^{2+}]/[Ag^+]^2 = 1.0\ M/[0.010\ M]^2 = 10{,}000$ $E_{cell} = E°_{cell} - (0.0592/n)\log Q = +1.03\ V - (0.0592/2)(4)$ The emf will be less than $+1.03\ V$
(C)	This option is incorrect. If there is a difference in concentration there will be a different emf, not the same.
(D)	This option is incorrect. There is sufficient information given to provide an answer.

6. Select one statement describing the difference between a Ni-Ag voltaic cell and a Ni-Ag electrolytic cell

   A) In a voltaic cell, oxidation occurs at the anode. In an electrolytic cell, oxidation occurs at the cathode.

   B) An electrolytic cell generates energy without outside help. A voltaic cell needs a continuous input of energy.

   C) In a Ni-Ag electrolysis cell, silver cations in the aqueous solution migrate toward the cathode. In a voltaic cell, the cations migrate toward the cathode.

   D) In an electrolysis cell, a continuous input of current forces a non-spontaneous reaction to occur, while in a voltaic cell chemical reactions occur to generate energy.

(A)	This option is incorrect. For any electrochemical cell, oxidation occurs at the anode and reduction occurs at the cathode.
(B)	This option is incorrect. An electrolytic cell generates energy without outside help. A voltaic cell needs a continuous input of energy.
(C)	This option is incorrect. In this voltaic cell, at the cathode cations gain electrons to form atoms.
(D)	This option is correct. In an electrolysis cell, a continuous input of current forces a non-favorable reaction to occur, while in a voltaic cell chemical reactions generate energy.

Section II Free Response

1. A student runs an experiment measuring the concentration of N_2O_5 several times after N_2O_5 dissolves in CCl_4 at 45 °C and obtains the following data for the decomposition reaction of N_2O_5.

$$2N_2O_5 \rightarrow 4NO_2 + O_2(g)$$

Time (sec)	[N₂O₅] (M)	Time (sec)	[N₂O₅] (M)
0.00	1.500	3600.0	0.160
900.0	0.857	4500.0	0.0913
1800.0	0.489	5000.0	?
2700.0	0.279		

The student plots a graph of concentration of N_2O_5 versus time.

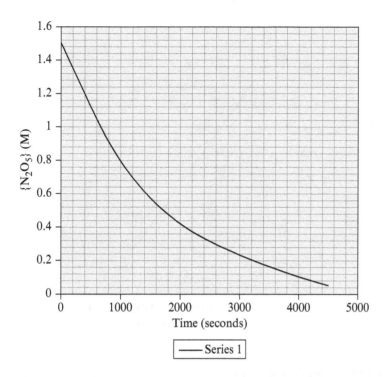

a) How is the average rate of disappearance of N_2O_5 related to the average rate of appearance of NO_2? Explain how to relate the relative rates of N_2O_5 and NO_2 to each other.

The average rate of appearance of NO_2 is twice as fast as the rate of disappearance of N_2O_5 because 4 moles of NO_2 are produced for every 2 moles of N_2O_5 that react.

b) Calculate the average rate of appearance of NO_2 between the start of the reaction and 1,800.0 seconds.

$$\text{Average Rate} = (-1/2)\Delta[N_2O_5]/\Delta t = (1/4)\Delta[NO_2]/\Delta t$$
$$\Delta[NO_2]/\Delta t = (-)2\,\Delta[N_2O_5]/\Delta t$$
$$\{[0.489\ M - 1.500\ M]/1800.0\ \text{sec} - 0.0\ \text{sec}\}$$
$$\text{Average rate} = \Delta[N_2O_5]/\Delta t = 2[5.62 \times 10^{-4}\ M/\text{sec}]$$
$$= 1.12 \times 10^{-2}\ M/\text{sec}$$

c) Determine the order of this reaction.

Since the plot of $[N_2O_5]$ vs. time is not linear, the reaction is not zero order with respect to $[N_2O_5]$. A plot of $\ln[N_2O_5]$ vs time is linear, therefore the reaction is first-order with respect to $[N_2O_5]$.

Time (sec)	$[N_2O_5]$ (M)	$\ln[N_2O_5]$
0.00	1.500	0.405
900.0	0.857	−0.154
1800.0	0.489	−0.715
2700.0	0.279	−1.276
3600.0	0.160	−1.832
4500.0	0.0913	−2.797
5000.0	?	

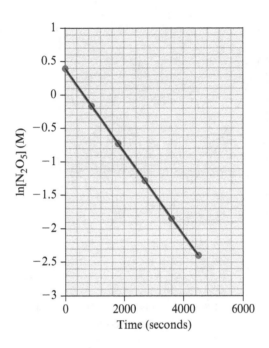

d) Determine the rate constant for this reaction at 45 °C. Include units with your answer.

A first-order reaction with respect to $[N_2O_5]$ with a 2 for a stoichiometric coefficient follows the equation for a straight line $\ln[N_2O_5]_t = -2kt + \ln[N_2O_5]_0$ where t is time and $2k$ is the slope of the line. The rate constant, k, is equal to (−slope/2) Using the information for 1,800.0 seconds

$$\ln[1.500\text{ M}] = m(1,800.0\text{ sec}) + \ln[0.489\text{ M}]$$

$$0.405 = m(1,800.0\text{ sec}) + (-0.715)$$

$$0.405 + 0.715 = m(1,800.0\text{ sec})$$

$$1.120/1,800.0\text{ sec} = m$$

$$-6.22 \times 10^{-4}\text{ sec}^{-1} = \text{slope} = -2k, \text{ rate constant} = 3.11 \times 10^{-4}\text{ sec}^{-1}$$

e) Determine or estimate the concentration of N_2O_5, in units of molarity, at 5,000.0 seconds. If you could not calculate a rate constant use may use $k = 4.50 \times 10^{-4}\text{ sec}^{-1}$.

$$\ln[N_2O_5]_t = -2kt + \ln[N_2O_5]_0 \quad \text{For } k = 3.11 \times 10^{-4}\text{ sec}^{-1}$$

$$\ln[x] = -2(3.11 \times 10^{-4}\text{ sec}^{-1})(5,000.0\text{ sec}) + \ln[1.500\text{ M}]$$

$$\ln[x] = -3.11 + 0.405 = -2.70$$

$$\ln[x] = -2.70 \quad \text{note: } e^{\ln x} = x$$

$$x = e^{(-2.70)} = x = 0.0669\text{ M}$$

Alternatively, since the average rate of disappearance of $[N_2O_5]$ between 4,500 sec and 3,600 sec is -7.60×10^{-5} M/sec, assume the average rate between 5,000 sec and 4,500 sec is -7.00×10^{-5} M/sec

$$\text{Average rate} = -\Delta[N_2O_5]/\Delta t = -7.00 \times 10^{-5}\text{ M/sec}$$

$$\text{rate} = -\Delta[N_2O_5]/\Delta t = [N_2O_5]_2 - [N_2O_5]_1/(t_2 - t_1)$$

$$-7.00 \times 10^{-5}\,\text{M/sec} = [N_2O_5]_2 - 0.0913\,\text{M/}$$
$$(5{,}000.0\,\text{sec} - 4{,}500.0\,\text{sec})$$

$$-7.00 \times 10^{-5}\,\text{M/sec} = (x - 0.0913\,\text{M})/500.0\,\text{sec}$$

$$(-7.00 \times 10^{-5}\,\text{M/sec})(500.0\,\text{sec}) = (x - 0.0913\,\text{M})$$

$$-0.035\,\text{M} = x - 0.0913\,\text{M}$$

$$x = 0.056\,\text{M}$$

Exercising the option of using $k = 4.50 \times 10^{-4}\,\text{sec}^{-1}$

$$\ln[N_2O_5]_t = -2kt + \ln[N_2O_5]_0$$

$$\ln[x] = -(9.00 \times 10^{-4}\,\text{sec}^{-1})(5{,}000.0\,\text{sec}) + \ln[1.500\,\text{M}]$$

$$\ln[x] = -4.50 + 0.405$$

$$-4.09 = \ln[x]$$

$$e^{(.155)} = x = 0.0166\,\text{M}$$

2. Several students conduct a series of experiments in which the conductivity of a solution was monitored as a function of how much titrant (or titrator) was added to the analyte (or titrand) during an acid–base titration. The procedure called for the slow addition of 0.500 M KOH(aq) solution in a buret to 500.0 mL of 0.500 M acetic acid solution, CH$_3$COOH(aq) in an Erlenmeyer flask.

Before collecting any data the students sketched graphs of how they thought electrical conductivity of the resultant solution would vary as base is added to the acid. The electrical conductance is shown in arbitrary units.

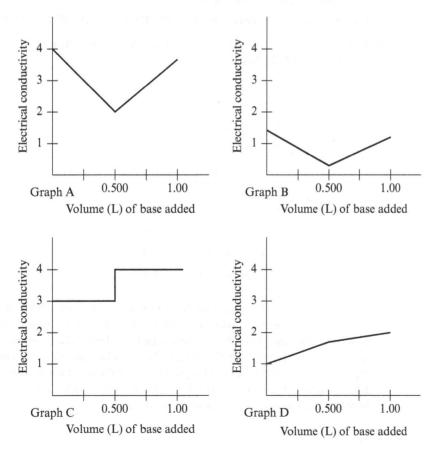

a) Which graph best matches your expectation for Experiment #1? Explain why the electrical conductivity changed from the point when the titrant was first added to the point at which all of the acid reacted.

Graph D. A weak acid has low conductivity because most of the acid is in the form of molecules which do not conduct, approximately 8% of the weak acid is ionized. KOH is a strong base. As KOH is added, some of the acetic acid molecules react and form acetate ions. For each acetate ion formed a K^+ ion is associated with it. This means for every one acetic acid molecule that reacts two ions form. Even though the solution becomes more dilute, there are more ions present in the solution. Electrical conductivity in a solution is a measure of the number of ions present. The more ions present, the greater the conductivity. Positive and negative ions migrating in solution constitutes a current. The relative electrical conductivity of the solution will increase steadily as KOH is added.

b) Write a balanced chemical equation representing the reaction of an aqueous acetic acid solution with an aqueous potassium hydroxide solution.

$$CH_3COOH(aq) + KOH(aq) \rightarrow K^+(aq), CH_3COO^-(aq) + H_2O(l)$$

c) What volume of base was added to react with all of the acid?

Moles of $CH_3COOH(aq)$ initially present

$0.500\,L \times 0.500\,mol/L = 0.250\,mol\ CH_3COOH(aq)$

Moles of KOH needed to react with all of the acid

$0.250\,mol\ CH_3COOH(aq) \times 1\,mole\ KOH/1\,mole\ CH_3COOH$

$= 0.250\,mol\ KOH$

$M = moles\ solute/L\ solution$

$L\ KOH\ solution = moles\ solute/M = 0.250\,mol/0.500\,mol/L = 0.500\,L$

d) Indicate the point on your graph (use the letter "P") just when all of the acid reacted with the base.

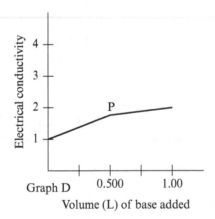

Graph D

e) The diagram on the next page, on the left represents a small volume of the acetic acid solution at the particulate nature of matter level before any base is added. Water molecules have been omitted for clarity. The diagram is not to scale. In the circle on the right, make a similar particulate drawing representing the important species present just at the point where enough KOH is added to react with all of the acid in the circle on the left. Be sure to include any newly formed water molecules.

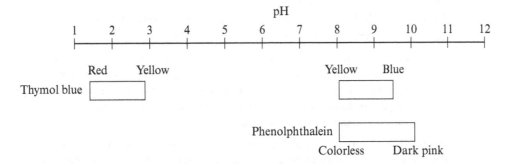

The point where all of the acid
has reacted with the base.

Initial

Acetate ion

f) Is the pH greater than, less than, or equal to 7 at the point in which all of
the acid reacts with KOH? Justify your answer.

The pH will be slightly greater than 7. At the equivalence point, all of the initial
acid reacts with the added KOH, creating acetate ions, $CH_3COO^-(aq)$ and $K^+(aq)$ ions. Some
of the acetate ions react with water to form new hydroxide ions (not from the KOH) and new
acetic acid molecules. The reverse reaction also occurs. An equilibrium system is established.

$$CH_3COO^-(aq) + H_2O(l) \rightleftharpoons CH_3COOH(aq) + OH^-(aq)$$

The acetic acid molecules stay intact as molecules and do not release H^+ ions.
The presence of hydroxide ions in solution, in addition to the hydroxide ions from the autoionization of water, creates a slightly basic solution.

3. Students perform an acid–base titration to standardize an HCl solution by placing 20.00 mL of HCl(aq) in an Erlenmeyer flask, then titrating with a known
concentration of NaOH(aq). Two laboratory technicians have determined the
concentration of a sodium hydroxide solution, NaOH(aq) to be 0.1482 M
$\pm$ 0.0002 M. and the concentration of the HCl(aq) solution to be 0.2223 M
$\pm$ 0.0002 M. The students have the following indicator color chart to consult.

pH

| 1 | 2 | 3 | 4 | 5 | 6 | 7 | 8 | 9 | 10 | 11 | 12 |

Red   Yellow   Yellow   Blue

Thymol blue

Phenolphthalein

Colorless   Dark pink

Student X adds a few drops of thymol blue indicator to the acid. Student X rinses a buret with water, then rinses a buret twice with 0.1482 M NaOH(aq) solution, before filling the buret
with fresh 0.1482 M NaOH(aq). Student X performs a titration of the acid using the 0.1482 M
NaOH solution and stops adding NaOH(aq) when the color of the solution in the Erlenmeyer
flask just turns from red to orange. Student X records in his notebook the volume of NaOH(aq)
required to neutralize the HCl(aq), then calculates the concentration of the HCl(aq) solution.

Student Y adds a few drops of phenolphthalein indicator to the acid. Student Y rinses a buret twice with water and does not allow most of the water to drain from the buret before filling the buret with 0.1482 M NaOH(aq). Student Y performs a titration of the acid using the NaOH solution and stops adding NaOH(aq) when the color of the solution in the Erlenmeyer flask just turns from colorless to faint pink. Student Y records in her notebook the volume of NaOH(aq) required to neutralize the HCl(aq), then calculates the concentration of the HCl(aq) solution.

a) Will the concentration of HCl(aq) reported by Student X be higher, lower, or about the same as the concentration of HCl(aq) reported by the technicians? Explain.

The concentration of the HCl(aq) solution as reported by Student X will be lower compared to the 0.2223 M value reported by the lab technicians. 20.00 mL of 0.2223 M HCl contains 0.00446 mole of HCl. The technicians used about 30.00 mL of 0.1482 M NaOH to neutralize the HCl. Student X stops the titration well before all of the acid is completely neutralized. Since thymol blue turns a solution orange around pH = 2, we can estimate Student X added about 15 mL of NaOH(aq). The student would show the following calculations:

$$0.01500 \text{ L NaOH} \times 0.1482 \text{ mol/L NaOH} = 0.002223 \text{ mol NaOH}$$

$$HCl(aq) + NaOH(aq) \rightarrow NaCl(aq) + H_2O(l)$$

$$0.002223 \text{ mol NaOH} \times 1 \text{ mole HCl/1 mole NaOH} = 0.002223 \text{ mol HCl}$$

$$M_{HCl} = 0.002223 \text{ mol HCl/0.02000 L} = 0.1112 \text{ M}$$

b) Will the concentration of HCl(aq) reported by Student Y be higher, lower, or about the same as the concentration of HCl(aq) reported by the technicians? Explain.

The concentration of the HCl(aq) solution as reported by Student X will be higher compared to the 0.2223 M value reported by the lab technicians. As stated above, 20.00 mL of 0.2223 M HCl contains 0.00446 mole of HCl. The technicians used about 30.00 mL of 0.1482 M NaOH to neutralize the HCl. Student Y did not rinse the buret with the sodium hydroxide solution, therefore when the sodium hydroxide solution was added to the buret some of the water in the buret mixed with the NaOH and diluted the solution. We can estimate the concentration of the NaOH(aq) in the buret as 0.120 M. Student Y stops the titration when all of the acid is completely neutralized. We can estimate about 35 mL of base was used to neutralize the acid because the NaOH solution in the buret was a bit more dilute compared to what the technicians used. The student would show the following calculations using a higher value for the concentration of NaOH compared to the true value.

$$0.03500 \text{ L NaOH} \times 0.1482 \text{ mol/L NaOH} = 0.005187 \text{ mol NaOH}$$

$$HCl(aq) + NaOH(aq) \rightarrow NaCl(aq) + H_2O(l)$$

$$0.005187 \text{ mol NaOH} \times 1 \text{ mole HCl/1 mole NaOH} = 0.005187 \text{ mol HCl}$$

$$M_{HCl} = 0.005187 \text{ mol HCl/0.02000 L} = 0.2593 \text{ M}$$

c) The term *error* indicates the numerical difference between a calculated (or measured) value and the true value. Errors can be classified as determinate (systematic), and indeterminate. Determinate errors can be further classified as *methodic*, *operative*, and *instrumental*. What type of error did Students X and Y make? Explain.

Although the measured values of volume do have some error, in this experiment, measurements of the volume of solutions are not the prime source of error. Students X and Y each made a different type of operative error. This type of error can be corrected in a subsequent trial of the experiment. Operative errors are a type of determinate error. Determinate errors are unidirectional with respect to the true value and can be reproduced by a scientist who understands the procedures, calculations and the theory of the experiment.

Sample questions of both multiple choice and data based free response questions are in each chapter.

AP Correlation Guide

This chart correlates the College Board's Advanced Placement Units and Unit Topics, which are aligned to the Enduring Understandings and Learning Objectives in the curriculum, to the corresponding chapters and sections in Chemistry: A Molecular Approach 5th Edition, AP® Edition.

Unit 1 Atomic Structure and Properties (8 topics) 7–9%

Big Ideas in this Unit are: Scale, Proportion, and Quantity (SPQ) and Structure and Properties (SAP)

SPQ-1: The mole allows different units to be compared.

SPQ-2. Chemical formulas identify substances by their unique combination of atoms.

SAP-1. Atoms and molecules can be identified by their electron distribution and energy.

SAP-2. The periodic table shows patterns in electronic structure and trends in atomic properties.

Unit Topic Number	Unit Section Topic	Enduring Understanding	Learning Objective	Chapter and Section
1.1	Moles and Molar Mass	SPQ-1	SPQ-1.A Calculate quantities of a substance or its relative number of particles using dimensional analysis and the mole concept.	2.9, 3.8, 3.9
1.2	Mass Spectroscopy of Elements	SPQ-1	SPQ-1.B Explain the qualitative relationship between the mass spectrum of an element and the masses of the element's isotopes.	2.6, 2.8
1.3	Elemental Composition of Pure Substances	SPQ-2	SPQ-2.A Explain the quantitative relationship between the elemental composition by mass and empirical formula of a pure substance.	1.3, 2.3, 3.3
1.4	Composition of Mixtures	SPQ-2	SPQ-2.B Explain the quantitative relationship between the elemental composition by mass and the composition of substances in a mixture.	1.3, 3.9, 3.10
1.5	Atomic Structure and Electron Configuration	SAP-1	SAP-1.A Represent the electron configuration of an element or ions of an element using the Aufbau principle.	2.5, 9.2–9.7
1.6	Photoelectron Spectroscopy	SAP-1	SAP-1.B Explain the relationship between the photoelectron spectrum of an atom or ion and • the electron configuration of the species. • the interactions between the electrons and the nucleus.	refer to the AP Test Prep book to accompany Tro
1.7	Periodic Trends	SAP-2	SAP-2.A Explain the relationship between trends in atomic properties of elements and electronic structure and periodicity.	9.4–9.8
1.8	Valence Electrons and Ionic Compounds	SAP-2	SAP-2.B Explain the relationship between trends in the reactivity of elements and periodicity.	4.5, 9.4, 13.4–13.5

Unit 2 Molecular and Ionic Compound Structure and Properties (7 topics) 7–9%

Big Idea in this Unit is: Structure and Properties (SAP)

SAP-3. Atoms or ions bond due to interactions between them, forming molecules.

SAP-4. Molecular compounds are arranged based on Lewis diagrams and Valence Shell Electron Pair Repulsion (VSEPR) theory.

Unit Topic Number	Unit Section Topic	Enduring Understanding	Learning Objective	Chapter and Section
2.1	Types of Chemical Bonds	SAP-3	SAP-3.A Explain the relationship between the type of bonding and the properties of the elements participating in the bond.	3.2–3.9, 10.2–10.6, 10.11, 11.5, 22.2
2.2	Intramolecular Force and Potential Energy	SAP-3	SAP-3.B Represent the relationship between potential energy and the distance between atoms, based on factors that influence the interaction strength.	10.2, 10.5, 11.6
2.3	Structure of Ionic Solids	SAP-3	SAP-3.C Represent an ionic solid with a particulate model that is consistent with Coulomb's law and the properties of the constituent ions.	10.4, 13.4, 13.5
2.4	Structure of Metals and Alloys	SAP-3	SAP-3.D Represent a metallic solid and/or alloy using a model to show essential characteristics of the structure and interactions present in the substance.	13.4, 25.4
2.5	Lewis Diagrams	SAP-4	SAP-4.A Represent a molecule with a Lewis diagram.	11.2–11.5
2.6	Resonance and Formal Charge	SAP-4	SAP-4.B Represent a molecule with a Lewis diagram that accounts for resonance between equivalent structures or that uses formal charge to select between nonequivalent structures.	10.8
2.7	VSEPR and Bond Hybridization	SAP-4	SAP-4.C Based on the relationship between Lewis diagrams, VSEPR theory, bond orders, and bond polarities— • Explain structural properties of molecules. • Explain electron properties of molecules.	11.2–11.8

Unit 3: Intermolecular Forces and Properties (13 topics) 18–22%

Big Ideas in this Unit are: Scale, Proportion, and Quantity (SPQ) and Structure and Properties (SAP)

SAP-5 Intermolecular Forces can explain the physical properties of a material.

SAP-6 Matter exists in three states: solid, liquid, and gas, and their differences are influenced by variances in spacing and motion of molecules.

SAP-7 Gas properties are explained macroscopically—using the relationships among pressure, volume, temperature, moles, and gas constant—and the molecularly by the motion of the gas.

SPQ-3 Interactions between intermolecular forces influence the solubility and separation of mixtures.
SAP-8 Spectroscopy can determine the structure and concentration in a mixture of a chemical species.

Unit Topic Number	Unit Section Topic	Enduring Understanding	Learning Objective	Chapter and Section
3.1	Intermolecular Forces	SAP-5	SAP-5.A Explain the relationship between the chemical structures of molecules and the relative strength of their intermolecular forces when— • The molecules are of the same chemical species. • The molecules are of two different chemical species.	12.3
3.2	Properties of Solids	SAP-5	SAP-5.B Explain the relationship among the macroscopic properties of a substance, the particulate-level structure of the substance, and the interactions between these particles.	12.3, 12.4, 13.4, 13.5, 13.6
3.3	Solids, Liquids, and Gases	SAP-6	SAP-6.A Represent the differences between solid, liquid, and gas phase using a particulate-level model.	12.2, 13.4, 13.5
3.4	Ideal Gas Law	SAP-7	SAP-7.A Explain the relationship between the macroscopic properties of a sample of a gas or mixture of gases using the ideal gas law.	6.3–6.6
3.5	Kinetic Molecular Theory	SAP-7	SAP-7.B Explain the relationship between the motion of particles and the macroscopic properties of gases with— • The kinetic molecular theory (KMT) • A particulate model • A graphical representation.	6.8, 6.9
3.6	Deviations from Ideal Gas Law	SAP-7	SAP-7.C Explain the relationship among nonideal behaviors of gases, interparticle forces, and/or volumes.	6.10
3.7	Solutions and Mixtures	SPQ-3	SPQ-3.A Calculate the number of solute particles, volume, or molarity of solutions.	5.2, 14.2, 14.5
3.8	Representations of Solutions	SPQ-3	SPQ-3.B Using particulate models for mixtures— • Represent interactions between components. • Represent concentrations of components.	14.2, 14.3
3.9	Separation of Solutions and Mixtures Chromatography	SPQ-3	SPQ-3.C Explain the relationship between the solubility of ionic and molecular compounds in aqueous and nonaqueous solvents, and the intermolecular interactions between particles.	14.2, 14.3, 14.4, refer to the AP Test Prep book to accompany Tro
3.10	Solubility	SPQ-3	SPQ-3.C2 Substances with similar intermolecular interactions tend to be miscible or soluble in one another.	12.3, 14.2

Unit Topic Number	Unit Section Topic	Enduring Understanding	Learning Objective	Chapter and Section
3.11	Spectroscopy and the Electromagnetic Spectrum	SAP-8	SAP-8.A Explain the relationship between a region of the electromagnetic spectrum and the types of molecular or electronic transitions associated with that region.	refer to the AP Test Prep book to accompany Tro
3.12	Photoelectric Effect	SAP-8	SAP-8.B Explain the properties of an absorbed or emitted photon in relationship to an electronic transition in an atom or a molecule.	8.2, 8.3
3.13	Beer–Lambert Law	SAP-8	SAP-8.C Explain the amount of light absorbed by a solution of molecules or ions in relationship to the concentration, path length, and molar absorptivity.	refer to the AP Test Prep book to accompany Tro

Unit 4 Chemical Reactions (9 topics) 7–9%

Big Ideas in this Unit are: Scale, Proportion, and Quantity (SPQ) and Transformations (TRA).

SPQ-4: When a substance changes into a new substance or when its properties change, no mass is lost or gained.

TRA-1: A substance that changes its properties, or that changes into different substances, can be represented by chemical equations and

TRA-2: A substance can change into another substance through different processes, and the change itself can be classified by the sort of processes that produced it.

Unit Section Number	Unit Section Topic	Enduring Understanding	Learning Objective	Chapter and Section
4.1	Introduction to Reactions	TRA-1	TRA-1.A Identify evidence of chemical and physical changes in matter.	1.4
4.2	Net Ionic Equations	TRA-1	TRA-1.B Represent changes in matter with a balanced chemical or net ionic equation— • For physical changes. • For given information about the identity of the reactants and/or product. • For ions in a given chemical reaction.	4.2, 5.6
4.3	Representation of Reactions	TRA-1	TRA-1.C Represent a given chemical reaction or physical process with a consistent particulate model.	3.1–3.3, 4.2, 5.6
4.4	Physical and Chemical Changes	TRA-1	TRA-1.D Explain the relationship between macroscopic characteristics and bond interactions for— • Chemical processes. • Physical processes.	1.4, 1.5
4.5	Stoichiometry	SPQ-4	SPQ-4.A Explain changes in the amounts of reactants and products based on the balanced reaction equation for a chemical process.	4.3, 4.4, 5.3, 6.4
4.6	Introduction to Titration	SPQ-4	SPQ-4.B Identify the equivalence point in a titration based on the amounts of titrant and analyte, assuming the titration reaction goes to completion.	5.7, 18.4

Unit Section Number	Unit Section Topic	Enduring Understanding	Learning Objective	Chapter and Section
4.7	Types of Chemical Reactions	TRA-2	TRA-2.A Identify a reaction as acid–base, oxidation–reduction, or precipitation.	5.4–5.9, 17.3
4.8	Introduction to Acid–Base Reactions	TRA-2	TRA-2.B Identify species as Bronsted–Lowry acids, bases, and/or conjugate acid–base pairs, based on proton-transfer involving those species.	5.7, 18.4
4.9	Oxidation–reduction (redox) reactions	TRA-2	TRA-2.C Represent a balanced redox reaction equation using half-reactions.	5.9, 20.3, 20.4, 20.5

Unit 5 Kinetics (11 Topics) 7–9%

Big Ideas in this Unit are: Transformations (TRA) and Energy (ENE)

TRA-3 Some reactions happen quickly, while others happen more slowly and depend on reactant concentrations and temperature.

TRA-4 There is a relationship between the speed of a reaction and the collision frequency of particle collisions.

TRA-5 Many chemical reactions occur through a series of elementary reactions when combined form a chemical equation.

ENE-1 The speed at which a reaction occurs can be influenced by a catalyst.

Unit Topic Number	Unit Section Topic	Enduring Understanding	Learning Objective	Chapter and Section
5.1	Reaction Rates	TRA-3	TRA-3.A Explain the relationship between the rate of a chemical reaction and experimental parameters.	15.2–15.7
5.2	Introduction to Rate Law	TRA-3	TRA-3.B Represent experimental data with a consistent rate law expression.	15.2, 15.3
5.3	Concentration Changes Over Time	TRA-3	TRA-3.C Identify the rate law expression of a chemical reaction using data that show how the concentrations of reaction species change over time.	15.2, 15.3, 15.4, 21.6
5.4	Elementary Reactions	TRA-4	TRA-4.A Represent an elementary reaction as a rate law expression using stoichiometry.	15.2, 15.3, 15.5
5.5	Collision Model	TRA-4	TRA-4.B Explain the relationship between the rate of an elementary reaction and the frequency, energy, and orientation of molecular collisions.	15.5, 15.6, 21.6
5.6	Reaction Energy Profile	TRA-4	TRA-4.C Represent the activation energy and overall energy change in an elementary reaction using a reaction energy profile.	15.5, 21.6
5.7	Introduction to Reaction Mechanisms	TRA-5	TRA-5.A Identify the components of a reaction mechanism.	15.6
5.8	Reaction Mechanism and Rate Law	TRA-5	TRA-5.B Identify the rate law for a reaction from a mechanism in which the first step is rate limiting.	15.6

Unit Topic Number	Unit Section Topic	Enduring Understanding	Learning Objective	Chapter and Section
5.9	Steady-State Approximation	TRA-5	TRA-5.C Identify the rate law for a reaction from a mechanism in which the first step is not rate limiting.	15.6
5.10	Multistep Reaction Energy Profile	TRA-5	TRA-5.D Represent the activation energy and overall energy change in a multistep reaction with a reaction energy profile.	15.5, 15.6
5.11	Catalysts	ENE-1	ENE-1.A Explain the relationship between the effect of a catalyst on a reaction and changes in the reaction mechanism.	15.7

Unit 6: Thermodynamics (9 Topics) 7–9%

Big Idea in this Unit is: Energy (ENE)

ENE-2 Changes in a substance's properties or change into a different substance requires an exchange of energy.

ENE-3 The Energy exchanged in a chemical transformation is required to break and form bonds.

Unit Topic Number	Unit Section Topic	Enduring Understanding	Learning Objective	Chapter and Section
6.1	Endothermic and Exo- thermic Processes	ENE-2	ENE-2.A Explain the relationship between experimental observations and energy changes associated with a chemical or physical transformation.	7.2–7.6, 14.3
6.2	Energy Diagrams	ENE-2	ENE-2.B Represent a chemical or physical transformation with an energy diagram.	7.3–7.5, 14.3
6.3	Heat Transfer and Thermal Pollution	ENE-2	ENE-2.C Explain the relationship between the transfer of thermal energy and molecu- lar collisions.	7.3–7.5
6.4	Heat Capacity and Calorimetry	ENE-2	ENE-2.D Calculate the heat q absorbed or released by a system undergoing heating/ cooling based on the amount of the sub- stance, the heat capacity, and the change in temperature.	7.3–7.7
6.5	Energy of Phase Changes	ENE-2	ENE-2.E Explain changes in the heat q absorbed or released by a system undergo- ing a phase transition based on the amount of the substance in moles and the molar enthalpy of the phase transition.	12.5–12.7
6.6	Introduction to Enthalpy of Reaction	ENE-2	ENE-2.F Calculate the heat q absorbed or released by a system undergoing a chemical reaction in relationship to the amount of reacting substance in moles and the molar enthalpy of reaction.	7.8–7.9
6.7	Bond Energies	ENE-3	ENE-3.A Calculate the enthalpy change of a reaction based on the average bond ener- gies of bonds broken and formed in the reaction.	7.8

Unit Topic Number	Unit Section Topic	Enduring Understanding	Learning Objective	Chapter and Section
6.8	Enthalpy of Formation	ENE-3	ENE-3.B Calculate the enthalpy change for a chemical or physical process based on the standard enthalpies of formation.	7.9
6.9	Hess's Law	ENE-3	ENE-3.C Represent a chemical or physical process as a sequence of steps.	7.8–7.9

Unit 7: Equilibrium (14 Topics) 7–9%

Big Ideas in this Unit are: Transformations (TRA) and Scale, Proportion, and Quantity (SPQ)

TRA-6 Some reactions can occur in both forward and reverse directions, sometimes proceeding in each direction simultaneously.

TRA-7 A system at equilibrium depends on the relationships between concentrations, partial pressures of chemical species, and the equilibrium constant K.

TRA-8 Systems at equilibrium respond to external stresses to offset the effect of the stress.

SPQ-5 The dissolution of a salt is a reversible process that can be influenced by environmental factors such as pH or other dissolved ions.

Unit Topic Number	Unit Section Topic	Enduring Understanding	Learning Objective	Chapter and Section
7.1	Introduction to Equilibrium	TRA-6	TRA-6.A Explain the relationship between the occurrence of a reversible chemical or physical process, and the establishment of equilibrium, to experimental observations.	16.2, 16.3, 16.7
7.2	Direction of Reversible Reactions	TRA-6	TRA-6.B Explain the relationship between the direction in which a reversible reaction proceeds and the relative rates of the forward and reverse reactions.	16.3, 16.7
7.3	Reaction Quotient and Equilibrium Constant	TRA-7	TRA-7.A Represent the reaction quotient Q_c or Q_p, for a reversible reaction, and the corresponding equilibrium expressions $K_c = Q_c$ or $K_p = Q_p$.	16.3, 16.4, 16.7
7.4	Calculating the Equilibrium Constant	TRA-7	TRA-7.B Calculate K_c or K_p based on experimental observations of concentrations or pressures at equilibrium.	16.5, 16.6
7.5	Magnitude of the Equilibrium Constant	TRA-7	TRA-7.C Explain the relationship between very large or very small values of K and the relative concentrations of chemical species at equilibrium.	16.3, 16.5, 16.7
7.6	Properties of the Equilibrium Constant	TRA-7	TRA-7.D Represent a multistep process with an overall equilibrium expression, using the constituent K expressions for each individual reaction.	16.3
7.7	Calculating Equilibrium Concentrations	TRA-7	TRA-7.E Identify the concentrations or partial pressures of chemical species at equilibrium based on the initial conditions and the equilibrium constant.	16.5, 16.6, 16.8

Unit Topic Number	Unit Section Topic	Enduring Understanding	Learning Objective	Chapter and Section
7.8	Representations of Equilibrium	TRA-7	TRA-7.F Represent a system undergoing a reversible reaction with a particle model.	16.2
7.9	Introduction to Le Châtelier's Principle	TRA-8	TRA-8.A Identify the response of a system at equilibrium to an external stress, using Le Châtelier's principle.	16.9
7.10	Reaction Quotient and Le Châtelier's Principle	TRA-8	TRA-8.B Explain the relationships between Q, K, and the direction in which a reversible reaction will proceed to reach equilibrium.	16.7, 16.9
7.11	Introduction to Solubility Equilibria	SPQ-5	SPQ-5.A Calculate the solubility of a salt based on the value of Ksp for the salt.	5.4, 5.5, 18.5, 18.6
7.12	Common-Ion Effect	SPQ-5	SPQ-5.B Identify the solubility of a salt, and/or the value of Ksp for the salt, based on the concentration of a common ion already present in solution.	18.5, 18.6
7.13	pH and Solubility	SPQ-5	SPQ-5.C Identify the qualitative effect of changes in pH on the solubility of a salt.	18.6
7.14	Free Energy of Dissolution	SPQ-5	SPQ-5.D Explain the relationship between the solubility of a salt and changes in the enthalpy and entropy that occur in the dissolution process.	14.3, 14.4, 19.2, 19.5, 19.10

Unit 8: Acids and Bases (7 Topics) 11–15%

Big Idea in this Unit is: Structure and Properties (SAP)

SAP-9 The chemistry of acids and bases involves reversible proton-transfer reactions, with equilibrium concentrations being related to the strength of the acids and bases involved.

SAP-10 A buffered solution resists changes to its pH when small amounts of acid or base are added.

Unit Topic Number	Unit Section Topic	Enduring Understanding	Learning Objective	Chapter and Section
8.1	Introduction to Acids and Bases	SAP-9	SAP-9.A Calculate the values of pH and pOH, based on K_w and the concentration of all species present in a neutral solution of water.	5.7, 17.5
8.2	pH and pOH of Strong Acids and Bases	SAP-9	SAP-9.B Calculate pH and pOH based on concentrations of all species in a solution of a strong acid or a strong base.	17.4–17.7
8.3	Weak Acid and Base Equilibria	SAP-9	SAP-9.C Explain the relationship among pH, pOH, and concentrations of all species in a solution of a monoprotic weak acid or weak base.	17.4–17.7
8.4	Acid–Base Reactions and Buffers	SAP-9	SAP-9.D Explain the relationship among concentrations of major species in a mixture of weak and strong acids and bases.	17.4–17.7, 18.4
8.5	Acid–Base Titrations	SAP-9	SAP-9.E Explain results from the titration of a mono-or polyprotic acid or base solution, in relation to the properties of the solution and its components.	5.7, 18.4

Unit Topic Number	Unit Section Topic	Enduring Understanding	Learning Objective	Chapter and Section
8.6	Molecular Structure of Acids and Bases	SAP-9	SAP-9.F Explain the relationship between the strength of an acid or a base and the structure of the molecule or ion.	17.3, 17.8, 17.10
8.7	pH and pKa	SAP-10	SAP-10.A Explain the relationship between the predominant form of a weak acid or base in solution at a given pH and pK_a of the conjugate acid or the pK_b of the conjugate base.	17.5–17.8, 18.4
8.8	Properties of Buffers	SAP-10	SAP-10.B Explain the relationship between the ability of a buffer to stabilize pH and the reactions that occur when an acid or a base is added to a buffered solution.	18.2
8.9	Henderson-Hasselbalch Equation	SAP-10	SAP-10.C Identify the pH of a buffer solution based on the identity and concentrations of the conjugate acid–base pair used to create the buffer.	18.2, 18.3
8.10	Buffer Capacity	SAP-10	SAP-10.D Explain the relationship between the buffer capacity of a solution and the relative concentrations of the conjugate acid and conjugate base components of the solution.	18.3

Unit 9: Applications of Thermodynamics (Thermodynamics) (10 Topics) 7–9 %

Big Idea in this Unit is: Energy (ENE)

ENE-4 Some chemical or physical processes cannot occur without intervention.
ENE-5 The relationship between $\Delta G°$ and K can be used to determine favorability of a chemical or physical transformation.
ENE-6 Electrical energy can be generated by chemical reactions.

Unit Topic Number	Unit Section Topic	Enduring Understanding	Learning Objective	Chapter and Section
9.1	Introduction to Entropy	ENE-4	ENE-4.A Identify the sign and relative magnitude of the entropy change associated with chemical or physical processes.	19.4, 19.7
9.2	Absolute Entropy and Entropy Change	ENE-4	ENE-4.B Calculate the entropy change for a chemical or physical process based on the absolute entropies of the species involved in the process.	19.7
9.3	Gibbs Free Energy and Thermodynamic Favorability	ENE-4	ENE-4.C Explain whether a physical or chemical process is thermodynamically favored based on an evaluation of $\Delta G°$.	19.9, 19.10
9.4	Thermodynamic and Kinetic Control	ENE-4	ENE-4.D Explain, in terms of kinetics, why a thermodynamically favored reaction might not occur at a measurable rate.	19.2
9.5	Free Energy and Equilibrium	ENE-5	ENE-5.A Explain whether a process is thermodynamically favored using the relationships among K, $\Delta G°$, and T.	19.10

Unit Topic Number	Unit Section Topic	Enduring Understanding	Learning Objective	Chapter and Section
9.6	Coupled Reactions	ENE-5	ENE-5.B Explain the relationship between external sources of energy or coupled reactions and their ability to drive thermodynamically unfavorable processes.	19.10, 19.9, 20.5, 25.3
9.7	Galvanic (Voltaic) and Electrolytic Cells	ENE-6	ENE-6.A Explain the relationship between the physical components of an electrochemical cell and the overall operational principles of the cell.	20.3
9.8	Cell Potential and Free Energy	ENE-6	ENE-6.B Explain whether an electrochemical cell is thermodynamically favored based on its standard cell potential and the constituent half-reactions within the cell.	20.3, 20.4, 20.5
9.9	Cell Potential Under Nonstandard Conditions	ENE-6	ENE-6.C Explain the relationship between deviations from standard cell conditions and changes in cell potential.	20.6
9.10	Electrolysis and Faraday's Law	ENE-6	ENE-6.D Calculate the amount of charge flow based on changes in the amounts of reactants and products in an electrochemical cell.	20.8

Upon publication, this text was correlated to the College Board's AP Chemistry Curriculum Framework that became effective in 2019 and is still current. We continually monitor the College Board's AP Course Description for updates to exam topics. For the most current AP correlation for this textbook, visit PearsonSchool.com/Advanced.

AP Chemistry is broken down into nine Units. These Units all have enduring understandings, science practices, and learning objectives which accompany them. Each chapter will identify the learning objectives and science practices within the chapter to be mastered. Some of the objectives may be listed for several chapters where different parts of an objective may be addressed.

Ten questions similar to the AP style questions accompany each chapter. Some of these questions are foundational in nature and will not be on an actual AP Chemistry Exam but will be expected as part of the steps to solve problems. For instance, the AP Exam will not ask you to change measurements from grams to moles and milliliters to liters as a test question but both of these will need to be done as a part of solving a problem to determine a molarity when the mass of the solute is given in grams and the volume of solution is given in milliliters.

This manual is a quick review of vocabulary and concepts needed to be successful in AP Chemistry. The reading guides that accompany each chapter also have recommended problems to do from the text. Refer to *Chemistry: A Molecular Approach* by Nivaldo Tro for additional examples and problems on each concept.

Upon publication, this text was correlated to the College Board's AP Chemistry Curriculum Framework for the 2019–2020 school year. We continually monitor the College Board's AP Course Description for updates to exam topics. For the most current AP correlation for this textbook, visit PearsonSchool.com/AdvancedCorrelations.

MATTER, MEASUREMENT, AND PROBLEM SOLVING

This is a foundational chapter and many of the concepts and skills discussed here will be review from your first-year chemistry course or other science classes. Every chapter has vocabulary you must recognize and understand to determine what a given problem on the AP Exam is asking you to address. It is important you recognize some vocabulary words have very specific definitions in chemistry, which may be different from how they are used in general language. Be sure to review Section 1.8 "Solving Chemical Problems" and the definitions in Section 1.5 "Energy: A Fundamental Part of Physical and Chemical Change" in the text. In addition, pay close attention to the following sections to review concepts:

1.3 **The Classification of Matter**

1.4 **Physical and Chemical Changes and Physical and Chemical Properties**

1.6 **The Units of Measurement**

1.7 **The Reliability of a Measurement**

The number and type of the learning objective is not important but knowing the content addressed is critical. This chapter addresses several foundational misconceptions that students often have. All parts of the learning objectives listed for Chapter 1 may not be addressed in this chapter but the foundations of each objective are.

Specific Learning Objectives Addressed in This Chapter:

Learning Objective SAP-6.A Represent the differences among solid, liquid, and gas phases using a particulate-level model.

Learning Objective TRA-1.A Identify evidence of chemical and physical changes in matter.

Learning Objective TRA-1.C Represent a given chemical reaction or physical process with a consistent particulate model.

Learning Objective SPQ-2.B Explain the quantitative relationship between the elemental composition by mass and the composition of substances in a mixture.

Concepts and Vocabulary to Review:

Section 1.1   # Atoms and Molecules

Atoms are the building blocks of matter. Atoms can combine to form molecules and compounds. In ordinary chemical reactions, atoms are "conserved"—they are never created or destroyed (except through radioactive nuclear processes). Molecules, on the other hand, can be restructured into other molecules through chemical reactions.

Chemistry is the study of atoms and molecules and their interactions. How atoms combine together affects the properties the resulting substance has.

Crystalline Solid:
Regular
three-dimensional pattern

Diamond
C (*s*, diamond)

Figure 1.1 Crystalline Solid   Diamond (first discussed in Section 1.1) is a crystalline solid composed of carbon atoms arranged in a regular, repeating pattern.

Graphite and diamonds are both made only of carbon atoms yet have very different properties due to the way the atoms are held together. Diamonds are hard because they are bound tightly in all directions while graphite is brittle because it is only bound in two directions. Owing to the difference in structure, carbon atoms flake off the graphite so it can be used in pencils while in diamond the carbon atoms do not flake off.

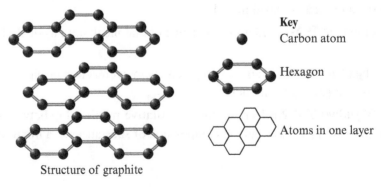

Key
Carbon atom
Hexagon
Atoms in one layer

Structure of graphite

The Scientific Approach to Knowledge   Section 1.2

The **Law of Conservation of Mass** states "In a chemical reaction, matter is neither created nor destroyed." Antoine Lavoisier and others demonstrated this law through very careful measurements. The Law of Conservation of Mass forms the basis of chemistry predictions for the amounts of products produced in chemical reactions, given the starting amounts. If a reaction starts with 32.0 g of reactants, there will be 32.0 g of product formed if the reaction goes to completion. This law remains true for chemical reactions in this course. For nuclear reactions, Albert Einstein explained the equation $E = mc^2$, which indicates matter and energy can be interchanged. The conservation of mass–energy as a combined property is now a fundamental principle in physics.

The Classification of Matter   Section 1.3

Matter has mass and takes up space, although the space may be very small. Atoms are the fundamental chemical components of matter and are not visible to the human eye. They can now be visualized using recently developed equipment called *atomic force microscopes*. Atoms make up molecules—atoms closely organized in small groups, ions—a group of atoms with an overall charge, and compounds. In the following descriptions, the term *species* applies to atoms, ions, compounds, molecules, and in some cases, mixtures of these.

Solid matter is closely packed together and the species composing the solid are in relatively fixed positions. A solid has a fixed volume and shape. The examples of diamond and graphite used earlier in Figure 1.1 are examples of atoms held together as solids. The atoms do vibrate while being held in position.

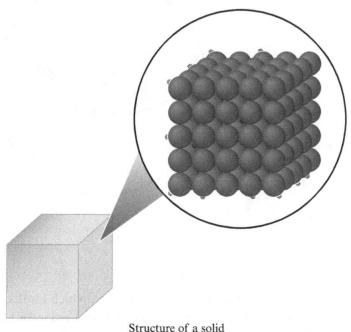

Structure of a solid

Crystalline solids have an ordered pattern in their shape. A few examples are salt (sodium chloride) and ice (solid water). Crystals generally have well-defined internal and external shapes, and can only be compressed under extremely high pressures.

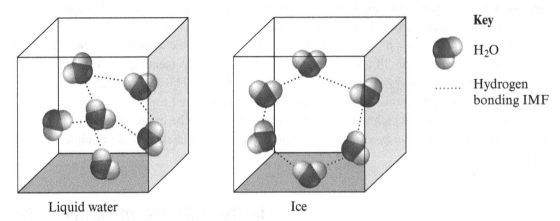

Liquid water   Ice

Key

H_2O

...... Hydrogen bonding IMF

In the first diagram, water molecules are moving around the container in the liquid form while in the second diagram the water molecules are being held in position. The forces involved will be discussed in a later chapter.

In **amorphous** solids, there is a lack of an ordered arrangement although the species composing the solid may be arranged in long chains or rings. An example of an amorphous solid is glass.

Liquid matter, like solid matter, is closely packed together. However, liquid matter can move independent to each other. Water molecules in liquid water move over, under, and around other water molecules. Liquids take the shape of the container they occupy and only compress under high pressure.

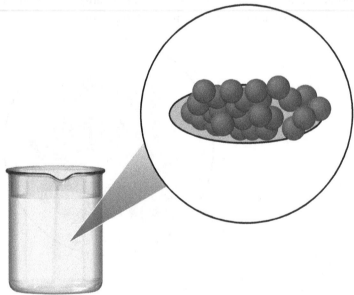

Structure of a liquid

Gases are a type of matter not closely packed together, which results in their ability to be easily compressed. If a substance is not a gas under standard conditions of 1 atmosphere and 25 °C, when it changes to a gas it is called a *vapor*. Liquid water when heated changes to gaseous water vapor.

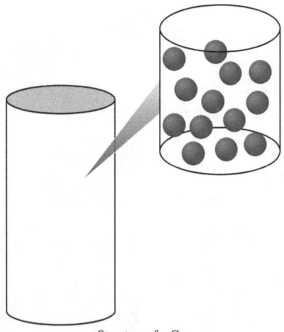

Structure of a Gas

Elements are composed of one or more atoms, each having the same number of protons. Elements cannot be chemically broken down into smaller substances.

Compounds are substances with two or more elements bonded together in fixed proportions, such as water with two hydrogen atoms and one oxygen atom has the formula H_2O. The formula H_2O_2 is hydrogen peroxide which has totally different properties than water.

Pure substances are composed of a single type of component (either an element or a compound) and the composition of the substance does not vary.

Mixtures are composed of more than one component and the composition can vary. There are two types of mixtures, heterogeneous and homogeneous. Sometimes, the two types are hard to distinguish from each other.

> **Heterogeneous mixtures** are mixtures with a varied composition. An example is hot cocoa with marshmallows on top.

> **Homogeneous mixtures** have a uniform composition as a result of mixing. An example of a homogeneous solution is lemonade (without pulp). The sugar, water, and lemon juice are uniformly mixed. Poorly stirred lemonade may well be heterogeneous! To be homogeneous it must be well mixed. Mixtures can also be gases. Air is such an example. While air seems homogenous, its composition varies from place to place and day to day, so it is classified as heterogeneous.

Classifying Matter can be quickly reviewed by using the chart below. You will be expected to know how to physically or chemically test to see what type of matter is present.

Some procedures or techniques used to determine the classification of matter include decanting, filtering, and distilling. Refer to Figure 1.3 and 1.4 for how to set up distillation and filtration.

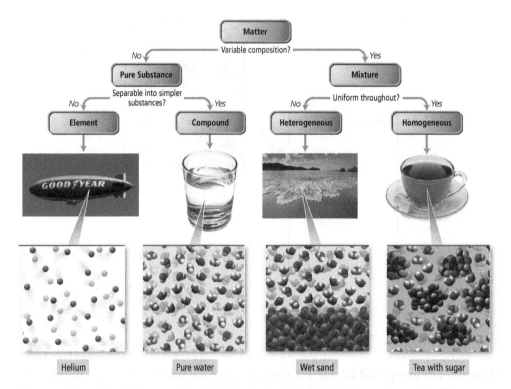

Figure 1.2 Classifying Matter according to Its Composition: Elements, Compounds, and Mixtures

Volatile is a term used for a liquid that is easily changed to its vapor state. Perfume contains volatile liquids that are easily changed to a vapor as evidenced by the way the odor moves through a room when a bottle of perfume is opened.

Decanting is a technique during which a heterogeneous mixture can be separated carefully by pouring one substance from the other. A mixture such as sand and water can be decanted by pouring off the layer of water.

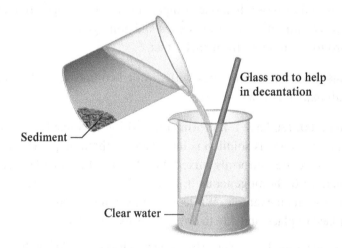

Distillation is a technique used to separate liquid substances, often in a homogeneous mixture, with different boiling points. The lower boiling point substance will boil off first and can be collected in a different flask, thereby separating two liquid substances. When a water and ethanol mixture is distilled, the ethanol will evaporate first.

Distillation

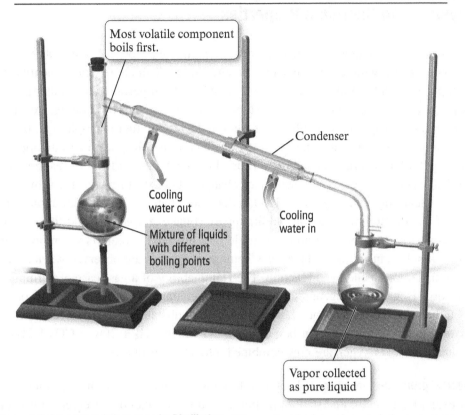

Most volatile component boils first.

Condenser

Cooling water out

Cooling water in

Mixture of liquids with different boiling points

Vapor collected as pure liquid

Figure 1.3 Separating Substances by Distillation   When a liquid mixture is heated, the component with the lowest boiling point vaporizes first, leaving behind less volatile liquids or dissolved solids. The vapor is then cooled, condensing it back to a liquid, and collected.

Filtration is a technique used to separate solids from liquids in a heterogeneous mixture. Filtration takes place by pouring a heterogeneous mixture through a funnel fitted with a piece of filter paper. Only liquids will move through the paper, separating solids such as precipitates from the liquid. Filtration will not separate a dissolved salt from water.

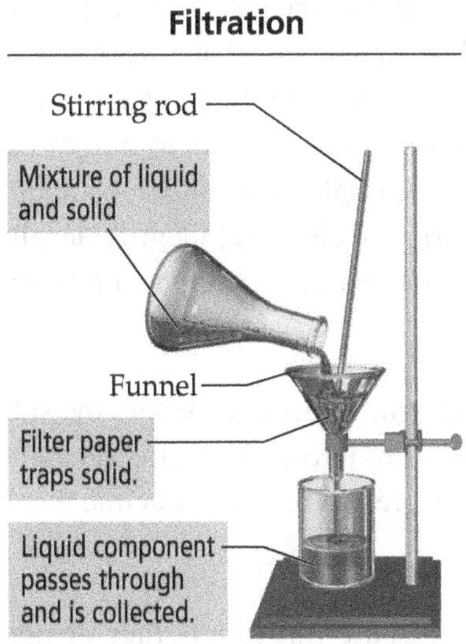

Filtration

Stirring rod

Mixture of liquid and solid

Funnel

Filter paper traps solid.

Liquid component passes through and is collected.

Figure 1.4 Separating Substances by Filtration   A solid and liquid mixture can be separated by pouring the mixture through a funnel containing filter paper designed to allow only the liquid to pass.

Section 1.4   **Physical and Chemical Changes and Physical and Chemical Properties**

The properties of matter are either physical or chemical properties. Physical properties are observed without the substance undergoing a chemical reaction. Identifying a sample as a white solid or blue solution are physical properties. Some other physical properties are the temperatures at which a substance undergoes boiling, freezing, condensation, evaporation, sublimation, and deposition. Other examples can be the observation that a substance has an odor, has a certain color, has a certain appearance, and/or has a certain density determined by a calculation from measurements. Physical changes occur when a substance changes state but it remains the same substance. Changing from $H_2O(s) \rightarrow H_2O(l)$ does not change the compound, only the state of matter. Boiling, freezing, subliming are some examples of conditions where a change of state occurs. Another example of a physical change is when one substance dissolves in another substance. Chemical properties are observed when a substance undergoes a chemical reaction. The flammability of a gas (ease of burning in air), corrosiveness, rusting, and toxicity are some examples. Chemical changes occur when the substance reacts and changes into a new substance. For instance, methane reacts with oxygen to make carbon dioxide and water. $CH_4 + 2O_2 \rightarrow CO_2 + 2H_2O$. The methane and oxygen are now combined into new substances.

Physical properties are observed without the substance undergoing change in identity. For example, the color and state of matter of a substance can be observed. However, some physical properties can only be observed by adding or removing energy, such as boiling or freezing, so the substance undergoes a change of state (see next page).

Chemical properties are only observed when the substance changes its composition in a chemical reaction. Gasoline is a flammable gas. Its chemical property of flammability is observed as gasoline undergoes a combustion reaction with oxygen to form the new substances of carbon dioxide and water.

Physical changes involve changes to the physical state or form of the substance without changing its identity. The changes in states from liquid water to water vapor by boiling or changing liquid water to ice by freezing are examples of physical changes. The composition is still two hydrogen atoms to one oxygen atom within the molecule. For example, cutting a sample of a solid substance in half will result in two pieces, both with the same original chemical identity despite their difference in physical appearance (shape). Some physical changes look very different in appearance such as ice and liquid water.

Chemical changes involve chemical reactions where the substances change into other substances. Gasoline combusting into carbon dioxide and water is an example. The original material is no longer present and new chemical substances can be identified as having been produced.

Looking at an equation is a good hint to whether or not a change is physical or chemical. If the formula is the same but only the phase has changed is physical and

Physical Change versus Chemical Change

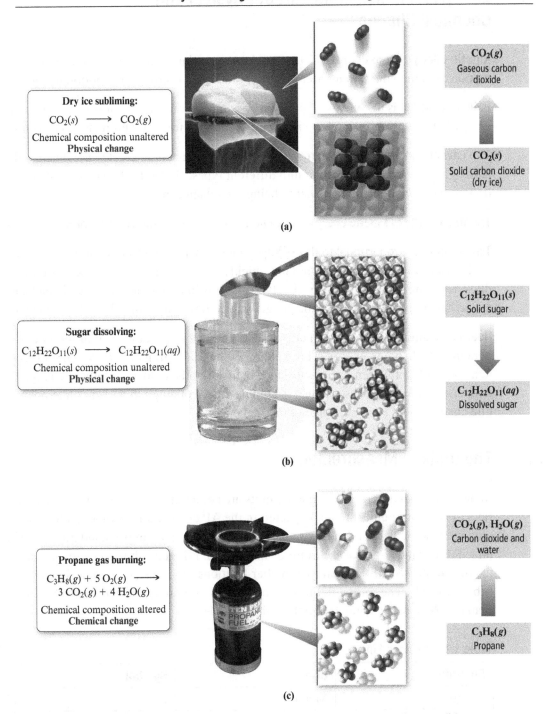

Figure 1.5 Physical and Chemical Changes   (a) The sublimation (the state change from a solid to a gas) of dry ice (solid CO_2) is a physical change. (b) The dissolution of sugar is a physical change. (c) The burning of propane is a chemical change.

if the formula has changed because the atoms have been rearranged is a chemical change. $H_2O(s) \rightarrow H_2O(l)$ is a physical change while $CH_4 + 2O_2 \rightarrow CO_2 + 2H_2O$ is a chemical change as new compounds have been made.

Section 1.5

Energy: A Fundamental Part of Physical and Chemical Change

Kinetic energy is the energy of motion. Atoms and/or molecules are constantly in motion as in the vibration motion within a solid or the translational motion in a gas.

Potential energy is the energy of position or composition. Compounds have potential energy in bonds. Substances have potential energy by virtue of their relative positions.

The **Law of Conservation of Energy** states that energy is neither created nor destroyed, although the energy may change into different types. (Refer to the law of conservation of mass *about* matter and energy being interchangeable.)

Thermal energy is kinetic energy associated with the temperature of an object.

Temperature is proportional to the average kinetic energy of a sample of matter. Molecules vibrating vigorously or moving quickly will have a higher temperature than those vibrating slowly or moving slowly. Note: It is important to understand that heat and temperature are NOT the same thing. Temperature is measured by a thermometer.

Heat is the amount of thermal energy transferred when two objects at different temperatures exchanging energy. Thermal energy naturally transfers from a hot object to a cooler object. When a pure substance melts or boils, it does so without changing temperature until the phase change is complete. Even though there is not a temperature change, there is an exchange of thermal energy.

Section 1.6

The Units of Measurement

In the U.S., both metric and nonmetric units are common. Conversions between metric and nonmetric units are not expected in the AP curriculum. Although chemistry only uses metric units, not all those units used are expressed in the standard basic SI unit. For instance, the basic SI unit of mass is the kilogram, but, in chemistry lab, the masses are usually in grams or smaller fractions of grams (such as milligrams, a sub-unit in SI). The formal definitions of each SI unit are not tested in the AP Curriculum. Review the symbols and the units in Table 1.1.

Table 1.1   SI Base Units

Quantity	Unit	Symbol
Length	Meter	m
Mass	Kilogram	kg
Time	Second	s
Temperature	Kelvin	K
Amount of substance	Mole	mol
Electric current	Ampere	A
Luminous intensity	Candela	cd

Mass is a measure of the quantity of matter. Mass is different from weight. Weight is gravitational force of attraction an object has toward a large body such as the Earth or moon. An object on the moon has the same mass on Earth but has a different weight since the gravitational force (gravity) is different in both locations.

Temperature was defined in the previous section. Knowledge of conversions between some units is necessary, such as converting between the temperature scales of Celsius and Kelvin. In this instance, the conversion is °C + 273.15 is the temperature in Kelvin since the degree itself is the same size in both scales, only the staring points of the scales differ. The AP Exam uses temperatures in Celsius and Kelvin. Most chemical equations that include temperature require the temperature in Kelvin.

Prefixes and how to use them to perform conversions between units are reviewed in Table 1.2, which shows the SI prefix multipliers. The highlighted rows are the most commonly used units. Common mistakes on the AP Exam are incorrect conversions between units. See Section 1.8 for examples.

Volume is a measure of the space matter occupies. Two volume units and equivalents important to be familiar with in AP chemistry are: 1 mL, which is equal in volume to 1 cm^3, and 1 L, which is equal to 1,000 mL or 1 dm^3 at standard conditions.

Derived units are units that are not directly observed because they are combinations of units, or in other words they are calculated units. Examples include units for density in g/mL and speed in m/s. Measurements of mass and volume can be observed and then used to determine the density of an object. Distance traveled and the time it took can be measured and then used to calculate speed. Derived units are usually ratios such us km/hr. It is important to be familiar with how to use them as conversion

Table 1.2 SI Prefix Multipliers.

Prefix	Symbol	Multiplier	
exa	E	1,000,000,000,000,000,000	(1×10^{18})
peta	P	1,000,000,000,000,000	(1×10^{15})
tera	T	1,000,000,000,000	(1×10^{12})
giga	G	1,000,000,000	(1×10^{9})
mega	M	1,000,000	(1×10^{6})
kilo	k	1000	(1×10^{3})
deci	d	0.1	(1×10^{-1})
centi	c	0.01	(1×10^{-2})
milli	m	0.001	(1×10^{-3})
micro	μ	0.000001	(1×10^{-6})
nano	n	0.000000001	(1×10^{-9})
pico	p	0.000000000001	(1×10^{-12})
femto	f	0.000000000000001	(1×10^{-15})
atto	a	0.000000000000000001	(1×10^{-18})

factors in problems. Sometimes a needed value can be measured or derived. For instance, volume can be directly measured in a graduated cylinder but volume can also be derived if length, width, and height were measured and the volume was calculated by multiplying the measurements together.

Density is a physical property that indicates the compactness of matter in a specific volume and is calculated from measurements of the mass and volume of an object. The density ratio is the mass divided by the volume of the object. No matter how the mass or volume of the substance changes, the ratio between the two variables for a given substance remains the same. Whether 175 g of water or 25 mL of water are present in a beaker, the ratio of mass to volume for water under standard conditions is 1.0 g/mL. A higher density indicates that more mass is found in the same volume. When identifying an unknown in a laboratory setting, the density of an object can be used as evidence for substance identification. For example, pure gold has a density of 19.3 g/cm^3. In jewelry, 24 carat gold is pure gold so if you buy a 24 carat bracelet, you can check to see if it is pure by checking its density using the following equation.

$$d = \frac{m}{V}$$

Since density is the ratio between mass and volume, density can also be determined from a graph with mass on the y axis and volume on the x axis. The slope of the line is the ratio of mass to volume and therefore the slope is also the density. Density is an intensive property since the amount of matter present does not change the value. In contrast, extensive properties change by how much matter is present. Examples of extensive properties are mass and volume.

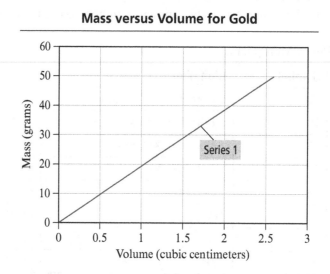

Mass versus Volume for Gold

Section 1.7   The Reliability of a Measurement

How to make or read others measurements is an important skill. Every scientific measurement is reported to a certain number of digits based on the device being used for the measurement. Every digit in the measurement is certain except for the last digit, which is approximate. A measurement reported as 22.46 g indicates for certain 22.4 grams are present but the last digit in the hundredths position indicates the 6 was close but not certain. The approximate digit is part of the significant figures in a measurement. This means the actual value was between 22.45 g and 22.47 g. In other words, there is a chance the last digit could be different by ± 0.01. In the reported measurement of 12.1 m, the uncertainty is ± 0.1 m.

Significant figures are the measured digits in a reported measurement and they do not include placeholders. The zero in 0.1 g is a placeholder and not significant while the one was measured is significant. The measurement 0.1 g has one significant figure.

Review how to determine the number of significant figures in a measurement with the following rules:

Nonzero digits are ALL significant. The measurement 234 g has three significant figures.

Zeros in a measurement

- Zeros between two nonzero digits were measured and are significant. The measurement 204 g has three significant figures. The hundreds and tens units were measured and the ones unit was the estimated digit.
- Zeros at the beginning of a number are placeholders and are not significant. The measurement 0.0021 cm has only two significant figures (the 2 and the 1).
- Zeros which are at the end of a number may or may not be significant. In 210 g, we do not know if the zero was measured. The key is the location and presence of a decimal point. When a decimal is present, the zeros were measured and are significant. 21.00 g has four significant figures. 20. g has two significant figures.
  - Zeros at the end of a number without a decimal are placeholders and are not significant figures. The measurement 210 g has two significant figures (the 2 and the 1). If all three digits were measured and the 210 g is exact, AP uses a decimal point after the zero to make the zero "significant," 210. g. It can also be written in scientific notation as 2.10×10^2 g. All digits in scientific notation are significant.

Exact numbers are counted, whole numbers and have unlimited significant figures. These include defined equivalency numbers used in conversion factor ratios, such as 1000 mL = 1 L. The 1 L has an unlimited number of significant figures. Be careful about how you write your measurements!

Significant Figures in Calculations

The proper use of significant figures is expected in all calculations. "Rounding" is the process used for reporting results of complex calculations correctly. Remember to only round once in a problem—at the end. Keeping track of the number of significant figures to record when there are multiple operations is important. Why only round once? Rounding each time there is a calculation compounds the error in the answer.

The following rules are used in calculations with significant figures:

- Multiplication and division both round to the least number of digits found in the measurements being used in the calculation. For example, to find the density of a compound the mass is divided by the volume. If the mass is 10.0 g, a three digit number, and the volume is 5.0 mL, a two digit number, then the density is 10.0 g ÷ 5.0 mL = 2.0 g/mL. The two digits in the volume indicate the final answer will have two significant figures.

- Addition and subtraction round to the least precise of the starting measurements. For instance in the example 120.0 g − 58 g, 120.0 g is measured to the tenth place and 58 g is measured to the whole number. 58 g has the least precise place value of the two measurements indicating the final answer should be rounded to the whole number or 62 g.

- Only look at the next digit to determine how to round to the correct number of significant figures. A 5 or higher in the next digit rounds up and a 4 or lower rounds down. 22.47 g rounded to the tenth is 22.5 g, whereas 22.445 g rounded to the tenth is 22.4 g.

These rules are how the scientists communicate about the tools that were used in making their measurements and are expected to be used in the AP Chemistry Course as well as on the AP Chemistry Exam.

Accuracy is how close a measurement is to its true value (when this is known).

Precision is how close a series of measurements are to each other. Often precision is expressed relative to the mean (average) value of a series of measurements of the same parameter. How close repeated measurements are to each other is an example of precision. For example, if one measures the mass of a bar of copper on the same balance three times: 5.258 g, 5.257 g, 5.257 g, the measurements are considered precise.

Measurements can be precise and accurate (a measurement close to the true value multiple times), precise and inaccurate (the same wrong measurement several times), and accurate and imprecise (averaging close to the true value, but the measurements are not close to each other).

Section 1.8   Solving Chemical Problems

Conversion factors are ratios using the relationship between the two units to convert from one unit to the other. The ratio is written so the units cancel to result in the new desired unit. For example, if you are converting between liters and milliliters there are you could say 1000 mL in 1 L or 1 L contains 1000 mL. $\dfrac{1000\ \text{mL}}{1\ \text{L}}$ is the conversion factor to cancel the L, but if the conversion is from milliliters to liters it would be written as $\dfrac{1\ \text{L}}{1000\ \text{mL}}$ to cancel the mL.

Dimensional analysis uses relationships among units as a way to solve problems. For instance, if converting the speed 21.4 km per hour (km·hr^{-1} or km/hr) to meters per second (m·s^{-1} or m/s), there will be two conversions steps. One step is converting kilometers to meters and the other step is converting hours to seconds. Using the conversion factors $\dfrac{1000\ \text{m}}{1\ \text{km}}$ and $\dfrac{1\ \text{hr}}{3600\ \text{s}}$, the problem would be written as

$$\frac{21.4\ \text{km}}{1\ \text{hr}} \times \frac{1000\ \text{m}}{1\ \text{km}} \times \frac{1\ \text{hr}}{3600\ \text{s}}$$

$$\frac{21.4\ \cancel{\text{km}}}{1\ \cancel{\text{hr}}} \times \frac{1000\ \text{m}}{1\ \cancel{\text{km}}} \times \frac{1\ \cancel{\text{hr}}}{3600\ \text{s}} = 5.94\ \text{m/s}$$

The first step converted the km unit to m and the second step converted the hr unit to s. You can see here the canceling of the units so you are left with the correct units. This process is used throughout the chemistry curriculum in numerical problems.

Analyzing and Interpreting Data   Section 1.9

Arranging data in tables and graphs often helps to identify patterns in the data. The units used in the graph, the intervals in the data, relationships such as direct and inverse can be identified and used. In each chapter, how to analyze and interpret data will be addressed specific to the content.

Additional Practice

Self-Assessment Quiz Questions Q2, Q3, Q4, Q6, Q7, Q8, Q9, Q11, Q12, and Q16
Problems:
Classify 37, 40–50
Units 59–61
Density 65, 66, 69, 70, 73–78, 80–82
Significant Figures 83–90
Unit Connections 91, 92, 100
Cumulative 105, 107, 115
Concept 143, 144, 148
Group 150
Data 155

Equations to know:
$K = °C + 273.15$
$d = m/v$

Practice AP Test Questions

1. This thermometer is measuring the temperature of a liquid in units of Celsius. What is the correct temperature using the proper number of significant figures?

A) 19.7

B) 20.3

C) 19.70

D) 19.59

2. Which of the following is not a physical property of chlorine gas?

   A) Chlorine gas has a pale green color.

   B) The normal boiling point of chlorine gas is 239 K.

   C) Chlorine gas irritates the mucus membranes.

   D) The density of chlorine gas at STP is 3.2 g/L.

3. Which of the following can be separated using filtration?

   A) A solution of sodium chloride.

   B) Copper turnings in water.

   C) Oxygen and helium gas in a gas cylinder.

   D) 5% skim milk.

4. Provide the reason for selection of your answer to the previous problem.

   A) All mixtures can be easily separated using physical techniques such as filtration, decanting, and evaporation.

   B) The solvent in a solution can be separated from the solute by filtration since the solute and solvent do not react.

   C) Any component of a homogeneous mixture that is visible can be separated by filtration because the particles are too large to pass through the small holes in the filter paper.

   D) If a substance is not soluble in a solvent, filtration can be used to separate the two components because the insoluble substance is too large to pass through the holes in the filter paper.

5. Which drawing at the particulate level of matter best represents a small sample of Helium gas?

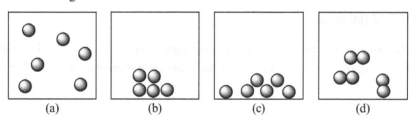

   (a)   (b)   (c)   (d)

6. The following particulate level model represents an initial state and a final state.

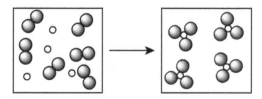

   This is a representation of a

   A) physical process   B) chemical reaction   C) nuclear reaction

7. A block of iron (*density* = 7.86 g/cm³) has a mass of 12.4 g. What is the mass of a block of silicon (*density* = 2.65 g/cm³) occupying the same volume as the block of iron?

   A) 4.19 g   B) 2.97 g   C) 1.68 g   D) 1.58 g

8. A cube of an unknown metal measures 10.41 mm on one side. The mass of the cube is 10.11 g. Which of the following is most likely the unknown metal?

	Metal	Density (g/cm³)
A.	gold	19.32
B.	copper	8.96
C.	iron	7.86
D.	zirconium	6.51

9. The following particulate level model represents a small volume of a sample of matter

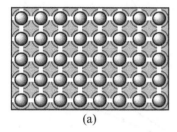 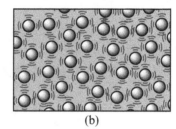 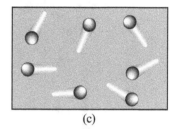

   (a)   (b)   (c)

   Which diagram represents a solid sample of matter?

   A) (a)   B) (b)   C) (c)

10. Which element is a good conductor of heat and electricity?

   A) carbon   B) oxygen   C) argon   D) sodium

Data Interpretation and Analysis Question: Thermal Conductance

When designing for insulation, it is important to know that metals such as copper and silver have high thermal conductivity, meaning copper and silver allow for quick transfer of heat and are not good insulators. Polystyrene, $(C_8H_8)_n$, and alumina have low thermal conductivity and are good insulators. The SI units of thermal conductivity are watts per meter kelvin $(W/(m \cdot K))$. One watt is defined as the energy consumption rate of one joule per second, $1W = 1J/1s$. When selecting insulating materials for the Space Shuttle, four different materials were subjected to increasing temperatures and the thermal conductivity was measured. The following graph plots thermal conductivity versus temperature.

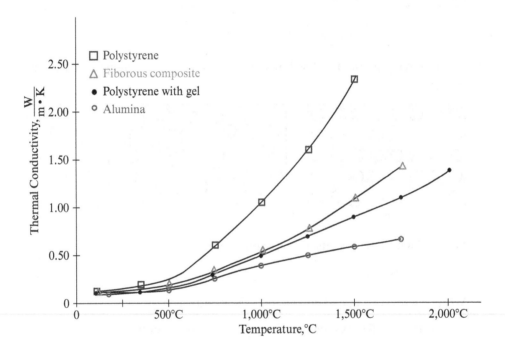

Answer the following questions based on the information presented above.

i. Which material is the best insulator at 1,500 °C?

   A) polystyrene   B) fibrous composite

   C) polystyrene-filled with gel foam   D) alumina

ii. Which material is the best insulator at 2,000 °C?

   A) polystyrene   B) fibrous composite

   C) polystyrene-filled with gel foam   D) alumina

iii. A length of 0.250 m of polystyrene was tested at four different temperatures. Which temperature allowed the most transfer of heat?

   A) 750 °C   B) 1,250 °C

   C) 1,000 °C   D) 1,500 °C

iv. A length of 0.250 m of alumina was tested for thermal conductivity at 1,000. °C for 2.00 minutes. How much heat was transferred in units of Joules?

A) 1.06 J   B) 200. J

C) 250. J   D) 15,300 J

v. *Thermal conductance* is the quantity of heat that passes in unit time through a metal plate of *particular area and thickness* when it is in contact with a second metal plate with a difference in temperature of one kelvin. For a plate of thermal conductivity k, area A and thickness L, the conductance calculated is kA/L, measured in $W \cdot K^{-1}$ (equivalent to: W/°C). The thermal conductance is the inverse of the thermal resistance. A sample of polystyrene with gel has the following dimensions (l × w × h): 50.0 cm × 25.0 cm × 5.00 cm. Calculate the *thermal conductance at 1,740 °C.*

A) 2.75 W/°C   B) 275 W/°C   C) 2750 W/°C   D) 2750 0 W/°C

Polystyrene has the following structure

vi. Classify polystyrene with as many of the following that apply.

A) pure substance, homogeneous   B) heterogeneous mixture

C) element   D) compound

Data Interpretation and Analysis Question Answers with Brief Explanations

i. D) Of the four materials, alumina has the lowest thermal conductivity, meaning it will not transfer heat very well.

ii. C) At 2000 °C, the only material on the graph with a data point is polystyrene filled with gel foam. Since the other materials do not have a data point, we can only assume the materials will break down after 1500 °C.

iii. C) At 1000 °C, polystyrene conducts heat faster compared to the other three materials.

iv. D) 15,300 J was transferred. 0.400 WmK(.250 m)(1,273K)(1J/Sec/W)(120. sec).

v. A) 2.75 W/°C Thermal conductance = kA/L = [1.10 (W/mK) × (1 m/100 cm) × 1250 cm²]/5.00 cm

vi. A) pure substance, homogeneous and D) compound.

READING GUIDE

This is a foundational chapter included in the AP Chemistry curriculum. Many of these concepts and skills are review from previous science classes. Be sure to read Chapter 1 in your book. The questions in the reading guide are written to have you synthesize material not to just "copy" an answer form the text. In AP, you need to be able to define, classify, compare similarities, explain differences, juxtapose (place side by side and compare and/or contrast), explain cause and effect, and explain consequences.

As you read, make a list of the Concepts and Vocabulary to Review in Chapter 1.

Section 1.1   Atoms and Molecules

1. What are atoms and how are they different than molecules? Provide an example of a substance that is comprised only atoms. Provide an example of a substance comprised of molecules. What is the difference between atoms and molecules? Graphite and diamond are made only of carbon atoms, why don't graphite and diamond have the same properties? Composed of the same atoms, hydrogen and oxygen, explain why water and hydrogen peroxide have different properties.

Section 1.2   The Scientific Approach to Knowledge

2. What is the scientific process? Explain the steps of this process. A diagram can be used to augment your explanation.

3. How does this scientific process lead to the development of laws and theories?

4. Explain the contributions of the following scientists (include evidence each scientist used):

   Antoine Lavoisier:

   John Dalton:

5. In your own words, explain the Law of Conservation of Mass and give an example.

Section 1.3   The Classification of Matter

6. What is matter? Explain the differences among solids, liquids, gases, crystal-line, and amorphous substances. Use drawings if appropriate. Justify your answer with evidence from the characteristics of each.

7. Fill in the chart below:

Type of Matter	Example	Shape	Volume
Solid			
Liquid			
Gas			
Amorphous Substance			
Crystalline Substance			

Which of these types of matter is compressible? Justify your answer.

8. Draw a concept map showing the relationship among matter, atoms, elements, substances, compounds, mixtures, homogeneous mixtures, and heterogeneous mixtures. In your map, include examples and linking words, explaining how each heading relates to the others.

9. Explain what a volatile substance is and how to determine which substance is more volatile in a distillation.

10. Draw diagrams to help explain the differences in the following techniques used in separating mixtures: decanting, distillation, and filtration. What does each technique separate? Give an example of a use for each technique.

   Decanting:

   Distillation:

   Filtration:

Physical and Chemical Changes and Physical and Chemical Properties   Section 1.4

11. What is a physical change? Give three examples. (Use drawings if appropriate.)

12. What is a chemical change? Give three examples. (Use drawings if appropriate.)

13. In lab, how could you distinguish between physical change and chemical change?

14. What is a physical property? Give three examples.

15. What is a chemical property? Give three examples.

16. How can you tell the difference between a physical property and a chemical property?

Section 1.5   **Energy: A Fundamental Part of Physical and Chemical Change**

17. What is energy? Explain the different types of energy and give an example of each. (Use drawings if appropriate.)

    Kinetic Energy:

    Potential Energy:

    Thermal Energy:

18. Explain the Law of Conservation of Energy, compare and contrast it to the Law of Conservation of Mass.

Section 1.6   **The Units of Measurement**

19. What type of unit system of measurement is used in chemistry?

20. For each quantity in the chart below, give the SI unit and symbol.

Quantity	Temperature	Time	Length	Mass	Amount of Substance	Electric Current
Unit						
Symbol						

21. Define each of the following units:

    Meter:

    Kilogram:

    Second:

    Kelvin:

22. List two reasons why chemists use mass instead of weight.

23. Define the following terms:

    Temperature:

    Heat:

24. Explain the difference between heat and temperature. Include an example in your answer.

25. How does one change from a temperature in degrees Celsius to a temperature in Kelvin?

26. Fill in the following table of prefixes often used in chemistry:

Prefix	Kilo-	Deci-	Centi-	Milli-	Nano-
Symbol					
Multiplier					

27. What is a derived unit?

28. Give three examples of a derived unit.

29. Explain what volume is. Include an example in your answer.

30. What are two common units of volume and their symbols used in chemistry?

31. What is the name of the relationship between the mass and the volume of a substance?

32. Liquid water and ice have different densities. Sketch a diagram of how the molecules in each substance are arranged. Use this diagram to explain why liquid water is denser than ice.

33. Look up the density of liquid water at 1.0°C, 4°C, 20°C, and 60°C and record the values. (Be sure to include units.) What is occurring at the molecular level causing the density of water to vary with temperature? Explain why density is an intensive property of matter?

The Reliability of a Measurement   Section 1.7

34. How is the reliability of a measurement indicated in science? How does one record uncertainty in a measurement?

35. Explain how to make a measurement correctly. Use an example in your answer such as finding the length of a strip of metal.

36. What are significant figures? Why are significant figures important to use?

37. Explain how to determine the number of significant figures in a measurement and how to record the uncertainty of a measurement.

38. State the number of significant figures present in each measurement and explain the rules used to determine the number of significant figures in the following measurements:

1.00350 g:

1.0020 g:

240 g:

What are exact numbers and how many significant figures are in an exact number?

39. Explain how to round a numerical value in a chemistry calculation.

40. In a series of calculations, why is it better to only round once at the end?

41. Explain how to determine the number of significant figures in the final result of a calculation using multiplication or division.

42. Explain how to determine the number of significant figures in the final result of a calculation using addition or subtraction.

43. Explain the difference between accuracy and precision. Include an example of each. What is the difference between systematic and random error?

Section 1.8   Solving Chemical Problems

44. What is a conversion factor?

45. How would you set up a problem to convert 37.0 mL to L?

46. What is dimensional analysis and why do chemists use it?

47. Show how to set up a problem to convert 0.075 km/hr to m/s. Why is it important to always include units in all set-ups and answers in chemistry?

Section 1.9   Analyzing and Interpreting Data

48. What are two ways to organize data to check for patterns in the data? In a graph, how can you identify what is being represented?

Self-Assessment Answers

1. _____   2. _____   3. _____

4. _____   5. _____   6. _____

7. _____   8. _____   9. _____

10. _____   11. _____   12. _____

13. _____   14. _____   15. _____

16. _____

ATOMS AND ELEMENTS

To understand the development of our current knowledge of atoms and their structure, there are several points in this chapter that require your attention. In the past, some concepts that we now accept regarding the atom were met with skepticism and were not readily accepted. Other ideas have been discarded in light of more recent evidence. In this chapter, pay particular attention to the **DATA** leading to the change or new concept being introduced and the new MODEL created by this evidence. The most important sections to review are as follows:

Specific Learning Objectives Addressed in This Chapter:

Learning Objective SPQ-1.A Calculate quantities of a substance or its relative number of particles using dimensional analysis and the mole concept.

Learning Objective SPQ-1.B Explain the quantitative relationship between the mass spectrum of an element and the masses of the element's isotopes.

Learning Objective SPQ-2.A Explain the quantitative relationship between the elemental composition by mass and the empirical formula of a pure substance.

Concepts and Vocabulary to Review:

Brownian Motion: Atoms Confirmed   Section 2.1

Historically, over two hundred years of experimental work including that of Albert Einstein and Jean Perrin explained the particulate nature of matter. Today there are about ninety-one naturally occurring elements and scientists through a variety of methods have formed over twenty synthetic elements. The actual number of natural elements is debated as some of the synthetic elements are thought to have trace amounts in nature.

Section 2.3   **Modern Atomic Theory and the Laws That Led to It**

Antoine Lavoisier stated in the **Law of Conservation of Mass** that the mass of reactants used in a chemical reaction will equal the mass of the products. This statement indicates atoms are conserved in chemical reactions. This concept is a building block of atomic theory. If 20.0 grams of reactant are reacted completely, 20.0 grams of product will form.

With the **Law of Definite Proportions,** Joseph Proust stated that all the elements composing a specific compound are always found in exact or fixed ratios of weight (mass) in the compound. In contrast, mixtures can have a variety of ratios. The compound water (H_2O) is always 16.0 g of oxygen atoms to 2.0 g of hydrogen atoms, which is a ratio of 8:1. Brass while made of copper and zinc atoms, can have differing amounts of each component resulting in different grades of brass. These are not in a definite proportion.

With the **Law of Multiple Proportions,** John Dalton stated that when two elements combine to form different compounds, the atoms in each of the compounds formed have a different fixed ratio. For instance, both water and hydrogen peroxide are both made of only hydrogen and oxygen atoms. Water as noted above has a ratio of 8:1 by mass, but hydrogen peroxide (H_2O_2) has 32.0 g of oxygen atoms to 2.0 g of hydrogen atoms, which is a ratio of 16:1 by mass. The ratio of mass of oxygen in water (8:1) to mass of oxygen in hydrogen peroxide (16:1) is 1:2. Using Dalton's theory, there must be twice as many oxygen atoms in hydrogen peroxide compared to the number of oxygen atoms in water.

The following data and the determination of a chemical formula would be an example of Learning Objective SPQ-2.A of using data to confirm conservation of matter and the law of definite proportions.

In a series of experiments, a chemist analyzed two different compounds containing only titanium and bromine and determined the mass of each element in each compound.

Compound	Mass of Bromine (g)	Mass of Titanium (g)
1	17.394	2.605
2	15.390	4.610

Calculate the mass of bromine per gram of titanium in each compound. How do the numbers support the atomic theory?

$$\text{Compound 1} \quad \frac{17.394 \text{ g Br}}{2.605 \text{ g Ti}} = \frac{6.69 \text{ g Br}}{1 \text{ g Ti}}$$

$$\text{Compound 2} \quad \frac{15.390 \text{ g Br}}{4.610 \text{ g Ti}} = \frac{3.34 \text{ g Br}}{1 \text{ g Ti}}$$

$$\frac{\text{Compound 1}}{\text{Compound 2}} = \frac{6.69 \text{ g Br}}{3.34 \text{ g Br}} = \frac{2}{1}$$

The ratio of the mass in units of grams of bromine in compound 1 to the mass of bromine in compound 2 is 2:1. This ratio uses small whole numbers. The two compounds obey the law of multiple proportions. The only way for this to occur is for the bromine and titanium to combine using atoms. For every one bromine atom in compound 2 there are two bromine atoms in compound 1. Possible compounds include $TiBr$, $TiBr_2$ and $TiBr_4$ or $TiBr_3$ and $TiBr_6$. Additional calculations can be done using the above data to determine which formulas fit the data.

Dalton reintroduced the idea of the existence of atoms, saying that all matter is composed of atoms; the atoms combine in whole number ratios; and in chemical reactions, atoms cannot change into other types of atoms. A hydrogen atom is always a hydrogen atom. (Only nuclear reactions can change the type.) He also stated ALL atoms of the same element have the same mass, which was later disproved. There is no single mass for a given element due to the existence of isotopes, which creates a range of masses for each element. A periodic table of the elements will list the weighted average mass of all of the naturally occurring isotopes of the element.

The Discovery of the Electron   Section 2.4

J.J. Thompson using cathode ray tubes discovered the electron, a negatively charged subatomic particle with very little mass. This was done by applying high electrical charges at the ends of a cathode ray tube.

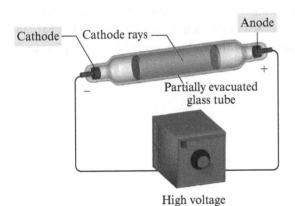
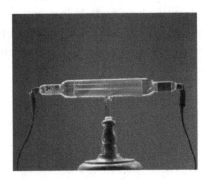

Figure 2.1 Cathode Ray Tube

The rays travel in straight lines and carry a negative electrical charge. The ray can be bent by approaching the ray with a positive charge. Thompson was able to calculate the charge to -1.76×10^8 Coulombs per gram indicating the electron was very small in comparison to the atom.

Robert Millikan followed this up with his oil drop experiment indicating the charge of a single electron was -1.60×10^{-19} C (coulombs). Combining this data with J.J. Thompson's charge to mass ratio, the mass of the electron was then calculated to be 9.10×10^{-28} g.

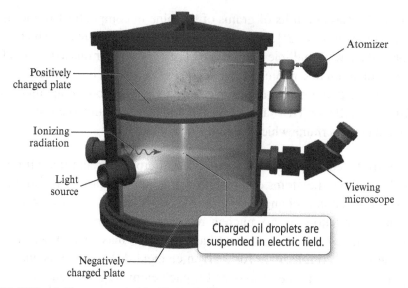

Figure 2.2 Millikan's Measurement of the Electron's Charge   Millikan calculated the charge on oil droplets falling in an electric field. He found that it was always a whole-number multiple of -1.60×10^{-19} C, the charge of a single electron.

Section 2.5   The Structure of the Atom

Henri Becquerel and Marie Curie discovered radioactivity of atoms. Ernest Rutherford was able to separate this radioactivity into alpha particles, beta particles, and gamma rays. These discoveries were used to help probe the atom. The alpha particle is positively charged and in a magnetic field is attracted to a negatively charged plate, the beta particle is negatively charged and is attracted to a positively charged plate, and the gamma ray has no charge and will not be attracted to either plate and will pass straight through a magnetic field.

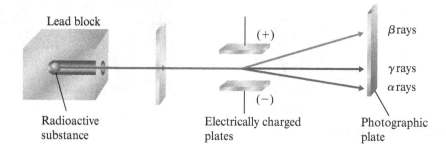

From the discovery of the electron, **J.J. Thompson** suggested the atom was like a positive pudding with electrons spread through it—this is known as the **plum pudding model**.

If the Thompson model of the atom was correct, the positively charged alpha particles should pass straight through gold foil. Ernest Rutherford and his co-workers set up a gold foil experiment to test this. Instead, he found some of the alpha particles were deflected and some bounced back. These results changed the concept of the plum pudding model to a **nuclear model**. Rutherford found there had to be a dense, positively charged area in the atom to repel alpha particles (He^{2+}) being shot through the atom. The core of the atom, where the dense positive charge was located, he called the nucleus of the atom. The positive particles were called protons. The protons accounted for about half of the mass of the atom. In contrast to the dense, closely packed nucleus, the rest of the atom where the electrons were found was mostly empty space (See Figures 2.4 and 2.5).

The last particle was hard to observe since it was neutral in charge. This was the neutron and was identified by James Chadwick although it had been observed earlier. This particle explained the unaccounted for mass of the atom.

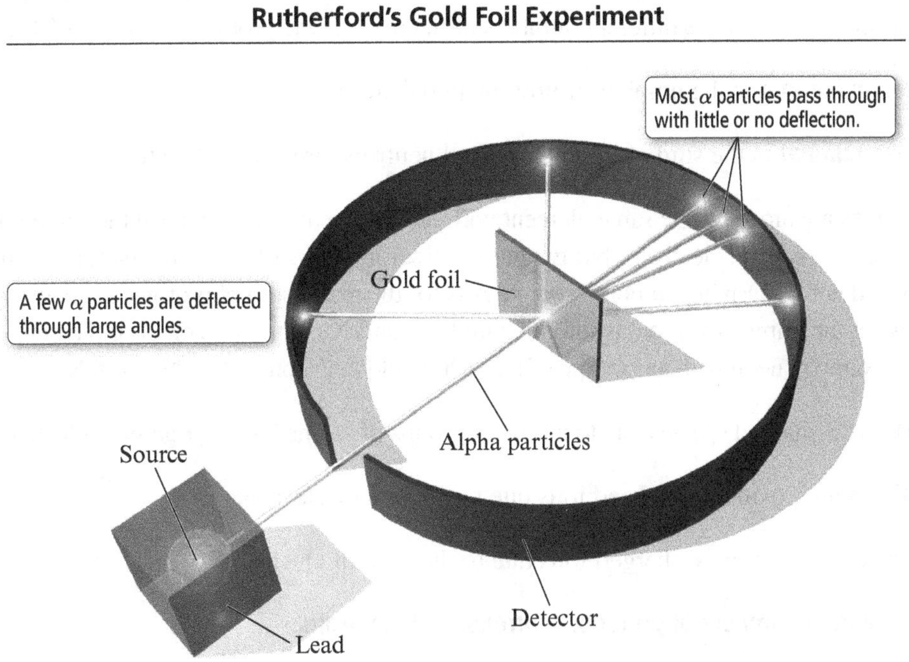

Rutherford's Gold Foil Experiment

Most α particles pass through with little or no deflection.

A few α particles are deflected through large angles.

Gold foil

Alpha particles

Source

Lead

Detector

Figure 2.3 Rutherford's Gold Foil Experiment   Alpha particles are directed at a thin sheet of gold foil. Most of the particles pass through the foil, but a small fraction are deflected, and a few even bounce backward.

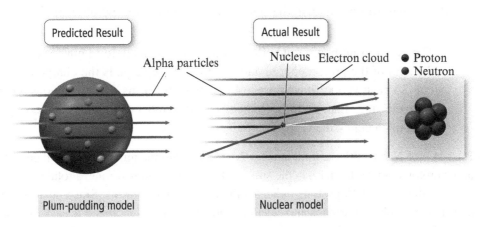

Predicted Result

Actual Result

Alpha particles

Nucleus   Electron cloud

● Proton
● Neutron

Plum-pudding model

Nuclear model

Figure 2.4 The Nuclear Atom   Rutherford's results could not be explained by the plum-pudding model. Instead, they suggest that the atom has a small, dense positively charged nucleus.

Section 2.6   **Subatomic Particles: Protons, Neutrons, and Electrons in Atoms**

Chemical symbols represent the elements on the periodic table. Even though the names of the elements may vary in different countries, the symbols are the same. The periodic table provided on the AP Exam has the symbols for each element, therefore you should know the names of the elements. These will not be test questions themselves but will help during testing to locate the information quickly. Some errors on the exam occur because students do not know the symbols and for example will use the mass of titanium (Ti) for the mass of tin (Sn).

Atomic mass unit is $1/12$ th the mass of a carbon-12 atom with six protons and six neutrons (carbon can have different numbers of neutrons). One proton has a mass of 1 amu.

Atomic number is the number of protons in the atom.

Mass number is the sum of the protons and neutrons present in the atom.

Isotopes are atoms of the same element with different masses. They have the same number of protons and electrons, but greater or lesser numbers of neutrons. Isotopes can be notated with a dash or symbol $^A_Z X$ where A is for the mass (sum of protons and neutrons), Z is for the number of protons (atomic number), and X is for the symbol of the element. For example, neon with an isotope of mass 20 could be Neon – 20, ^{20}Ne, or $^{20}_{10}$Ne.

Ions are a charged species due to atoms or groups of atoms losing or gaining electrons.

Cations are positively charged ions due to the loss of electrons.

Anions are negatively charged ions due to the gain of electrons.

Calculating numbers of protons, neutrons, and electrons:

   ✓ The proton number is the atomic number of the atom. $A\# = \#p$
   ✓ The mass number is the sum of the number of protons and neutrons. $Mass\# = p + n$
   ✓ The neutron number is the mass number minus the number of protons. $Mass\# - p = n$
   ✓ The electron number equals the proton number in an atom but for an ion, the sum of the proton charge and electron charge equals the charge of the ion. So positive ions have more protons than electrons whereas anions have more electrons than protons. Remember, the number of protons can't change without changing the type of atom it is.

In the case of Neon – 20, the total mass is 20. Neon is atomic number 10 and therefore has 10 protons. Since the mass is the sum of the protons and neutrons, a total mass of 20 minus the mass of 10 protons indicates the mass of 10 neutrons. Since neon is not charged, the number of protons and electrons must be equal. Note that it is easier to use mass values in amu or Daltons (symbol Da) than grams because the mass is so small. A carbon-12 atom is defined to have a mass of 12.0000 Da or 12.0000 amu.

Summary table of subatomic particles:

Particle	Charge (Relative)	Mass (g)	Mass (amu or Da)
Proton	+1	1.672×10^{-24}	1.00727
Neutron	0	1.674×10^{-24}	1.00866
Electron	−1	9.10×10^{-20}	0.00055

Finding Patterns: The Periodic Law and the Periodic Table   Section 2.7

Many scientists suggested ways of organizing the elements into a table based on repeating patterns of similarities in elements. The modern table base is attributed to Dmitri Mendeleev. While there are many correct important elements in the table he proposed, he incorrectly suggested elements increased by mass and not by an elements atomic number (number of protons). Mendeleev also suggest the presence of eka-silicon which was later discovered and named germanium.

The periodic table is arranged with metals on the left and nonmetals on the right. Where there is a transition between metals and nonmetals is the location of the semi-metals or metalloids. Most of the table is comprised of metals.

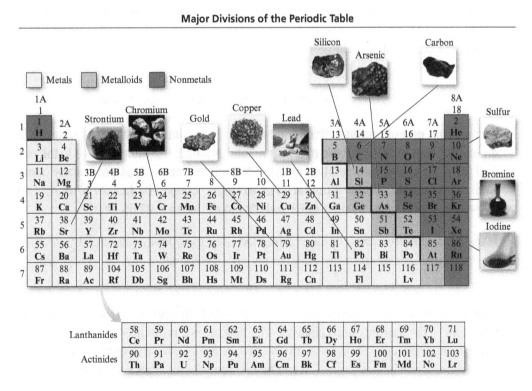

Figure 2.5 Metals, Nonmetals, and Metalloids   The elements in the periodic table fall into these three broad classes.

Several of the columns or families are given names. Column 1 is called the Alkali metals, Column 2 is called the Alkaline earth metals, column 16 is called the chalcogens, column 17 is called the halogens, and 18 is called the noble gases. All the elements in columns 3 – 12 are transition elements filling d orbitals and the two rows pulled out below are filling f orbitals. This will be discussed in chapter 9.

When metals form cations, they lose electrons. The number of electrons lost is one of the patterns within a family. The alkali metals all lose one electron and form cations with a 1+ charge. When nonmetals form anions, they gain electrons. The number of electrons gained is a pattern within families of nonmetals. The halogens all gain one electron to form a 1− charge.

Section 2.8   Atomic Mass: The Average Mass of an Element's Atoms

Atomic mass is the average mass of an atom of an element. Because elements can have isotopes, the mass on the periodic table is a weighted average of the isotopic masses. The main isotopes of carbon have masses of 12 amu, 13 amu, and 14 amu, and the mass on the table is 12.01 amu, therefore, we know there must be a much higher percentage of carbon with a mass of 12 than carbon with a mass of 13 amu or 14 amu since the average mass is closest to the isotope with a mass of 12 amu.

$$\text{Atomic mass} = \sum (\text{fraction of isotope } z \times \text{mass of isotope } z)$$
$$+ (\text{fraction of isotope } y \times \text{mass of isotope } y).$$

Copper has two isotopes: copper 63(62.94) with an abundance of 69.17% and copper 65(64.93) with an abundance of 62.94%. The weighted average atomic mass of copper can be calculated as follows:

$$\text{Atomic mass Cu} = (0.6917 \times 62.94 \text{ amu})$$
$$+ (0.3083 \times 64.93 \text{ amu}) = 63.55 \text{ amu}$$

Be sure you do not confuse atomic mass and mass number. The mass number is an integer sum of the numbers of neutrons and protons; the atomic mass is the actual mass (in appropriate relative units) of the atoms and so does not usually come to an exact whole number (integer). For example, copper-63 has 29 protons and 34 neutrons for a mass number of 63 and it's atomic mass is 63.55 amu.

Mass spectrometry is a technique or method used to separate particles by mass. It separates isotopes of atoms by mass so the relative abundance of an isotope can be determined.

Vaporized atoms are ionized and then accelerated through a magnetic field. The trajectory of the ionized atoms changes. The lighter ones move more, separating them from the heavier ones. From knowing the percentage of each mass in the sample, the average mass can be determined. It can be used to identify what is in a sample.

Mass Spectrometer

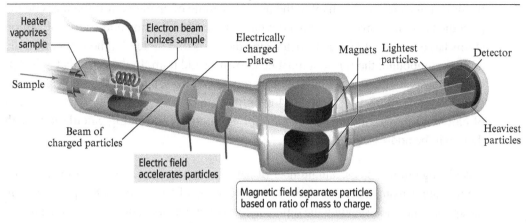

Figure 2.6 The Mass Spectrometer Atoms are converted to positively charged ions, accelerated, and passed through a magnetic field that deflects their path. The heaviest ions undergo the least deflection.

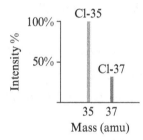

Figure 2.7 The Mass Spectrum of Chlorine The position of each peak on the *x*-axis indicates the exact mass of each isotope. The intensity (or height) of the peak indicates the relative abundance of the isotope. The intensity of the highest peak is usually set to 100% and the intensity of all other peaks is reported relative to the most intense one.

The intensity indicates relative abundance. The one in the greatest abundance is set at 100% (normalized) and the others are in relationship to it. From a spectrum such as this, the weighted average mass of an element can be calculated. In Figure 2.7, Cl-35 has the largest abundance so it is artificially set to 100%. The Cl-37 isotope is set as a relative ratio of about 32% intensity. To calculate the % abundance of Cl-35, take $\{100/(100 + 32)\} = 0.758$ or 75.8%. To calculate the % abundance of Cl-37, take $\{32/(100 + 32)\} = 0.242$ or 24.2%. From these percentages, the isotopic mass can be calculated. $(35 \times 0.758) + (37 \times 0.242) = 35.5$ amu.

Molar Mass: Counting Atoms by Weighing Them   Section 2.9

1 Mole represents 6.022×10^{23} particles. It is similar to using the word dozen. When we hear one dozen, we think of the number 12. It could be oranges, apples, anything. Two dozen is 24, half a dozen is 6 and so on. When you hear mole, think of 6.022×10^{23}. You can also have multiples or fractions of a mole. By definition, a mole is equal to the number of atoms in exactly 12.0 grams of carbon-12.

Avogadro's number (he did not determine the number, but it is named after him) is the number of things (usually atoms or molecules) in a mole, so 6.022×10^{23}.

Molar mass is the mass of one mole of the same thing; this could be atoms, molecules, formula units, etc. In this chapter, the mass of a mole of an element is the mass on the periodic table in grams. A carbon atom has a mass of 12.01 amu and 1 mole of carbon atoms has a mass of 12.01 g. To determine the mass of a mole of a molecule, formula unit, or compound, the formula must be known to add it up. In the formula $Ca(NO_3)_2$ there is one calcium, two nitrogen and six oxygen atoms. The molar mass is calculated as follows: $1(40.08 \text{ g/mol}) + 2(14.01 \text{ g/mol}) + 6(16.00 \text{ g/mol}) = 164.10 \text{ g/mol}$ of calcium nitrate. Adding molar mass of compounds and doing calculations with them will be addressed in Chapter 4.

Calculating grams, moles, and number of particles in a species and converting between them requires using a periodic table to find the mass of a mole of each type of atom in the species and understanding the different conversion factors between each of the units.

Additional Practice

Self-Assessment Questions Q1, Q3, Q5, Q6, Q7, Q8, Q10, Q11, Q12, Q13, Q14, and Q15
Problems:
Atomic Theory, Nuclear Theory, and subatomic particles 39–42, 46–48
Isotopes and Ions 51–54, 56, 58, 61, 62
The Periodic Table and Atomic Mass 68–72, 74, 76–80
The Mole Concept 81–89
Cumulative Problems 104, 105, 117
Conceptual 132
Data Analysis 142

Equations to know:

$n = m/M$

number of moles = mass/molar mass

Practice AP Test Questions

1. Iodine–131 is radioactive and is used to treat thyroid cancer. In $^{131}I^{1-}$, there are _____ protons, _____ neutrons, and _____ electrons.

   A) 131, 53, 54
   B) 131, 53, 52
   C) 53, 78, 54
   D) 53, 131, 53

2. The elements in Groups 1, 16, and 17 are called _____, _____, and _____, respectively.

   A) alkaline earth metals, halogens, chalcogens
   B) alkali metals, chalcogens, halogens
   C) alkali metals, halogens, noble gases
   D) alkaline earth metals, transition metals, halogens

3. A cathode-ray beam passes through an electric field between charged parallel plates. In which direction is the beam deflected?

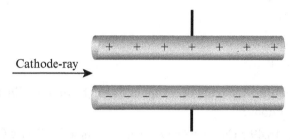

Cathode-ray

A) up, toward the positive plate   B) down, toward the negative plate

C) into the page   D) out of the page

E) There will be no deflection

4. How many xenon atoms are contained in 1.18 moles of xenon?

A) 1.96×10^{24} xenon atoms

B) 1.27×10^{23} xenon atoms

C) 0.710×10^{24} xenon atoms

D) 4.55×10^{26} xenon atoms

5. Chlorine has two naturally occurring isotopes chlorine-35 and chlorine-37 with masses and natural abundances 34.97 amu (75.77%) and 36.97 amu (24.23%) respectively. Which mass spectrum most likely will look like the mass spectrum of the charged molecular ions of chlorine gas, Cl_2?

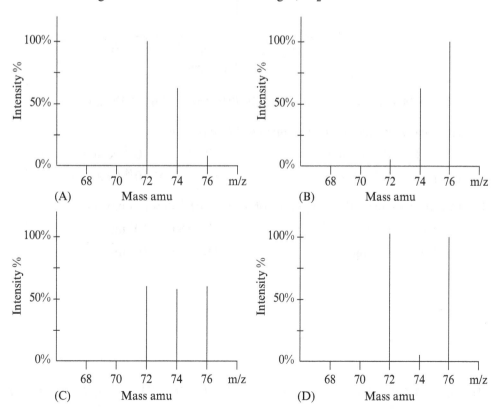

6. Which pair of substances could be used to illustrate the law of multiple proportions?
   A) SO_3, H_2SO_3
   B) H_2O, H_2O_2
   C) H_2CO_3, CO_2
   D) NaCl, $CaCl_2$

7. Which of the following pairs of compounds can be used to illustrate the law of definite proportions?
   A) sample 1 16.49 g Cu   3.58 g Oxygen   sample 2 12.37 g Cu 7.63 g Oxygen
   B) sample 1 32.98 g Cu   7.16 g Oxygen   sample 2 17.66 g Cu 2.22 g Oxygen
   C) sample 1 65.96 g Cu 14.32 g Oxygen   sample 2 17.66 g Cu 2.22 g Oxygen
   D) sample 1 16.49 g Cu   3.58 g Oxygen   sample 2 10.66 g Cu 1.22 g Oxygen

8. Gallium has a weighted average atomic mass of 69.723 amu and according to its mass spectrum has two main isotopes that can be detected. The Ga-69 (68.926 amu) isotope has a natural abundance of 60.110%. What is the calculated mass, in units of amu, of the other main isotope of Gallium?

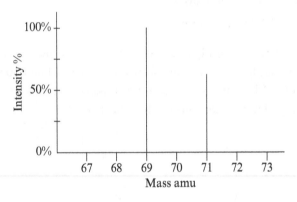

   A) 70.924 amu   B) 70.928 amu   C) 70.932 amu   D) 70.920 amu

9. How many iron atoms are contained in 177 g of iron?
   A) 1.31×10^{25} Fe atoms   C) 2.34×10^{24} Fe atoms
   B) 1.06×10^{26} Fe atoms   D) 1.91×10^{24} Fe atoms

10. Calculate the mass (in milligrams) of 3.73×10^{20} atoms of oxygen.
    A) 6.19×10^{6} mg   C) 9.91×10^{3} mg
    B) 1.62×10^{7} mg   D) 3.73×10^{6} mg

Data Interpretation and Analysis Question: Lead in Air

Lead in the form of tetraethyllead (TEL) was used as a gasoline additive because it decreased engine knocking and increased fuel economy. When TEL reacted with oxygen gas in the air, it produced lead.

$$(CH_3CH_2)_4Pb + 13 O_2 \rightarrow 8 CO_2 + 10 H_2O + Pb$$

TEL destroyed automotive catalytic converters and was found to contribute to lead poisoning in humans living in areas where many cars operated. In the United States, the Environmental Protection Agency's (EPA's) regulations stipulated beginning decreasing lead content in motor vehicle gasoline between 1973 and 2000 and eventually eliminating lead in gasoline sold to the public by 2004 for use on US highways and roads. Figure a plots the maximum 3-month average concentration of lead in air (ug/m^3) over a 24-year period between 1990 and 2014.

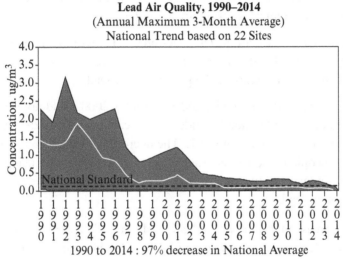

Figure a

Source: EPA https://www3.epa.gov/airtrends/lead.html National Service Center for Environmental Publications (NSCEP).

Figure b plots the amount of lead used in gasoline and the average amount of lead in blood (ug/dL) between 1976 and 1980.

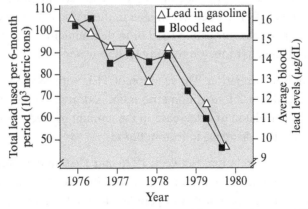

Figure b Blood lead values and amounts of lead consumed in gasoline between 1976 and 1980 (U.S. EPA 1986).
Source: U.S. EPA. 1986. Air Quality Criteria for Lead. I. Washington, DC:U.S. Environmental Protection Agency.

Environ Health Perspect; DOI:10.1289/ehp.0800534 Kenneth Bridbord,[1] and David Hanson[2]

Personal Perspective on the Initial Federal Health-Based Regulation to Remove Lead from Gasoline

i. Can the EPA regulations decreasing the amount of lead used as an additive in gasoline be correlated with a decrease in the amount of lead in the air between 1990 and 2005?

A) No, there is no direct evidence linking the lead used in gasoline to the lead detected in air. An experiment involving isotopic labeling of lead in TEL to determine if the lead in TEL is the same lead in the atmosphere is needed to provide such evidence.

B) No, there is no direct evidence linking the lead used in gasoline to the lead detected in air. The decrease in lead in the atmosphere could be due to some other chemical reaction involving lead.

C) Yes, there is a correlation. The reaction of TEL with oxygen in the air produces lead in a 1:1 stoichiometric ratio. A decrease in lead additive in gasoline is tied to a decrease in the production of lead.

D) Because cars made in the United States after 2000 could not use TEL in gasoline, as people traded in older model cars for new models, people did not purchase gasoline with TEL. The decrease of lead in the atmosphere is due to people in the United States not using gasoline with lead in it. A decrease in lead additive in gasoline is correlated with a decrease in the production of lead.

ii. Can the decrease in the amount of lead used as an additive in gasoline be correlated with a decrease in the amount of lead in blood between 1976 and 1980?

A) No, there is no direct evidence linking the lead used in gasoline to the lead detected in blood. An experiment involving isotopic labeling of lead in TEL to determine if the lead in TEL is the same lead in blood is needed to provide such evidence.

B) No, there is no direct evidence linking the lead used in gasoline to the lead detected in blood. The decrease in lead in the blood could be due to people changing their behavior eating food or to the municipal water treatment plants doing a better job at removing lead in water.

C) Yes, there is a correlation. The reaction of TEL with oxygen in the air produces lead in a 1:1 stoichiometric ratio. A decrease in lead additive in gasoline is correlated to a decrease in the amount of lead in the air, which is correlated with a decrease in lead in blood.

D) Yes, there is a correlation. Between 1976 and 1980 in the United States, there was a gradual decrease in TEL in gasoline. At the same time, there was an increase in the number of people who could drive cars, in the number of cars, and in mileage driven. As more people breathed in air, drank water, and consumed food with less lead in it, there was less lead to get into the bloodstream. The average concentration of lead in blood decreased because there were more people in the sample who did not have lead in their blood.

iii. Using the maximum 3-month average, how many lead atoms were in one cubic meter of the air in 1992?

    A) 207   B) 8.72×10^{15} C) 9.30×10^{15} D) 9.30×10^{21}

iv. On average, how many lead atoms were in one dL of the blood in 1978?

    A) 207   B) 2.56×10^{15} C) 2.56×10^{17} D) 3.00×10^{17}

Data Interpretation and Analysis Question Answers with Brief Explanations

i. C) The 1:1 stoichiometry provides a link to a correlation between TEL and Pb.

ii. C) The 1:1 stoichiometry provides a link to a correlation between TEL and Pb and lead in the blood.

iii. B) 9.30×10^{15} Pb atoms in one cubic meter of air.

iv. A) 2.56×10^{17} Pb atoms in one dL of blood.

CHAPTER 2

READING GUIDE

This chapter is foundational to concepts in the AP Chemistry curriculum. The concepts covered include the building materials of matter and changes in matter. To understand the development of our current knowledge about atoms, we must understand how our ideas came to be. While reading, pay particular attention to data or observations leading to the change in an understanding or a new concept being developed. Please note, some of the material covered here is not in the AP Chemistry curriculum but may be required material by some colleges and universities. This material is designated with an asterisk (*) next to the question.

Section 2.1   Brownian Motion: Atoms Confirmed

1. Explain the contribution to scientific knowledge by Robert Brown. How did Albert Einstein explain his observation? Who confirmed Einstein's observation with data?

2. What is an STM? What can it do?*

3. How many naturally occurring elements are there?

4. So far, how many synthetic elements are there?

Section 2.2   Early Ideas About the Building Blocks of Matter

5. Who proposed the early ideas about the atom? Why were they rejected?

6. What chemist from the 1800s reintroduced the idea of atoms?

Section 2.3   Modern Atomic Theory and the Laws That Led to It

7. Explain the concept of the Law Conservation of Mass.

8. Explain the Law of Definite Proportions as stated by Joseph Proust.

9. What data led to the development of the Law of Definite Proportions?

10. Give an example of the Law of Definite Proportions. Explain why this law is important in chemistry.

11. Explain the Law of Multiple Proportions as stated by John Dalton.

12. What data led to the development of the Law of Multiple Proportions?

13. Give an example of the Law of Multiple Proportions. Explain why this law is important in chemistry.

14. What are the four parts of Dalton's Theory about atoms?

15. Which part of Dalton's Theory was later proven incorrect?

16. What modern instrumentation led to the need for a change in Dalton's ideas?

17. Fill in the following table:

Law or Theory	Scientist	Data to Support
Law of Definite Proportions		
Law of Multiple Proportions		
Atomic Theory		

The Discovery of the Electron   Section 2.4

18. Draw a cathode ray tube and explain how it works. What properties did Thomson discover about the cathode ray?

19. Using diagrams, explain the properties of electric charge. What are electrostatic forces?

20. Draw a diagram to illustrate your explanation of how the charge of a single electron was determined. What is the charge of a single electron? What is the mass of an electron?

21. Fill in the following chart:

Scientist	Discovery	Experiment and Data to Support
J.J. Thompson		
Robert Millikan		

The Structure of the Atom   Section 2.5

22. What particles allowed researchers to probe the atom? Who discovered these particles?

23. Describe three experiments, run prior to 1930, and the types of energies or particles used to probe the structure of the atom. It will help to make a sketch of the basic parts of the experiment. What did each experiment investigate? Include the names of the scientists associated with each experiment in your answer.

24. Draw a picture of Rutherford's nuclear model of the atom and explain how it differs from J.J. Thomson's Plum Pudding Model.

25. What data led to changing from the Plum Pudding Model to the nuclear model of the atom? Explain the three parts of his nuclear theory. What was missing from Rutherford's model of the atom?

26. In 1932, a neutral particle as massive as a proton was detected in the nucleus of an atom. Describe the experiment used to detect this particle. Name this particle.

27. Fill in the following chart:

Subatomic Particle Found	Scientist	Experiment	Data Supporting Discovery

28. If matter is mostly empty space, why does it appear to be solid?

Section 2.6 — Subatomic Particles: Protons, Neutrons, and Electrons in Atoms

29. Define the following terms in your own words:

Atomic mass unit:

Atomic number:

Mass number:

Isotopes:

Natural abundance:

Why is matter usually charge-neutral?

30. Explain how to calculate or find each of the following for an atom:

The proton number:

The mass number:

The neutron number:

The electron number:

Which of these particles determines the type of atom present?

31. Fill in the following table of subatomic particles:

Particle	Charge (Relative)	Mass (kg)	Mass (amu)	How to Determine/ Calculate?
Proton				
Neutron				
Electron				

32. Draw a diagram showing the general location of each of the subatomic particles in an atom. What are two ways to write an isotope?

33. What is an ion? What is the difference between a cation and an anion? Give an example of each. What happens to the proton and electron number when forming a cation? What happens to the proton and electron number when forming an anion?

34. How are elements named? Give three examples?

Finding Patterns: The Periodic Law and the Periodic Table   Section 2.7

35. Who was Dmitri Mendeleev and why was he an important scientist?

36. Explain the concept of Periodic Law.

37. What new elements were predicted by Mendeleev? How correct were his predictions?

38. Indicate on the following table where metals, nonmetals, and metalloids would be found.

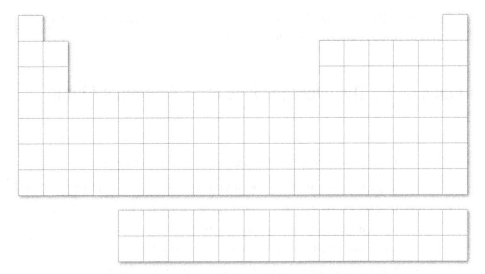

39. Identify three properties that define an element as a metal.

40. Identify three properties that define an element as a nonmetal.

41. Which group of elements is the least reactive? Explain why these elements are less reactive. Which group of metals are the most reactive? Which group of nonmentals are the most reactive?

42. What properties distinguish metalloids from other elements?

43. Label the following periodic table to show where to find alkali metals, alkaline earth metals, halogens, transition metals, and noble gases. Number the columns. Which columns are considered main group elements?

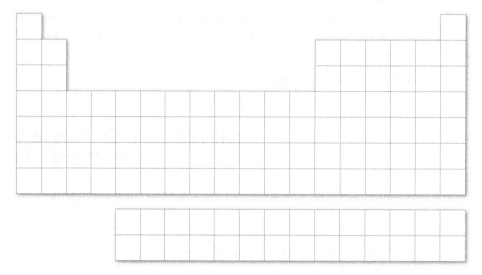

44. Explain how to predict the charge usually observed for a monatomic ion.

45. Explain how the charge properties of metals and nonmetals are different.

46. Which elements form predictable charges to use in making compounds? Circle these elements and add the charge.

Section 2.8   Atomic Mass: The Average Mass of an Element's Atoms

47. Explain what isotopes are. How do you write a symbol for an isotope?

48. Explain how isotopes can be the same element, yet are different.

49. Explain atomic mass. How is this different from the atomic mass number?

50. Explain how to calculate, in general, the weighted average atomic mass provided for each element on the periodic table. Why are mass numbers whole numbers but atomic masses are usually not?

51. What is mass spectrometry? What is it used for? What does a mass spectrum of chlorine look like? How is this graph normalized to find % abundance? What are two uses of mass spectrometry by scientists? How does the atomic mass indicate the most common isotope?

Section 2.9   Molar Mass: Counting Atoms by Weighing Them

52. What is a mole in chemistry and why is it so useful?

53. What does Avogadro's number represent?

54. Explain the term *molar mass*.

55. Explain how to determine the number of atoms by weighing a sample of an element.

56. Draw a conceptual plan with relationships used (including equations) showing how to change from grams to moles and then moles to number of atoms (see example 2.6, 2.7, 2.8, and 2.9 in the text).

57. Draw a conceptual plan with relationships used (including equations) showing how to change from number of atoms to moles and then moles to grams.

58. Explain the term *dimensional analysis*. Why is it important to use units when doing these types of calculations?

Self-Assessment Answers

1. _____   2. _____   3. _____

4. _____   5. _____   6. _____

7. _____   8. _____   9. _____

10. _____   11. _____   12. _____

13. _____   14. _____   15. _____

CHAPTER

3

MOLECULES AND COMPOUNDS

To understand chemistry, you must first learn the language of chemistry, including all the naming systems of different types of compounds. The majority of this chapter is reviewing the basics of naming ionic- and covalent-bonded compounds. You need to know the molecular and atomic elements in Section 3.4. There is also a short introduction to naming organic compounds, but this will be covered more thoroughly in a later chapter. All of this is foundational knowledge that must be mastered in order to complete any of the problems on the AP exam. While not all the information in this chapter may have a specific learning objective, it is a foundational part of most of the learning objectives.

Calculation of molar mass, percent composition, empirical formulas, molecular formulas, and converting in to and out of moles are calculations in this chapter that must be mastered. The most important sections to review are as follows:

3.2 **Chemical Bonds**

3.3 **Representing Compounds: Chemical Formulas and Molecular Models**

3.4 **An Atomic-Level View of Elements and Compounds**

3.5 **Ionic Compounds: Formulas and Names**

3.6 **Molecular Compounds: Formulas and Names**

3.8 **Formula Mass and the Mole Concept for Compounds**

3.9 **Composition of Compounds**

3.10 **Determining a Chemical Formula from Experimental Data**

Specific Learning Objectives Addressed in This Chapter:

SPQ-1 The mole allows different units to be compared.

SPQ-1.A Calculate quantities of a substance or its relative number of particles using dimensional analysis and the mole concept.

SPQ-2 Chemical formulas identify substances by their unique combination of atoms.

SPQ-2.A Explain the quantitative relationship between the elemental composition by mass and empirical formula of a pure substance.

SPQ-2.B Explain the quantitative relationship between the elemental composition by mass and the composition of substances in a mixture.

SAP-3 Atoms or ions bond due to interactions between them, forming molecules.

SAP-3.A Explain the relationship between the type of bonding and the properties of the elements participating in the bond.

Concepts and Vocabulary to Review:

Hydrogen, Oxygen, and Water   Section 3.1

Hydrogen gas is a diatomic molecule made of two hydrogen atoms, H_2. Oxygen gas is also a diatomic molecule, O_2. When hydrogen and oxygen gas molecules react to form water, there is a tremendous release of energy. While energy is required to break the bonds holding the hydrogen and oxygen molecules together, energy is released when the two new hydrogen–oxygen bonds form to make water. The water has totally different properties than the molecules it was made from.

The following table shows some characteristics of the atoms and of the compound formed when they are reacted together.

Selected Properties	Hydrogen	Oxygen	Water
Boiling Point	−253 °C	−183 °C	100 °C
State at Room Temperature	Gas	Gas	Liquid
Flammability	Explosive	Necessary for combustion	Used to extinguish flame

Chemical Bonds   Section 3.2

What holds the atoms in compounds together? This is called *chemical bonding*. Two types of bonds are—ionic and covalent. Some types of atoms typically bond by one type than the other. See Figure 3.1.

Ionic bonds result when a positive ion interacts with a negative ion. Ions are formed when one or more electrons are removed from an atom of one element and transferred to an atom of a second element. This results in an actual charge on the atoms. Metal atoms lose electrons while nonmetal atoms gain electrons. Atoms losing electrons to form a positive ion are called cations. Atoms gaining electrons to form negative ions are called anions. The electrostatic attractions between the positively and negatively charged ions hold the solid compound together in a three-dimensional lattice. The positively charged ions (cations) and negatively charged ions (anions) are arranged in specific patterns. An ionic compound is NOT a discrete molecule. The

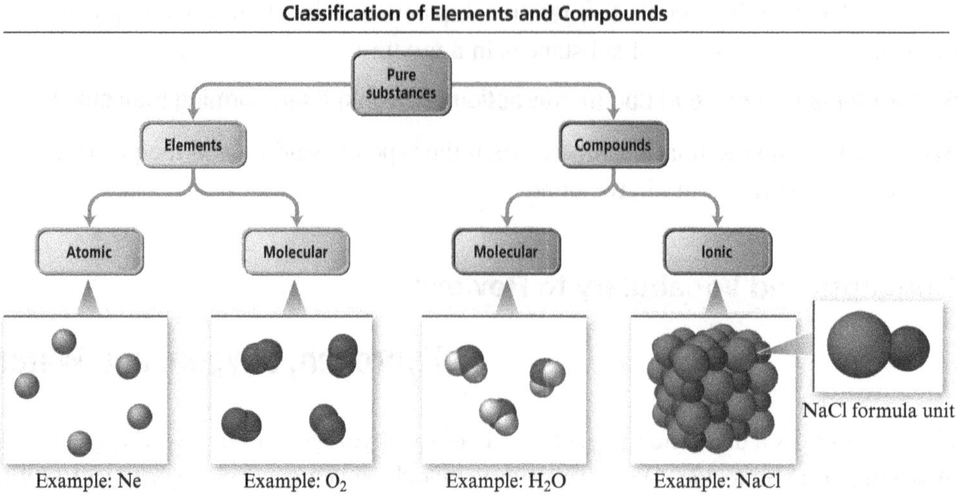

Classification of Elements and Compounds

Figure 3.1 **A Molecular View of Elements and Compounds**

basic unit (the smallest number ratio of each ion in the solid) of the lattice is called a *formula unit* (Section 3.4). The formula unit of an ionic compound is what is used for the formula of a compound in a chemical equation. See Figure 3.4. These compounds have a set ratio of atoms to atoms such as NaCl which is one-to-one, which is reflected in its formula. The one-to-one ratio indicates that sodium and chloride ions alternate in the lattice. In contrast, mixtures do not have a set formula like brass.

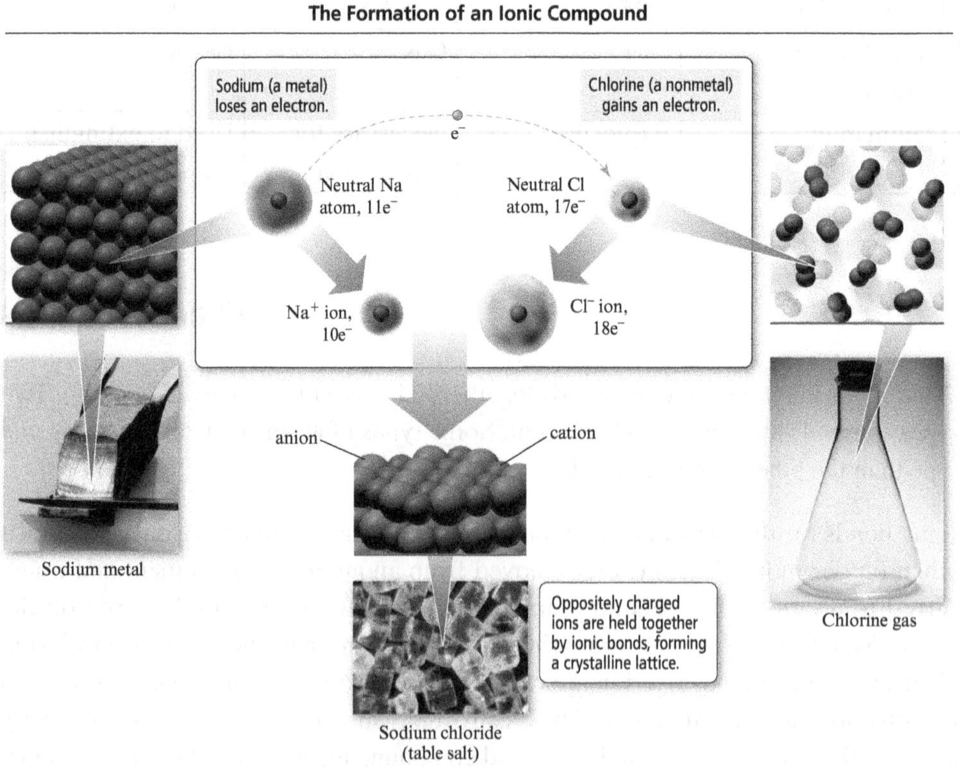

The Formation of an Ionic Compound

Figure 3.2 **The Formation of an Ionic Compound**   An atom of sodium (a metal) loses an electron to an atom of chlorine (a nonmetal), creating a pair of oppositely charged ions. The sodium cation is attracted to the chloride anion, and the two are held together as part of a crystalline lattice.

Covalent bonds, by contrast, are formed by the sharing of electrons between two or more nonmetal atoms. The atoms may be of the same element (as in hydrogen, H_2, or oxygen, O_2), or they may be between atoms of differing elements (as in carbon monoxide, CO, or nitrogen dioxide, NO_2). The sharing of electrons takes place because the resulting compound is more stable than the individual atoms, meaning that it has a lower potential energy compared to the atoms. When atoms use covalent bonds to form discrete units, they are called *molecules*. When two chlorine atoms combine to share electrons equally, as in Cl_2, the Cl — Cl bond is called a covalent bond. Substances held together by covalent bonds are called molecules. Cl_2 is a molecule.

Vocabulary can be confusing but remember formula units are the ratio of cation to anion, and how ionic compounds are represented while molecules are formed by covalent bonds.

Representing Compounds: Chemical Formulas and Molecular Models

Section 3.3

There are many ways to represent a chemical substance on paper and it is important to understand what each type of representation indicates and does not indicate.

The chemical formula indicates the atoms present and the number of each atom present. CO represents one atom of carbon and one atom of oxygen are in the molecule.

The **empirical formula** is the reduced, whole-number formula giving the smallest whole-number ratio of each atom to each of the others. H_2O_2 can be reduced to HO; a ratio of one atom of oxygen to every atom of hydrogen. H_2O cannot be reduced and has a ratio of two hydrogen atoms to every oxygen atom. Only integers are used in empirical formulas so $HO_{0.5}$ would not be correct.

A **molecular formula** is the unreduced, full formula of the compound representing the actual composition found by an experiment. In an experiment, data would indicate the ratio of hydrogen atoms to oxygen atoms in hydrogen peroxide is one to one or HO. The molecular formula is always a whole-number multiple of the empirical formula. In the case of hydrogen peroxide, the empirical formula HO is multiplied by 2 to give the molecular formula of H_2O_2. While this type of formula fully describes the constituent parts and is used in many calculations, it does not give any idea of the actual geometry or of the arrangement of the atoms in the compound.

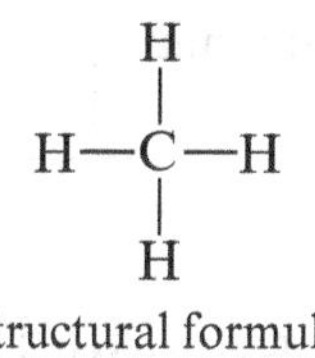

A **structural formula** shows how atoms are arranged in the molecule and how they are connected with bonds (represented by lines), providing the position of covalent bonds. If two lines are between two atoms, they are sharing four electrons and the connecting bond is called a double bond; if there are three lines, the bond is a triple bond and they are sharing six electrons. A triple bond is the highest order bond between two atoms. There are no quadruple bonds, and so on. While the structural formula tells us more about the connectivity and orders of bonding within the molecule, it still does not tell us anything about the geometry of the molecule.

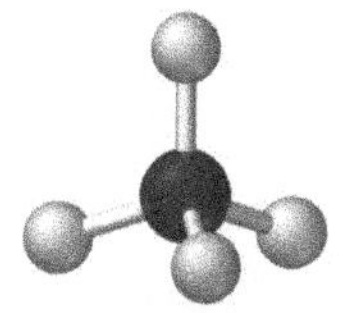

The **ball-and-stick molecular model** represents atoms as balls and bonds as sticks. This model is a good representation of the connectivity of the atoms in a molecule, and of

$$H-\overset{\displaystyle H}{\underset{\displaystyle H}{C}}-H$$

Structural formula

Figure 3.3

Ball-and-stick model

Figure 3.4

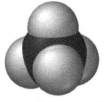

Space-filling model

Figure 3.5

the three dimensional structure and bond angles. At the same time, however, it is much less convenient in many cases, particularly where calculations are being performed.

The **space-filling molecular model** represents how the model would look scaled to size, with the electron orbitals included from the outside of the molecule. It is a fair approximation to how the molecule would look, should we be able to see something that small.

The following table shows a comparison of several molecules between the different representations.

Table 3.1   Benzene, Acetylene, Glucose, and Ammonia

Name of Compound	Empirical Formula	Molecular Formula	Structural Formula	Ball-and-Stick Model	Space-Filling Model
Benzene	CH	C_6H_6			
Acetylene	CH	C_2H_2	$H-C\equiv C-H$		
Glucose	CH_2O	$C_6H_{12}O_6$			
Ammonia	NH_3	NH_3			

Section 3.4   An Atomic-Level View of Elements and Compounds

Atomic elements exist in nature as atoms. Molecular elements do not exist as single atoms but groups of atoms in nature. Oxygen is not found as O atoms but as two atoms combined, O_2 or three atoms combined, O_3. Elements that exist as two atoms together are called diatomic elements. They are elements whose names end in -gen or -ine: Hydrogen, nitrogen, oxygen, fluorine, chlorine, bromine, and iodine. Polyatomic elements include sulfur existing as S_8 and phosphorus as P_4.

Compounds are combinations of different elements. Molecular compounds are two nonmetals combined such as H_2O. They exist with exact numbers between each of the elements in their formula. In water, there are always two hydrogen to one oxygen atom. In contrast, ionic compounds exist as formula units that repeat when forming a lattice in a solid. The formula unit is the ratio of ion to ion. In NaCl, the repeating pattern is one Na^+ to one Cl^-. See Figure 3.2.

Some ionic compounds are formed from an ion that is made from a group of covalently bonded atoms with an overall charge. These are called polyatomic ions. They can be cations or anions. The polyatomic ion is treated as a unit within the compound. In $Mg_3(PO_4)_2$, the formula unit of the ionic compound is three magnesium ions and two phosphate ions.

Ionic Compounds: Formulas and Names   Section 3.5

Ionic compounds are usually stable because the force of attraction between the cations and anions are strong, especially when the ions are packed close together in a solid lattice. The most familiar is common salt, NaCl, which consists of Na^+ and Cl^- ions in a closely packed lattice. To determine the formula of ionic compounds, write the cation symbol first and the anion symbol second; determine what ratio of cations and anions add up to zero (neutral in charge); and then write the smallest whole-number ratio in the formula. For NaCl, the Na^+ is the cation, the Cl^- the anion, and the ratio is 1:1. In calcium fluoride, there are two fluoride ions, F^-, for each calcium ion Ca^{2+}, resulting in a ratio of 1:2. The resulting formula is, then, CaF_2. See Figure 3.6.

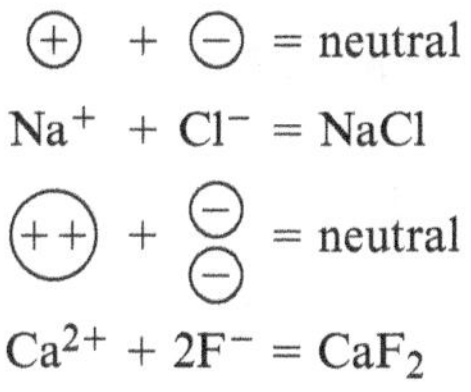

$\oplus$ + $\ominus$ = neutral
Na^+ + Cl^- = NaCl
$(++)$ + $\ominus\ominus$ = neutral
Ca^{2+} + $2F^-$ = CaF_2

Figure 3.6

Table 3.2   Metals Whose Charge Is Invariant from One Compound to Another

Metal	Ion	Name	Group Number
Li	Li^+	Lithium	1A
Na	Na^+	Sodium	1A
K	K^+	Potassium	1A
Rb	Rb^+	Rubidium	1A
Cs	Cs^+	Cesium	1A
Be	Be^{2+}	Beryllium	2A
Mg	Mg^{2+}	Magnesium	2A
Ca	Ca^{2+}	Calcium	2A
Sr	Sr^{2+}	Strontium	2A
Ba	Ba^{2+}	Barium	2A
Al	Al^{3+}	Aluminum	3A
Zn	Zn^{2+}	Zinc	*
Sc	Sc^{3+}	Scandium	*
Ag**	Ag^+	Silver	*

*The charge of these metals cannot be inferred from their group number.
**Silver sometimes forms compounds with other charges, but these are rare.

Table 3.3 Some Common Monoatomic Anions

Nonmetal	Symbol for Ion	Base Name	Anion Name
Fluorine	F^-	fluor	Fluoride
Chlorine	Cl^-	chlor	Chloride
Bromine	Br^-	brom	Bromide
Iodine	I^-	iod	Iodide
Oxygen	O^{2-}	ox	Oxide
Sulfur	S^{2-}	sulf	Sulfide
Nitrogen	N^{3-}	nitr	Nitride
Phosphorus	P^{3-}	phosph	Phosphide

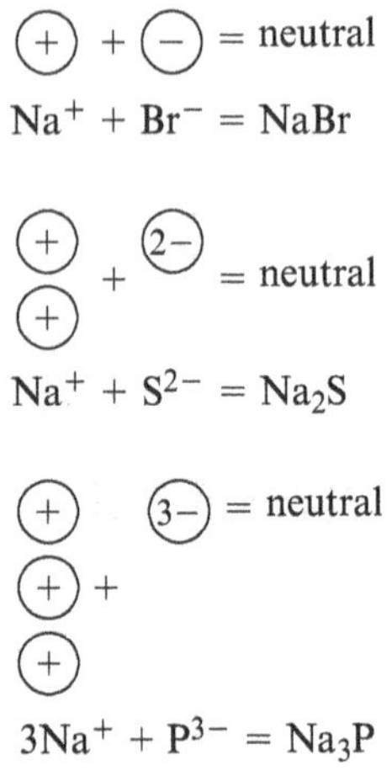

$(+) + (-)$ = neutral

$Na^+ + Br^- = NaBr$

$(+) + (2-)$ = neutral
$(+)$

$Na^+ + S^{2-} = Na_2S$

$(+)$ $(3-)$ = neutral
$(+) +$
$(+)$

$3Na^+ + P^{3-} = Na_3P$

Figure 3.7

Naming ionic compounds requires knowledge of the different cation and anion names. In AP, you need to know the rules for naming ionic compounds. The general format is write the metal name (Roman numeral if needed) and then the anion name. Roman numerals are needed if a metal has more than one possible valence state (or oxidation number) leading to alternative formulas for

Table 3.4 Some Metals That Form Cations with Different Charges

Metal	Ion	Name	Older Name*
Chromium	Cr^{2+}	Chromium(II)	Chromous
	Cr^{3+}	Chromium(III)	Chromic
Iron	Fe^{2+}	Iron(II)	Ferrous
	Fe^{3+}	Iron(III)	Ferric
Cobalt	Co^{2+}	Cobalt(II)	Cobaltous
	Co^{3+}	Cobalt(III)	Cobaltic
Copper	Cu^+	Copper(I)	Cuprous
	Cu^{2+}	Copper(II)	Cupric
Tin	Sn^{2+}	Tin(II)	Stannous
	Sn^{4+}	Tin(IV)	Stannic
Mercury	Hg_2^{2+}	Mercury(I)	Mercurous
	Hg^{2+}	Mercury(II)	Mercuric
Lead	Pb^{2+}	Lead(II)	Plumbous
	Pb^{4+}	Lead(IV)	Plumbic

*An older naming system substitutes the names found in this column for the name of the metal and its charge. Under this system, chromium(II) oxide is named chromous oxide. Additionally, the suffix *-ous* indicates the ion with the lesser charge, and *-ic* indicates the ion with the greater charge. We will *not* use the older system in this text. It is also not used in the AP Chemistry curriculum.

the compound. Be sure to be able to name the ions and compounds from all the different types of examples given in the text. While no AP test question will ask this directly as a question, you should know all of the cations and anions listed in the previous tables in Tables 3.2 and 3.3. Note, those metals in column 1A of the periodic table all have a +1, and those from column 2A all have a +2. This pattern will be explained in a later chapter, knowing this will help determining formulas.

Combining monoatomic cations and anions results in binary compounds. Binary compounds are composed of two types of atoms. Examples include $NaBr$, Na_2S, and Na_3P. In these examples, Na^+ is combined with anions Br^-, S^{2-}, and P^{3-}. The number of sodium cation needed to balance each anion differs.

The compounds Fe_2O_3 and FeO are both made of only iron and oxygen but are very different compounds. The roman numeral is used to designate the state of the iron used. In FeO, the iron and oxygen must have the same but opposite charge to be neutral. Oxygen forms oxide with a $2-$ charge so the iron must be $2+$ ($+2 + -2 = 0$). Therefore the name of the compound is iron(II) oxide. In Fe_2O_3, it takes two iron ions to balance three oxide ions. The three oxide ions have a total charge of (-2×3) or $6-$ charge which must be balanced by the two iron ions. This indicates each iron must have a $3+$ charge. The name of the compound is iron(III) oxide See Figure 3.8.

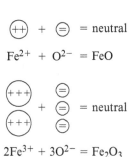

$$Fe^{2+} + O^{2-} = FeO$$

$$2Fe^{3+} + 3O^{2-} = Fe_2O_3$$

Figure 3.8

Table 3.5 Some Common Polyatomic Ions

Name	Formula	Name	Formula
Acetate	$C_2H_3O_2^-$	Hypochlorite	ClO^-
Carbonate	CO_3^{2-}	Chlorite	ClO_2^-
Hydrogen carbonate (or bicarbonate)	HCO_3^-	Chlorate	ClO_3^-
Hydroxide	OH^-	Perchlorate	ClO_4^-
Nitrite	NO_2^-	Permanganate	MnO_4^-
Nitrate	NO_3^-	Sulfite	SO_3^{2-}
Chromate	CrO_4^{2-}	Hydrogen sulfite (or bisulfite)	HSO_3^-
Dichromate	$Cr_2O_7^{2-}$	Sulfate	SO_4^{2-}
Phosphate	PO_4^{3-}	Hydrogen sulfate (or bisulfate)	HSO_4^-
Hydrogen phosphate	HPO_4^{2-}	Cyanide	CN^-
Dihydrogen phosphate	$H_2PO_4^-$	Peroxide	O_2^{2-}
Ammonium	NH_4^+		

$(NH_4)_2SO_4$, Na_2CO_3, and $Al(OH)_3$ are examples of compounds with polyatomic ions. Notice that if more than one unit of a polyatomic ion is present in the formula, the polyatomic ion is put inside parenthesis. NH_{42} would indicate one nitrogen and forty-two hydrogen whereas the $(NH_4)_2$ indicates two of the ammonium ion are present for a total of two nitrogen atoms and eight hydrogen atoms.

$$NH_4^+ \quad SO_4^{2-}$$

$$\oplus + \ominus \quad = neutral$$

$$\oplus$$

$$\overline{2NH_4^+ + SO_4^{2-}} = (NH_4)_2SO_4$$

Figure 3.9

If the polyatomic ion contains oxygen, it is called an oxyanion. Sulfate is an example of an oxyanion. Some ionic compounds have enough space between the ions and have enough attraction for water molecules that they actually incorporate the water into the lattice. This makes the lattice even more stable. These types of compounds are called **hydrates**. *Hydrates* are indicated by a molecular formula followed by a dot and a number of water molecules such as in copper(II) sulfate pentahydrate: $CuSO_4 \cdot 5H_2O$. The formula will be the smallest whole number ratio of the compound to the hydrate. The number of water molecules incorporated into the hydrate is called the water of hydration. You will need to know how to name and write the formula of hydrated ionic compounds.

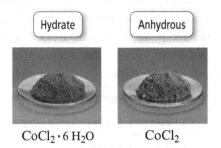

Hydrate   Anhydrous

$CoCl_2 \cdot 6 H_2O$ $CoCl_2$

Figure 3.10 Hydrates   Cobalt(II) chloride hexahydrate is pink. Heating the compound removes the waters of hydration, leaving the blue anhydrous cobalt(II) chloride.

The water of hydration contained in hydrates can be removed by heating. After waters of hydration are removed from the compounds the remaining **anhydrous** (literally "without water" in Latin) forms have different properties. An example is copper(II) sulfate pentahydrate, whose formula is given above, which is blue, whereas anhydrous copper sulfate $(CuSO_4)$ appears white.

Section 3.6 Molecular Compounds: Formulas and Names

Molecular (covalently bonded) compounds have a different naming system. These compounds are made of two nonmetals. The format for naming is prefix (except *mon-*) name of first element, prefix and base name of second element, then *–ide*. For N_2O_5, the prefix for 2 is di, N is the base nitrogen the prefix for 5 is penta- the base with suffix is oxide. N_2O_5 is dinitrogen pentoxide, CO is carbon monoxide (NOT monocarbon monoxide), and CO_2 is carbon dioxide (NOT monocarbon dioxide). You should know the first ten prefixes.

Table 3.6 Prefixes and the Number of Atoms Present in a Molecule

mono = 1	hexa = 6
di = 2	hepta = 7
tri = 3	octa = 8
tetra = 4	nona = 9
penta = 5	deca = 10

A few compounds go by common names, such as water (which would be dihydrogen monoxide). Another common name to know is ammonia, which has the formula NH_3.

Another group of compounds frequently encountered are acids. *Acids* are molecular compounds that release hydrogen ions (H^+) when dissolved in water. Acid have a sour taste and many acids dissolve metals. Naming acids depends on which anion is present in the acid. Generally, compounds are only named as acids when dissolved in water or when water is present. Two types are binary acids and oxyacids. Binary acids will have an anion ending in –ide and oxyacids include a polyatomic ion that includes an oxygen and can end in -ite or -ous.

Binary acids:

- If the anion ends in *–ide*, the acid name follows the pattern *hydro* (base name of the nonmetal)*ic acid*. In HCl, the anion is chloride, Cl^-, so it is named is hydrochloric acid. When in the complete absence of water and it is a gas at room temperature, its name is simply hydrogen chloride. Cl^- needs one H^+ to balance to HCl as seen in Figure 3.10.

$\oplus + \ominus$ = neutral
$H^+ + Cl^- = HCl$

Figure 3.10

Acids with polyatomic anions without oxygen:

- Some anions end in –ide that are not single atoms like cyanide, CN^-. When these anions are used in an acid, it is named using binary rules. HCN is hydrocyanic acid.

$(+) + (-)$ = neutral
$H^+ + CN^- = HCN$

Oxyacids:

- If the anion ends in *–ate*, the acid name follows the pattern (base name of the nonmetal)*ic acid*. In HNO_3, nitrate is NO_3^- and therefore requires one H^+ to balance the formula resulting in HNO_3. The anion is nitrate, indicating the acid name should end in –ic so the acid name is nitric acid, NOT hydronitric acid.
- If the anion ends in *–ite*, the acid name follows the pattern (base name of the nonmetal)*ous acid*. In HNO_2, nitrite is NO_2^- and therefore requires one H^+ to balance the formula resulting in HNO_2. The anion is nitrite indicating the acid name should end in –ous. Hence, the acid name is nitrous acid.

Section 3.7   # Summary of Inorganic Nomenclature

All the naming rules are summarized in the following table:

Inorganic Nomenclature Flow Chart

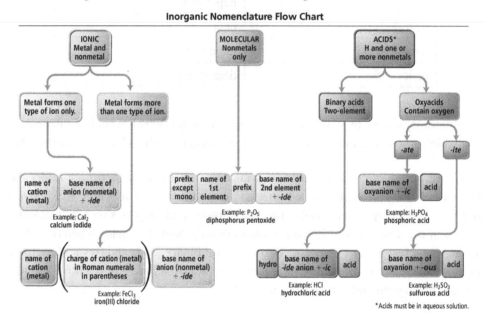

Figure 3.12 Inorganic Nomenclature Flowchart   The chart summarizes how to name inorganic compounds. Begin by determining if the compound is ionic, molecular, or an acid. Then follow the flowchart for that category from top to bottom until you arrive at a name for the compound.

You should practice both approaches—writing formulas from names and writing names from formulas. See questions 33–58 on page 131 in the text for practice.

Section 3.8   # Formula Mass and the Mole Concept for Compounds

Remember formula mass or more commonly molecular mass is in amu.

Molar Mass is the mass of 1 mole of a substance. A mole represents 6.022×10^{23} atoms or molecules and is the number necessary to make the number of atomic mass units on the periodic table equal to the mass in grams. 1 amu has a mass of 1.660×10^{-24} g. For carbon with a mass of 12.01 amu then

$$12.01 \text{ amu} \times (1.660 \times 10^{-24} \text{ g}/1 \text{ amu}) \times (6.022 \times 10^{23} \text{ atoms of C}/1 \text{ atom C})$$
$$= 12.01 \text{ g of C}$$

Therefore, the mass an atom of an element in amu and of a mole of those same atoms in grams per mole are the same. A carbon atom has a mass of 12.01 amu and a mole of carbon atoms (6.022×10^{23} atoms C) has a mass of 12.01 g. To calculate the molar mass of a compound, add the molar masses of all the atoms making up the compound from the atomic masses on the periodic table. The units of molar mass are g/mol. Determination of the correct molar mass is a calculation that must be mastered at the AP level. Be sure to use all given digits on the periodic table and to use correct significant figures for the result. For example, the mass of carbon on the periodic table is 12.01 g/mol and the mass of oxygen is 16.00 g/mol. Thus, the molar mass of CO_2 is 12.01 g/mol + 2(16.00 g/mol) = 44.01 g/mol. Remember, this works because the data given on the periodic table can be interpreted two ways: (1) as the relative mass of the atoms in atomic mass units OR (2) the molar mass in grams/mol of the atoms.

Composition of Compounds   Section 3.9

Mass percent or mass percent composition can be determined from the molar mass and the atomic masses. After determining the molar mass, use the mass each element contributed to the total molar mass and put it over the total molar mass to form a ratio. This ratio is multiplied by 100 to indicate the mass percent. For CO_2, the C is 12.0 g/mol of the total 44.01 g/mol, which would be 27.29% C.

Grams of X/total mass of XY × 100 = % of X.

The same ratio of masses in grams without the multiplier of 100 can be used as a conversion factor, such as

$$\frac{12.01 \frac{g}{mol} \text{ of C}}{44.01 \frac{g}{mol} \text{ of } CO_2}.$$

There are a variety of problems in which this can be used, such as calculating the number of grams used to form a certain amount of compound.

It is important to recognize percent literally means "out of 100". In some cases, it is convenient to assume the sample size is 100 grams of the compound. What is the mass of C in 50.0 g CO_2? If we assume we have 100 grams of CO_2, then we can ask what is the mass of C in 100.00 grams of CO_2? Since the percentage of C in CO_2 is 27.29%, the mass of carbon in 100.0 g of CO_2 is 27.29 grams. This also means that oxygen is 100.00 g − 27.29 g = 72.71 grams, so the mass percent of oxygen in CO_2 is 72.71%. In 50 grams there would be half of each amount or 13.65 g of carbon and 36.35 g of oxygen.

Example:
How many grams of iron are in 40.00 g of iron(III) sulfate?

The formula mass or molar mass of $Fe_2(SO_4)_3$ is 400.0 g/mol.

$$\frac{111.7 \text{ g Fe}}{400.0 \text{ } Fe_2(SO_4)_3} \times 100\% = 27.92\% \text{ Fe}$$

$$40.00 \text{ g } Fe_2(SO_4)_3 \times 0.2792 = 11.17 \text{ g Fe}$$

Chemical formulas can also provide ratios to help solve problems. For instance, in $C_6H_{12}O_6$, the ratio of moles of carbon atoms per mole of compound is 6:1 or 6 mol of C/1 mol of $C_6H_{12}O_6$. Mastery of conversions between grams of one species to grams of another species using mass and molar conversion factors is a necessity.

Example:

How many grams of sulfur are in 40.0 g of $Fe_2(SO_4)_3$?
From the formula, there are 3 moles of S in every 1 mol of $Fe_2(SO_4)_3$

$$40.00 \text{ g} \times \frac{1 \text{ mol Fe}_2(SO_4)_3}{400.0 \text{ g Fe}_2(SO_4)_3} \times \frac{3 \text{ mol S}}{1 \text{ mol Fe}_2(SO_4)_3} \times \frac{32.06 \text{ g S}}{1 \text{ mol S}} = 9.619 \text{ g S}$$

Another source of a ratio sometimes needed in solving problems is the density of the substance. For example, the density of water is 1.00 g/mL. In this case, the ratio of mass to volume can be used to determine the total mass or total volume present.

Example:

How many molecules of methanol (CH_3OH) are in 14.8 mL of methanol? The density of methanol is 0.7918 g/mL.

$$14.8 \text{ mL CH}_3\text{OH} \times \frac{0.7918 \text{ g}}{1 \text{ mL}} \times \frac{1 \text{ mol CH}_3\text{OH}}{32.01 \text{ g CH}_3\text{OH}} \times \frac{6.02 \times 10^{23} \text{ molecules CH}_3\text{OH}}{1 \text{ mol CH}_3\text{OH}}$$

$$= 2.20 \times 10^{23} \text{ molecules CH}_3\text{OH}$$

It is always required to show work and use units on the AP Test. If properly set up, the units will cancel so the desired final units are left. Well-practiced, problem-solving skills for problems of varying types and approaches are needed to be a successful student in AP chemistry. The number of steps needed to be done in a problem depends on what the question is asking. This is a critical foundational skill and MUST be mastered.

Section 3.10   Determining a Chemical Formula from Experimental Data

The AP course is data driven, so understanding how to determine a formula from data is an important skill. This also works with chemical equations.

Example:

Assuming a 100.0 gram sample, 69.94 g is iron and 30.06 g is oxygen. Convert the mass of each element to moles. Calculate the mole to mole Fe to O ratio.

$$69.94 \text{ g Fe} \times \frac{1 \text{ mol Fe}}{55.845 \text{ g Fe}} = 1.252 \text{ mol Fe}$$

$$30.06 \text{ g O} \times \frac{1 \text{ mol O}}{16.00 \text{ g O}} = 1.879 \text{ mol O}$$

$$\frac{1.879 \text{ mol O}}{1.252 \text{ mol Fe}} = \frac{1.50 \text{ mol O}}{1 \text{ mol Fe}} \times \frac{2}{2} = \frac{3 \text{ mol O}}{2 \text{ mol Fe}}$$

The empirical formula is Fe_2O_3.

This experimental data only leads to the determination of the empirical formula, not the molecular formula. When working on these problems, remember the ratios of atom to atom must be whole numbers, so you must recognize what certain decimals need to have as a multiplier to get the nearest whole number. For instance, 0.50 needs to be multiplied by 2 to get the whole number 1, 0.3 would most likely be multiplied by 3. Additionally, experiments rarely give perfect data as all experiments have some measureable error. Sometimes the data will not result in a perfect whole number ratio. For instance, if the data results in the calculations yielding a ratio of 1.9:1, it is much more likely to really be a 2:1 ratio.

To determine the molecular formula from your calculated empirical formula and empirical formula mass, the molar mass of the compound must be known. The ratio of the molar mass to the empirical mass will yield the multiplier needed to transform the empirical formula into the molecular formula.

$$\frac{\text{molar mass}}{\text{empirical mass}} = \text{multiplier}$$

Example:

Caffeine contains 49.50% C, 5.15% H, 28.90% N, and 16.50% O by mass. Determine the empirical formula and the molecular formula of caffeine. The formula mass or molar mass of caffeine is 195 g/mol.

From the percent by mass data the empirical formula is $C_4H_5N_2O$. The empirical mass is 97.5 g/mol.

$$\frac{\text{Molar Mass}}{\text{Empirical Mass}} = \frac{195\frac{g}{mol}}{97.5\frac{g}{mol}} = \frac{2}{1}$$

$$\text{Molecular formula} = C_4H_5N_2O \times 2 = C_8H_{10}N_4O_2$$

One way to get the data to calculate the percent composition is to burn the material. Burning in the presence of oxygen is called combustion. In **combustion analysis**, organic compounds are burned in oxygen or air completely to produce CO_2 and H_2O. The amounts of these products can be used to determine the amount of starting reactants. In complete combustion of a hydrocarbon, all the carbon in the hydrocarbon is combined with oxygen to make carbon dioxide. All the hydrogen combines with oxygen to make water. From the amount of carbon dioxide, the amount of the original carbon can be determined and from the amount of water formed, the amount of the original hydrogen in the hydrocarbon can be determined. With this data, the formula of the compound can be determined. In these types of experiments, it is safe to assume that no other products have been formed.

Example:

A 0.1507 g sample of menthol, a substance used in mentholated cough drops and composed of C, H, and O was combusted and produced 0.4243 g of carbon dioxide and 0.1738 g of water. Determine the empirical formula of menthol.

All of the carbon in the carbon dioxide must be from the carbon in the sample of menthol. In the formula CO_2, there is 1 mole of carbon to two moles of oxygen. Calculate the number of moles and grams of carbon present in the carbon dioxide.

$$0.4243 \text{ g CO}_2 \quad \times \quad \frac{1 \text{ mol CO}_2}{44.0 \text{ g CO}_2} \quad \times \quad \frac{1 \text{ mol C}}{1 \text{ mol CO}_2} = 0.00964 \text{ mol C}$$

Changing grams of CO$_2$ to moles of CO$_2$ Changing from mol CO$_2$ to moles of C

All of the hydrogen in the water must be from the hydrogen in the sample of menthol. Calculate the number of moles and grams of hydrogen present in the water.

$$0.1738 \text{ g H}_2\text{O} \times \frac{1 \text{ mol H}_2\text{O}}{18.01 \text{ g H}_2\text{O}} \times \frac{2 \text{ mol H}}{1 \text{ mol H}_2\text{O}} = 0.01930 \text{ mol H}$$

In order to determine the moles of oxygen in the sample, the mass of oxygen in the sample should be calculated. First, determine the mass of carbon and hydrogen present in the sample of menthol.

$$0.00964 \text{ mol C} \times \frac{12.01 \text{ g C}}{1 \text{ mol C}} = 0.1158 \text{ g C}$$

$$0.01930 \text{ mol H} \times \frac{1.007 \text{ g H}}{1 \text{ mol H}} = 0.0195 \text{ g H}$$

mass of oxygen = total mass sample − mass C − mass H

mass of oxygen = 0.1507 g − 0.1158 g C − 0.0195 g H = 0.0156 g O

$$\text{moles of O} = 0.0156 \text{ g O} \times \frac{1 \text{ mol of O}}{16.00 \text{ g O}} = 0.000964 \text{ mol O}$$

Determine the mole to mole ratio of the elements.

$$\frac{0.01930 \text{ mol H}}{0.00964 \text{ mol C}} = \frac{2 \text{ mol H}}{1 \text{ mol C}}$$

$$\frac{0.00964 \text{ mol C}}{0.000975 \text{ mol O}} = \frac{10 \text{ mol C}}{1 \text{ mol O}}$$

Since the ratio is 1 mol of O to 10 mol C and the number of moles of H is twice C, there must be 20 mol of H.

The empirical formula of menthol is C$_{10}$H$_{20}$O.

Section 3.11   Organic Compounds

This section is a brief introduction to organic compounds. You do not need to memorize all the organic compounds you will encounter but being familiar with them will help you to recognize the properties of them. The majority of the compounds in the world are organic which indicates they have a base composition of carbon and hydrogen although many other atoms such as nitrogen, oxygen, and sulfur may be in the formula. Organic chemistry has its own naming system based on the composition of the compound.

Hydrocarbons are a group of compounds with only carbon and hydrogen. The carbon atoms form chains and the hydrogen atoms bond to the carbons in the chain. The alkane group of molecules only have single bonds between the carbon atoms in the chain, alkenes have at least one double bond in the chain between carbon atoms, and alkynes have at least one triple bond in the chain between carbon atoms. If other atoms are added to the compound, the compound is functionalized. There are several functional groups such as alcohols. CH_4 is an alkane called methane. CH_3OH is called methanol. It contains an R-OH group, which is the functional group called alcohols.

Table 3.7 contains a list of various functional groups found in organic molecules.

Table 3.7   Families of Organic Compounds

Family	Name Ending	General Formula	Example	Name	Occurrence/Use
Alcohols	–ol	R—OH	CH_3CH_2—OH	Ethanol (ethyl alcohol)	Alcohol in fermented beverages
Ethers	ether	R—O—R′	CH_3CH_2—O—CH_2CH_3	Diethyl ether	Anesthetic; laboratory solvent
Aldehydes	–al	$\overset{\displaystyle O}{\overset{\displaystyle \|}{R-C-H}}$	$\overset{\displaystyle O}{\overset{\displaystyle \|}{H_3C-C-H}}$	Ethanal (acetaldehyde)	Perfumes; flavors
Ketones	–one	$\overset{\displaystyle O}{\overset{\displaystyle \|}{R-C-R'}}$	$\overset{\displaystyle O}{\overset{\displaystyle \|}{H_3C-C-CH_3}}$	Propanone (acetone)	Fingernail polish remover
Carboxylic acids	acid	$\overset{\displaystyle O}{\overset{\displaystyle \|}{R-C-OH}}$	$\overset{\displaystyle O}{\overset{\displaystyle \|}{H_3C-C-OH}}$	Acetic acid	Vinegar
Esters	–ate	$\overset{\displaystyle O}{\overset{\displaystyle \|}{R-C-OR'}}$	$\overset{\displaystyle O}{\overset{\displaystyle \|}{H_3C-C-OCH_3}}$	Methyl acetate	Laboratory solvent
Amines	amine	RNH_2	$\overset{\displaystyle H}{\overset{\displaystyle \|}{CH_3CH_2-N-H}}$	Ethyl amine	Smell of rotten fish

Organic compounds will be explored more deeply in chapters 22 and 23.

This chapter contains a variety of fundamental skills you must master to be successful in AP chemistry. Practice and continue to practice these foundations throughout the year.

Additional Practice

Equations to know:

$$\left(\begin{array}{c} \text{No. of atoms of 1st element} \\ \text{in chemical formula} \end{array} \times \begin{array}{c} \text{atomic mass} \\ \text{of 1st element} \end{array} \right) +$$

$$\left(\begin{array}{c} \text{No. of atoms of 2nd element} \\ \text{in chemical formula} \end{array} \times \begin{array}{c} \text{atomic mass} \\ \text{of 2nd elements} \end{array} \right) + \dots$$

$$\text{Mass \% of element X} = \frac{\text{mass of X in 1 mol compound}}{\text{mass of 1 mol compound}} \times 100\%$$

$$\text{Molecular formula} = n \times (\text{empirical formula})$$

$$n = \frac{\text{molar mass}}{\text{empirical formula molar mass}}$$

Practice AP Test Questions

While the AP test will not ask you to name compounds, it is important that you can recognize the type of compound given and determine its formula. This is the most basic skill to master the language of chemistry.

1. Which one of the following is the formula of hypochlorous acid?

   A) $HClO_3$ C) $HClO$

   B) $HClO_2$ D) H_2ClO_2

2. The correct name for $Fe(NO_2)_2$ is _____.

   A) Iron(II) nitrite   C) Ferric nitrite

   B) Iron(II) nitrate   D) Iron dinitrite

3. The correct name for K_2O_2 is _____.

   A) Potassium oxide

   B) Potassium dioxide

   C) Dipotassium oxide

   D) Potassium peroxide

4. The formula for the compound formed between aluminum ions and carbonate ions is _____.

   A) $Al_3(CO_3)_3$

   B) $Al_2(CO_3)_3$

   C) $AlCO_3$

   D) $Al(CO_3)_3$

5. The name of the compound N_2O_4 is ___.

   A) Dinitrogen tetroxide

   B) Dinitrogen quatroxide

   C) Nitrogen(IV) oxide

   D) Nitric oxide

6. Which series of compounds have a common empirical formula?

   A) C_2H_6 C_3H_8 C_4H_{10}

   B) $HClO$ $HClO_2$ $HClO_3$

   C) $Al_2(CO_3)_3$ Al_2S_3 Al_2O_3

   D) C_2H_4 C_3H_6 C_4H_8

7. The definitive distinction between ionic bonding and covalent bonding is that:

   A) ionic bonding involves a sharing of electrons and covalent bonding involves a transfer of electrons.

   B) ionic bonding involves a transfer of electrons and covalent bonding involves a sharing of electrons.

   C) ionic bonding requires two nonmetal atoms and covalent bonding requires a metal cation and a nonmetal anion.

   D) covalent bonding requires two nonmetal atoms and ionic bonding requires a metal cation and a nonmetal anion.

8. Which of the compounds, Li_3P, PH_3, C_2H_6, $AlBr_3$, are ionic compounds?

   A) only C_2H_6

   B) only $AlBr_3$

   C) Li_3P and $AlBr_3$

   D) PH_3 and C_2H_6

9. Determine the molecular formula of a compound that has a molar mass of 122.2 g/mol and an empirical formula of $C_2H_5O_2$.

   A) $C_2H_5O_2$

   B) $C_6H_{15}O_6$

   C) $C_3H_7O_3$

   D) $C_4H_{10}O_4$

   E) $C_8H_{20}O_8$

10. How many iron(II) ions, Fe^{2+}, are there in 2.50 g of $FeSO_4$ (MM $= 151.9$)?

    A) 2.73×10^{-26} iron (II) ions

    B) 9.99×10^{21} iron (II) ions

    C) 9.15×10^{24} iron (II) ions

    D) 2.29×10^{26} iron (II) ions

Data Interpretation and Analysis Question: Did Water on Earth Come from Comets or Asteroids? Analysis of Deuterium-Hydrogen Ratios

Scientists running computer simulations have speculated that a bombardment of comets or asteroids might have delivered enough ice to account for how water arrived on planet Earth. Water, H_2O, is a compound, consisting of two hydrogen atoms bonded on either side of an oxygen atom. However, hydrogen and oxygen atoms have isotopes. Table 1 lists the three naturally occurring isotopes of hydrogen along with the atomic mass and relative abundance. The nucleus of a deuterium atom contains one proton and one neutron; hydrogen has one proton and no neutrons. Tritium, containing one proton and two neutrons, is rare.

Table 1   Natural Isotopes of Hydrogen

Natural Isotopes	Number of Protons	Number of Neutrons	Atomic Mass	Relative Abundance
^1H	1	0	1.0078	99.985%
^2H	1	1	2.0141	0.015%
^3H	1	2	3.0161	0.0000001%

There are three naturally occurring stable isotopes of oxygen, O^{16}, O^{17}, O^{18}. All three isotopes of oxygen have the same number of protons, but different number of neutrons. Oxygen-16 is the most abundant of the three isotopes. Table 2 lists the natural isotopes of oxygen.

Table 2   Natural Isotopes of Oxygen

Isotope	Symbol	Protons	Neutrons	% on Earth
Oxygen-16	^{16}O	8	8	99.63%
Oxygen-17	^{17}O	8	9	0.04%
Oxygen-18	^{18}O	8	10	0.20%

On Earth, for every 1 million water molecules, 156 water molecules contain deuterium. Comets contain about 20% ice. Measurements from Halley's comet (from the Oort Cloud) reveal for every 1 million water molecules, 312 water molecules contain deuterium. Measurements from the Kuiper Belt comet 103P/Hatley 2 indicates for every 1 million water molecules, 157 water molecules contain deuterium. Measurements from the Kuiper Belt comet 67P/C-G 2 indicate that for every 1 million water molecules, 468 water molecules contain deuterium.

i. Select all statements that are true.

   If water arrived on Earth from comets bombarding Earth,

   A) there should be very little difference in chemical composition between water on Earth and water on comets.

B) there would have to be millions of comets in order to account for all of the water on Earth.

C) half of the comets would have to have a lower percentage of deuterium in water molecules compared to 67P/C-G 2 and 103P/Hatley 2 in order to have the average be similar to the water on Earth. However, there are no comets known that have a hydrogen–deuterium ratio less than Earth's.

D) most of the comets would have to originate in the Kuiper Belt and have ice with a chemical composition close to the comet 103P/Hatley 2.

ii. In a sample of water containing one million water molecules, what percentage of the molecules would be D_2O^{16}, deuterium oxide, molecules?

A) 99.63%   B) 99.60%   C) 0.030%   D) 0.015%

iii. How many different combinations of all the isotopes of hydrogen and oxygen are possible that result in different isotopes of water?

A) 6   B) 9   C) 12   D) 18

iv. Of all of the possible isotope combinations for water molecules, which combinations result in the most abundant and which in the least abundant?

A) $^1H_2{}^{16}O$, $^3H_2{}^{18}O$ B) $^1H_2{}^{18}O$, $^3H_2{}^{18}O$

C) $^2H^3H^{16}O$, $^2H^3H^{18}O$ D) $^1H^2H^{16}O$, $^1H_2{}^{18}O$

v. Given the mass spectrum of water in this figure identify the species responsible for peaks at m/z = 17 and 18.

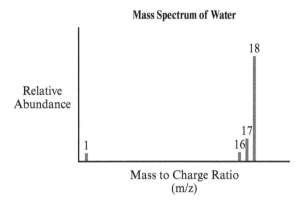

A) $(^{17}O)^+$, $(^1H^{17}O)^+$ B) $(^{17}O)^+$, $(^{18}O)^+$

C) $(^1H^{16}O)^+$, $(^1H_2{}^{16}O)^+$ D) $(^1H^{16}O)^+$, $(^1H^{17}O)^+$

vi. Select all statements that are true.

If water arrived on Earth from asteroids bombarding Earth,

A) the asteroids could not have been large because large asteroids bombarding Earth would have left extremely large impact craters and there are not enough large impact craters on Earth.

B) a significant number of medium sized asteroids would have had to hit Earth, all with the same isotopic composition of water now on Earth.

C) the asteroids would have had to be unique asteroids with lots of water because there are no asteroids known that have the same hydrogen–deuterium ratio as Earth's.

D) there would also have to be comets bombarding Earth at the same time and the comets would have to originate in the Kuiper Belt.

Data Interpretation and Analysis Question Answers with Brief Explanations

i. A) and D)

ii. D)

iii. $^1H_2{}^{16}O$, $^2H_2{}^{16}O$, $^3H_2{}^{16}O$
$^1H_2{}^{17}O$, $^2H_2{}^{17}O$, $^3H_2{}^{17}O$
$^1H_2{}^{18}O$, $^2H_2{}^{18}O$, $^3H_2{}^{18}O$

$^1H^2H^{16}O$, $^1H^3H^{16}O$, $^2H^3H^{16}O$
$^1H^2H^{17}O$, $^1H^3H^{17}O$, $^2H^3H^{17}O$
$^1H^2H^{18}O$, $^1H^3H^{18}O$, $^2H^3H^{18}O$

iv. A) $^1H_2{}^{16}O$, $^3H_2{}^{18}O$

v. C) $(^1H^{16}O)^+$, $(^1H_2{}^{16}O)^+$

vi. B)

READING GUIDE

Chapter 3 has concepts crossing Units 1, 2, and 3 in the AP Chemistry curriculum. These concepts are foundational to all the other big ideas. Naming compounds, balancing equations, and the mathematical routines to use data to determine formulas are important to have mastered. Differentiating between the different types of compounds by name or by formula will be imperative to success in later chapters and on the AP Chemistry exam. Applications of concepts addressed across the science practices and reasoning processes of AP Chemistry are also included in the reading guide.

Hydrogen, Oxygen, and Water Section 3.1

1. What are three properties of hydrogen gas? Classify each property as a chemical property or a physical property.

2. What are three properties of oxygen gas? Classify each property as a chemical property or a physical property.

3. Explain how the properties of the components of water, namely hydrogen, and oxygen differ from the properties of water.

4. Compare and contrast the components of a mixture and a compound.

Chemical Bonds Section 3.2

5. What ion needs to be reduced in the diet of patients with hypertension?*

6. What two basic forces in atoms are responsible for chemical bonding?

7. Name the two main types of chemical bonds.

8. Usually ionic bonds are formed between what types of elements?

9. Generally speaking, what makes a bond ionic in nature? How do the components you named in your response to Question #8 form this bond? Draw a picture to support your explanation.

10. In the reaction of sodium metal with chlorine gas to form sodium chloride, how does sodium form a cation? Write an equation to support your answer.

11. In the reaction of sodium metal with chlorine gas to form sodium chloride, how does chlorine form an anion? Write an equation to support your answer.

12. Using Figure 3.2, make two observations about sodium, two observations about chlorine, and two observations about sodium chloride. Why are the properties of sodium chloride not the same as the elements it is composed of?

The Formation of an Ionic Compound

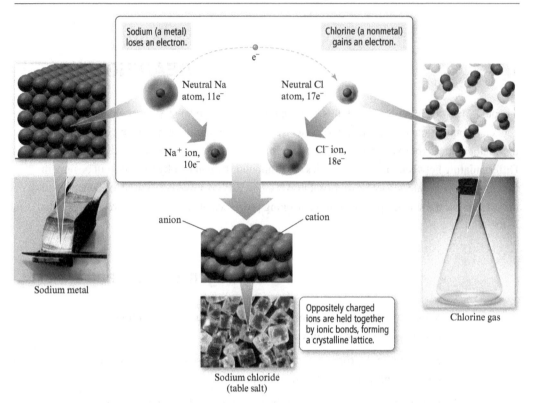

Sodium (a metal) loses an electron.

Chlorine (a nonmetal) gains an electron.

e^-

Neutral Na atom, 11e$^-$

Neutral Cl atom, 17e$^-$

Na$^+$ ion, 10e$^-$

Cl$^-$ ion, 18e$^-$

anion

cation

Sodium metal

Oppositely charged ions are held together by ionic bonds, forming a crystalline lattice.

Chlorine gas

Sodium chloride (table salt)

13. Explain which types of elements form the anion and the cation in an ionic bond?

14. What holds an ionic bond together?

15. Explain what an ionic lattice is and include a diagram in your answer.

16. Draw a diagram showing how the constituent elements, Na and Cl_2, combine to form NaCl.

17. Covalent bonds are formed between what general classes of elements?

18. What makes a bond covalent? How do the components you named in your response to Question #17 explain what is happening?

19. What happens to the potential energy of an electron when it is shared in a covalent bond? Why?

20. Explain what a molecule is. Identify an element consisting of molecules. Identify a compound consisting of molecules.

21. Explain why covalently bonded compounds are called molecular compounds. Provide two examples. Explain why ionic compounds are not called molecular compounds.

22. Explain how does the terminology used in the name of a substance indicate something about a substance?

Representing Compounds: Chemical Formulas and Molecular Models   Section 3.3

23. In a chemical formula, what element is usually listed first and which is last? What is a subscript and what does it indicate?

24. Explain how the formulas for H_2O and NaCl provide different information about the composition of these two compounds.

25. Using an example, explain the difference between a structural formula, an empirical formula, and a molecular formula.

26. In a structural formula, how are single bonds and double bonds depicted? What does each represent?

27. Select a compound and explain the advantages and disadvantages of using ball-and-stick molecular models, space-filling molecular models, and structural formulas (Lewis structures) to represent a compound. Make a table to support your answer.

An Atomic-Level View of Elements and Compounds   Section 3.4

28. Explain the difference between atomic elements and molecular elements.

29. Identify and write the formulas of molecular elements that are diatomic molecules and polyatomic molecules.

30. Explain the difference in composition between molecular compounds and ionic compounds.

31. Explain why ionic compounds are not called molecules. What is a formula unit and why is the term used for ionic compounds? What is a lattice? Draw a lattice and indicate a formula unit.

32. Draw a flow chart showing how to identify atomic elements, molecular elements, molecular compounds, and ionic compounds.

33. What is a polyatomic ion? Give an example of one polyatomic cation and one polyatomic anion? Show how these ions combine to make a compound.

Ionic Compounds: Formulas and Names   Section 3.5

34. Why are ionic compounds generally stable?

35. Summarize the three parts of writing an ionic formula and include examples.

36. What is the difference between a common name and a systematic name? Why do chemists prefer the use of the systematic name over the common name?

37. What is a binary compound? Select a binary compound and explain the necessary steps to name it as an ionic binary compound.

38. Explain the basic format and the steps needed to name an ionic compound composed of a cation that has a possibility of existing in more than one oxidation state (charge).

39. Select two compounds as examples to explain when are Roman numerals used in the name of an ionic compound and when Roman numerals are not used.

40. How are ionic compounds with polyatomic ions named? Can a compound have two polyatomic ions?

41. What are oxyanions? Choose two oxyanions and list their chemical formulas and names.

42. Fill in the following chart for oxyanions formed by bromine and oxygen atoms:

Ionic Ending	per___ate	____ate	___ite	hypo___ite
Formula		Bromate BrO_3^-		
# Oxygens Compared to the –ate Ending		standard		

43. What are hydrates and how are waters of hydration indicated in a formula?

44. Fill in the following chart on the prefixes used in naming to identify the number of waters in a hydrate:

1/2	1	2	3	4	5	6	7	8

How are hydrates named? What does the term anhydrous mean? How is a hydrate changed to an anhydrous form?

Section 3.6   Molecular Compounds: Formulas and Names

45. What is the basic format used in naming a binary molecular compound? How does one decide which element should be first in the formula of a molecule?

46. Fill in the following table with the prefixes used in molecular compound naming:

1	2	3	4	5	6	7	8	9	10

47. Use the compounds CO and CO_2 to explain the rules for naming a molecular compound.

48. What does (aq) mean after the formula of a substance?

49. What are acids?

50. What are three characteristics of acids?

51. What are the two main types of acids?

52. What is the basic format used for writing the name of a binary acid?

53. What is the basic format used for writing the names of the two types of oxyacids?

54. What is acid rain? Identify three environmental problems it can cause.

Summary of Inorganic Nomenclature   Section 3.7

55. Fill in the following chart summarizing how to name inorganic compounds:

Inorganic Nomenclature Flow Chart

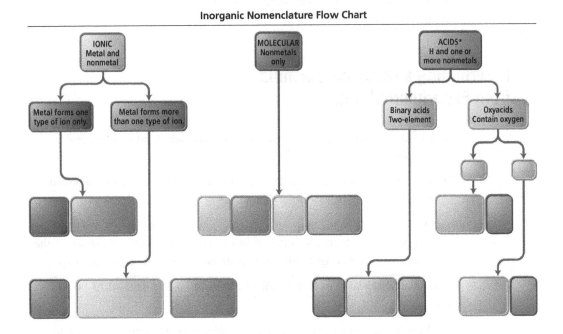

56. How do you decide which part of the flowchart to use for naming?

57. Explain how to use the flowchart to name $CuCl_2$, CO, and H_2CO_3. Differentiate how to name NCl_3 and $AlCl_3$.

Formula Mass and the Mole Concept for Compounds   Section 3.8

58. What is formula mass? How is it calculated? Explain how to calculate the molar mass of a compound.

59. Show how to calculate the molar mass of $HClO_4$.

60. How is a molar mass different from atomic mass?

61. How can the molar mass and number of grams present in a sample be used to determine the number of species present in the sample?

62. How many molecules of CO_2 are contained in a sample of 43.5 g of CO_2? How many oxygen atoms and carbon atoms are present in the sample? Be sure to show all your work and label all quantities with the correct units. Explain how you obtained your answers.

Composition of Compounds   Section 3.9

63. What is mass percent?

64. Explain how to calculate mass percent of species A in the Compound A_2B.

65. Using water as an example, show how to calculate mass percent of hydrogen.

66. Explain how to use mass percent as a conversion factor.

67. How are chemical formulas used as conversion factors?

68. Show how to calculate the empirical formula of a compound using 42.88% C and 57.12% O.

Section 3.10   Determining a Chemical Formula from Experimental Data

69. Explain the steps to determine an empirical formula from mass percent composition.

70. Why does the calculation described in Question #69 provide the empirical formula and not the molecular formula?

71. Fill in the chart below indicating the multiplier to use to find the whole-number subscripts for an empirical formula from the fractional subscripts the experimental data might provide. Explain how these multipliers are used.

Fractional Subscript	0.20	0.25	0.33	0.40	0.50	0.66	0.75	0.80
Multiplier								

72. What specific quantity is needed to be able to change an empirical formula to a molecular formula?

73. Explain how to calculate the molecular formula from the empirical formula. Write a mathematical expression to support your answer.

74. Explain the process of combustion analysis for a hydrocarbon compound.

75. If the combustion of a hydrocarbon forms 1.60 g of carbon dioxide and 0.819 g of water, write out a conceptual plan and indicate the relationships needed to calculate the empirical formula of the hydrocarbon.

Section 3.11   Organic Compounds

76. What are organic compounds and how has this definition changed over time?

77. Give two reasons why carbon chemistry is unique.

78. What are hydrocarbons?

79. Explain the bond differences among an alkane, alkene, and alkyne. (Look at the examples in Table 3.1.)

Table 3.1 Common Hydrocarbons

Name	Molecular Formula	Structural Formula	Space-filling Model	Common Uses
Methane	CH_4	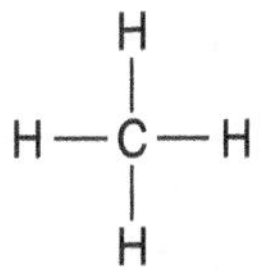	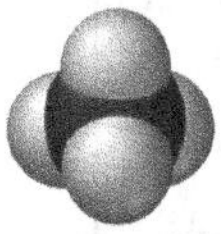	Primary component of natural gas)
Propane	C_3H_8	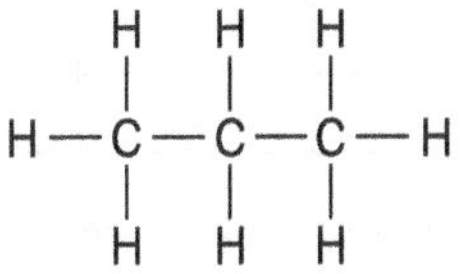	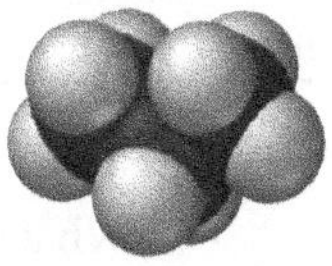	LP gas for grills and outdoor stoves
n-Butane*	C_4H_{10}	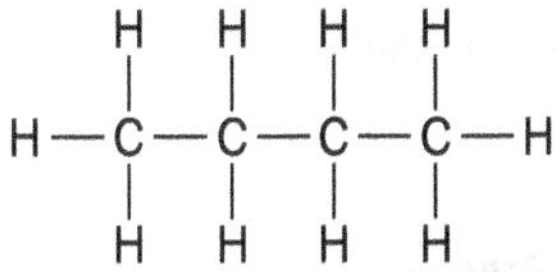	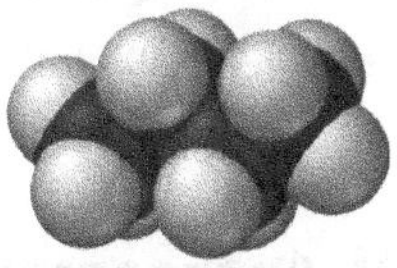	Common fuel for lighters
n-Pentane*	C_5H_{12}	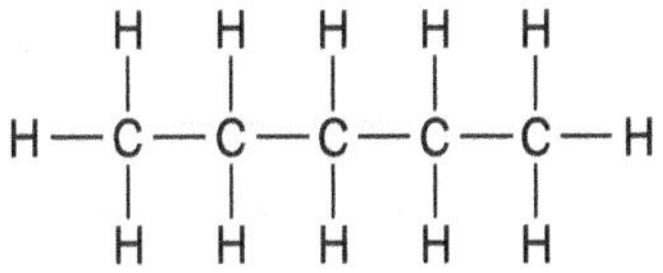	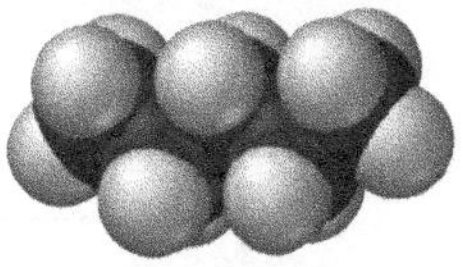	Component of gasoline
Ethene	C_2H_4	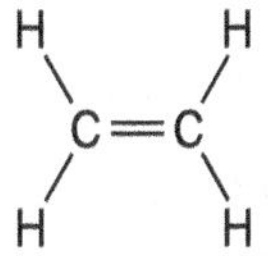	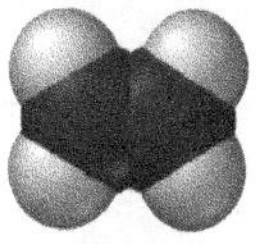	Ripening agent in fruit
Ethyne	C_2H_2			Fuel for welding torches

*The "n" in the names of these hydrocarbons stands for "normal", which means straight chain.

80. Fill in the following chart for the prefixes used in organic naming:

# Carbons	1	2	3	4	5	6	7	8	9	10
Prefix										

81. What is an organic chemistry functional group?

82. What functional group must be present in an alcohol? Draw methanol and circle the functional group.

83. Fill in the following chart on organic functional groups:

Family	Alcohol	Carboxylic Acids	Ketones	Esters	Ethers	Aldehydes	Amines
Functional Group/ General Formula							
Name Ending							
Example							

84. What does the R stand for in the general formulas found in the chart in Question #83? Why is it important to recognize the functional group present in an organic compound?

Self-Assessment Answers

1. _____   2. _____   3. _____

4. _____   5. _____   6. _____

7. _____   8. _____   9. _____

10. _____   11. _____   12. _____

13. _____   14. _____

CHEMICAL REACTIONS AND CHEMICAL QUANTITIES

This chapter has two parts: mathematical calculations and types of chemical reactions. Mathematical calculations are important to master because they are the basis of many other types of problems in later chapters and all are tested on the AP exam. The math here should be mostly review. The calculations in regards to reactions going to equilibrium will be in later chapters. The introduction in this chapter to types of reactions are useful ways to classify many chemical reactions we see everyday. Understanding how to decide on a specific type of reaction is important. There is a lot packed into this chapter, but the most important sections for quantitative calculations are as follows:

4.2 **Writing and Balancing Chemical Equations**

4.3 **Reaction Stoichiometry: How Much Carbon Dioxide?**

4.4 **Stoichiometric Relationships: Limiting Reactant, Theoretical Yield, Percent Yield, and Reactant in Excess**

4.5 **Three examples of Chemical Reactions: Combustion, Alkali Metals, and Halogens**

Specific Learning Objectives Addressed in This Chapter:

SPQ-1 The mole allows different units to be compared.

SPQ-1.A Calculate quantities of a substance or its relative number of particles using dimensional analysis and the mole concept.

SPQ-4 When a substance changes into a new substance, or when its properties change, no mass is lost or gained.

SPQ-4.A Explain changes in the amounts of reactants and products based on the balanced reaction equation for a chemical process.

Concepts and Vocabulary to Review:

Section 4.2   Writing and Balancing Chemical Equations

A **chemical reaction** can be represented by symbols, using the molecular formulas that you have learned to write. The **reactants** are the starting materials and are found on the left-hand side of the equation; the **products** that are formed are found on the right-hand side. An arrow which means "to form", is placed between the reactants and the products. Sometimes an equals sign is used instead of an arrow, hence the words *chemical equation*. Once the skeleton equation with the chemical species is present, **coefficients** are put in front of each chemical species to balance the equation to get the same number of each type of atom on each side of the equation. This is what an equals sign would indicate. If it is unbalanced then it really isn't an equation. This is called *conservation of atoms* and it is the foundation of writing and balancing equations. Atoms cannot be changed into other types of atoms nor can they be lost in the reaction (unless it is a nuclear reaction which is not covered here). The coefficients are applied to every element in the chemical species they are placed in front of; $2CO_2$ indicates 2C atoms and 4O atoms. Using proper math notations, this would be written $2(CO_2)$, but chemists leave out the parentheses.

Example:

Balance the following equation and write a sentence describing what occurs at the atom level and at the mole level.

$$\underline{}Fe(s) + \underline{}O_2(g) \rightarrow \underline{}Fe_2O_3(s)$$

At first look, you may think you only need 2 Fe but the oxygen atoms need to be balanced first. Putting a 3 in front of the O_2 gives 6 O atoms. This requires putting a 2 in front of the Fe_2O_3 to also have 6 oxygen atoms. This results in 4 Fe.

$$4\,Fe(s) + 3\,O_2(g) \rightarrow 2\,Fe_2O_3(s)$$

Four atoms of iron react with 3 molecules of oxygen gas to form two formula units of iron(III) oxide.

Four moles of iron react with three moles of oxygen gas to form two moles of iron(III) oxide.

Section 4.3   Reaction Stoichiometry: How Much Carbon Dioxide?

The foundation of most chemistry problems is stoichiometry. When reactions occur, how can we predict how much product can be made? We use stoichiometry: using the coefficients from a balanced equation to provide the mole ratios of one chemical to another. Often, we refer to the mathematical calculation of changing from one type of chemical substance to another as a conversion.

Mole: Mole Stoichiometry. In the equation $2H_2(g) + O_2(g) \rightarrow 2H_2O(g)$ there are several ratios of moles to moles: $\dfrac{2\text{ mol }H_2}{1\text{ mol }O_2}, \dfrac{2\text{ mol }H_2O}{1\text{ mol }O_2}, \dfrac{1\text{ mol }O_2}{2\text{ mol }H_2}, \dfrac{1\text{ mol }O_2}{2\text{ mol }H_2O}, \dfrac{2\text{ mol }H_2}{2\text{ mol }H_2O},$

and $\dfrac{2 \text{ mol } H_2O}{2 \text{ mol } H_2}$. The ratio you would choose to use depends on what substance you are starting with and to which one you want to convert. If you have 3 moles of oxygen and you want to convert to moles of water, you would use $\dfrac{2 \text{ mol } H_2O}{1 \text{ mol } O_2}$. This ratio will cancel the unit of moles of oxygen and convert to the unit moles of water.

$$3 \text{ mol } O_2 \times \frac{2 \text{ mol } H_2O}{1 \text{ mol } O_2} = 6 \text{ mol } H_2O$$

$$3 \text{ mol } O_2 \times \frac{2 \text{ mol } H_2O}{1 \text{ mol } O_2} = 6 \text{ mol } H_2O$$

There are two types of conversions to review: mole–mole conversions as shown above and mass–mass conversions.

Unfortunately, there is no way to directly go from mass of one species to moles or mass of another species in the reaction. The chemical equation used indicates the relationships between all the species but only in molecules, or, more conveniently, moles. Mass-mass conversions must include mole-to-mole conversions as a step as well as adding a gram conversion step before and after the mole–mole step. Converting the starting substance from grams to moles occurs first, then the moles to mole stoichiometry step is done, and the final step is converting the formed substance from moles to grams. Of course, there are different types of combinations in which you can start in grams but end in moles. Throughout all conversions, it is important to recognize that atoms are being conserved. They MUST add up!

The steps for gram to gram stoichiometry for A → B: (1) mass of substance A convert to moles of A, (2) convert from moles of A to moles of B, and (3) convert from moles of B to grams of B. If you start with 18.0 grams of hydrogen, how many grams of oxygen will be required to react completely to form water? The first step is to identify the chemical equation to know the moles ratios needed.

$$2H_2 + O_2 \rightarrow 2H_2O$$

The equation indicates the ratio of two moles of hydrogen gas is needed to completely react with one mole of oxygen gas. In the calculation grams of hydrogen are converted to moles of hydrogen followed by the stoichiometry step of multiplying by the ratio 1 mole of oxygen to two moles of hydrogen (1:2) and finally converting the moles of oxygen to grams:

$$18.0 \text{ g } H_2 \quad \times \quad \frac{1 \text{ mol } H_2}{2.016 \text{ g } H_2} \quad \times \quad \frac{1 \text{ mol } O_2}{2 \text{ mol } H_2} \quad \times \quad \frac{32.00 \text{ g } O_2}{1 \text{ mol } O_2} = 143 \text{ g } O_2$$

Convert from grams to moles of H_2	Convert from moles of H_2 to moles of O_2 (Stoichiometry step)	Convert from mole to grams of O_2

You need to be able to read a problem and determine where you need to start—moles or grams—and where you need to stop. Practice this skill and performing the necessary set up. On the AP exam, you are required to show work for all your calculations in the free response section, so always write everything out with units and labels even during practice sessions. There are also calculations in the multiple-choice section of the exam; if you do the set-up, units will cancel and the problem will be easy to solve.

Section 4.4   Stoichiometric Relationships: Limiting Reactant, Theoretical Yield, Percent Yield, and Reactant in Excess

Using the skills in the above section, we can also calculate to further analyze chemical reaction yields. There are several types of calculations you need to be able to do.

A *limiting reactant* is the reactant you do not have enough of to fully react the other reactant(s). In other words, it is the ingredient that runs out first. This is also calculated through stoichiometry. If you were making cookies and the recipe called for 1 cup of sugar and 1 cup of flour to make 6 cookies, and you had 12 cups of sugar, but only 2 cups of flour, the flour is the limiting reactant. You could not make 72 cookies, but only 12 cookies, at the most. At this point, you have run out of flour, and can make no more cookies. In chemistry, the recipe, in the analogy above, is the chemical reaction. The coefficients are the guide to how much of each reactant are needed to make the products, and those coefficients count atoms and molecules. This means the number of grams of each reactant does not indicate which reactant is the limiting reactant because it is NOT a direct count of atoms; you must do the mathematical calculations to determine the numbers by converting to moles. The reactant you have a surplus of is called the *excess reactant*. For the cookies, the excess reactant was the sugar. You will be expected to be able to determine how much excess reactant is present after the reaction occurs as well. For the cookies, it would be 12 – 2 cups of sugar, or 10 cups of sugar.

The amount of product indicated by stoichiometry is the *maximum yield*; this predicted amount is called the *theoretical yield*. In reality, things external to the reaction can affect the amount that actually gets made—and the amount is always less than or equal to the amount predicted should be made. When the reaction is actually completed, the amount really made is called the *actual yield*. If stoichiometry predicted 50.0 grams of water to be made, this is the theoretical yield. If the reaction only made 40.0 grams, this is the actual yield. These two numbers are used to calculate percent yield, which is calculated by taking the actual yield and dividing it by the theoretical yield, then multiplying by 100% to make it a percent.

$$\frac{\text{actual yield}}{\text{theoretical yield}} \times 100\% = \% \text{ yield.}$$

In the cookies example, the theoretical yield was 12 cookies, but suppose you left some batter on the sides of the mixing bowl, so only 10 cookies were made. This is the actual yield. The percent yield is 10 cookies/12 cookies $\times$ 100% = 83%. Note percent yield has no units.

It is vital in all chemistry calculations to associate every quantity with a unit. Rarely will a quantity be unitless. Even *grams* have an associated label, e.g., grams of hydrogen, and so does *moles*. This is important as grams/grams may appear to cancel, but grams hydrogen/grams water does NOT cancel.

Three Examples of Chemical Reactions: Combustion, Alkali Metals, and Halogens

Section 4.5

These are three common types of reactions. Combustion is reacting with oxygen such as hydrogen reacting with oxygen to make water. Alkali metals are the most reactive metals and halogens are the most reactive nonmetals and are therefore found in many reactions.

Combustion reactions emit heat. Organic compounds combusting with oxygen will have products of water and carbon dioxide. If the reaction is incomplete, it will also have other products such as carbon soot and carbon monoxide. The complete combustion of methane would be:

$$CH_4(g) + 2O_2(g) \rightarrow CO_2(g) + 2H_2O(g).$$

Reactions with Alkali metals involve cations that are all +1. The reactivity of the alkali metals increases down a column on the periodic table. If the alkali metal is reacting with a halogen, the general format is $2M + X_2 \rightarrow 2MX$ where M is the metal and X_2 is a halogen. The metal has a +1 and although the charge of a halide is -1 because the metal is reacting with a diatomic molecule, two of the products are formed. This type of reaction forms ionic bonds and also emits heat. An example is $2Li(s) + Cl_2(g) \rightarrow 2LiCl(s)$.

Alkali metals also react with water to form metal hydroxides and hydrogen gas. This equates to

$2M(s) + H_2O(l) \rightarrow 2M^+(aq) + 2OH^-(aq) + H_2(g).$ An example would be

$2Na(s) + H_2O(l) \rightarrow 2Na^+(aq) + 2OH^-(aq) + H_2(g).$ Again the alkali metals are more reactive as you go down the column on the periodic table.

Halogens react with metals to form metal halides. The general formula is $2M + nX_2 \rightarrow MX_n$. An example would be $2Al(s) + 3Cl_2(g) \rightarrow 2AlCl_3(s)$. Hydrogen halides form when hydrogen reacts with a halogen. $H_2(g) + Cl_2(g) \rightarrow 2HCl(g)$.

Covalent bonds form when two nonmetal halogens react together. These compounds are called interhalogen compounds. $Br_2(l) + F_2(g) \rightarrow 2BrF(g)$.

Additional Practice

Self-Assessment Quiz Questions Q1, Q2, Q3, Q4, Q5, Q6, Q7, Q8, Q9, and Q10

Equations to know:

mass A $\rightarrow$ amount A(in moles) $\rightarrow$ amount B(in moles) $\rightarrow$ mass B

$$\% \text{ yield} = \frac{\text{actual yield}}{\text{theoretical yield}} \times 100\%$$

Practice AP Test Questions

1. Molybdenum sulfide can react with oxygen gas to produce molybdenum oxide and sulfur dioxide.

$$\text{MoS}_2(s) + \text{O}_2(g) \rightarrow \text{MoO}_3(aq) + \text{SO}_2(g)$$

   When the above equation is balanced and all coefficients are reduced to lowest whole number terms, what is the coefficient for $\text{O}_2(g)$?

   A) 3   B) 4   C) 5   D) 7

2. Silicon can be produced by reacting silicon dioxide with carbon in an electric arc furnance as represented by the following unbalanced chemical equation:

$$\text{SiO}_2(s) + \text{C}(s) \rightarrow \text{Si}(s) + \text{CO}(g)$$

Compound	Molar Mass (g/mole)
SiO_2	60.08
CO	28.01

   What mass of silicon can be produced when excess silicon dioxide reacts with 12. g of carbon?

   A) 0.018 g   B) 6.0 g   C) 14 g   D) 28 g

3. When 0.600 mole of phosphorus, P_4, and 0.600 mole of fluorine gas, F_2, react as completely as possible, to produce phosphorus trichloride, PF_3, what mass of reactant would remain?

A) 61.5 g P_4 B) 73.8 g P_4 C) 22.8 g F_2 D) 12.3 g P_4

4. When aluminum reacts with chlorine gas, aluminum chloride, $AlCl_3$, can form.

$$2Al(s) + 3Cl_2\ (g) \rightarrow AlCl_3(s)$$

If the percentage yield for the above reaction is 50.0%, how many grams of aluminum must react to produce 27 g of $AlCl_3$.

A) 11 g   B) 19 g   C) 22 g   D) 43 g

5. The following diagram represents the reaction of A_2 (two joined triangles) with X_2 (two joined shaded spheres) at the particulate nature of matter level representation.

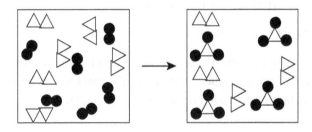

Write a balanced chemical equation for the process, and identify the limiting reagent.

A) $A + X_2 \rightarrow AX_3$ C) $A_2 + 3X_2 \rightarrow 2\,AX_3$

   A_2 is the limiting reagent A_2 is the limiting reagent

B) $2A + 6X \rightarrow 2\,AX_3$ D) $A_2 + 3X_2 \rightarrow 2\,AX_3$

   X_2 is the limiting reagent X_2 is the limiting reagent

6. Based on the picture diagram in the previous problem, how many moles of product, AX_3, can be made if 2.0 moles of A_2 are allowed to react with 2.0 moles of X_2?

A) 1.3 mol AX_3 B) 2.0 mol AX_3 C) 4.0 mol AX_3 D) 6.0 mol AX_3

7. Iron reacts with oxygen gas in the presence of some water to form iron(III) oxide.

$$4\,Fe(s) + 2\,O_2(g) \rightarrow 2\,Fe_2O_3\ (s)$$

When 16 g of oxygen gas are allowed to react with 28 g of iron, calculate the maximum amount of iron(III) oxide that can form.

A) 20. g   B) 40. g   C) 44 g   D) 53 g

8. When 20. g of barium metal is reacted with water, 10.00 g of barium hydroxide is produced. Using the following balanced equation, calculate the percent yield for the reaction?

$$Ba(s) + 2\,H_2O(l) \rightarrow Ba(OH)_2(aq) + H_2(g)$$

A) 13%   B) 25%   C) 50.%   D) 90.%

9. Determine the limiting reactant (LR) and the moles of hydrogen cyanide that can be formed when 8.0 g of CH_4, 16. g of O_2, and 17. g of NH_3 are allowed to react. Some possibly useful molar masses are as follows:

CH_4 = 16. g/mol, NH_3 = 17 g/mol, HCN = 27 g/mol.

$$2CH_4(g) + 3O_{2g}(l) + 2NH_3(g) \rightarrow 2HCN(g) + 6H_2O(g)$$

A) LR = CH_4, 0.50 mole HCN formed

B) LR = O_2, 0.50 mole HCN formed

C) LR = NH_3, 0.33 mole HCN formed

D) LR = O_2, 0.33 mole HCN formed

10. Hydrogen gas reacts with chlorine gas in a combination reaction. The molecular diagram represents an initial mixture of the reactants, prior to any reaction. After the reaction occurs, identify the limiting reagent.

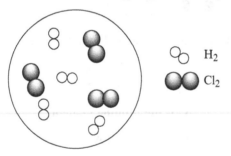

A) H_2 B) Cl_2 C) HCl   D) There is no limiting reagent.

Data Interpretation and Analysis Question: The Synthesis of Bromopropane

When propene (C_3H_6) reacts with hydrogen bromide (HBr) two products form, 2-bromopropane and 1-bromopropane.

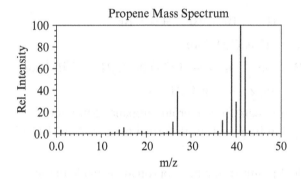

Bromine has two naturally occurring isotopes, ^{79}Br (50.7%) and ^{81}Br (49.3%). Prior to the reaction a mass spectrum was obtained for propene and for hydrogen bromide.

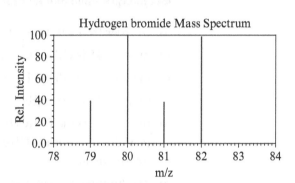

a) Given the mass spectrum of hydrogen bromide, identify what species are represented by each of the four peaks.

b) Given the mass spectrum of propene, identify what species are represented by the m/z = 41 and m/z = 42 peaks.

After the reaction occurs the two products are collected, separated, and a mass spectrum is obtain for each product.

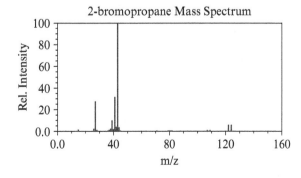

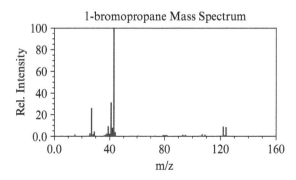

The mass spectra for the two bromopropane compounds are nearly identical.

c) Identify what species are represented by the m/z = 124, 122, 43, and 41 peaks in the bromopropane mass spectrum.

d) Explain how both bromopropanes have a m/z = 27 peak. One of the bromo-propane compounds has a small peak at m/z = 29, the other does not. Explain why the ion fragment represented by m/z = 29 peak must be from the 1-bromopropane and not the 2-bromopropane.

e) When 20.0 grams of propene are allowed to react with 20.0 grams of hydrogen bromide, 20.0 grams of bromopropane (a mixture consisting of 1-bromopropane and 2-bromopropane compounds) is actually collected in the laboratory. Determine the limiting reagent and estimate the overall percent yield.

f) What laboratory procedures would not separate a mixture of the two bromopropane compounds?

g) How would you separate the two bromopropane compounds and how would you determine the percentage of each compound collected?

Data Interpretation and Analysis Question Answers with Brief Explanations

a) In order from left to right: ^{79}Br $^1H-^{79}Br$ ^{81}Br $^1H-^{81}Br$

b) m/z = 41 is $C_3H_5^+$ ion   m/z = 42 is $C_3H_6^+$ ion

c) m/z = 124 is the $C_3H_7-^{81}Br^+$ ion   m/z = 122 is the $C_3H_7-^{79}Br^+$ ion
m/z = 43 is the $C_3H_7^+$ ion   m/z = 41 is $C_3H_5^+$ ion

d) m/z = 29 is the $CH_3CH_2^+$ ion fragment from 1-bromopropane. 2-bromopropane does not form a $CH_3CH_2^+$ ion fragment. Both form a m/z = 27 CH_2CH^+ ion fragment.

e) The limiting reagent is HBr, 30.4 grams of the bromopropane is made in the lab. The overall percent yield is 66.6%.

f) One can not use gravity filtration, distillation, or suction filtration.

g) HPLC

READING GUIDE

This chapter combines mathematical concepts and reactions which are included in the AP Chemistry curriculum as well as forming foundational concepts. Understanding the different types of reactions, their reactants, products and how to predict them will be valuable tools to use in the laboratory section of your course.

Climate Change and the Combustion of Fossil Fuels*   Section 4.1

1. What is meant by Earth's average temperature? What factors determine this? What data is used to determine the Earth's average temperature? Has the Earth's average temperature changed over the previous forty years?*

2. Explain what is meant by *the Greenhouse Effect*.

3. What is a "greenhouse gas"? Which greenhouse gases are scientists most concerned with and why? What data is used to determine the amount of greenhouse gases present in the atmosphere?

Writing and Balancing Chemical Equations   Section 4.2

4. Why must a chemical equation be balanced?
5. What are chemical reactions? How are they represented by using chemical formulas?
6. Where are the reactants found in a chemical equation? Where are the products found in a chemical equation? What separates the reactants and products in a chemical equation?
7. What is the difference between a reactant and a product?
8. Explain what is meant by a balanced chemical equation. What law is a balanced equation based on?
9. Explain how you can check that a chemical equation is balanced. Explain how to balance the following chemical equation which represents the decomposition of hydrazine. $N_2H_4(l) \rightarrow NH_3(g) + N_2(g)$.
10. Explain the difference between a coefficient and a subscript in a chemical equation.
11. How are the states of matter indicated in a chemical reaction?

Section 4.3   Reaction Stoichiometry: How Much Carbon Dioxide?

12. Gasoline used as a fuel for cars is a complex mixture. What compound is a major component of gasoline? Write a balanced chemical equation for the combustion of this major component. What does this equation indicate?

13. How many moles of carbon dioxide are produced for every two moles of octane burned?

14. Define *stoichiometry*.

15. What is stoichiometry similar to in cooking?*

16. In stoichiometry, what are coefficients and how are they used?

17. Given a simple chemical reaction $A + B \rightarrow C$, what is the general plan for determining how the mass, in grams, of one reagent consumed in a chemical reaction is related to the mass, in grams, of another reagent consumed in a chemical reaction? How does this plan apply to determining the mass of product formed knowing the mass of reactant consumed?

18. Set up a problem with units showing how to convert from 2.5 grams of hydrogen to grams of oxygen used during the reaction: $2H_2(g) + O_2(g) \rightarrow 2H_2O(g)$.

Section 4.4   Limiting Reactant, Theoretical Yield, Percent Yield, and Reactant in Excess

19. Define the following terms:

    Limiting reactant:

    Theoretical yield:

    Percent yield:

    Actual yield:

20. What is the relationship between actual yield and theoretical yield?

21. Explain how to identify the limiting reactant.

22. Explain how to calculate the theoretical yield of a reaction.

23. What is meant by an excess reactant?

24. Write the equation for the synthesis of ammonia from the elements nitrogen and hydrogen. Given 50.0 g of N_2 and 20.0 g of H_2, determine the limiting reactant and theoretical yield.

25. In problem #24, if 19.0 grams of ammonia is formed when the experiment is performed, what is the percent yield?

Three Examples of Chemical Reactions: Combustion, Alkali Metals, and Halogens

Section 4.5

26. What reactant is needed for a combustion reaction?

27. What are some characteristics of a combustion reaction?

28. What are typical products of organic combustion?

29. Which metals are the most reactive? Compare the reactivity of these metals going down a column of the periodic table. What is the general formula when these metals react with halogens and when they react with water?

30. What is a metal halide? What is the general formula when a metal reacts with a halogen?

31. What are interhalogen compounds? List an example.

Self-Assessment Answers

1. _____   2. _____   3. _____

4. _____   5. _____   6. _____

7. _____   8. _____   9. _____

10. _____   11. _____   12. _____

13. _____   14. _____   15. _____

CHAPTER

5

INTRODUCTION TO SOLUTIONS AND AQUEOUS REACTIONS

This chapter has two main focuses: (1) how to make solutions and calculate their concentrations and (2) types of reactions with solutions. Both of these topics need to be mastered as basic skills in the AP curriculum. Included in this chapter are several lab skills you need to be able to do including making solutions and doing titrations with acids and bases. The following sections all have important material to understand.

5.2 **Solution Concentration**

5.3 **Solution Stoichiometry**

5.4 **Types of Aqueous Solutions and Solubility**

5.5 **Precipitate Reactions**

5.6 **Representing Aqueous Reactions: Molecular, Ionic, and Net Ionic Equations**

5.7 **Acid–Base Reactions**

5.8 **Gas-Evolution Reactions**

5.9 **Oxidation–Reduction Reactions**

Specific Learning Objectives Addressed in This Chapter:

SPQ-3 Interactions between intermolecular forces influence the solubility and separation of mixtures.

SPQ-3.A Calculate the number of solute particles, volume, or molarity of solutions.

SPQ-3.B Using particulate models for mixtures:

- Represent interactions between components
- Represent concentrations of components

TRA-1 A substance that changes its properties, or that changes into a different substance, can be represented by chemical equations.

TRA-2 A substance can change into another substance through different processes, and the change itself can be classified by the sort of processes that produced it.

TRA-2.A Identify a reaction as acid–base, oxidation–reduction, or precipitation.

TRA-2.C Represent a balanced redox reaction equation using half-reactions.

SPQ-4 When a substance changes into a new substance, or when its properties change, no mass is lost or gained.

SPQ-4.A Explain changes in the amounts of reactants and products based on the balanced reaction equation for a chemical process.

SPQ-4.B Identify the equivalence point in a titration based on the amounts of titrant and analyte, assuming the titration reaction goes to completion.

Concepts and Vocabulary to Review:

Solution Concentration   Section 5.2

To discuss solutions, you must remember the following vocabulary words.

Solute is the substance being dissolved.

Solvent is the substance doing the dissolving, and in water solutions, the solvent is the water.

A **dilute solution** is one containing only a few solute particles in a large amount of solvent. A **concentrated solution** has much more solute than a dilute solution. In a **saturated solution**, the solution contains the maximum amount of solute that the solvent can dissolve. This **solubility limit** depends on several factors and is different for different substances; there is no standard rule.

Molarity (M) is used to indicate the concentration of a solution in moles solute per liter of solution. The definition of molarity is the ratio of $\dfrac{\text{mol solute}}{\text{liters of solution}}$. In many problems, you will need to change grams of solute to moles of solute in order to calculate molarity.

How to make a solution is an important LAB SKILL. Make sure you know the steps. You may be asked to make a whole liter of solution, but more often than not, you will be asked to make another amount on the AP test, such as 250 mL. You need to be able to calculate the number of grams needed to make any amount of solution. To solve this, you can set up a proportion:

$$\frac{\text{mol solute}}{\text{liters solution}} = \frac{\text{x mol solute}}{\text{desired liters of solution}}$$

In this proportion, the given molarity is on one side and the desired volume in liters is on the other to determine how many moles of solute is needed. This can then be converted into grams of solute. Once this number is known, there are three basic steps to follow after putting on proper personal protection equipment (PPE) such as goggles: (Note these steps may vary at your institution.) See Figure 5.1.

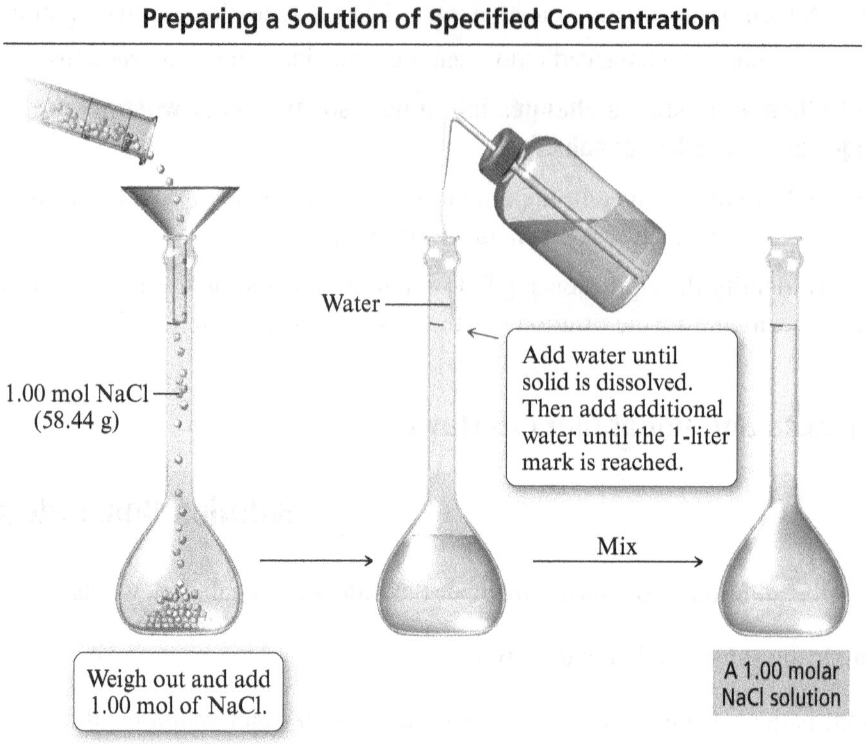

Preparing a Solution of Specified Concentration

1.00 mol NaCl (58.44 g)

Water

Add water until solid is dissolved. Then add additional water until the 1-liter mark is reached.

Mix

Weigh out and add 1.00 mol of NaCl.

A 1.00 molar NaCl solution

Figure 5.1 Preparing a 1 Molar NaCl Solution

1. Measure out the grams of solute needed on a balance. Dissolve the solute in a small amount of water (solvent) in a volumetric flask.** see note below if using acids.

2. Add water (solvent) to the mark in the flask.

Since molarity is a ratio, it can be used in stoichiometry calculations too because molarity times volume in liters equals moles; $\dfrac{\text{Mol solute}}{\text{L solution}} \times \text{L} = \text{mol}$.

Another lab-related skill is to make a dilute solution from a concentrated solution. The concentrated solution is called a *stock solution*. The equation for solution dilution is $M_1 V_1 = M_2 V_2$, where the subscript 1 refers to the stock solution and the subscript 2 refers to the new diluted solution. See Figure 5.2.

Solution dilution steps, after putting on PPE, are as follows:

1. Measure out the specific volume of stock solution.

2. Pour into the appropriate volumetric flask.**

3. Add water to the mark.

**Regardless of which steps your institution follows, if you are diluting an acid solution on the AP test, pour 1/2 to 2/3 of the water needed in the appropriate flask. Then SLOWLY add the acid while swirling it. Finish by adding the last amount of water to the mark. This is a safety issue.

Diluting a Solution

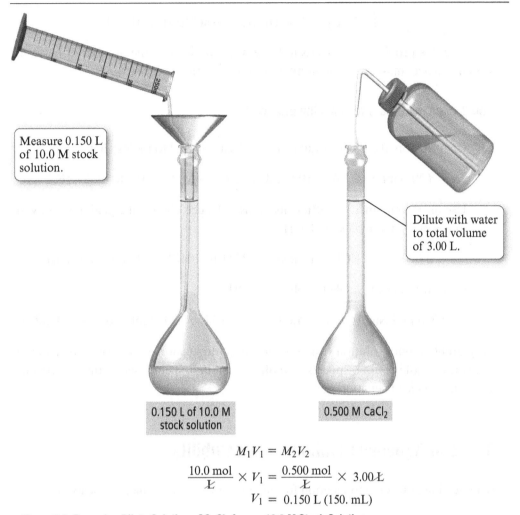

Measure 0.150 L of 10.0 M stock solution.

Dilute with water to total volume of 3.00 L.

0.150 L of 10.0 M stock solution

0.500 M CaCl₂

$$M_1V_1 = M_2V_2$$

$$\frac{10.0\ \text{mol}}{\cancel{L}} \times V_1 = \frac{0.500\ \text{mol}}{\cancel{L}} \times 3.00\ \cancel{L}$$

$$V_1 = 0.150\ \text{L (150. mL)}$$

Figure 5.2 Preparing Dilute Solution of CaCl₂ from a 10.0 M Stock Solution

Solution Stoichiometry   Section 5.3

Reactants and products can be expressed in terms of volumes and concentrations. Using the definition of Molarity = moles solute/Liter of solution, the moles of solute can be calculated by multiply the volume (in units of Liters) times the Molarity, $V \times M$ = moles of solute.

Given a balanced chemical reaction involving reactants in the aqueous phase, we can use the coefficients in the balanced equation to calculate a volume of concentration in another species in the reaction. For instance, given 20.0 mL of 2.0 M HCl, what volume of 4.0 M NaOH is needed to react with all of the HCl?

The balanced chemical reaction

$$HCl(aq) + NaOH(aq) \rightarrow NaCl(aq) + H_2O(l)$$

To solve this problem, one needs to know the "big idea"—the number of moles of acid that reacts must equal the number of moles of base that reacts.

The 3 steps necessary to solve the problem:

1. Convert from the given volume and Molarity of HCl to moles HCl

$$(20.0 \text{ mL}) \times 1.0 \text{ L}/1000 \text{ mL} \times 2.0 \text{ moles}/\text{L} = 0.040 \text{ moles HCl}$$

2. Use the stoichiometry coefficients in the balanced chemical equation to convert moles of HCl to moles of NaOH

$$0.040 \text{ moles HCl} \times 1 \text{ mole NaOH}/1 \text{ mol HCl} = 0.040 \text{ mol NaOH}$$

3. Convert moles of NaOH to volume NaOH

$$0.040 \text{ mol NaOH} \times 1 \text{ L}/4.0 \text{ mol} = 0.10 \text{ L} \times 1000 \text{ ml}/1.0 \text{ L} = 10. \text{ mL}$$

Any problem with solution stoichiometry uses dimensional analysis with a step of converting moles of one species to moles of another species using the coefficients from the balanced equation.

Section 5.4   Types of Aqueous Solutions and Solubility

This section builds the foundation for other sections by introducing vocabulary.

Strong electrolytes are differentiated from nonelectrolytes and weak electrolytes. The strong electrolytes, which include the strong acids, disassociate (break apart into ions) completely in water. The individual ions of the strong electrolytes are more attracted to the water molecules than they are to themselves. An aqueous solution of sodium chloride or table salt is an example of a strong electrolyte. See Figures 5.3 and 5.6.

Weak electrolytes, which include weak acids and bases, do not disassociate completely in solution and will actually have only some degree of ionization (dissociation). Acetic acid is an example of a weak electrolyte solution. See Figure 5.4. Water molecules are not being shown in Figures 5.3 and 5.4.

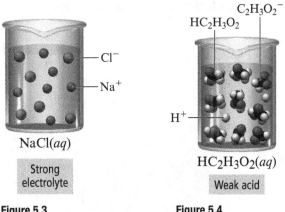

Figure 5.3   **Figure 5.4**

Nonelectrolytes also dissolve in water because they are more attracted to the water molecules than they are to themselves, BUT when they dissolve they stay intact as molecules. Typically, non-electrolytes are made up of covalently bonded molecules. Sugar dissolved in water is an example of a nonelectrolyte.

Sugar Solution

Figure 5.5 A Sugar Solution   Sugar dissolves because the attractions between sugar molecules and water molecules, which both contain a distribution of electrons that results in partial positive and partial negative charges, overcome the attractions between sugar molecules to each other.

It is important to be able to draw and explain the solute–solvent interactions seen below in Figures 5.6 and 5.7. These are often asked on the AP exam and indicate an understanding of how different species dissolve.

Those compounds that dissolve in a solute are called *soluble* and those that do not are *insoluble*. There are rules to predict if a compound will be soluble in water. These are used to see if newly formed products will be soluble as well. Alkali metal ions,

Dissolution of an Ionic Compound

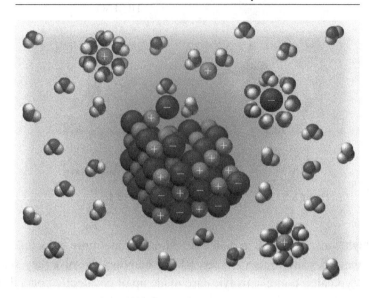

Figure 5.6 Sodium Chloride Dissolving in Water   The attraction between water molecules and the ions of sodium chloride causes NaCl to dissolve in the water.

Interactions between Sugar and Water Molecules

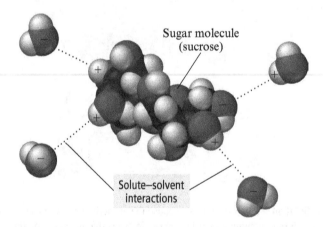

Figure 5.7 Sugar and Water Interactions   Partial charges on sugar molecules and water molecules (which we will discuss more fully in Chapter 11) result in attractions between the sugar molecules and water molecules.

nitrate, and ammonium ions are always soluble are the only rules you are expected to know. You do not need to memorize the table below, but you should be familiar with its data. It is the forces within and between the solute and solvent molecules determining the type of solution that will form.

Table 5.1 Solubility Rules for Ionic Compounds in Water

Compounds Containing the Following Ions Are Generally Soluble	Exceptions
Li^+, Na^+, K^+, and NH_4^+	None
NO_3^- and $C_2H_3O_2^-$	None
Cl^-, Br^-, and I^-	When these ions pair with Ag^+, Hg_2^{2+}, or Pb^{2+}, the resulting compounds are insoluble.
SO_4^{2-}	When SO_4^{2-} pairs with Sr^{2+}, Ba^{2+}, Pb^{2+}, Ag^+, or Ca^{2+}, the resulting compound is insoluble.
Compounds Containing the Following Ions Are Generally Insoluble	**Exceptions**
OH^- and S^{2-}	When these ions pair with Li^+, Na^+, K^+, or NH_4^+, the resulting compounds are soluble.
	When S^{2-} pairs with Ca^{2+}, Sr^{2+}, or Ba^{2+}, the resulting compound is soluble.
	When OH^- pairs with Ca^{2+}, Sr^{2+}, or Ba^{2+}, the resulting compound is slightly soluble.
CO_3^{2-} and PO_4^{3-}	When these ions pair with Li^+, Na^+, K^+, or NH_4^+, the resulting compounds are soluble.

Precipitation Reactions   Section 5.5

During a reaction in solution (usually in water) in which insoluble compounds form, the insoluble compound is called a *precipitate*. You should be able to describe what is occurring in a precipitation reaction. Usually these reactions start by combining two aqueous solutions. By trading the cations in the two solutions, you can predict what possible products could form.

For example, when aqueous solutions of silver nitrate and sodium chloride are mixed, the new products are sodium nitrate and silver chloride. Knowing compounds containing sodium ions and nitrate ions are ALWAYS soluble, the compound forming the precipitate must be silver chloride. This is the same logic one would use on the AP exam.

Keep in mind–even soluble compounds reach a point where no more solid can dissolve in a given amount of water. If enough salt is added to a fixed amount of water, the solution eventually gets saturated and no more can dissolve.

Not all precipitate reactions produce the same amount of precipitate. This concept will be addressed in the mathematics of K_{sp} in Chapter 17. Even in reactions where precipitate is formed, a certain number of ions remain in solution and go to equilibrium.

Precipitation Reaction

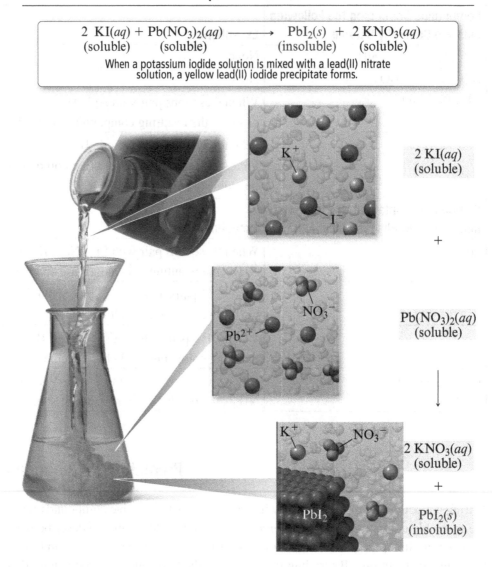

$$2\ KI(aq) + Pb(NO_3)_2(aq) \longrightarrow PbI_2(s) + 2\ KNO_3(aq)$$
(soluble)   (soluble)   (insoluble)   (soluble)

When a potassium iodide solution is mixed with a lead(II) nitrate solution, a yellow lead(II) iodide precipitate forms.

2 KI(aq)
(soluble)

+

Pb(NO₃)₂(aq)
(soluble)

2 KNO₃(aq)
(soluble)

+

PbI₂(s)
(insoluble)

Figure 5.8 Precipitation of Lead(II) Iodide   When a potassium iodide solution is mixed with a lead(II) nitrate solution, a yellow lead(II) iodide precipitate forms.

Section 5.6   Representing Aqueous Reactions: Molecular, Ionic, and Net Ionic Equations

Molecular equations, balanced net ionic equations, and complete ionic equations have different uses. Molecular equations keep all the reactants and products as whole species with their coefficients. These equations are used to indicate all the reactants and products, atom conservation, and the mole-to-mole ratios between them. Sometimes, however, it is more convenient to only look at the species as they exist in solution, rather than as complete molecules. For this, we use **ionic equations**. In balanced complete ionic equations, strong electrolytes are written as disassociated ions, so all reactants and products are written showing how they exist in the solution before and after the reaction also with coefficients to balance the equation. In other cases, we are only concerned with the ions that are actually reacting in the experiment. So, in balanced **net ionic equations**, species not participating in the reaction are crossed out and only the species undergoing a change are left. It is important to understand what each type of equation indicates. The following is a common example.

Molecular equation: $AgNO_3(aq) + NaCl(aq) \rightarrow NaNO_3(aq) + AgCl(s)$

Ionic equation: $Ag^+(aq) + NO_3^-(aq) + Na^+(aq) + Cl^-(aq) \rightarrow Na^+(aq) + NO_3^-(aq) + AgCl(s)$

Net ionic equation: $Ag^+(aq) + Cl^-(aq) \rightarrow AgCl(s)$

The unchanged ions in the complete ionic equation (NO_3^- and Na^+) were removed as spectator ions to create the net ionic equation.

Acid–Base Reactions   Section 5.7

This section includes introductory vocabulary and background about acid and base concepts which are in chapters 16 and 17. An acid–base reaction is also called a **neutralization** reaction because the acid neutralizes the base. When the acid and base react, they form a salt and water. The salt contains the cation of the base and the anion of the acid. For example, in the reaction, $KOH + HCl \rightarrow KCl + H_2O$, the cation K^+ and the anion Cl^- produce the salt KCl. The net ionic representation of the whole reaction of a strong acid with a strong base is $OH^- + H^+ \rightarrow H_2O$ because the salt ions are water soluble and thus the K^+ and Cl^- are spectator ions.

Arrhenius developed a theory of acids and bases. His theory states acids produce H^+ in solution and bases produce OH^- in solution. When an acid disassociates into an H^+ and an anion, the H^+ combines with a water molecule to form a hydronium ion, H_3O^+.

Polyprotic acids have more than one hydrogen ion that can disassociate into solution. If there are two hydrogen ions going into solution, it is called a *diprotic acid*. H_2SO_4 is an example of a diprotic acid. Triprotic acids, such as H_3PO_4, phosphoric acid, can release three protons into solution.

In the laboratory, acid–base reactions are done quantitatively using a process called *titration*. Often, an indicator is added to show progress. When the reaction reaches its endpoint or equivalence point, there will be a color change. Different indicators turn different colors and are sensitive to different pH points. At the equivalence point, the moles of acid will equal the moles of base. This relationship can be used to determine an unknown concentration using the equation Molarity of the acid (H^+) multiplied by the Volume of the acid is equal to the Molarity of the base (OH^-) multiplied by the Volume of the base ($M_aV_a = M_bV_b$). Titrations will be addressed in more detail in chapters 16 and 17.

A very important LAB SKILL is to be able to do a titration as shown in the following figure. You may be asked to describe such an experiment and perform calculations with the data from an experiment on the AP exam.

Acid–Base Titration

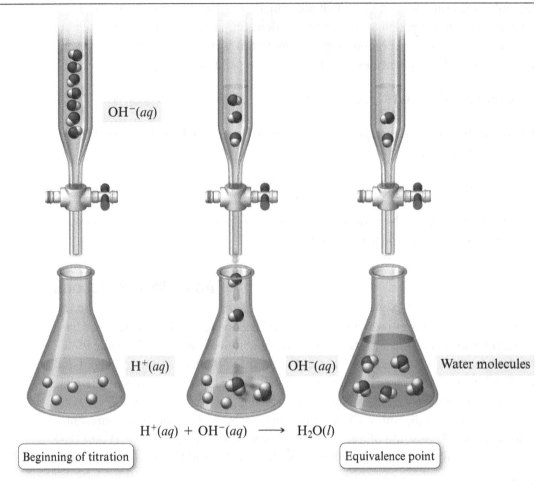

$$H^+(aq) + OH^-(aq) \longrightarrow H_2O(l)$$

Beginning of titration

Equivalence point

Figure 5.9 Acid–Base Titration of a Strong Acid and Strong Base

Section 5.8   Gas-Evolution Reactions

Gas evolution reactions in aqueous solutions produce observable bubbling. Predicting which reactions will produce gas is outlined in the table below.

Table 5.2 Types of Compounds That Undergo Gas-Evolution Reactions

Reactant Type	Intermediate Product	Gas Evolved	Example
Sulfides	None	H_2S	$2\,HCl(aq) + K_2S(aq) \rightarrow H_2S(g) + 2\,KCl(aq)$
Carbonates and bicarbonates	H_2CO_3	CO_2	$2\,HCl(aq) + K_2CO_3(aq) \rightarrow H_2O(l) + CO_2(g)$ $+ 2\,KCl(aq)$
Sulfites and bisulfites	H_2SO_3	SO_2	$2\,HCl(aq) + K_2SO_3(aq) \rightarrow H_2O(l) + SO_2(g)$ $+ 2\,KCl(aq)$
Ammonium	NH_4OH	NH_3	$NH_4Cl(aq) + KOH(aq) \rightarrow H_2O(l) + NH_3(g)$ $+ KCl(aq)$

Gas evolution reactions can be tricky since often intermediates form that react to form the actual products. For instance, when solutions of HCl and K_2CO_3 are mixed, one would predict H_2CO_3 or carbonic acid as a product along with KCl. H_2CO_3 is an intermediate which then produces CO_2 gas and H_2O. Intermediates are not listed in the final equation.

Oxidation–Reduction Reactions   Section 5.9

Oxidation–reduction, or *redox*, reactions are reactions in which there is a transfer of electrons from one species to another. The species losing electrons is **oxidized** and the species accepting electrons is being **reduced**. It is important to recognize which species is being oxidized and which is reduced in an equation. To do this, you must identify an oxidation state or oxidation number for each atom in a species. Rules used to identify an oxidation state are as follows:

1. The oxidation state of an atom in a free element is 0.

2. The oxidation state of a monoatomic ion is equal to its charge.

3. The sum of the oxidation states of all atoms in:
    - A neutral molecule or formula unit is 0.
    - An ion is equal to the charge of the ion.

4. In their compounds, metals have positive oxidation states.
    - Group 1A metals *always* have an oxidation state of +1.
    - Group 2A metals *always* have an oxidation state of +2.

5. In their compounds, nonmetals are assigned oxidation states according to the table shown here. Entries at the top of the table take precedence over entries at the bottom of the table.

Nonmetal	Oxidation State	Example
Fluorine	−1	MgF_2 −1 ox state F × 2 indicates Mg is +2
Hydrogen	+1	H_2O +1 ox state H × 2 indicates O is −2
Oxygen	−2	CO_2 −2 ox state O × 2 indicates C is +4
Group 7A	−1	CCl_4 −1 ox state Cl × 4 indicates C is +4
Group 6A	−2	H_2S −2 ox state S indicates each H is +1
Group 5A	−3	NH_3 −3 ox state N indicates each H is +1

When assigning oxidation states, keep these points in mind:

- The oxidation state of any given element generally depends on what other elements are present in the compound. (The exceptions are the group 1A and 2A metals, which are *always* +1 and +2, respectively.)

- Rule 3 must always be followed. Therefore, when following the hierarchy shown in rule 5, give priority to the element(s) highest on the list and then assign the oxidation state of the element lowest on the list using rule 3.

- When assigning oxidation states to elements that are not covered by rules 4 and 5 (such as carbon), use rule 3 to deduce their oxidation state once all other oxidation states have been assigned.

For example, to find the oxidation number of the Mn in $KMnO_4$, you write an equation assigning Mn oxidation state as x, assign the known oxidation states, in this case K is always $+1$ and each O is almost always -2 (except in peroxides), and then set the equation equal to zero since it is a neutral compound; $+1 + x + -8 = 0$. Thus, Mn is in the $+7$ oxidation state. This section must be mastered before the electrochemistry chapter.

Redox reactions can be recognized because there are changes in oxidation states. Many reactions are redox.

In a reaction such as $Cu(s) + 2\,AgNO_3(aq) \rightarrow Cu(NO_3)_2(aq) + 2Ag(s)$, canceling the spectator nitrate ion and writing the net ionic equation. $Cu + 2Ag^+(aq) \rightarrow Cu^{2+}(aq) + 2Ag(s)$ emphasizes the electron transfer that is occurring. Cu loses two electrons and changes to Cu^{2+} (oxidation), whereas each Ag^+ gains an electron to form Ag (reduction). The oxidation half reaction is $Cu \rightarrow Cu^{2+}(aq) + 2\,e^-$ and the reduction half reaction is $Ag^+(aq) + 1\,e^- \rightarrow Ag(s)$. Since the number of electrons lost must equal the number of electrons gained, the silver half reaction must be doubled to $2Ag^+(aq) + 2\,e^- \rightarrow 2Ag(s)$. Once the net ionic equation half reactions are written, it is easier to see that this is an oxidation–reduction reaction. It is important to note that a reaction must have both to occur. LEO goes GER is a way to remember Losing Electrons is Oxidation and Gaining Electrons is Reduction.

Identifying oxidizing agents and reducing agents are not part of the AP curriculum.

In combustion reactions, a compound reacts with oxygen. These are always redox reactions because elemental oxygen has an oxidation state of zero, changes in the reaction to -2, and is therefore reduced. If an organic hydrocarbons or substance containing only C, H, and O atoms is completely combusted, the products will be water and carbon dioxide. An example reaction is methane reacting with oxygen:

$$CH_4(g) + 2\,O_2(g) \rightarrow CO_2(g) + 2\,H_2O(l).$$

Note the C atom is unchanged at $+4$ and each of the 4H atoms are oxidized from -1 to $+1$ while oxygen is reduced from 0 to -2.

Keys to recognizing a reaction has occurred are formation of a precipitate, bubbling, flames, and possibly a color change. Some color changes are phase changes and not reactions like the change from ice to liquid water.

Is there a way to predict if certain oxidation reactions will occur? The answer is yes. The reactivity of metals can be used to predict metal reacting with solution reactions.

Table 5.4 Solution Stoichiometry

What volume (in L) of a 0.150 M KCl solution will completely react with 0.150 L of a 0.175 M Pb(NO$_3$)$_2$ solution according to the following balanced chemical equation? $$2 \text{ KCl}(aq) + \text{Pb(NO}_3)2(aq) \rightarrow \text{PbCl}_2(s) + 2 \text{ KNO}_3(aq)$$	
SORT You are given the volume and concentration of a Pb(NO$_3$)$_2$ solution. You are asked to find the volume of KCl solution (of a given concentration) required to react with it.	**GIVEN:** 0.150 L of Pb(NO$_3$)$_2$ solution, 0.175 M Pb(NO$_3$)$_2$ solution, 0.150 M KCl solution **FIND:** volume KCl solution (in L)
STRATEGIZE The conceptual plan has the form: volume A → amount A (in moles) → amount B (in moles) → volume B. Use the molar concentrations of the KCl and Pb(NO$_3$)$_2$ solutions as conversion factors between the number of moles of reactants in these solutions and their volumes. Use the stoichiometric coefficients from the balanced equation to convert between number of moles of Pb(NO$_3$)$_2$ and number of moles of KCl.	**CONCEPTUAL PLAN** 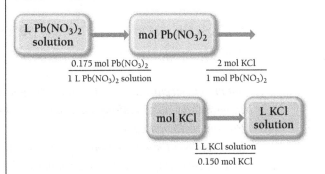 **RELATIONSHIPS USED** $$\text{M Pb(NO}_3)_2 = \frac{0.175 \text{ mol Pb(NO}_3)_2}{1 \text{ L Pb(NO}_3)_2 \text{ solution}}$$ 2 mol KCl : 1 mol Pb(NO$_3$)$_2$ $$\text{M KCl} = \frac{0.150 \text{ mol KCl}}{1 \text{ L KCl solution}}$$
SOLVE Begin with L Pb(NO$_3$)$_2$ solution and follow the conceptual plan to arrive at L KCl solution.	**SOLUTION** $0.150 \text{ L Pb(NO}_3)_2 \text{ solution} \times \dfrac{0.175 \text{ mol Pb(NO}_3)_2}{1 \text{ L Pb(NO}_3)_2 \text{ solution}}$ $\times \dfrac{2 \text{ mol KCl}}{1 \text{ mol Pb(NO}_3)_2} \times \dfrac{1 \text{ L KCl solution}}{0.150 \text{ mol KCl}}$ $= 0.350 \text{ L KCl solution}$
CHECK The final units (L KCl solution) are correct. The magnitude (0.350 L) is reasonable because the reaction stoichiometry requires 2 mol of KCl per mole of Pb(NO$_3$)$_2$. Since the concentrations of the two solutions are not very different (0.150 M compared to 0.175 M), the volume of KCl required is roughly two times the 0.150 L of Pb(NO$_3$)$_2$ given in the problem.	
FOR PRACTICE 5.4 What volume (in mL) of a 0.150 M HNO$_3$ solution will completely react with 35.7 mL of a 0.108 M Na$_2$CO$_3$ solution according to the following balanced chemical equation? $$\text{Na}_2\text{CO}_3(aq) + 2 \text{ HNO}_3(aq) \rightarrow 2 \text{ NaNO}_3(aq) + \text{CO}_2(g) + \text{H}_2\text{O}(l)$$	
FOR MORE PRACTICE 5.4 In the previous reaction, what mass (in grams) of carbon dioxide forms?	

Metals that give up their electrons easily are on the top of the list. These half-reactions always move in the direction written and are oxidizing. The metals on the bottom of the list do not give up electrons easily and is why precious metals are at the bottom of the list, they tend to stay as metals since they are not very reactive. If a forward running oxidation reaction combines with a reverse reducing reaction found below it, the reaction will happen. For example, if combining the half reactions remember in oxidation–reduction, one species must be oxidized (give up electrons) and another species must be reduced (accept electrons). If copper metal reacts with silver nitrate, copper metal gives up 2 electrons to become Cu^{2+} and is oxidized while Ag^+ takes in electrons and is reduced to become Ag.

Additional Practice

Self-Assessment Quiz Questions Q1, Q2, Q3, Q4, Q5, Q6, Q7, Q8, Q9, Q10, Q11, and Q12.

Problems:
Solution Concentration, and Solution Stoichiometry 21, 23, 25, and 27–38
Types of Aqueous Solutions and Solubility 39–41
Precipitate Reactions 43–45
Ionic and Net Ionic Equations 47, 48, and 50
Acid–Base and Gas Evolution Reactions 51, 53–55, and 57–59
Oxidation–Reduction 61, and 63–72
Cumulative Problems 79, 80, 84, and 85
Conceptual Problems 91–93
Data Interpretation and Analysis 98

Equations to know:

$M = n_{solute}/L_{solution}$, $M_1V_1 = M_2V_2$ *Solution Dilution*

Practice AP Test Questions

1. What is the concentration, in units of molarity, of a solution of potassium nitrate, that contains 25.0 grams of KNO_3 (molar mass 101.1 g) in 200.0 mL of solution?

   A) 0.200 M   B) 0.900 M   C) 2.00 M   D) 5.00 M

2. How many mL of 2.00 M KNO_3 are needed to prepare 40.0 mL of 0.200 M KNO_3?

   A) 0.0075 mL   B) 8.00 mL   C) 12.0 mL   D) 13.3 mL

3. When 1.0 gram of each of the following ionic compounds are added separately to 100 mL of room temperature water, all will be soluble except:

   A) MgO   B) NH_4NO_3 C) $CuBr_2$ D) $Al(C_2H_3O_2)_3$

4. The balanced net ionic equation for the reaction of $AgNO_3(aq)$ with $KBr(aq)$ is:

   A) $AgNO_3(aq) + KBr(aq) \rightarrow AgBr(aq) + KNO_3(s)$
   B) $Ag^+(aq) + NO_3{-}(aq) + K^+(aq) + Br^-(aq) \rightarrow Ag^+(aq) + Br^-(aq) + KNO_3(s)$

C) $Ag^+(aq) + NO_3{}^-(aq) + K^+(aq) + Br^-(aq) \rightarrow AgBr(s) + K^+(aq) + NO_3{}^-(aq)$

D) $Ag^+(aq) + Br^-(aq) \rightarrow AgBr(s)$

5. A 0.200 M K_2SO_4 solution is produced by _____.

   A) dilution of 250.0 mL of 1.00 M K_2SO_4 to 1.00 L
   B) dissolving 43.6 g of K_2SO_4 in water and diluting to a total volume of 250.0 mL
   C) diluting 20.0 mL of 5.00 M K_2SO_4 solution to 500.0 mL
   D) dilution of 1.00 mL of 250 M K_2SO_3 to 1.00 L

6. In an acid–base neutralization reaction, 20.00 mL of 0.60 M potassium hydroxide reacts with 60.00 mL of sulfuric acid solution. What is the concentration of the H_2SO_4 solution?

   _____ $KOH(aq)$ + _____ $H_2SO_4(aq) \rightarrow$ _____ $K_2SO_4(aq)$ + _____ $H_2O(l)$
   A) 0.10 M   B) 0.20 M   C) 0.40 M   D) 2.0 M

7. The following diagram represents the reaction of a strong acid HX (a square joined to an X) with strong base, NaOH (the Na+ ion, and a circle joined to a square) at the particulate nature of matter level representation.

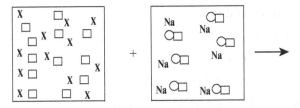

   The volume represented by the interior of the square A is the same as square the volume represented by the interior of Square B. If the concentration of the acid is 0.50 M, what volume of base is required to neutralize the acid?

   A) 10. mL   B) 20. mL   C) 30. mL   D) 40. mL

8. What mass (g) of CaF_2 (molar mass 78 g) is formed when 40.0 mL of 0.40 M NaF is treated with an excess of aqueous calcium nitrate?

   A) 2.5   B) 1.3   C) 0.64   D) 0.00010

9. Which of the following is an oxidation–reduction reaction?
   A) $Mg(s) + 2AgNO_3(aq) \rightarrow 2Mg(s) + Mg(NO_3)_2 (aq)$
   B) $HCl(aq) + NaOH(aq) \rightarrow NaCl(aq) + H_2O(l)$
   C) $AgNO_3(aq) + HBr(aq) \rightarrow AgBr(s) + HNO_3(aq)$
   D) $H_2CO_3(aq) + Ba(NO_3)_3(aq) \rightarrow 2HNO_3(aq) + BaCO_3(s)$

10. Of the 0.50 M aqueous solutions listed below, all are electrolytes except _____.

    A) $HCl(aq)$ B) $Rb_2SO_4(aq)$ C) $CH_3OH(aq)$ D) $KOH(aq)$

1. C); 2. C); 3. A); 4. D); 5. C); 6. A); 7. D); 8. C); 9. A); 10. C)

Chapter 5 Practice AP Test Questions Answers:

Data Interpretation and Analysis Question: Production of Hydrogen Peroxide from Water and Oxygen Gas Using a Catalyst: Clean Energy

Hydrogen peroxide, H_2O_2, is identified as a clean energy fuel because decomposition in the presence of the catalyst MnO_2 produces pure water, oxygen gas, and energy.

$$2H_2O_2(aq) \xrightarrow{MnO_2(s)} 2H_2O(l) + O_2(g) + \text{Energy}$$

Since there are no natural deposits of hydrogen peroxide on Earth, hydrogen peroxide is manufactured, which consumes energy. A new process was published in 2013 for producing hydrogen peroxide from water and oxygen gas using $Ir(OH)_3$ as a catalyst and $[Ru^{II}(Me_2phen)_3]SO_4$ as a photosensitizer and sunlight (hv).

$$2H_2O(l) + O_2(g) \xrightarrow{Ir(OH)_3} 2H_2O_2(aq)$$

Note: $[Ru^{II}(Me_2phen)_3]^{2+}$ (Me_2phen = 4,7-dimethyl-1,10-phenanthroline)

  i. If 10.0 g of water with 10.0 g oxygen gas produces hydrogen peroxide using $Ir(OH)_3$ and $[Ru^{II}(Me_2phen)_3]^{2+}$, what is the maximum mass of hydrogen peroxide, in grams, that could be produced?

   A) 21.25   B) 20.0 g   C) 18.8 g   D) 10.0 g

 ii. The oxygen atoms from oxygen gas are being

   A) oxidized.   B) reduced.   C) displaced.

   D) both oxidized and reduced.   E) used as an electrolyte.

iii. The oxygen atoms from water are being

   A) oxidized.   B) reduced.   C) displaced.

   D) both oxidized and reduced.   E) used as an electrolyte.

Satoshi Kato[a], Jieun Jung[a], Tomoyoshi Suenobu[a] and Shunichi Fukuzumi.
Energy Environ. Sci., 2013, **6**, 3756–3764

 iv. The graph shows the concentration of H_2O_2 produced, in units of microMolar, when the amount of $Ir(OH)_3$ is varied from 0.0 mg to 8.0 mg, all other variables being fixed. In order to produce the maximum amount of H_2O_2, what amount of $Ir(OH)_3$ should be used?

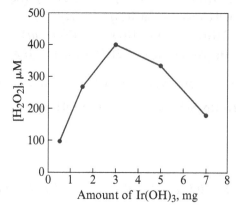

   A) 1.0 mg   B) 2.0 mg   C) 3.0 mg   D) 4.0 mg

v. Based on the information in the graph, if 1.0 mg of $Ir(OH)_3$ are used, approximately what is the percent yield?

A) 90%   B) 70%   C) 50%   D) 30%

vi. During the reaction, the photosensitized $[Ru^{II}(Me_2phen)_3]SO_4$ undergoes the following reaction:

$$2\left[Ru^{II}(Me_2phen)_3\right]^{2+} + O_2 + 2H^+ \xrightarrow{hv} 2\left[Ru^{III}(Me_2phen)_3\right]^{3+} + H_2O_2$$

The Ru atoms are being

A) oxidized.   B) reduced.   C) displaced.

D) both oxidized and reduced.   E) used as an electrolyte.

vii. In order to determine if the oxygen in hydrogen peroxide is coming from water or from oxygen gas, it was necessary to do an isotope-labeling experiment. Instead of using $^{16}O^{16}O$ gas, $^{18}O^{18}O$ oxygen gas was used. Water was 99.6% $H_2^{16}O$. After the reaction, helium gas bubbled through the resultant solution to remove any remaining oxygen gas. Next, a small amount of MnO_2 was added to the newly formed hydrogen peroxide, which catalyzed the decomposition of H_2O_2 to O_2 and water. The following mass spec was obtained from the oxygen gas generated by the decomposition of hydrogen peroxide.

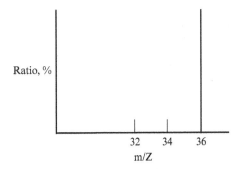

Which of the following statements are true?

A) The purpose of the experiment was to show direct evidence for the photocatalytic production of H_2O_2 from oxygen gas and water.

B) The purpose of the experiment was to show evidence that most of the hydrogen peroxide came from the photocatalytic production of H_2O_2 from oxygen gas and water, rather than the reaction of $[Ru^{II}(Me_2phen)_3]SO_4$ with oxygen gas.

C) The results of the mass spec indicate that the $^{18}O^{18}O$ from oxygen gas rather than the ^{16}O from water served as the source of oxygen atoms for H_2O_2.

D) The amount of evolved O_2 in water oxidation reaction was very small as compared with the amount of introduced $^{18}O^{18}O$. This is the reason the evolution of O_2 containing ^{16}O from water was negligible.

Data Interpretation and Analysis Question Answers with Brief Explanations

i. C) 18.8 g

10.0 g $H_2O \times (1 \text{ mol}/18.0 \text{ g } H_2O) \times (2 \text{ mol } H_2O_2/2 \text{ mol } H_2O) \times$
(34.0 g H_2O_2/1 mol) H_2O_2)

ii. B) $O^0 \rightarrow O^{-1}$

iii. A) $O^{-2} \rightarrow O^{-1}$

iv. C) according to the information in the graph, 3.0 mg

v. D) assuming the maximum amount is at 400 uM as noted in the graph
% Yield $= (120 \text{ uM}/400 \text{ uM}) \times 100\% = 30\%$

vi. A) $Ru^{2+} \rightarrow Ru^{3+}$

vii. B)

READING GUIDE

This chapter combines mathematical concepts and reactions which are included in the AP Chemistry curriculum in Unit 4 on Chemical Reactions. Understanding the different types of reactions, their reactants, products and how to predict them will be valuable tools to use in the laboratory section of your course.

Molecular Gastronomy and the Spherified Cherry   Section 5.1

1. What is a common reaction in food preparation? Give an example.

Solution Concentration   Section 5.2

2. Define the following terms:

    Solution:

    Solvent:

    Solute:

    Aqueous solution:

    Dilute solution:

    Concentrated solution:

    Molarity:

3. Explain how to make a solution of a specified molarity and include a diagram in your answer.

4. If 32.4 g of NaCl are dissolved in 500 mL of water, what is the molarity of the resulting NaCl solution? Explain how you arrived at this answer.

5. How can molarity be used as a conversion factor in calculations involving the mass of a solute?

6. What is a stock solution?

7. What equation is used to determine the amount of stock solution needed to dilute to a different molarity and what does each symbol in the equation represent?

8. For any aqueous solution, what does molarity times volume in liters equal?

9. Explain, in general, how to take a stock solution and prepare a dilute solution. Include a diagram in your answer.

10. Calculate the amount of stock solution needed to make 250.0 mL of 3.00 M KOH from a stock solution of 5.50 M KOH.

11. What is the safety rule to follow when diluting concentrated acids?

Section 5.3   Solution Stoichiometry

12. Explain the strategy to use with stoichiometry problems when given the molarities of the reactants in reactions with solutions.

13. According to the reaction $2KCl(aq) + Pb(NO_3)_2(aq) \rightarrow PbCl_2(s) + 2KNO_3(aq)$, what volume of 0.100 M KCl would be needed to react completely with 25.0 mL of 0.150 M $Pb(NO_3)_2$? Explain how you arrived at this answer.

Section 5.4   Types of Aqueous Solutions and Solubility

14. What happens when a solid is put into a liquid solvent? Why is water able to dissolve so many substances?

15. Explain how a common salt dissolves in water. Include an ionic-level diagram in your answer.

16. Explain why a common salt solution like $NaCl(aq)$ can conduct electricity, but a sugar solution cannot.

17. Explain how sugar dissolves in water and include a diagram in your answer. Explain the differences from your answer to Question #15.

18. Define the following terms:

    Electrolyte:

    Strong electrolyte:

    Nonelectrolyte:

    Strong acid:

    Weak acid:

    Weak electrolyte:

    Insoluble:

    Soluble:

19. When an equation is written to illustrate what happens when a strong acid is put in water, what type of arrow goes in the equation and why?

20. When an equation is written to illustrate what happens when a weak acid is put in water, what type of arrow is put in the equation and why? Compare and contrast strong and weak acids.

21. What is the solubility of ionic compounds with elements from Group one on the periodic table?

22. What is the solubility of ammonium ions and nitrate ions?

Note: For the AP Chemistry Exam, students need to know any compounds containing the "sodium, potassium, ammonium, and/or nitrate ions" are soluble in water. Students do not have to memorize the other "solubility rules", although knowledge of them could be helpful. On the AP Chemistry Exam, students will have to make decisions about whether or not a compound is soluble in water, and know what products form.

Precipitation Reactions   Section 5.5

23. What does the term *hard water* refer to? What makes water hard?

24. What are precipitate reactions?

25. What types of compounds form precipitates?

26. How do you predict the products of a precipitation reaction?

27. After predicting products, how do you determine if one of the products is going to actually precipitate?

Representing Aqueous Reactions: Molecular, Ionic, and Net Ionic Equations   Section 5.6

28. Explain the difference between molecular, complete ionic, and net ionic equations.

29. What are spectator ions and how are they identified in an equation?

30. How does one decide if a species should be written together as a substance or as distinct ions in an ionic equation?

31. Using the reaction of aqueous solutions of silver nitrate and sodium sulfide, write a balanced molecular, a balanced ionic, and a balanced net ionic equation.

Acid–Base Reactions   Section 5.7

32. What is observed in a gas-evolution reaction?

33. What is a neutralization reaction? What are antacids and what are they used for?

34. What is the difference between an Arrhenius acid and an Arrhenius base?

35. How do hydronium ions form? Include the equation for their formation. What is the difference in the equation when a weak acid is present compared to a strong acid? Symbol is often used for hydronium?

36. What are polyprotic acids?

37. Give an example of a diprotic acid. Write the two equations for the successive release of its hydrogen ions.

38. Why does H_2SO_4 have different types of arrows in the equations for the successive release of its hydrogen ions?

39. Write the names and formulas of three common acids.

40. Write the names and formulas of three common bases.

41. What products are formed when aqueous solutions of strong acids and strong bases react together?

42. Explain the chemical definition of a salt. Write chemical equations showing how two salts are formed.

43. Explain the process of titration.

44. What is the equivalence point of a titration and how is it determined?

45. What are indicators?

46. When used appropriately, what color does the indicator phenolphthalein show in acid? What would the color of the phenolphthalein be at the equivalence point of a titration of a strong base with a strong acid?

Section 5.8   Gas-Evolution Reactions

47. What are the reactants in gas-evolution reactions?
48. What gas or gases are formed when carbonates are added to an acid solution?

49. What types of compounds produce SO_2 when reacted with acid?

50. Write a balanced molecular equation and a balanced net ionic equation for the reaction between sodium bicarbonate and hydrochloric acid.

Section 5.9   Oxidation–Reduction Reactions

51. What is another name for an oxidation–reduction reaction?

52. Explain what happens in oxidation–reduction reactions?

53. Do all oxidation–reduction reactions involve oxygen as a reactant?

54. Explain the difference between oxidation and reduction.

55. What is an oxidation number?

56. What is the oxidation state of an atom in a free element?

57. What is the oxidation state of Group I ions? How can you determine the oxidation state of a monoatomic ion?

58. What is the normal oxidation state of Group II ions?

59. Explain how to determine the oxidation state of S in SO_4^{2-}. What is it?

60. What is the difference between a charge of a polyatomic ion and the oxidation state of its constituent atoms?

61. Explain how to determine which atom is oxidized and which is reduced by examining a balanced chemical equation.

62. For the reaction represented by $Mg(s) + 2H_2O(l) \rightarrow Mg(OH)_2(aq) + H_2(g)$, identify which constituent is oxidized and which is reduced.

63. Define the following terms:

    Oxidizing agent:*

    Reducing agent:*

64. In a combustion reaction, what species is oxidized and what species is reduced? Include an example equation in your explanation.

65. How can a redox reaction be predicted to occur? What is the activity series of the metals? Give an example of how the activity series of metals can be used.

Self-Assessment Answers

1. _____   2. _____   3. _____

4. _____   5. _____   6. _____

7. _____   8. _____   9. _____

10. _____   11. _____   12. _____

GASES

Gases were the first state of matter to be effectively explained. Since gases automatically fill the container they are in, their volume can be externally controlled. This behavior introduces many unique concepts the AP student must know and are the easiest to model both qualitatively and quantitatively. Students should also be able to look at data and graphs and determine the type of relationship between the variables being measured. It is important to understand the concepts conceptually, not just mathematically. The most important sections to know are:

6.2   **Pressure: The result of Molecular Collisions**

6.3   **The Simple Gas Laws: Boyle's Law, Charles's Law, and Avogadro's Law**

6.4   **The Ideal Gas Law**

6.5   **Applications of the Ideal Gas Law: Molar Volume, Density, and Molar Mass of a Gas**

6.6   **Mixtures of Gases and Partial Pressures**

6.8   **Kinetic Molecular Theory: A Model for Gases**

6.10 **Real Gases: The Effects of Size and Intermolecular Forces**

Specific Learning Objectives Addressed in This Chapter:

SAP-6 Matter exists in three states: solid, liquid, and gas, and their differences are influenced by variances in spacing and motion of molecules.

SAP-6.A Represent the differences between solid, liquid, and gas phase using a particulate-level model.

SAP-7 Gas properties are explained macroscopically—using the relationships among pressure, volume, temperature, moles, and gas constant—and the molecularly by the motion of the gas.

SAP-7.A Explain the relationship between the macroscopic properties of a sample of a gas or mixture of gases using the Ideal Gas Law. To include Ideal Gas Law, Dalton's law of partial pressures, mole fraction and partial pressure, and graphical representations of gas laws.

SAP-7.B Explain the relationship between the motion of particles and the macroscopic properties of gases with: The kinetic molecular theory (KMT), A particulate model, and A graphical representation.

SAP-7.C Explain the relationship among nonideal behaviors of gases, interparticle forces, and/or volumes.

Concepts and Vocabulary to Review:

The Simple Gas Laws: Boyle's Law, Charles's Law, and Avogadro's Law

Section 6.3

Gases take up and fill the space of the container they are in and are readily compressible if the container changes its volume. Measurements can be taken of their pressure, temperature, volume, and the number of gas particles present. Changes in these parameters affect the other gas parameters. Each simple gas law shows a relationship between two of these variables. It is not important to know the names of the laws, but it is important to understand and be able to explain the concepts behind them, as well as perform calculations using them. For each simple law, be able to draw a graphical relationship, explain what the relationship is, and using a model of an ideal gas, explain why the relationship exists.

Handling quantitative problems about gases involves having a good understanding of the different units used, and their interrelationships. In AP, the pressure (P) units used can be measured in atm, mmHg, and torr. Temperatures (T) may be given in °C or K but must always be converted to K when solving numerical gas problems, volumes (V) may be given in mL, cm^3, or L, but should be in liters when performing calculations such as the Ideal Gas Law, and the amount of gas should be expressed in moles (n).

Historically, scientists studied the effects of changing one variable on another and their conclusions have become known as the *gas laws*. Each can be represented by a graph and/or an equation of change comparing one set of conditions to another. However, eventually it was realized these individual laws could be combined under most conditions into a single statement that became known as the Ideal Gas Law. Remember that in each of the following "single laws," only TWO variables are considered at a time. THIS MEANS ALL THE OTHER VARIABLES MUST REMAIN CONSTANT, OR THE LAW DOES NOT HOLD. The combined gas law does allow more than one variable changing at once. The Ideal Gas Law can solve for one variable at one set of conditions.

Boyle's Law states the inverse relationship between pressure and volume when the other variables are held constant. When either P or V goes up, the other goes down. If you push down on a capped off syringe with a gas inside, the pressure on the gas goes up due to increased numbers of collisions with the sides of the container, while the volume occupied by the gas decreases. If you pull on the syringe, the gas volume will go up, but its pressure will go down due to the decreased number of collisions with the sides of the container. See figure 6.1. This is evidence of the inverse relationship. Only by plotting the INVERSE of one variable on a graph will a straight-line relationship appear.

The mathematical formula for Boyle's Law is: $P_1V_1 = P_2V_2$ where P_1 is the starting pressure, V_1 is the starting volume, P_2 is the ending pressure, and V_2 is the ending volume.

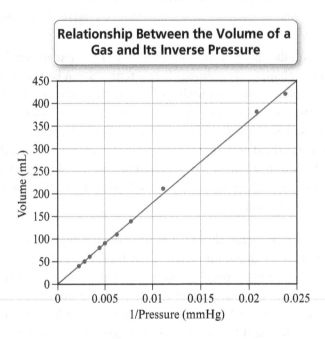

Figure 6.1 Volume versus Pressure   A plot of the volume of a gas sample versus pressure. The plot shows that volume and pressure are inversely related.

Charles's Law states the direct relationship between temperature and volume, while the other variables are held constant. The evidence of the direct relationship is when either temperature or volume changes the other has the same degree of change. In a graph, this will appear as a linear relationship. If the temperature (T) in Kelvin doubles, the volume (V) will correspondingly double. Note that the simple numerical relationship only works for Kelvin temperature units, which are based on Charles's results. This explains why warm air rises. As the gases temperature increases, the volume expands, which in turn lowers the density of the gas. Remember density is mass per unit volume, so this assumes the mass of the gas in the air remains constant. The least dense gas rises the most. See figure 6.2.

The mathematical formula for Charles's Law is: $\dfrac{V_1}{T_1} = \dfrac{V_2}{T_2}$ The volume units must be the same, such as liters or milliliters, and the temperature units must be in Kelvin.

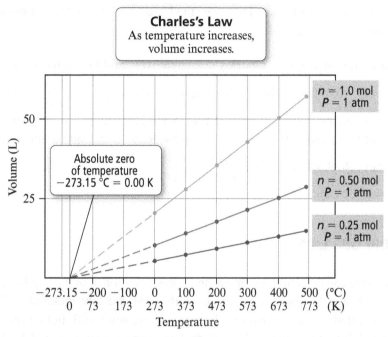

Figure 6.2 Volume versus Temperature   The volume of a fixed amount of gas at a constant pressure increases linearly with increasing temperature in kelvins. (The extrapolated lines cannot be measured experimentally because all gases condense into liquids before −273.15 °C is reached.)

Avogadro's Law explains the direct relationship between volume and the number of moles (n) of a gas present when the other variables are held constant. As a direct relationship, when the volume and number of moles (not mass in grams) are plotted in a graph, the graph will appear linear indicating when the number of moles or the volume increases or decreases, so does the other.

The mathematical formula for Avogadro's Law is: $\dfrac{V_1}{n_1} = \dfrac{V_2}{n_2}$. This relationship is shown in figure 6.3.

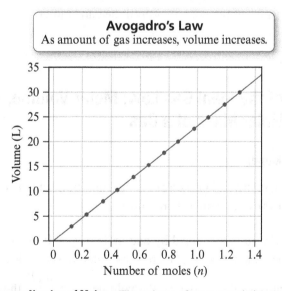

Figure 6.3 Volume versus Number of Moles   The volume of a gas sample increases linearly with the number of moles of gas in the sample.

Two other gas laws students need to know, the Ideal Gas Law and Gay-Lussac's Law, will be covered in Section 6.4.

A simplification of Boyle's, Charles's, Avogadro's, and Gay-Lussac (mentioned below in section 6.4) laws is the combined gas law where $\dfrac{P_1V_1}{n_1T_1} = \dfrac{P_2V_2}{n_2T_2}$. This is useful as only one equation is used instead of four. Each law can be seen by removing the variables held constant. For instance if the number of moles and the temperature are held constant, Boyles Law results. $\dfrac{P_1V_1}{\cancel{n_1}\cancel{T_1}} = \dfrac{P_2V_2}{\cancel{n_2}\cancel{T_2}}$.

Section 6.4   The Ideal Gas Law

The laws above can be combined into a single law/equation. Combining Boyle's Law, Charles's Law, and Avogadro's law results in the **ideal gas law equation**, $PV = nRT$, where R is called the gas constant. The units of pressure will dictate the value of R used in solving any numerical problem, but as previously noted, T is always in Kelvin, V is in liters, and n is always numbers of moles. R can be $0.0821 \dfrac{\text{L} \cdot \text{atm}}{\text{K} \cdot \text{mol}}$ or another value provided on the AP test is $62.4 \dfrac{\text{L} \cdot \text{mmHg}}{\text{K} \cdot \text{mol}}$. Notice that K stands in for T in kelvin units. In the other laws, conditions like temperature or volume were changing whereas the Ideal Gas Law is determining a factor at one set of conditions.

Another gas law is **Gay-Lussac's Law,** which describes the direct relationship between pressure and temperature, while the other variables are held constant. This direct relationship when graphed results in a linear relationship where if one increases, so does the other. This explains why an aerosol can explodes upon heating. If the temperature increases, the pressure increases due to increased numbers of collisions with the sides of the container until the can "blows".

$$\frac{P_1}{T_1} = \frac{P_2}{T_2}$$

Section 6.5   Applications of the Ideal Gas Law: Molar Volume, Density, and Molar Mass of a Gas

Key definitions to know:

STP (standard temperature and pressure) are the conditions of $0\,°\text{C}$ or 273 K (standard temperature) and 1.00 atm (standard pressure).

Molar volume is the volume occupied by one mole of gas. If one mole of gas is present ($n = 1$) and the conditions of STP are substituted into the ideal gas law equation $PV = nRT$ and rearranged to solve for the volume, $V = \dfrac{nRT}{P}$, the resulting volume

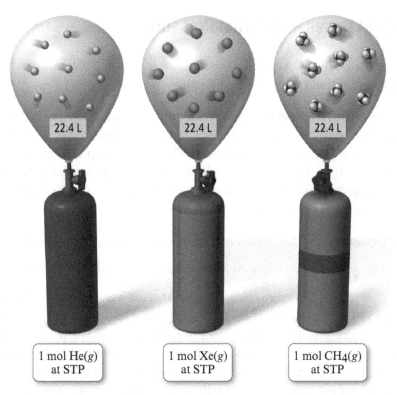

Figure 6.4 One mole of any gas occupies approximately 22.4 L at standard temperature (273 K) and pressure (1.0 atm).

is 22.4 liters. This is true regardless of the gas present. Watch for these conditions! It also follows 0.5 moles of any gas at STP would occupy 11.2 liters.

Gas density: At STP, the density of a gas equation becomes $d = \dfrac{M}{22.4 \frac{g}{L}}$ or $\dfrac{\text{Molar mass}}{\text{Molar volume}}$. When comparing 1 mole of gases at STP, the density of a gas is directly proportional to the molar mass; therefore, the larger the molar mass, the more dense the gas. If the conditions are not at STP, the equation to use for density of a gas is $d = \dfrac{PM}{RT}$. This is derived from substituting $\dfrac{m}{M}\left(\dfrac{\text{mass in grams}}{\text{molar mass}}\right)$ for n and rearranging the ideal gas equation to $\dfrac{m}{V} = \dfrac{PM}{RT}$. This same equation can be rearranged to solve for the molar mass of a gas: $M = \dfrac{mRT}{PV}$, which can also be written as $M = \dfrac{dRT}{P}$. It is important to note that gases have concentrations. The concentration is $\dfrac{n}{V}$. One can solve for the concentration using the Ideal Gas Equation $PV = nRT$ rearranged to $\dfrac{n}{V} = \dfrac{P}{RT}$.

Section 6.6   **Mixtures of Gases and Partial Pressures**

In earlier gas laws, it was assumed a single gas was present. Dalton showed several gases can be present and the gas laws still apply.

Dalton's Law of Partial Pressures: In any mixture of gases, each gas contributes to the total pressure present. Each gas contributes a **partial pressure** and when combined add up to the total gas pressure in the container. This relationship is represented by the equation $P_{total} = P_a + P_b + P_c + \ldots$ where a, b, and c represent the different gases. If gas A has a partial pressure of 0.50 atm and gas B has a partial pressure of 0.25 atm, then the total pressure is 0.75 atm.

The **mole fraction** of any gas (moles of a gas present compared to the total moles of gas present or $\dfrac{X_a}{X_{total}}$) can also be used to determine the partial pressure. For gas a this would be $P_a = X_a P_{total}$. In other words, the part that the gas is of the total moles, it is the same part of total pressure. If the gas is half of the moles present, it will be half of the pressure present. This comes about because each gas independently follows the combined gas equation as reviewed in the previous section. Deep sea divers and mountain climbers have to be very aware of partial pressures as it affects breathing. At high altitudes there is less pressure and the partial pressure of oxygen is also less so one can die from a lack of oxygen (hypoxia) and at deep sea conditions the pressure is increased resulting in oxygen toxicity (too much oxygen) or nitrogen narcosis (too much nitrogen) both of which can cause death.

Collecting a Gas over Water

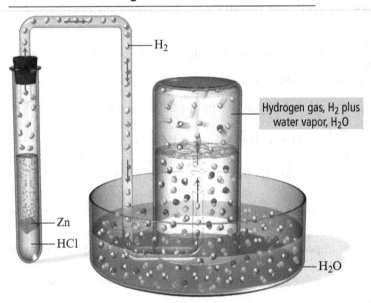

Figure 6.5 Collecting a Gas over Water   When the gaseous product of a chemical reaction is collected over water, the product molecules (in this case H_2) mix with water molecules. The pressure of water in the final mixture is equal to the vapor pressure of water at the temperature at which the gas is collected. The partial pressure of the product is the total pressure minus the partial pressure of water.

Often in reactions to prepare a sample of a gas that does not dissolve in water, the gas is collected over water. Some of the water at the surface escapes as a vapor and must be accounted for in the total pressure. Using the concept of Dalton's Law of Partial Pressure, the total pressure is the sum of the pressure of the gas collected and the pressure of the water vapor present. Water vapor pressure in equilibrium with liquid water can be determined by knowing the temperature of the water and looking at a table of water vapor pressures in a handbook or in an online table. In normal lab conditions, the temperature of the water is room temperature and total pressure is local atmospheric pressure. The water vapor pressure is subtracted from the total pressure to determine the pressure of the gas.

Table 6.1   Vapor Pressure of Water versus Temperature

Temperature (°C)	Pressure (mm Hg)	Temperature (°C)	Pressure (mm Hg)
0	4.58	55	118.2
5	6.54	60	149.6
10	9.21	65	187.5
15	12.79	70	233.7
20	17.55	75	289.1
25	23.78	80	355.1
30	31.86	85	433.6
35	42.23	90	525.8
40	55.40	95	633.9
45	71.97	100	760.0
50	92.6		

A gas is collected over water at 35 °C. What is the pressure of the gas if the total pressure is 760.00 torr? 760.00 torr −42.23 torr = 717.77 torr

Kinetic Molecular Theory: A Model for Gases   Section 6.8

Kinetic Molecular Theory is a model used to explain how gases behave under varying conditions. It can be used to explain all the gas laws. The model is based on three assumptions:

1. The size of a gas particle does not matter since gas particles are tiny and are spread out.

2. The average kinetic energy (KE) of a gas particle is proportional to its temperature. The total kinetic energy of all the gas particles in a sample is proportional to the overall gas temperature.

3. Collisions between gas molecules (or within container walls) are totally elastic (no energy is lost as they collide).

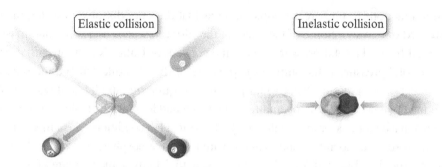

Figure 6.6 Elastic versus Inelastic Collisions   When two billiard balls collide, the collision is elastic—the total kinetic energy of the colliding bodies is the same before and after the collision. When two lumps of clay collide, the collision is inelastic—the kinetic energy of the colliding bodies dissipates in the form of heat during the collision.

One misconception is that all gas molecules in any gas move at the same speed because they have the same average kinetic energy. Remember, gases with the same average kinetic energy must be at the same temperature. In reality, the higher the molar mass of a gas is, the slower its velocity or speed will be.

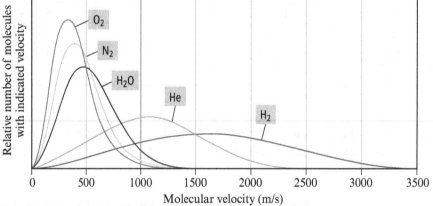

Figure 6.7 Velocity Distribution for Several Gases at 25 °C   At a given temperature, there is a distribution of velocities among the particles in a sample of gas. The exact shape and peak of the distribution vary with the molar mass of the gas. Notice the gas with the lowest molar mass is hydrogen, H_2, and also has the highest velocity where as oxygen gas, O_2, has the greatest molar mass and the slowest velocity.

KMT explanation of Boyle's Law: As the volume of a gas decreases, the gas molecules will hit the sides of a container more often creating a greater pressure. More hits in the same time means more force is transfered to an area of the container surface. (Remember temperature and the number of gas particles are held constant.)

KMT explanation of Charles's Law: As the temperature increases, the average kinetic energy of the gas increases. This indicates the gas particles are moving at a higher average velocity so the collisions with the sides of the container are more frequent, creating a higher pressure. This increased pressure of a non-rigid container causes the volume to increase to keep pressure constant. (Remember the variables of pressure and the number of gas particles are held constant.)

KMT explanation of Avogadro's Law: If the number of gas molecules increases in the same volume of a non-rigid container, there will be more collisions with the sides of the container, increasing the volume to maintain the same pressure. (Remember the variables of pressure and temperature are held constant.)

KMT explanation of Dalton's Law: Because all gas molecules present have the same average kinetic energy (they are at the same temperature), all the molecules will exert the same force. The partial forces will add up to give the total pressure, so the fraction of particles of each type (mole fraction) will determine each gas's contribution to that total. Total pressure will be the partial pressure of all the gases added together.

At higher temperatures, more molecules of the same gas are moving at faster speeds. The graph of this will show the range of velocities of the same gas at different temperatures as shown in the graph below.

In addition, there is a distribution of velocities within a gas sample known as a **Maxwell–Boltzmann** distribution as seen below.

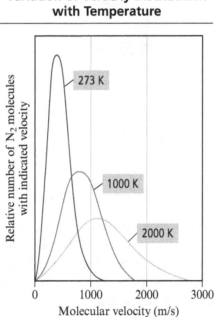

Figure 6.8 Velocity Distribution for Nitrogen at Several Temperatures As the temperature of a gas sample increases, the velocity distribution of the molecules shifts toward higher velocity and becomes less sharply peaked.

At any temperature, lighter gases travel faster *on average* than heavier gases. Some gas molecules will be faster and some will be slower and in fact, the rate of movement of a gas is inversely proportional to its molar mass. The root mean square speed (u_{rms}) of a gas is represented by the equation $u_{\text{rms}} = \sqrt{\dfrac{3RT}{M}}$. The variations of velocities can be seen in a velocity graph at the same temperature of different gases.

Figure 6.2 shows N_2 at several temperatures. The same molecules at 273 K are moving with a slower velocity than at 1000 K and 2000 K.

Section 6.9   Mean Free Path, Diffusion, and Effusion of Gases

Gas particles travel at high speeds but they are colliding with each other. Between collisions, they travel in straight line paths but they collide often. The distance between collisons is called the mean free path. The distance traveled between collisions increases when the pressure decreases.

Effusion

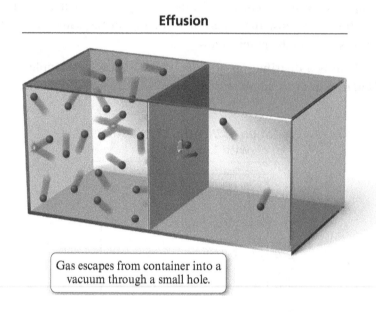

Gas escapes from container into a
vacuum through a small hole.

Diffusion is how gas molecules spread out in response to a concentration gradient. At the same temperature, Heavier molecules will move slower than lighter ones. If two containers of gas are opened at the same time, the molecules with the lower molar mass will reach a person in the back of the room first. Effusion is the process where a gas escapes from a container into a vacuum through a small hole. Graham's law of effusion is $\dfrac{\text{rate}_A}{\text{rate}_B} = \sqrt{\dfrac{\mathcal{M}_B}{\mathcal{M}_A}}$. Comparing the rates of helium and neon would take the square root of 20.18 g/mol over 4.003 g/mol. $\dfrac{\text{rate helium}}{\text{rate neon}} = \sqrt{\dfrac{201.8 \text{ g/mol}}{4.003 \text{ g/mol}}}$
The calculation indicates helium gas is moving at a rate 2.23 times faster than neon gas.

Section 6.10   Real Gases: The Effects of Size and Intermolecular Forces

Do gases always behave ideally? No! Remember KMT is based on three assumptions. If any of these are not true, then we would expect deviations.

If the gas particles are forced close enough together, the size of the gas particle does matter. As the particles move more slowly, the collisions may be less elastic and more inelastic indicating forces between molecules are interacting more. The two conditions causing this to happen are high pressure and/or low temperatures. Johannes van der Waals explained this by adding terms to the ideal gas equation for all gases at any condition. His equation is $\left[P + a\left(\dfrac{n}{V}\right)^2 \right] \times [V - nb] = nRT$ where a is a correction value for the attraction between gas particles (leading to nonelastic collisions) and b is the correction value for the volume of the gas particles. The numerical values for a and b are unique to each gas. If collisions are not elastic, fewer collisions will occur; the resulting pressure will be less than predicted by the ideal gas law, so the correction is added. If the container volume decreases enough, the space occupied by the actual gas particles becomes significant compared to the actual "empty space"; the volume used in the ideal gas law is too high, so the correction is subtracted. The size of gas particles and attractive forces between gas particles can be compared to an ideal gas in the below graph.

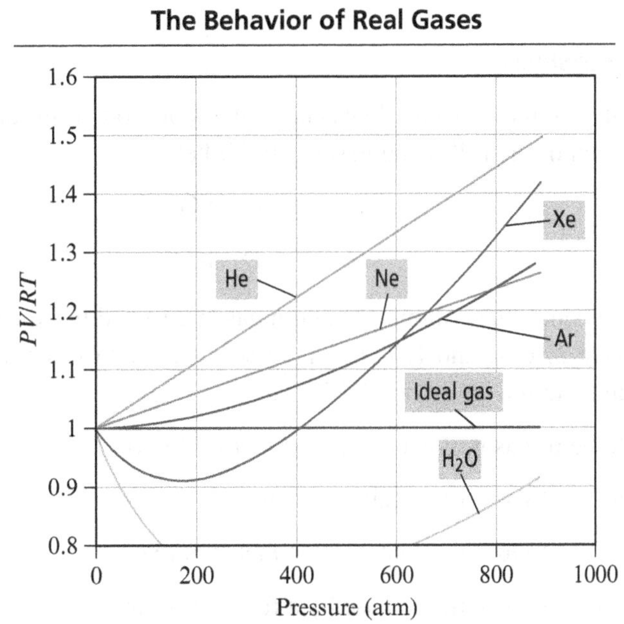

The Behavior of Real Gases

Figure 6.9 Real versus Ideal Behavior For 1 mol of an ideal gas, *PV/RT* is equal to 1. The combined effects of the volume of gas particles and the interactions among them cause each real gas to deviate from ideal behavior in a slightly different way. These curves were calculated at a temperature of 500 K.

Each gas is slightly different due to the combination of factors, including intermolecular forces. Helium has little attraction and a small atomic size compared to water vapor with high attractions between molecules and a much larger molecular size. Usually gas molecules are so far apart from each other, intermolecular forces do not affect gas properties but as the volume of a gas decreases or pressure increases, the gas particles get closer together and eventually get close enough that the forces make a difference. This is when gases do not behave ideally.

Additional Practice

Self-Assessment Quiz Questions Q1, Q2, Q3, Q4, Q5, Q6, Q7, Q8, Q9, Q10, Q11, Q12, Q13, Q14, and Q15

Problems:

Review 7

Converting between Pressure Units 29 and 30

Simple Gas Laws 31, 33, and 35

Ideal Gas Law 37, 44, 45, 49, 50, and 51

Molar Volume, Denisty, and the Molar Mass of a Gas 53, 57, 60, and 61

Partial Pressure 65 and 67

Reaction Stoichiometry Involving Gases 71 and 77

Kinetic Molecular Thoery 81, 82, 83, 86, 87, 89 and 90

Real Gases 91, 92, 95, 97, 102, 104, 107 and 108

Conceptual Problems 139, 142, 143, 144, 145, and 146

Data interpretation and Analysis 153

Practice AP Test Questions

1. If a 600.0 mL volume of a sample gas has a mass of 1.60 grams at 2.00 atm and 27.00 °C, which of the following gases could it be?

   A) NH_3 C) SO_2

   B) O_2 D) Kr

2. What will happen to the volume of helium gas in a sealed weather balloon if the gas starts at 27.0 °C and 1.00 atm and rises to a height where the pressure is 0.333 atm and a temperature of −73.0 °C?

   A) The volume of gas will decrease by a factor of two.

   B) The volume of gas will remain the same.

   C) The volume of gas will increase by a factor of two.

   D) The volume of gas will increase by a factor of four.

3. The diagram below represents a ratio of a mixture of gases at the molecule level in a small volume of gas within a sealed container, X. Oxygen molecules are represented by two joined grey spheres, helium atoms by unshaded spheres, and neon atoms by black spheres.

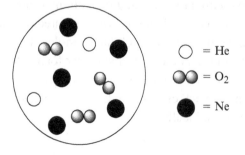

If the total pressure of the gases in sealed container, X, is 450 mm Hg, what is the partial pressure of helium?

A) 45 mm Hg   C) 135 mm Hg

B) 90 mm Hg   D) 225 mm Hg

4. When 7.50 g of zinc metal reacts with excess HCl, how many liters of H_2 gas can form at STP? Don't forget to write a balanced chemical equation.

A) 0.114 L   C) 2.57 L

B) 0.229 L   D) 5.15 L

5. If 1.00 mole of O_2 and Xe gases is allowed to effuse through a small hole under identical conditions of pressure and temperature, the rate of effusion of oxygen gas will be _____ times faster compared to xenon gas.

A) 0.25   C) 2

B) 0.50   D) 4

6. As the temperature of a sample of argon gas is raised from 40 °C to 80 °C, the average kinetic energy of the argon atoms changes by a factor of:

A) 0.5   B) $(353/313)^{0.5}$ C) 353/313   D) 2

7. A rigid closed steel 10.0 L cylinder contains nitrogen gas, $N_2(g)$ at 298K. Which of the following applies to the sample of gas in the cylinder when an additional 0.20 mole of nitrogen gas is added at constant temperature?

A) The volume of the gas increases.

B) The pressure of the gas decreases.

C) The average distance between the gas molecules increases.

D) The average speed of the gas molecules remains the same.

8. The graph below plots relative number of gas particles versus molecular speed for 0.10 mole of four gases at 298K. Given the identity of the four gases, identify Gas A.

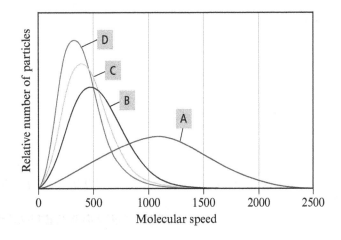

A) CH_4

B) Ar

C) Cl_2

D) SF_6

9. A hydrocarbon gas with an empirical formula CH_2 has a density of 2.50 grams per liter at 0.0 °C and 1.00 atmospheres (STP). Given the following four gases, identify the hydrocarbon.

A) C_2H_4 B) C_3H_6 C) C_4H_8 D) C_5H_{10}

10. The following graph of PV/RT versus pressure for real gases and for an ideal gas at 400K.

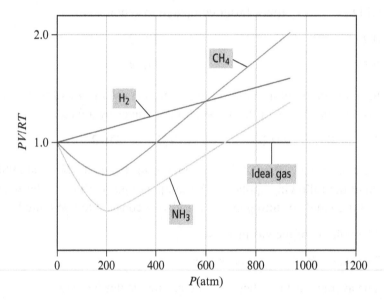

Which of the following real gases, all at 400K has the greatest positive deviation from an ideal gas at 600 atm?

A) N_2 B) Ne   C) CO_2 D) He

Data Interpretation and Analysis Question: Partial Pressure of Cyclopropane and Propene

Cyclopropane gas, C_3H_6, rearranges to form propene gas, C_3H_6, according to the following equation

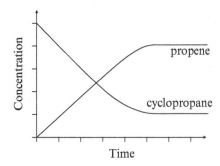

The graph below shows a plot of the concentration, in units of mol/L, of cyclopropane and propene versus time.

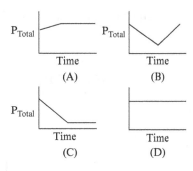

A 0.200-mole sample of cyclopropane gas is placed in a 1.00-L sealed rigid container at 800.0 K, and the reaction proceeds.

i. Which graph best represents the total pressure, in units of mole/L., versus time for this system?

P_{Total} ... Time (A)

P_{Total} ... Time (B)

P_{Total} ... Time (C)

Time (D)

ii. What is the total pressure in units of atm., when the partial pressure of cyclopropane is equal to the partial pressure of propene?

A) 0.050 atm   B) 0.10 atm   C) 6.56 atm   D) 13.13 atm

iii. At some point in time, the reaction of cyclopropane to propene is matched by the reaction of propene to cyclopropane. The concentration of each gas does not change. At this point, the concentration of cyclopropane is 0.0766 mol/L. How many moles of propene are there in the container.

A) 0.0766 mol   B) 0.124 mol   C) 0.152 mol   D) 0.200 mol

iv. After 50.0 seconds, the concentration of cyclopropane is 0.174 M, and the concentration of propene is 0.026 M. If suddenly, the volume of the container was decreased to 0.500 L while holding the temperature constant, what will happen to the pressure?

A) decrease by half   B) remain the same

C) increase by a factor of two   D) increase by a factor of four

v. The mass spectrum of cyclopropane is given below. The peaks less than $m/z = 42$ represent loss of hydrogen atoms and/or carbon atoms to produce fragments. Identify what the peak at $m/z = 42$ represents.

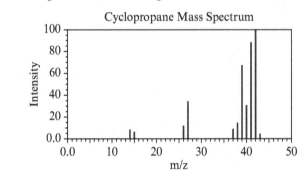

vi. The mas spectrum of propene has a peak at $m/z = 42$. What does this peak represent?

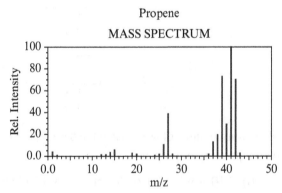

Source: NIST Chemistry WebBook (http://webbook.nist.gov/chemistry)

Data Interpretation and Analysis Question Answers with Brief Explanations

   i. D) The total pressure does not change with time since there is a 1:1 stoichiometry between cyclopropane and propene.

  ii. D) When the number moles of cyclopropane is equal to 0.100 mole it is also equal to the number of moles of propene and therefore the partial pressures are equal and the total moles of gas present is 0.200 moles. $P = nRT/V = 0.200$ mol R (800. K)/1.00 L = 13.13 atm.

 iii. B) 0.200 mol − 0.076 mol = 0.124 mol.

 iv. C) $PV = nRT$

  v. C) This ion has a mass of 42 amu and does not involve a rearrangement.

 vi. A) This ion has a mass of 42 amu and does not involve a rearrangement.

READING GUIDE

Gases and their properties are the focus of this chapter. Focus on understanding the concepts and the relationships between different variables and its effect on a gas.

Section 6.1 **Supersonic Skydiving and the Risk of Decompression**

1. Define pressure.

2. How do gases apply pressure on objects? Explain why pressure varies with different altitudes?

3. How does the concentration of a gas affect pressure?

Section 6.2 **Pressure: The Result of Molecular Collisions**

4. What are three everyday occurrences caused by the pressure of gases?

5. What is the mathematical formula for pressure?

6. On a weather map, what do the "H" and "L" stand for?*

7. What kind of weather is generally associated with an "H"?*

8. What kind of weather is generally associated with an "L"?*

9. Explain why the pressure of a gas depends on the number of gas molecules.

10. How does a change in altitude affect gas pressure? Explain why.

11. Explain why your ears "pop" as you go up and down mountains.

12. What is a barometer? Who invented it? How does one read a barometer?

13. Explain why pressure can be measured in millimeters of mercury even though millimeters measure length.

14. What is another term for mmHg? Where did the term come from?

15. How does the density of mercury compare to the density of water? How tall would a water barometer need to be to measure standard room pressure? Why?

16. What causes the liquid in the barometer column to rise and fall?

17. What is the abbreviation for an atmosphere and what is the relationship between it and mmHg?

18. What are three other units used to measure pressure?

19. Draw and explain what a manometer is and why it is useful.

20. For each of the following situations, draw a manometer illustrating the relative readings in the two arms. Then, explain the height difference of the liquid in the two arms of the manometer.

   a. The confined gas has a pressure equal to atmospheric pressure.

   b. The confined gas has a pressure less than atmospheric pressure.

   c. The confined gas has a pressure greater than atmospheric pressure.

21. If a manometer is used, what other information is needed to find the actual pressure. Explain why.

22. What is the difference between systolic pressure and diastolic pressure?*

23. What is the value for "normal" blood pressure in humans?*

24. What instrument measures blood pressure?*

25. What is another term for high blood pressure and what are risk factors for it?*

The Simple Gas Laws: Boyle's Law, Charles's Law, and Avogadro's Law   Section 6.3

26. What are the four basic properties used in measuring a gas?

27. What variables does Boyle's Law relate to each other?

28. What is the relationship between the two variables in Boyle's Law?

29. Explain what happens to the second property in Boyle's Law if one property is increased?

30. Explain two real-world examples in which the relationship in Boyle's Law is observed, and explain how these illustrate Boyle's Law.

31. Draw a graph illustrating the general relationship between volume and pressure. How would the axis on this graph need to be changed to show a straight line relationship?

32. Why must deep-sea divers ascend slowly?

33. Write the equation for Boyle's Law and include a statement specifying the two variables kept constant. What happens to the volume of a gas if you double the pressure of the gas?

34. What two properties are variables in Charles's Law?

35. What is the relationship between the two variables in Charles's Law?

36. Draw a graph showing the general relationship between the two variables in Charles's Law.

37. What is "absolute zero"? What is the connection between Charles's Law and absolute zero? Why must the numerical value for absolute zero be determined by extrapolation?

38. Can long reeds be used to snorkel? Why or why not? What is the limit on depth?*

39. Explain what happens to the other variable when one variable in Charles's Law increases and why.

40. What are two real-world examples of Charles's Law? Explain how these illustrate Charles's Law.

41. Why do warm gas molecules rise?

42. Write the equation for Charles's Law and include a statement specifying the two variables kept constant. If the volume of a gas is doubled, what happens to the absolute temperature?

43. What units are used for each variable in Charles's Law? Why is the choice of units important in these calculations?

44. What two properties are related to each other in Avogadro's Law?

45. What is the relationship between the two variables in Avogadro's Law?

46. Draw a graph showing the general relationship between the two variables in Avogadro's Law.

47. Write the equation for Avogadro's Law and include a statement specifying the two variables kept constant. What factors must be held constant when applying Avogadro's Law?

48. What are two real-world examples of Avogadro's Law?

Section 6.4   The Ideal Gas Law

49. What laws are combined to make the Ideal Gas Law?

50. Explain what R is, write the numerical value, and include its units when working with gases.

51. Write the Ideal Gas Equation and indicate the unit of each variable. In order to use the Ideal Gas Law, ideal gas behavior is assumed. List the properties of an ideal gas.

52. What two properties are variables in Gay-Lussac's Law? Which properties must be constant?

53. Explain why one should not heat aerosol cans.

Applications of the Ideal Gas Law: Section 6.5
Molar Volume, Density, and Molar Mass of a Gas

54. Define molar volume.

55. In order to make comparisons among gas samples, the properties of gases are often measured or calculated at STP. What is STP and what are its conditions?

56. At STP, what is the value for the molar volume of an ideal gas?

57. How does one calculate the density of a gas at STP using its molar volume?

58. Identify two examples of gases in a balloon that would cause the balloon to rise in air? Why would these two gases cause the balloon to rise? What types of gases would cause the balloon to sink? Explain your answer.

59. What is the equation to calculate the density of a gas?

60. On your own, combine the equations for molar mass and ideal gases to write one equation, for calculating the molar mass of a gas. Combine the equations for density and ideal gases to write one equation for the density of a gas.

Mixtures of Gases and Partial Pressures   Section 6.6

61. What are the four largest components of dry air, and what are the relative amounts of each?

62. Although air is a mixture of gases, why can the Ideal Gas Law often be used to calculate pressure, temperature, volume or moles of a gas?

63. Define the term "partial pressure of a gas."

64. What is the equation used to determine the partial pressure of a gas?

65. In a mixture of gases, if the partial pressure of each gas is known, what is the equation to determine the total pressure? What is the name of this relationship?

66. Define mole fraction.

67. What is the equation used to determine a mole fraction?

68. What are the partial pressures of nitrogen gas, oxygen gas, and argon gas in air?

69. What is the optimal partial pressure of oxygen in human lungs?*

70. What is hypoxia? What are its symptoms and what causes it?*

71. What is oxygen toxicity? What are its symptoms and what causes it?*

72. What is nitrogen narcosis? What are its symptoms and what causes it?*

73. What is heliox and why is it used?*

74. In a science laboratory, how are gases from chemical reactions often collected?

75. When collecting a gas through water displacement, what needs to be done to determine the pressure of the gas being collected? What other value needs to be measured?

76. Write an equation to use for the calculation used to answer Question #75.

77. In a chemistry lab, what common reaction is used to produce hydrogen gas? Why is this most easily collected "over water"?

78. What is another name for the partial pressure of a gas over a solution?

79. How is the vapor pressure of water determined? Write the vapor pressure of water at 25 °C and 55 °C. Explain why there is a difference in pressure.

Section 6.7   Gases in Chemical Reactions: Stoichiometry Revisited

80. Explain how stoichiometry problems with gases are different from other stoichiometry problems.

81. When performing stoichiometry problems with gases, what conditions must be met in order to use the molar volume of 22.4 L/mol?

Section 6.8   Kinetic Molecular Theory: A Model for Gases

82. What is Kinetic Molecular Theory (KMT)?

83. What are the three postulates of KMT?

1.

2.

3.

84. Why is it usually safe to assume gas particle/molecule size does not make a difference when measuring the volume of a gas?

85. What is true of two gases at the same temperature?

86. What is the difference between an elastic collision and an inelastic collision of gas particles?

87. Use KMT to explain Boyle's Law.

88. Use KMT to explain Charles's Law.

89. Use KMT to explain Avogadro's Law.

90. Use KMT to explain Dalton's Law.

91. Use KMT to explain the Ideal Gas Law. In a mixture of gases at the same temperature, how are the masses of gases related to their velocities? At the same temperature, how does the velocity of a light gas compare to a heavier gas. Explain.

92. What is the equation for the root-mean-square velocity of a collection of gas particles?

93. Draw a diagram showing what a sample velocity distribution with temperature would look like. Explain what the distribution would look like if the temperature of the gas was increased?

Mean-Free Path, Diffusion, and Effusion of Gases   Section 6.9

94. Explain the concept of a mean-free path for a gas.

95. How does the mean-free path of a gas change as a result of changing the temperature and pressure?

96. What is diffusion of a gas?

97. In a mixture of gases, which molecules diffuse the fastest? Slowest?

98. What is the process of effusion?

99. How is effusion different from diffusion?

100. Explain Graham's Law of Effusion in terms of KMT.

101. If two balloons are inflated to the same volume, one with air and the other with hydrogen, what differences would be observed over time in the volume between the two balloons. Explain why.

Real Gases: The Effects of Size and Intermolecular Forces   Section 6.10

102. What are two differences between a real gas and an ideal gas?

103. At what two conditions do the ideal gas assumptions break down?

104. At high pressure, how will the volume of a real gas change? Explain why.

105. How do real gas molecular attractions affect the pressure of gases? Explain why.

106. Write Van der Waals Equation and indicate what part corrects for intermolecular forces and what part corrects for particle size.

107. Explain why deviations from the Ideal Gas Law are not the same for all gases.

108. Explain the difference in deviations from ideal gas behavior between helium and water vapor.

Self-Assessment Answers

1. _____   2. _____   3. _____

4. _____   5. _____   6. _____

7. _____   8. _____   9. _____

10. _____   11. _____   12. _____

13. _____   14. _____   15. _____

THERMOCHEMISTRY

In the AP Curriculum, the concepts of thermochemistry are enveloped in Unit 6. The first part of the chapter reviews types of energy and energy units. The units used on the AP chemistry exam will be joules or kilojoules. Section 7.5 on constant-volume calorimetry is not directly tested in the AP curriculum, but it is the source of most heat of reaction data, important, for example, to the food industry. Section 7.10 covers many environmental applications of energy in the environment including air pollutants such as SO_x, CO, NO_x and O_3. These may be used as examples so be sure to read this section.

The most important sections to review are:

7.3 **The First Law of Thermodynamics: There Is No Free Lunch**

7.4 **Quantifying Heat and Work**

7.6 **Enthalpy: The Heat Evolved in a Chemical Reaction at Constant Pressure**

7.7 **Constant-Pressure Calorimetry: Measuring ΔH_{rxn}**

7.8 **Relationships Involving ΔH_{rxn}**

7.9 **Determining Enthalpies of Reaction from Standard Enthalpies of Formation**

Specific Learning Objectives Addressed in This Chapter:

ENE-2 Changes in a substance's properties or change into a different substance requires an exchange of energy.

ENE-2.A Explain the relationship between experimental observations and energy changes associated with a chemical or physical transformation.

ENE-2.B Represent a chemical or physical transformation with an energy diagram.

ENE-2.C Explain the relationship between the transfer of thermal energy and molecular collisions.

ENE-2.D Calculate the heat q absorbed or released by a system undergoing heating/cooling based on the amount of the substance, the heat capacity, and the change in temperature.

ENE-2.E Explain changes in the heat q absorbed or released by a system undergoing a phase transition based on the amount of the substance in moles and the molar enthalpy of the phase transition.

ENE-2.F Calculate the heat q absorbed or released by a system undergoing a chemical reaction in relationship to the amount of reacting substance in moles and the molar enthalpy of reaction.

ENE-3 The Energy exchanged in a chemical transformation is required to break and form bonds.

ENE-3.A Calculate the enthalpy change of a reaction based on the average bond energies of bonds broken and formed in the reaction.

ENE-3.B Calculate the enthalpy change for a chemical or physical process based on the standard enthalpies of formation.

ENE-3.C Represent a chemical or physical process as a sequence of steps.

Concepts and Vocabulary to Review:

Section 7.2

The Nature of Energy: Key Definitions

Heat is the flow of energy in a system. Units of energy used in chemistry include primarily the calorie (cal) and the joule. Converting between the two units requires knowing 1 cal is equivalent to 4.184 joules. A food Calorie (Cal) is 1000 calories or a kilocalorie. A watt (W) is a joule per second so a 100 watt bulb uses 100 joules per second.

In the field of thermodynamics, scientists realized it was very important to carefully define what was being measured or studied. Everything in the universe is to be included, but a small part called the *system* will be studied. Everything outside the *system* is the *surroundings*. We could write an equation:

$$\text{Universe} = \text{SYSTEM} + \text{SURROUNDINGS}$$

Each law is a general finding (meaning nothing has ever been identified as not following the rule) about the relationships with a system and/or its surroundings. Many general misconceptions arise from misunderstanding the concept of the system. Thermodynamics is full of definitions of quantities and terms that must be precisely understood and applied. Remember the terms were defined for convenience for communication among scientists trying to understand how nature works. Nature proceeds by its own rules without having to learn the definitions.

Section 7.3

The First Law of Thermodynamics: There Is No Free Lunch

The first law of thermodynamics is: The total of energy in the universe is constant.

In other words, energy lost by a system must be equal to what is gained by its surroundings. This is represented $q_{loss} + q_{gain} = 0$

A *state function* is a defined property of a system. State functions depend only on the beginning and ending conditions of the system and not the path of the reaction or change. You can travel from Chicago to New York by several different routes, but Chicago and New York look just the same no matter which route you take! The same is true with state functions and chemical or physical change. *Internal energy*, the sum of kinetic and potential energies in a system, is a state function. Work and heat are not state functions as they depend on the pathway of the change.

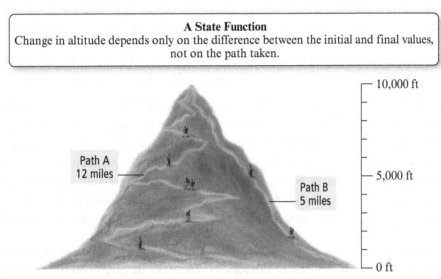

A State Function
Change in altitude depends only on the difference between the initial and final values, not on the path taken.

Figure 7.1 Altitude as a State Function The change in altitude during a climb depends only on the difference between the final and initial altitudes, not on the route traveled.

In chemical and physical change measurements, the goal is to determine what happens to the system. For a chemical reaction, the system is the chemical reaction. The container is part of the surroundings although it is up to the scientist doing the experiment to define the system and the surroundings. As long as accurate accounting of thermal energy changes is done, it all works out. If the internal energy is higher in the reactants than the products, energy will be given off by the reaction. When energy is released by a reaction, the sign of the energy change is defined as negative since the system loses energy to the surroundings. If the internal energy in reactants is lower than the products, energy must be absorbed by the system's products from its surroundings, so the sign of the energy change is positive.

$$\Delta E = q + w$$

Table 7.1 Sign Conventions for q, w, and ΔE

q (heat)	+ system *gains* thermal energy	− system *loses* thermal energy
w (work)	+ work done *on* the system	− work done *by* the system
ΔE (change in internal energy)	+ energy flows *into* the system	− energy flows *out* of the system

Section 7.4   Quantifying Heat and Work

Many students have a misunderstanding of temperature and heat. *Temperature* is a measure of thermal energy within a small volume of a sample of matter. *Heat* is thermal energy being transferred. All around us, we can observe when objects with different temperatures come into contact with each other. Thermal energy will transfer until both objects have the same temperatures (thermal energy). When the same temperature is reached, thermal equilibrium is reached. We also observe this transfer from the object with the higher temperature to the object with the lower temperature, so this was established as the conventional direction for thermal energy transfer.

Different materials have a different capacity to absorb heat because they have different ways of distributing the energy internally. This is called *heat capacity* (C) and is defined in the equation $C = \dfrac{q}{\Delta T}$ where, C is the heat capacity, q is heat transferred, and ΔT is the change in temperature. The amount of heat needed to change the temperature of a substance by one degree is dependent on the amount of substance present. A small amount of water requires less energy to raise its temperature than a large amount of water. This means heat capacity is an extensive property. Water has a high specific heat indicating it takes a lot of energy to raise its temperature, specifically 4.184 Joules per degree C. This explains why a large body of water like a lake takes a lot of energy to raise its temperature.

Often, it is more convenient to compare the amount of heat necessary to raise the temperature by 1°C for different substances. This task involves comparing the heat needed to raise similar masses of the different substances. *Specific heat capacity* is defined as the amount of heat needed to raise the temperature of 1.0 g by 1°C. Because specific heat capacity is based on a fixed amount of mass (1.0 g), it becomes an intensive property. Another intensive property is created by comparing the heat required to raise a mole of substance by 1°C; this is called *molar heat capacity*. The specific heat equation used in this book is $q = m \times C_s \times \Delta T$ where the subscript s distinguishes it as the specific heat, rather than heat capacity. On the AP test equation pages, the equation given is $q = mc\Delta T$, where c stands for specific heat.

The specific heat is equal to the heat capacity, divided by the number of grams present; $\dfrac{C}{m} = C_s$ or c. Pay attention to the units given to know whether c is specific heat capacity (J/g · °C), or molar heat capacity (J/mol · °C). When a hot object, like a hot piece of metal, is placed in cold water, the hot metal will lose heat while the water gains heat until thermal equilibrium is established. The amount of energy lost by the metal is equal in magnitude, but opposite in sign of the water: $q_{metal} = -q_{water}$ as long as the metal-water is the system and no energy is lost to the surroundings. This concept allows us to write the equation: $m_1 c_1 \Delta T_1 = -m_2 c_2 \Delta T_2$. This equation is not listed on the AP test equation pages. It is expected that you can set the two equations opposite each other recognizing that energy lost equals energy gained. It is also expected you know the specific heat of water is 4.18 J/g °C. Although the AP curriculum focuses on joules, one should know 1 calorie = 4.18 joules. Besides water, there are no other specific heat values you must know. Be able to solve problems for the final temperature when two objects are placed together, problems involving calculation of a specific heat, and problems solving for a mass of a substance, given the temperature changes and circumstances.

If a reaction occurs in a confined cylinder such as gasoline combustion in an automobile, the gases expand with the increased temperature and cause the cylinders to push a piston upward. This mechanical work is defined in physics as force x distance, which in this case is equal to pressure x volume change so $W = -P\Delta V$, where P is the pressure in atmospheres and ΔV is the change in volume in liters. The negative sign results as work is done by the system on the surroundings, so is counted as a loss to the system. This results in work having the unit of $L \cdot atm$. To convert to the energy unit of joules the $L \cdot atm$ answer must be multiplied by $\dfrac{101.3 \text{ J}}{1 \text{ L} \cdot atm}$.

Type of reaction	Sign of ΔH	Direction of heat	Surroundings
Exothermic	$-$	Releases heat to surroundings	Get warmer
Endothermic	$+$	Absorbs heat from surroundings	Get colder

Measuring ΔE for Chemical Reactions: Constant-Volume Calorimetry
Section 7.5

Constant pressure calorimetry is tested on the AP Chemistry exam but constant volume or bomb calorimetry is not. Calorimetry is a method of determining the thermal energy exchanged between the system (chemical reaction) and the surroundings (the resultant solution). Coffee cup calorimetry is constant pressure calorimetry since atmospheric pressure is exerted on the system and the surroundings equally. This is in Section 7.7.

Enthalpy: The Heat Evolved in a Chemical Reaction at Constant Pressure
Section 7.6

Enthalpy (H) is defined as the sum of internal energy and the product of pressure and volume for a system. ΔH, or the change in enthalpy of a system, is the heat transferred under constant pressure. The change of enthalpy can be positive or negative for the system, and the opposite sign for the surroundings.

In a chemical reaction, as reactant bonds break the system takes in energy from its surroundings. As new product bonds form, thermal energy is released. If more energy is taken in by the reaction than released the surroundings, the temperature of the surroundings decreases. This is an endothermic reaction and the sign of ΔH is positive $(+)$. If thermal energy is released to the surroundings, then the surroundings temperature will increase. This is an exothermic reaction and the sign of ΔH is negative $(-)$. This is happening when you use a hand warmer where your hand is part of the surroundings. The relationship between the energies of bonds breaking and bonds forming in chemical reactions will be covered in Chapter 10.

Thermochemical equations include information about enthalpy. The enthalpy is specific to the reaction written with its stoichiometric coefficients and is therefore written as: ΔH_{rxn}. The values will have a sign to indicate if the reaction is endothermic or exothermic as it proceeds in the conventional manner—from left to right.

$$C_3H_8(g) + 5\,O_2(g) \rightarrow 3\,CO_2(g) + 4\,H_2O(g) \quad \Delta H_{rxn} \ -2044\,kJ$$

In this reaction equation, the reaction is exothermic, hence the negative sign. The values can be used in ratios to determine the amount of heat with a different amount of reactant. For example $\dfrac{-2044\,kJ}{1\,mol\,C_2H_2}$ is one ratio that can be used. It also can be expressed as $-2044\,kJ/3\,mol\,CO_2$ produced.

Section 7.7   Constant-Pressure Calorimetry: Measuring ΔH_{rxn}

In a chemical reaction, bonds break (an input of energy) and bonds form (an output of energy). The net process produces heat or absorbs heat. Using a coffee-cup calorimeter is a common laboratory method to find the ΔH_{rxn}. During the reaction, energy of reaction will result in a temperature rise or lowering of a known amount of solution in which the reactants are dissolved; by taking temperature measurements of the solution before and after, knowing the mass of solution, and the specific heat of solution, the amount of heat (thermal energy transferred) can be determined. This assumes the calorimeter is well insulated so no heat is lost to the calorimeter or coffee cup. The thermometer measure what the solution is doing, not what the reaction is doing. $q_{rxn} + q_{sol} = 0$

$$q_{soln} = (mass_{soln})(c_{soln})\,(\Delta T)$$

The surroundings is the resultant solution, i.e., the mass of the water and dissolved chemicals.

$$\Delta H_{rxn} = q_{rxn}/\text{moles of limiting reagent at constant pressure}$$

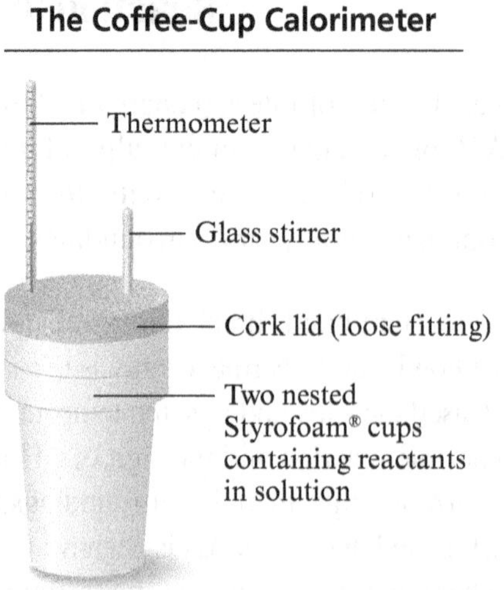

The Coffee-Cup Calorimeter

Figure 7.2 The Coffee-Cup Calorimeter   A coffee-cup calorimeter enables one to measure temperature changes of a solution. Enthalpy changes for chemical reactions in solution can then be calculated.

For aqueous systems, the system is the chemicals reacting. If the reaction is the result of mixing two solutions, for instance an acid with a base, the heat released by the reaction is the heat absorbed by the resultant solution,

$$q_{reaction} + q_{solution} = 0$$

The assumption that the solution has the same specific heat as water usually introduces only a very small error. We can make this assumption because the solution is mostly water. When the solution absorbs heat, the initial and final temperature of the solution can be measured. The difference in temperature $\Delta T = T_{final} - T_{initial}$.

Known mass of solution will be in the calorimeter. The heat of the solution is calculated using the equation $q_{soln} = m_{sol}c_{sol}\Delta T$ or $q = mc\Delta T$. The q_{rxn} will have the same value but opposite sign compared to q_{soln}. Usually, the solution is mostly water and so the specific heat is assumed to be 4.18 J/g·°C. $q_{sol} + q_{rxn} = 0$ To determine the ΔH_{rxn}, a balanced equation will be needed. Then a calculation can be set up to determine the amount of energy that would be released or absorbed per mole. When a reaction is in solution, the total mass of the solution is used for the mass in the calculation. (This is one of labs specified in the AP curriculum.) For instance, if 12.6 grams of KCl is dissolved in 100.0 grams of water, the total mass of the solution is 112.6 g. If the temperature decreased 6.2°C and the specific heat of the solution was 4.17 J/g°C, the $\Delta H/mol_{rxn}$ can be calculated.

$$H_2O + KCl(s) \rightarrow KCl(aq) \quad \text{dissolving process}$$

Step 1: $q_{loss} + q_{gain} = 0 \quad q_{solution} + q_{dissolving\ process} = 0$

Step 2: $m\Delta T_c = q_{solution}$

$(112.6\ g)(-6.2°C)(4.17\ J/g°C) = q_{solution}$

$q_{solution} = -(q_{solution}) = -(-2.9\ kJ) = +2.9\ kJ$

Step 3: $q_{dissolving\ process} = -(-q_{solution}) = -(-2.9\ kJ) = +2.9\ kJ$

Step 4: mass/molar mass $=$ moles of limiting reactant

12.6 g KCl/74.54 g/mol $= 0.169$ mol KCl

Step 5: $q_{dissolving\ process}/$mol approximates $\Delta H/mol_{rxn}$ at constant pressure

$+2.9\ kJ/0.169\ mol\ KCl = +17\ kJ/mol_{rxn}$

Relationships Involving ΔH_{rxn} Section 7.8

Remember ΔH_{rxn} is for a particular reaction and a particular number of moles. If the reaction is multiplied by a factor such as 2, the ΔH_{rxn} is also multiplied by the same factor. If the reaction is reversed, then the numerical value ΔH_{rxn} is the same, but the sign reverses. If the reaction is endothermic in the forward direction, it will be exothermic in the reverse direction.

$$2A + B \rightarrow 2C \quad \Delta H\ 180\ kJ \text{ then } 2C \rightarrow 2A + B \quad \Delta H\ -180\ kJ$$

Another relationship used to find ΔH_{rxn} is called Hess's Law. If a series of chemical equations can be added or subtracted to get a final desired equation, the net sum of the ΔH's of each reaction will sum to the overall ΔH_{rxn} of the desired equation. In other words, $\Delta H_1 + \Delta H_2 + \Delta H_3 = \Delta H_{rxn}$. It is vital to retain proper signs for the ΔH values during this procedure.

For instance, given the following two equations:

$$Ca(s) + CO_2(g) + 1/2O_2(g) \rightarrow CaCO_3(s) \quad \Delta H = -812.8 \text{ kJ}$$

$$2Ca(s) + O_2(g) \rightarrow 2CaO(s) \quad\quad\quad\quad\quad \Delta H = -1269.8 \text{ kJ}$$

Find the ΔH_{rxn} for the equation $CaO(s) + CO_2(g) \rightarrow CaCO_3(s)$. The product in the first reaction is the product wanted in the desired reaction, so it remains. The second equation needs the product as a reactant, so the equation needs to be reversed, re-membering to reverse the sign of ΔH. It also needs to be cut in half as only one mole of CaO is needed, not two. These will now add to the desired equation. Using Hess's Law, the ΔH_{rxn} is $-812.8 \text{ kJ} + \dfrac{1269.8 \text{ kJ}}{2}$ or -177.9 kJ.

Section 7.9   Determining Enthalpies of Reaction from Standard Enthalpies of Formation

Earlier chemists realized that when a compound is synthesized from its elements, a spe-cific amount of enthalpy is used or released. Thus, it was convenient to define this quantity as *standard enthalpy of formation* when carried out under specified conditions. This was made more useful when it was realized only enthalpy changes were being considered. It was possible to define the starting point as the system including the required amounts (moles) of elements required to form the compound and it was possible to define each element's contribution to the enthalpy when in their "standard state" of zero. Thus, a set of values for standard enthalpies of formation can be determined and published in a table.

Standard State

- *For a Gas:* The standard state for a gas is the pure gas at a pressure of ex-actly 1 atm.
- *For a Liquid or Solid:* The standard state for a liquid or solid is the pure sub-stance in its most stable form at a pressure of 1 atm and at the temperature of interest (often taken to be 25 °C).
- *For a Substance in Solution:* The standard state for a substance in solution is a concentration of exactly 1 M.

Standard enthalpies of formation from tables provide a very convenient way to calcu-late ΔH_{rxn}, because these, like other thermodynamic quantities, are additive as seen in Hess's Law. Note the following equation is slightly different than the one appear-ing in the textbook, but this one is the equation given on the AP test equation pages.

$$\Delta H° = \sum \Delta H_f° \text{ products} - \sum \Delta H_f° \text{ reactants}$$

Note the degree sign indicates standard state. The (algebraic) sum of standard enthal-pies of formation of all products minus the (algebraic) sum of the standard enthalpies of formation of all reactants will give the overall standard enthalpy *change* for the reaction. The standard values will be provided in a table, but you should know that the tables assume that the standard heat of formation of any element in its standard state

Table 7.2 Standard Enthalpies (or Heats) of Formation, ΔH_f°, at 298 K

Formula	ΔH°_f (kJ/mol)	Formula	ΔH°_f (kJ/mol)	Formula	ΔH°_f (kJ/mol)
Bromine		C_3H_8O(*l*, isopropanol)	−318.1	*Oxygen*	
Br(*g*)	111.9	C_6H_6(*l*)	49.1	O_2(*g*)	0
Br_2(*l*)	0	$C_6H_{12}O_6$(*s*, glucose)	−1273.3	O_3(*g*)	142.7
HBr(*g*)	−36.3	$C_{12}H_{22}O_{11}$(*s*, sucrose)	2226.1	H_2O(*g*)	−241.8
Calcium		*Chlorine*		H_2O(*l*)	−285.8
Ca(*s*)	0	Cl(*g*)	121.3	*Silver*	
CaO(*s*)	−634.9	Cl_2(*g*)	0	Ag(*s*)	0
$CaCO_3$(*s*)	−1207.6	HCl(*g*)	−92.3	AgCl(*s*)	−127.0
Carbon		*Fluorine*		*Sodium*	
C(*s*, graphite)	0	F(*g*)	79.38	Na(*s*)	0
C(*s*, diamond)	1.88	F_2(*g*)	0	Na(*g*)	107.5
CO(*g*)	−110.5	HF(*g*)	−273.3	NaCl(*s*)	−411.2
CO_2(*g*)	−393.5	*Hydrogen*		Na_2CO_3(*s*)	−1130.7
CH_4(*g*)	−74.6	H(*g*)	218.0	$NaHCO_3$(*s*)	−950.8
CH_3OH(*l*)	−238.6	H_2(*g*)	0	*Sulfur*	
C_2H_2(*g*)	227.4	*Nitrogen*		S_8(*s*, rhombic)	0
C_2H_4(*g*)	52.4	N_2(*g*)	0	S_8(*s*, monoclinic)	0.3
C_2H_6(*g*)	−84.68	NH_3(*g*)	−45.9	SO_2(*g*)	−296.8
C_2H_5OH(*l*)	−277.6	NH_4NO_3(*s*)	−365.6	SO_3(*g*)	−395.7
C_3H_8(*g*)	−103.85	NO(*g*)	91.3	H_2SO_4(*l*)	−814.0
C_3H_6O(*l*, acetone)	−248.4	N_2O(*g*)	81.6		

is 0 or $\Delta H_f^\circ = 0$. It is also vital to find the correct physical state for each substance in a provided table as the solid, liquid, and gaseous states will differ in their values for ΔH_f°.

There are two ways of determining ΔH_{rxn} for a chemical reaction. One can perform an experiment and measure the mass and change in temperature of the solution, and calculate $q_{solution}$, then calculate q_{rxn}. Or, one can look up the ΔH_f°. values of the reactants and products and calculate ΔH_{rxn}°.

For the chemical reaction $2H_2O(l) \rightarrow 2H_2(g) + O_2(g)$, the mathematics would be [2(0 kJ/mol) + 0 kJ/mol] − [2(−285.8 kJ/mol)] = 571 kJ/mol. This along with the change in entropy, ΔS, will explain why liquid water does not spontaneously decompose into oxygen gas and hydrogen gas without adding energy in electrolysis.

In coffee-cup calorimetry, there are sources of error. Some of the heat goes into the cup and some is taken in by the air, especially if the coffee-cup has no lid. These errors will cause the change in temperature to be too small resulting in a smaller q_{sol} and also a smaller q_{rxn}. More of thermodynamics will be covered in a later chapter.

Additional Practice

Self-Assessment Quiz Questions Q1, Q2, Q3, Q4, Q5, Q6, Q7, Q8, Q9, Q10, Q11, Q12, Q13, Q14, and Q15

Problems:
Review 8, 10, 11, 12, 14, 15, 17, 21, 23, and 25
Energy Units 33
Internal Energy, Heat, and Work 37, 39, and 41
Heat, Heat Capacity, and Work 45, 46, 47, and 49
Enthalpy and Thermochemical Stoichiometry 55, 57, 58, 60, 65, 67, and 69
Calorimetry 76
Quantitative Relationships Involving ΔH and Hess's Law 77, 78, and 79
Enthalpies of Formation and ΔH 83, 86, and 87
Energy Use and the Environment 99, 102, 103, 114, and 115
Challenge Problems 123, 128, 131, 132, 136, and 138
Conceptual Problems 139
Data Interpretation and Analysis 144

Equations to know:

$$KE = \frac{1}{2}mv^2$$

$$\Delta E = E_{products} - E_{reactants}$$

$$\Delta E_{system} = -\Delta E_{surroundings}$$

$$\Delta E = q + w$$

$$q = C \times \Delta T$$

$$q = m \times C_s \times \Delta T$$

$$q_{cal} = C_{cal} \times \Delta T$$

$$q_{cal} = -q_{rxn}$$

$$\Delta H = \Delta E + P\Delta V$$

$$\Delta H = q_p$$

$$\Delta H^\circ_{rxn} = \sum n_p \Delta H^\circ_f \text{ (products)} - \sum n_r \Delta H^\circ_f \text{ (reactants)}$$

Practice AP Test Questions

1. Nutrition scientists recommend cooking with vegetable oils instead of animal fats to lower the risk of heart disease. Olive oil is often used in cooking. One of the main compounds in olive oil is oleic acid ($C_{18}H_{24}O_2$). The equation (not balanced) for the combustion of olive oil is:

$$\_\_ C_{18}H_{24}O_2(l) + \_\_ O_2(g) \rightarrow \_\_ CO_2(g) + \_\_ H_2O(g) \ \Delta H$$
$$= -1.11 \times 10^4 \text{ kJ/mole}$$

Use the data in the table below and calculate the change in enthalpy of formation for oleic acid.

Substance	ΔH_f° Standard enthalpy of formation (kJ/mol)
$C_{18}H_{24}O_2(l)$	?
$CO_2(g)$	−393.5
$H_2O(g)$	−241.8

A) −2026 kJ   C) +1115 kJ

B) −1115 kJ   D) +2026 kJ

2. Vegetable oils can also be used as fuel for car or truck engines. These engines have moving pistons. When the combustion reaction in the previous problem occurs in an insulated container with a movable piston under a constant pressure of 12.00 atm, what will happen to the volume of the container and what is the work performed?

   A) The volume will decrease and work will be done on the system.

   B) The volume will decrease and work will be done by the system.

   C) The volume will increase and work will be done on the system.

   D) The volume will increase and work will be done by the system.

3. NO_2 gas is formed in automotive engines as a byproduct and contributes to atmospheric pollution. Given the following equations:

$$N_2(g) + O_2(g) \rightarrow 2NO(g) \qquad \Delta H = +180.8 \text{ kJ}$$
$$NO(g) + 1/2 \, O_2(g) \rightarrow NO_2(g) \qquad \Delta H = -56.0 \text{ kJ}$$

Calculate the heat of formation of NO_2 gas.

   A) +34 kJ

   B) +68 kJ

   C) +124.8 kJ

   D) +236.8 kJ

4. In a coffee-cup calorimeter, 50.0 mL of 0.800 M calcium nitrate are added to 50.0 mL of 1.600 M sodium fluoride, and a precipitate forms. The initial temperature of both solutions is 20.00 °C. Assume the specific heat of the resulting solution is 4.18 J/(g · °C) and the density is 1.00 g/mL. Calculate the final temperature of the solution.

$$Ca^{2+}(aq) + 2 F^-(aq) \rightarrow CaF_2(s) \qquad \Delta H° = -11.5 \text{ kJ}$$

A) 18.1 °C   C) 21.10 °C

B) 20.55 °C   D) 22.55 °C

5. The above chemical reaction (in question #4) is _____, and the _____ releases heat and the _____ gains heat.

A) exothermic; reaction; resultant solution

B) exothermic; reactants; products

C) endothermic; reaction; resultant solution

D) endothermic; reactants; products

6. A piece of iron (C=0.449 J/g°C) and a piece of gold (C=0.449 J/g°C) have identical masses. If the iron has an initial temperature of 488 K and the gold has an initial temperature of 308 K, which of the following statements is TRUE of the outcome when the two metals are placed in contact with one another in a calorimeter? Assume no heat is lost to the surroundings.

A) Since the two metals have the same mass, the final temperature of the two metals will be 398 K, exactly halfway between the two initial temperatures.

B) Since the two metals have the same mass, but the specific heat capacity of gold is much smaller than that of iron, the final temperature of the two metals will be closer to 308 K than to 488 K.

C) Since the two metals have the same mass, but the specific heat capacity of gold is much smaller than that of iron, the final temperature of the two metals will be closer to 488 K than to 308 K.

D) Since the two metals have different specific heats, the thermal energy contained in each metal after thermal equilibrium is reached will be different.

7. A 10.0 g piece of each of the following metals, initially at 25°C, is placed individually into 10.0 g of boiling water, initially at 100°C. Which metal will have the highest final temperature? Shown after each metal is its specific heat in J/(g°C).

A) gold (0.129)

B) iron (0.450)

C) aluminum (0.902)

D) copper (0.385)

8. How much heat (in units of kJ) is required to get a 10.0 g sample of liquid isopropanol (MM 60.09) at 22.6°C to 10.0 g of gas phase isopropanol at 82.6°C?

isopropanol	
Specific heat of $C_3H_8O(l)$	2.68 J/g°C
Heat of vaporization $C_3H_8O(l)$	44.4 kJ/mol
b.p. at 1 atm.	82.6°C

A) 10. kJ

B) 79 kJ

C) 0.30 kJ

D) 1.6 kJ

9. How much energy is <u>required</u> to decompose 765 g of PCl_3 (Molar Mass 137.32) according to the reaction below?

$$4\ PCl_3(g) \rightarrow P_4(s) + 6\ Cl_2(g) \qquad \Delta H°_{rxn} = +1207\ kJ$$

A) 2.31×10^3 kJ

B) 4.33×10^3 kJ

C) 6.74×10^3 kJ

D) 1.68×10^3 kJ

10. A 100.0 mL sample of 0.300 M NaOH is mixed with a 100.0 mL sample of 0.300 M HNO_3 in a coffee cup calorimeter. If both solutions were initially at 35.00°C and the temperature of the resulting solution was recorded as 37.00°C, determine the $\Delta H°_{rxn}$ (in units of kJ/mol NaOH) for the neutralization reaction between aqueous NaOH and HNO_3. Assume (1) that no heat is lost to the calorimeter or the surroundings, and (2) that the density and the heat capacity of the resulting solution are the same as water.

A) −55.7 kJ/mol NaOH

B) −169 kJ/mol NaOH

C) −27.9 kJ/mol NaOH

D) −34.4 kJ/mol NaOH

Data Interpretation and Analysis Problem: Heat of Reaction of Alkanes

Linear alkanes have the molecular formula $C_nH_{(2n+2)}$. Cycloalkanes have the formula, $C_nH_{(2n)}$. For example, the molecular formula and Lewis structure for propane and cyclo-propane are:

$$C_3H_8 \qquad\qquad C_3H_6$$

When propane undergoes combustion with excess oxygen gas carbon dioxide and water are formed, heat is released ($\Delta H_{rxn} = -2100$ kJ/mol), and the balanced chemical equation is

$$C_3H_8(g) + 5O_2(g) \rightarrow 3CO_2(g) + 4H_2O(l)$$

Table 1 lists the change in enthalpy or the heat of reaction for four alkanes.

Table 1

Name and Formula	Number of Carbon Atoms	ΔH_{rxn} (kJ/mol)	ΔH_{rxn} /Carbon Atom (kJ/mol)
Propane, C_3H_8	3	−2200	
Butane, C_4H_{10}	4	−2900	
Pentane, C_5H_{12}	5	−3537	
Hexane, C_6H_{14}	6	−4075	
Heptane, C_7H_{16}	7		

Figure 1 plots the average heat of combustion in units of kJ/mol per carbon atom in a series of linear alkanes.

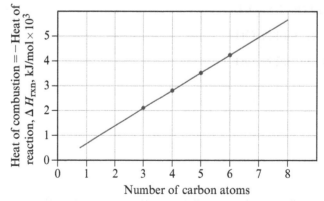

Figure 1 Heat of Combustion per Carbon Atom

Table 2 lists the change in enthalpy or heat of reaction for four cycloalkanes.

Table 2

Name and Formula	Number of Carbon Atoms	ΔH_{rxn} (kJ/mol)	ΔH_{rxn} /Carbon Atom (kJ/mol)
Cyclopropane, C_3H_8	3	−2090	
Cyclobutane, C_4H_{10}	4	−2700	
Cyclopentane, C_5H_{12}	5	−3291	
Cyclohexane, C_6H_{14}	6	−3920	
Cycloheptane, C_7H_{16}	7		

a) As the number of carbon and hydrogen atoms increase in a linear alkane the change in enthalpy of reaction increases. Explain.

b) As the number of carbon and hydrogen atoms increase in a cycloalkane, does the change in enthalpy of reaction increase, decrease or stay the same? Explain.

c) Calculate the ΔH_{rxn} /Carbon atom in units of kJ/mol for the first four linear alkanes. Does the ΔH_{rxn} /Carbon atom increase, decrease or stay the same with increasing number of carbon atoms?

d) Estimate the ΔH_{rxn} in units of kJ/mol for heptane.

e) Calculate the ΔH_{rxn} /Carbon atom in units of kJ/mol for the first four cycloalkanes. Does the ΔH_{rxn} / Carbon atom increase, decrease or stay the same with increasing number of carbon atoms? Why is there a difference in the ΔH_{rxn} / Carbon atom of the cycloalkanes compared to the ΔH_{rxn} /Carbon atom of the linear alkanes.

f) Estimate the ΔH_{rxn} in units of kJ/mol for cycloheptane. Compare this value to the ΔH_{rxn} in units of kJ/mol for heptane. If there is a difference explain.

Data Interpretation and Analysis Question Answers with Brief Explanations

a) It takes an input of energy to break a chemical bond. When a chemical bond forms, energy is released. With an increase in the number of atoms, there is an increase in the number of bonds. As more C−H and C−C bonds break to form C=O bonds and H−O bonds there is a net output or released energy.

b) For cycloalkanes the change in energy increases.

c) For linear alkanes, the trend is a decrease in energy per carbon atom.

Name and Formula	Number of Carbon Atoms	ΔH_{rxn} (kJ/mol)	ΔH_{rxn} /Carbon Atom (kJ/mol)
propane, C_3H_8	3	−2220	−740
butane, C_4H_{10}	4	−2900	−725
pentane, C_5H_{12}	5	−3537	−707
hexane, C_6H_{14}	6	−4075	−679
heptane, C_7H_{16}	7	−4465	−637

d) $\Delta H_{\text{combustion}}$ for heptane should be about -1150 kJ/mol.

e) For cycloalkanes, there is a gradually trend of a decrease in energy per carbon atom.

Name and Formula	Number of Carbon Atoms	ΔH_{rxn} (kJ/mol)	ΔH_{rxn} /Carbon Atom (kJ/mol)
cyclopropane, C_3H_8	3	-2090	-697
cyclobutane, C_4H_{10}	4	-2700	-675
cyclopentane, C_5H_{12}	5	-3291	-658
cyclohexane, C_6H_{14}	6	-3920	-653
cycloheptane, C_7H_{16}	7	-4300	-614

f) $\Delta H_{\text{combustion}}$ for cycloheptane should be about -4300 kJ/mol which is a lower compare to $\Delta H_{\text{combustion}}$ for heptane of -4500 kJ/mol. Although there are the same number of carbon atoms in heptane and cycloheptane, cycloheptane has fewer hydrogen atoms, thus fewer C$-$H bonds. This means there are fewer C$-$H bonds broken and fewer H$-$O bonds to make water. Since fewer water molecules form, less net energy is being produced.

READING GUIDE

Concepts in the AP Chemistry curriculum found in Chapter 7 include the energy changes in Unit 3 and the thermochemistry concepts Unit 6.

Chemical Hand Warmers

Section 7.1

1. What is thermochemistry?

2. What happens to the temperature of the surroundings in an exothermic reaction?

3. What is the chemical reaction frequently used in hand warmers? What is the useful product of hand warmers?

The Nature of Energy: Key Definitions

Section 7.2

4. Define the following in your own words:

   Heat:

   Kinetic energy:

   Thermal energy:

   Potential energy:

   Chemical energy:

   Law of Conservation of Energy:

5. If energy is conserved, what can energy do? Give an example. What important conclusion was reached for nuclear reactions in Einstein's postulate, $E = mc^2$ in terms of mass and energy?

6. What is the difference between a system and its surroundings? Why is this important?

7. During an energy exchange between a system and the surroundings, explain what happens.

8. What unit is represented by J? How many joules are in one calorie? How many calories are in 1 joule?

9. What is the relationship between a food *Calorie* (Cal) and a science *calorie* (c)?

10. What is a watt (W)?

11. How many joules are in a kilowatt-hour (kWh)? What is the most common use for kWh?

Section 7.3   The First Law of Thermodynamics: There Is No Free Lunch

12. What does the first law of thermodynamics state? Explain what this means.

13. What is internal energy?

14. What are state functions? Give three examples.

15. Draw an energy diagram in which the reactants have a higher internal energy than the products. What direction does the energy flow in this diagram? What is the sign of ΔE? (What is this kind of reaction called?)

16. Draw an energy diagram in which the reactants have a lower internal energy than the products. What direction does the energy flow in this diagram? What is the sign of ΔE? (What is this kind of reaction called?)

17. What is the sign of q when a system gains thermal energy? Where does the thermal energy come from?

18. What is the sign of q when a system loses thermal energy? Where does the thermal energy go?

19. What is the sign of ΔE when energy flows into a system? What is the sign of ΔE when energy flows out of a system?

20. What is the difference among ΔE, q, and w? Are work and heat state functions? Justify you answer.

Section 7.4   Quantifying Heat and Work

21. Explain the difference between heat and temperature. Incorporate an example in your explanation. Can you measure how much heat an object has? In what direction does thermal energy travel?

22. Explain the concept of thermal equilibrium.

23. Define and give the symbol for heat capacity. If two different substances each have 50 J of energy added, which substance will have the greater temperature change?

24. Define and give the symbol for specific heat. Explain the difference between specific heat and heat capacity? Which is an intensive property and which is an extensive property? Explain your answer. What is molar heat capacity?

25. In the following equation, identify what all the symbols represent and the usual units used for them: $q = mC_s\Delta T$. (note: on the AP equations page, this will be $q = mC\Delta T$)

26. What will happen when Object A and Object B come into contact with each other if they are at different temperatures? When will the transfer stop?

27. What equation can be used in calculations when there is a thermal energy transfer between a sample of water and a metal object?

28. What is meant by pressure–volume work? Explain one application using this concept.

29. What is the sign of work if work is done on the system by expanding gases? Justify your answer.

Measuring ΔE for Chemical Reactions: Constant-Volume Calorimetry

Section 7.5

30. Define calorimetry. Why are calorimetry experiments useful in science and engineering?

31. What is a bomb calorimeter and what does it measure? What sort of reaction are they often used for?*

32. Explain how to determine the change of energy, ΔE, in a combustion reaction carried out in a bomb calorimeter.*

Enthalpy: The Heat Evolved in a Chemical Reaction at Constant Pressure

Section 7.6

33. Define enthalpy (H) in your own words. Explain the difference between H and ΔH.

34. Compare and contrast ΔE from ΔH.

35. What does a $+\Delta H$ indicate? What is the term used for a reaction with this sign of change? Give an example of this type of reaction.

36. What does a $-\Delta H$ indicate? What is the term used for a reaction with this sign of change? Give an example of this type of reaction.

37. If an endothermic reaction absorbs heat, why does the reaction container feel cold?

38. What is the symbol for the enthalpy change of a chemical reaction?

39. Explain why the enthalpy change of a chemical reaction is an extensive property and not an intensive property. Is enthalpy a state function? Why or why not? How is this related to KMT learned about in the previous chapter? Can KMT apply to solids and liquids as well as gases?

40. What factors determine the magnitude of the enthalpy change of a chemical reaction? How is this usually indicated in a chemical reaction equation statement.

41. Using bonds forming and bonds breaking, explain what happens in exothermic and endothermic reactions.

42. Explain how to write a thermochemical equation. Give an example.

Section 7.7

Constant-Pressure Calorimetry: Measuring ΔH_{rxn}

43. Draw a simple coffee-cup calorimeter and explain how it works. Explain why this is a constant-pressure calorimeter.

44. What equation is used to determine how the heat lost is related to the heat gained by physical or chemical process in a coffee-cup calorimeter? What is the relationship between the sign of q of the reaction and q of the solution? Explain.

45. Explain the difference between a bomb calorimeter and a coffee-cup calorimeter in terms of what is held constant and what is measured. Explain why the results are different for the same chemical reaction carried out in the different types of calorimeters.*

Section 7.8

Relationships Involving ΔH_{rxn}

46. Why is it important to have the reaction designated when referring to ΔH_{rxn}? If the chemical reaction $2H_2 + O_2 \rightarrow 2H_2O$ is instead written as $4H_2 + 2O_2 \rightarrow 4H_2O$, what should be done to the value of ΔH_{rxn}? Justify your answer.

47. If a chemical reaction reverses to $2H_2O \rightarrow 2H_2 + O_2$, what should be done to the value of ΔH_{rxn}?

48. If a chemical reaction can be expressed as the sum of several equations, then how can the ΔH_{rxn} be found?

49. What concept is explained by Hess's law?

50. Use the following two equations and use a Hess's law energy level diagram to explain how to solve for the ΔH_{rxn} of $3H_2(g) + O_3(g) \rightarrow 3H_2O(g)$:

$$2H_2(g) + O_2(g) \rightarrow 2H_2O(g) \qquad \Delta H = -483.6 \text{ kJ}$$

$$3O_2(g) \rightarrow 2O_3(g) \qquad \Delta H = +285.4 \text{ kJ}$$

Section 7.9

Determining Enthalpies of Reaction from Standard Enthalpies of Formation

51. Explain the concept of standard state for a gas, a liquid, a solid, and a substance in solution.

52. What is standard enthalpy change? What are the conditions for a standard enthalpy change? What is the symbol?

53. What is standard enthalpy of formation? Write the equation for the standard enthalpy of formation of water. What is the symbol?

54. How are standard enthalpy change and standard enthalpy of formation different?

55. Explain how a table of standard enthalpies of formation can be used to find the enthalpy of a reaction. Include an example in your answer.

56. What is the equation for ΔH_{rxn}? What does each variable represent? Solve for ΔH_{rxn} using $2Al(s) + Fe_2O_3(s) \rightarrow Al_2O_3(s) + 2 Fe(s)$

Energy Use and the Environment"   Section 7.10

57. List three examples of fossil fuels. What are three environmental problems associated with the use of fossil fuels?

58. Fill in the following table with the four major air pollutants, identify the main source of each, and identify the affects on humans:

Pollutant	Source	Affect(s) on Humans

59. Explain the difference between stratospheric ozone and ground-level (tropospheric) ozone.

60. What is photochemical smog? What compounds contribute to smog? How are these compounds formed?

61. What U.S. agency regulates limits on air pollutants?*

62. What is meant by a "renewable" source of energy? What are two renewable sources of energy?*

Read the following and answer questions 63–65.

On May 9, 2013 the daily mean concentration of carbon dioxide in the atmosphere of Mauna Loa, Hawaii, surpassed 400 parts per million (ppm) for the first time since measurements began in 1958. Independent measurements of the concentration of carbon dioxide were made using calibrated instruments from the National Oceanic and Atmospheric Administration (NOAA) and the Scripps Institution of Oceanography. Scientists from NOAA and the Scripps Institution of Oceanography independently recorded the concentration of carbon dioxide on an hourly basis, calculated the daily mean concentration of CO_2 and reported it. The report marks an important milestone because Mauna Loa, as the oldest continuous carbon dioxide (CO_2) measurement station in the world, is the primary global benchmark site for monitoring the concentration of carbon dioxide in the atmosphere. Before the Industrial Revolution in the 19th century, the global average concentration of CO_2 was about 280 ppm. http://www.sciencedaily.com/releases/2013/05/130510180610.htm

63. Explain why carbon dioxide is called a *greenhouse gas*? Name three other greenhouse gases.*

64. What do computer models suggest as five possible effects if the amounts of greenhouse gases in the atmosphere continue to increase?*

65. How is the concentration of carbon dioxide in the atmosphere measured?*

Self-Assessment Answers

1. _____   2. _____   3. _____

4. _____   5. _____   6. _____

7. _____   8. _____   9. _____

10. _____   11. _____   12. _____

13. _____   14. _____   15. _____

THE QUANTUM-MECHANICAL MODEL OF THE ATOM

This chapter discusses the electron and its behavior in atoms. Chemistry is fundamentally determined by the behavior of electrons in and between atoms, so understanding this concept helps to understand the atom, including models such as the quantum-mechanical model and interactions in chemical bonding and structure. The chapter has mathematical reasoning to accompany the experiments as well as explanations about how each experiment contributed to understanding electrons behavior. The most important sections to review are as follows:

8.2 **The Nature of Light**

8.3 **Atomic Spectroscopy and the Bohr Model**

8.4 **The Wave Nature of Matter: The de Broglie Wavelength, the Uncertainty Principle, and Indeterminacy**

8.5 **Quantum Mechanics and the Atom**

8.6 **The Shapes of Atomic Orbitals**

Some other relevant review concepts are how electrons exist in orbitals, how they "transition" between orbitals, how this transition may release or absorb energy, how to determine the number of orbitals present and the number of electrons present.

Specific Learning Objectives Addressed in This Chapter:

SAP-8 Spectroscopy can determine the structure and concentration in a mixture of a chemical species.

SAP-8.A Explain the relationship between a region of the electromagnetic spectrum and the types of molecular or electronic transitions associated with that region.

SAP-8.B Explain the properties of an absorbed or emitted photon in relationship to an electronic transition in an atom or a molecule.

Concepts and Vocabulary to Review:

Section 8.1   ## Schrödinger's Cat

Edwin Schrödinger explained that electrons are small particles that can exist in two different states at the same time. This strange behavior of electrons gave rise to the quantum-mechanical model of the atom and an understanding of chemical bonding and periodicity.

Section 8.2   ## The Nature of Light

Like electrons, light has many properties such as wave-particle duality. It can behave as a wave or behave as a particle. Certain properties are best described as waves and others are best described as particles.

Light exhibits transverse wave properties—the variations occur perpendicular to its motion. Such waves can be described based on amplitude, wavelength, and frequency. The height or depth of a wave is its *amplitude*. The *wavelength* is the distance between analogous points of two peaks of a wave.

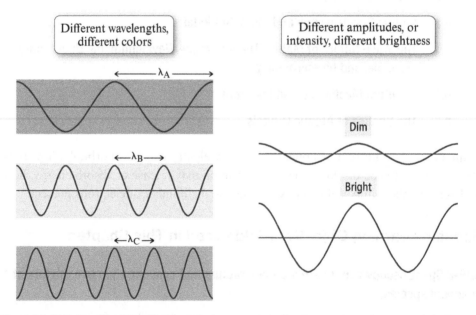

Figure 8.1 Wavelength and Amplitude   Wavelength and amplitude are independent properties. The wavelength of light determines its color. The amplitude, or intensity, determines its brightness.

The most energetic waves have the shortest wavelengths. *Frequency* is the number of variations (vibrations) of the wave passing a certain point in a second. A hertz (Hz) is one cycle per second. The higher the frequency, the shorter the wavelength, and the more energy the wave has. Since all light travels at the same speed in vacuum, there is an inverse relationship between wavelength and frequency. Wavelengths (λ)

can be calculated by knowing the speed of light (c) and the frequency (v) of the wave using the equation: $\lambda = \dfrac{c}{v}$. A photon is an elementary particle that is the smallest discrete unit of electromagnetic radiation or light. Photons are always in motion and in a vacuum travel at the speed of light. The energy of a photon can be calculated using the equation $E = \dfrac{hc}{\lambda}$, where h is 6.626×10^{-34} J·s. This proportionality constant is called Plank's constant.

In the visible light range, red light has the longest wavelength and lowest energy, whereas violet light has the shortest wavelength and highest energy.

The color we see when we observe an object corresponds to the wavelength reflected by the object. The other wavelengths of white light are absorbed by the object.

The full electromagnetic spectrum is shown below. Students should have a relative idea of the scale and the types of high and low energy waves.

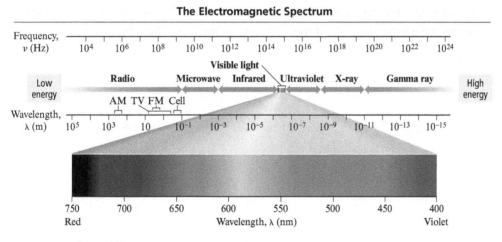

Figure 8.2 The Electromagnetic Spectrum   The right side of the spectrum consists of high-energy, high-frequency, short-wavelength radiation. The left side consists of low-energy, low-frequency, long-wavelength radiation. Visible light constitutes a small segment in the middle.

The high energy 10^{24} Hz gamma ray is the shortest wavelength of 10^{-15} nm while the low energy radio waves at 10^{6} Hz have the longest wavelengths of 10^{3} nm.

Some high energy waves such as gamma rays, UV, and X-rays can damage biological molecules. They do this by creating ions from neutral atoms or molecules. Radio waves are the longest waves and the least damaging. Microwave radiation is associated with transitions in molecular rotations, infrared radiation is associated with transitions in molecular vibrations and ultraviolet and visible radiations are associated with transitions in electronic energy levels.

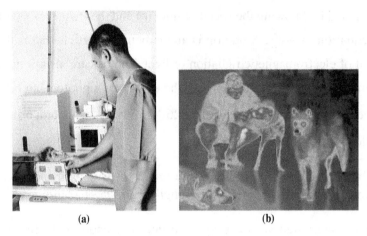

(a)   (b)

Figure 8.3 **(a)** To produce a medical X-ray, short-wavelength electromagnetic radiation passes through the skin and creates an image of bones and internal organs. **(b)** Warm objects emit infrared light, which is invisible to the eye but can be captured on film or by detectors to produce an infrared photograph.

Waves can interfere with each other. Constructive interference increases the wave amplitude and destructive interference cancels out a wave. Waves also exhibit diffraction or bending of light when it hits an object or slit. It is from studying diffraction patterns that lead to the development of X-ray crystallography. This method has been used to understand the inner structure of molecules including DNA. See figure 8.4.

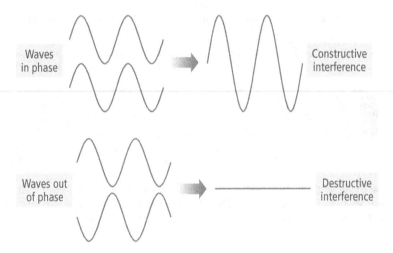

Figure 8.4

The discovery of the photoelectric effect helped to explain more about light and electrons in atoms. The data showed that it took a threshold frequency to dislodge an outer electron from a metal surface. Light not meeting the threshold energy will not dislodge an electron no matter how long or how brightly the light shines on the metal. Even if the intensity is low, if the light meets the threshold frequency, called the electron binding energy, electrons will be ejected. Albert Einstein explained this by explaining light energy comes in packets called *photons*. If the light has energy beyond the threshold the extra energy is transferred to the electron as kinetic energy.

The Photoelectric Effect

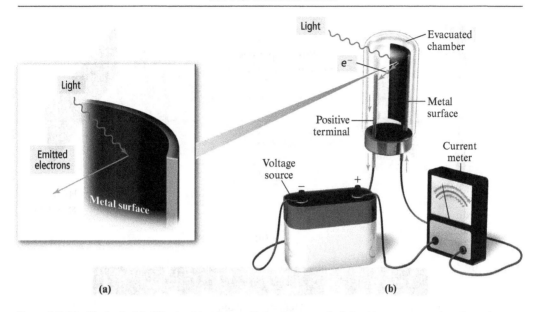

Figure 8.5 The Photoelectric Effect   **(a)** When sufficiently energetic light shines on a metal surface, the surface emits electrons. **(b)** The emitted electrons can be measured as an electrical current.

It is frequently more convenient to think of light (and all other electromagnetic waves), as photons rather than as waves (see Section 8.4). When the photon interacts with an electron in a photoelectric effect, the photon's energy is transferred to the electron, the photon disappears and the electron gains all the photon energy. A high energy photon is thus able to transfer sufficient energy for the electron to break away from the atom. Therefore, energy conservation is:

$$E_{photon} = E_{(electron\ binding)} + E_{(electron\ kinetic)}.$$

More recently, photoelectron spectroscopy (PES) has been used to measure accurately the energies of all electrons in atoms. Through the discoveries discussed in this section, electrons were observed to behave either as a wave or as a particle depending on the experiment.

Atomic Spectroscopy and the Bohr Model   Section 8.3

Atomic spectroscopy is the study of electromagnetic radiation being absorbed or emitted by atoms. When an atom absorbs energy, it's electrons form excited higher energy states and as the electron returns to the ground state where it started, the energy it absorbed to reach the higher energy state will be emitted. Elements in the gas state can be uniquely identified by observing the patterns in their emission spectrum when the electrons in atoms are excited with electrical energy, then the electrons relax and undergo a transition losing energy.

These patterns are also reflected by an element's characteristic color in flame tests. The color of the flame corresponds to the energy released by electrons undergoing a transition from an excited energy state to a lower energy state. The color also corresponds to the wavelengths of the electromagnetic spectrum.

Emission Spectra

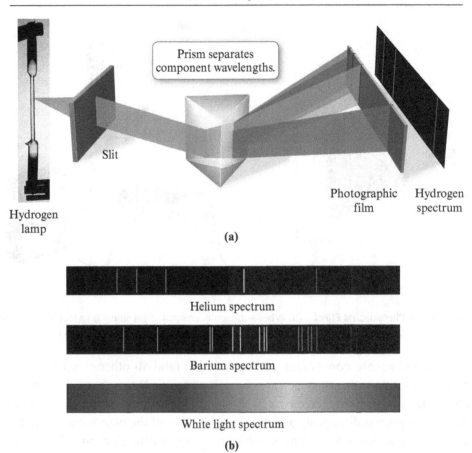

(a)

Hydrogen lamp

Slit

Prism separates component wavelengths.

Photographic film

Hydrogen spectrum

Helium spectrum

Barium spectrum

White light spectrum

(b)

Figure 8.6 Emission Spectra (a) The light emitted from a hydrogen, helium, or barium lamp consists of specific wavelengths that can be separated by passing the light through a prism. (b) The resulting bright lines constitute an emission spectrum characteristic of the element that produced it.

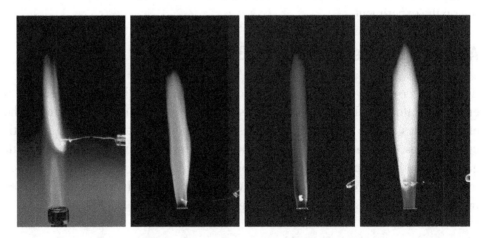

Figure 8.7 Flame Tests (from left to right) for Sodium, Potassium, Lithium, and Barium We can identify elements by the characteristic color of the light they produce when heated. The colors derive from especially bright lines in their emission spectra. The flame of sodium is orange, potassium is lavender, lithium is crimson red, and barium is yellow green.

The color observed in a flame test derives from the brightest line in the atom's emission spectra.

To summarize, when an electron makes a transition to another energy state, it absorbs energy to go to a higher energy level and releases energy to go to a lower energy state.

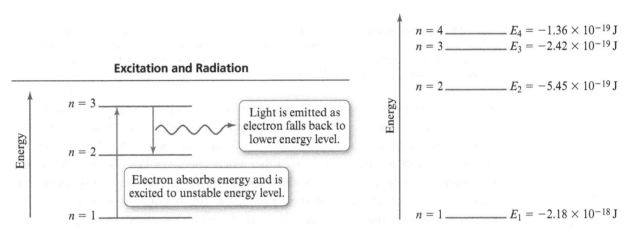

Figure 8.8 Excitation and Radiation   When an atom absorbs energy, an electron can be excited from an orbital in a lower-energy level to an orbital in a higher-energy level. The electron in this "excited state" is unstable, however, and relaxes to a lower-energy level, releasing energy in the form of electromagnetic radiation. The equation used to calculate the energy of each energy level is

$$E_n = -2.18 \times 10^{-18} \, J \left(\frac{1}{n^2} \right) \quad (n = 1, 2, 3, \dots).$$

Investigating the energy resulting from these transitions helped in the understanding of electron behavior in hydrogen. These transitions were correctly explained by Neils Bohr, although he was incorrect in making the assumption that electrons circled the atom in orbits like planets around the sun.

The Wave Nature of Matter: The de Broglie Wavelength, the Uncertainty Principle, and Indeterminacy   Section 8.4

Like an electromagnetic wave and a photon, an electron can behave both as a particle and as a wave. However, the wave characteristics and particle characteristics cannot be observed at the same time. On a very small scale, we cannot know position and velocity at the same time of any part of matter. The more known about position, the less is known about velocity (or energy). Heisenberg established this rule, called the Heisenberg uncertainty principle.

In an atom, the strong coulombic force of attraction between the electron and the positive nucleus causes the electron to stay in the atom, the question is where it "stays." The electron location can be described according to a probability map.

This is a theoretically calculated statistical representation of where an electron might be located. These are created using mathematical derivations from the Schrodinger

Figure 8.9 Trajectory versus Probability   In quantum mechanics, we cannot calculate deterministic trajectories. Instead, it is necessary to think in terms of probability maps: statistical pictures of where a quantum-mechanical particle, such as an electron, is most likely to be found. In this hypothetical map, darker shading indicates greater probability.

wave equation and can demonstrate the shape and energy of an electron in an atom, called an orbital. They are a human's best guess at what an atom really looks like inside. Detailed models of the electron orbitals in atoms and molecules with lots of electrons are still an area of research by theoretical chemists. The nature of the chemical bonding and the shapes of molecules can, however, be predicted fairly accurately using elaborate models based on these principles. The electron orbitals described by the models cluster into shells and subshells based on energies. These explain the chemical properties and the periodicity found in the periodic table remarkably well. This is explored in the following chapter.

The wavelength of an electron can be calculated by knowing the electrons velocity and mass using the de Broglie relationship. When we assign an electron a mass, its wavelength can be calculated. An object that has mass and a velocity emits a wave.

$$\lambda = \frac{h}{mv} \quad \text{de Broglie relation}$$

Section 8.5   Quantum Mechanics and the Atom

Each orbital of an atom has a probability distribution map. The orbital can be described by its energy (n), shape (l), its orientation in space(m_l) and the spin (ms) of its electrons. While the AP test will not test knowing the quantum numbers themselves, the concepts about orbitals they explain will be. The energy of an electron is based on its distance from the nucleus. The number of possible orbitals is equal to the principal quantum number. For elements in the first period of the periodic table, only the $1s$ orbital exists. For elements in the 2nd energy level, $2s$ and $2p$ are available. This is explained in more detail in chapter 9 that when electrons are filling sublevels of orbitals, Hund's rule and the Pauli exclusion principle are in effect. One electron will fill each sublevel with the same spin before pairing an electron with an opposite spin.

Section 8.6   The Shapes of Atomic Orbitals

Since electrons have wavelike properties, they are not located in an atom in a certain exact location but they cannot be just anywhere, they are limited to certain energy levels (quantized). The probability of orbital density is a plot of where one is most likely to find an electron in a particular orbital. The plot of a $1s$ orbital is below. The plots for the other orbitals of s are larger due to a bigger radius.

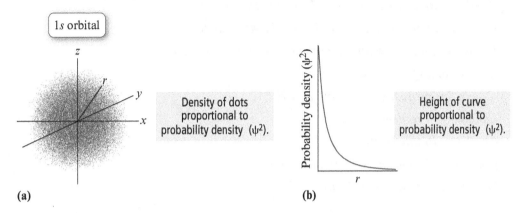

Figure 8.10 The 1s Orbital: Two Representations In (**a**) the dot density is proportional to the electron probability density. In (**b**), the height of the curve is proportional to the electron probability density. The x-axis is r, the distance from the nucleus.

The s orbital is spherical in shape compared to p orbitals which have a lobed distribution shown below. The shapes of the d and f orbitals are not in the AP curriculum although students should know d orbitals have five sublevels and f orbitals have seven sublevels.

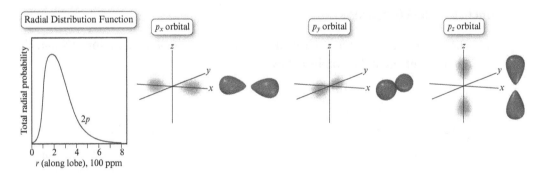

Figure 8.11 The 2p Orbitals and Their Radial Distribution Function The radial distribution function is the same for each of the three $2p$ orbitals when the x-axis of the graph is taken as the axis containing the lobes of the orbital.

It is the combination of orbitals around one x, y, z axis that gives the atom its shape and volume.

Additional Practice

Self-Assessment Quiz Questions Q1, Q2, Q3, Q4, Q5, Q7, Q8, and Q10
Problems: Review Questions 6, 7, 10, 11, 14, and 23
Electromagnetic Radiation 37, 39, 40, 44, 45, and 46
The Wave Nature of Matter and the Uncertainty Principle 51
Orbitals and Quantum numbers 57
Atomic Spectroscopy 65, 66, 69, and 70
Cumulative Problems 80 and 85
Challenge Problems 104
Conceptual Problems 105, 106, and 108
Data Interpretations and Analysis 114

Equations to know:

$$\nu = \frac{c}{\lambda}$$

$$E = h\nu$$

$$E = \frac{hc}{\lambda}$$

$$\lambda = \frac{h}{mv}$$

$$\Delta x \times m\Delta v \geq \frac{h}{4\pi}$$

$$E_n = -2.18 \times 10^{-18} \, \text{J}\left(\frac{1}{n^2}\right) \quad (n = 1, 2, 3, \ldots)$$

$$\Delta E = -2.18 \times 10^{-18} \, \text{J}\left(\frac{1}{n_f^2} - \frac{1}{n_i^2}\right)$$

Practice AP Test Questions

1. The electric field vectors for two different electromagnetic radiations (X and Y) are represented in the graphs below.

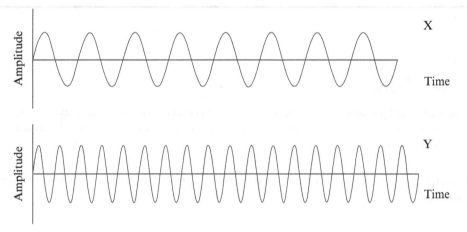

Wave X has:

    A) A longer wavelength and higher energy compared to Y

    B) The same wavelength and same energy as Y

    C) A longer wavelength and a lower energy compared to Y

    D) A shorter wavelength and a higher energy compared to Y

2. Calculate the frequency of electromagnetic radiation having a wavelength of 60.0 nm. The speed of light is 3.00×10^8 m/s.

A) 5.00×10^6 s^{-1}

B) 5.00×10^{15} s^{-1}

C) 2.00×10^{-16} s^{-1}

D) $200.$ s^{-1}

3. Results from several photoelectric effect experiments provided evidence for which of the following claims:

A) Electrons in atoms have quantized energies.

B) Electromagnetic radiation has characteristics of wave behavior.

C) Electromagnetic energy has characteristics of particle behavior.

D) Electrons in atoms exhibit properties characteristic of waves.

4. What is the minimum wavelength of a photon of electromagnetic radiation that can be absorbed by an electron in a hydrogen atom to cause it to undergo a transition from the $n = 2$ energy level to the $n = 4$ energy level? *Hint*: Calculate the energy of each, find the difference, and then solve for wavelength.

A) 500 nm

B) 600 nm

C) 700 nm

D) 800 nm

5. Calculate the de Broglie wavelength (in m) of an electron (mass $= 9.11 \times 10^{-31}$ kg) traveling at a speed of 7.45×10^6 m/s. ($h = 6.6 \times 10^{-34}$ J·s)

A) Greater than 1×10^{-5}

B) Between 10^{-5} and 10^{-7}

C) Between 10^{-7} and 10^{-9}

D) Less than 1×10^{-10}

6. When one electron transitions from the 4th shell to the 3rd shell in a hydrogen atom, is energy emitted or absorbed?

A) Emitted

B) Absorbed

C) No energy change of the atom occurs

D) The answer depends upon other, unknown, conditions

$n = \infty$ _ _ _ _ _ _ $E = 0$
$n = 4$ ═══════ $E = -0.85$ eV
$n = 3$ ─────── $E = -1.51$ eV

$n = 2$ ─────── $E = -3.40$ eV

$n = 1$ ─────── $E = -13.6$ eV

7. Using the information in the above question, estimate the energy (in units of joules) associated when an electron undergoes a transition from the $n = 4$ energy level to $n = 3$ energy level in a hydrogen atom.

1 electron volt $= 1.60218 \times 10^{-19}$ Joule

A) 1.1×10^{-19} J

C) 2.4×10^{-19} J

B) $1.4\ 1 \times 10^{-19}$ J

D) $3.8\ 1 \times 10^{-19}$ J

8. The existence of discrete (quantized) energy levels in an atom may be inferred from:

A) different threshold frequencies for each metal in photoelectric effect experiments

B) diffraction of electrons by crystals.

C) X-ray diffraction by crystals.

D) gas discharge tube experiments emitting atomic line spectra.

9. The orbital with an electron probability density depicted to the right side of the page is likely to be:

A) an s orbital, with $l = 0$.

B) a p orbital with $l = 1$.

C) an s orbital with $l = 1$.

D) a d orbital with $l = 2$.

E) a p orbital with $l = 0$.

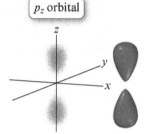

p_z orbital

10. In a photoelectric effect experiment, the maximum kinetic energy, KE_e, of ejected electrons (photoelectrons) is given by $KE_e = h\nu - BE$. Where BE is the binding energy of a surface electron in an atom. The following table provides data collected from several photoelectric effect experiments involving different metals. Some of the data is deliberately missing.

Metal	Threshold Frequency	Incoming Radiation Frequency	Ejected Electron Velocity	Binding Energy to Remove One Mole of Electrons
Lithium	5.51×10^{14} s^{-1}	5.51×10^{14} s^{-1}	minimal	279.7 kJ/mole of e-
Lithium	5.51×10^{14} s^{-1}	1.01×10^{15} s^{-1}	??	279.7 kJ/mole of e-
Gold	1.23×10^{15} s^{-1}	1.23×10^{15} s^{-1}	minimal	890.1 kJ/mole of e-
Gold	1.23×10^{15} s^{-1}	1.01×10^{15} s^{-1}	No ejected e-	890.1 kJ/mole of e-
unknown	6.71×10^{14} s^{-1}	6.71×10^{14} s^{-1}	minimal	??
unknown	6.71×10^{14} s^{-1}	1.01×10^{15} s^{-1}	6.95×10^5 m/s	??

The unknown metal could be

A) Li   B) Na   C) Ag   D) Au   E) Pt

Data Interpretation and Analysis Question: Xenon²¹⁺ Ions Created Using Ultrahigh Energy

Scientists from three countries collaborated to study the photoelectric effect at ultrahigh intensities on Xenon atoms. Energy pulses of 10 fs duration impacted Xenon atoms; the results are displayed in Figure 1.

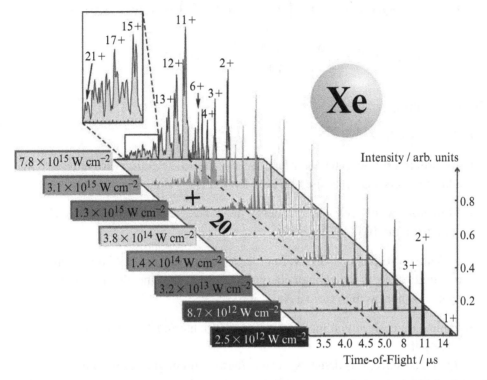

Figure 1 Ion time-of-flight mass/charge spectra of xenon taken at a photon energy of 93 eV (93 eV/photon) and different pulse irradiance levels.

Source: A. A. Sorokin, S. V. Bobashev, T. Feigl, K. Tiedtke, H. Wabnitz, and M. Richter, Photoelectric effect at ultra-high intensities, *Phys. Rev. Lett.* 99, 213002 (2007).

When 13.3 nm radiation of 7.8×10^{15} W/cm² impacted Xenon atoms, ions of Xenon from Xe^{2+} to Xe^{21+} were detected.

a) What energy, $E = h\nu$ in units of electron volts (eV) corresponds to a wavelength 13.3 nm?

b) What type of radiation is 13.3 nm?

c) Write the complete electron configuration for a neutral Xe atom.

d) When a Xe^{21+} ion forms, which electrons are removed from a neutral Xe atom?

e) An energy input of 5300 eV is required to form a Xe^{21+} ion. How many photons must a Xenon atom absorb in order to form one Xe^{21+} ion?

f) When 13.3 nm radiation of 2.5×10^{12} W/cm² impacted Xenon atoms, no Xe^{21+} ions were detected. Only $Xe^{1+} - Xe^{4+}$ were detected. Explain.

Data Interpretation and Analysis Question Answers with Brief Explanations

a) $E = h\nu$ $\nu = \dfrac{c}{\lambda}$ $\nu = \dfrac{3.00 \times 10^8 \frac{m}{s}}{13.3 \text{ nm} \times \dfrac{1 \text{ m}}{1 \times 10^9 \text{ nm}}} = 2.25 \times 10^{16} \dfrac{cyc}{s}$

$E = h\nu = 6.63 \times 10^{-34} \text{ J} \cdot \text{s}\left(2.25 \times 10^{16} \dfrac{cyc}{s}\right) = 1.49 \times 10^{-17} \text{ J}$

$E = 1.49 \times 10^{-17} \text{ J} \times \dfrac{6.242 \times 10^{18} \text{ eV}}{1 \text{ J}} = 93.0 \text{ eV}$

b) photon energy.

c) $[Kr]3d^{10}4s^24p^6$.

d) To form a Xe^{21+} ion, the outer $5p^6$, $5s^2$ and the $4d^{10}$ electrons are removed. In addition, three electrons are removed from the $4p^6$ shell.

e) 57 photons with 93 eV photon energy must have been absorbed by the Xenon atom from the 10 fs XUV pulse.

f) 13.3 nm corresponds to 93 eV. In order to form a Xe^{21+} ion, 5300 eV are required. 93 eV is not enough energy to remove all of the electrons required from a Xenon atom to form a Xe^{21+} ion.

http://online.itp.ucsb.edu/online/atomixrays-c10/richter/pdf/Richter_XrayConf_
    KITP.pdf
http://photonscience.desy.de/news__events/news__highlights/archive/archive_
    of_2007/flash_photoelectric_effect_at_ultrahigh_intensities/index_eng.html

READING GUIDE

Concepts in this chapter include photons, light, the photoelectric effect, transitions in electronic energy levels, understanding the historical perspective how the model of the atom changed and the evidence leading to each change. These concepts are part of Unit 3. The drawing of orbitals, and learning quantum numbers are not part of the curriculum.

Schrödinger's Cat   Section 8.1

1. Why do we need to understand the properties and behaviors of electrons?

2. What is true of the quantum electron that is not true in the macroscopic world?

3. How did Erwin Schrödinger explain the quantum electron?*

4. What atom properties does the Quantum Mechanical Model explain?

The Nature of Light   Section 8.2

5. What atomic particle has characteristics similar to light? What is wave-particle duality?

6. What is electromagnetic radiation? Name two energies included in the electromagnetic spectrum.

7. Explain the difference between a magnetic field and an electric field. *Not directly tested on the AP Chemistry Exam. However, students should know how a magnetic field and an electric field operate together to make the electromagnetic spectrum.

8. Explain what happens when you see lightning and hear thunder.*

9. Draw a wave and label amplitude and wavelength. Which of these properties determines the color of light and which determines the intensity of the color?

10. What is the relationship between frequency and wavelength?

11. Explain the difference in frequency and wavelength in high-energy waves and low-energy waves.

12. Explain the concept of wave frequency and include the units it is measured in.

13. What is a hertz and what is its symbol?

14. What range of wave lengths exhibit visible light to the human eye? What colors are seen when white light passes through a prism?

15. What is the relationship between frequency and wave speed?

16. Write the equation relating wavelength to other wave parameters. Identify each of the variables in the equations and their units.

17. In visible light, which colors have the lowest energy light? Which colors have the highest energy?

18. Explain what determines the color of an object we see.

19. Make an electromagnetic spectrum chart indicating types of waves from lowest energy to highest energy.

20. Fill in the following table:

Wave Type	Source	Biological Impact
Gamma Rays		
X-rays		
UV Light		
Visible Light		
IR		
Microwaves		
Radio Waves		

21. What types of waves are called ionizing radiation? Explain why.

22. Explain how radiation therapy works.*

23. What are the possible side effects of radiation therapy?*

24. Using diagrams, explain the concept of constructive interference and destructive interference.

25. Explain the difference between interference and diffraction.

26. What is the photoelectric effect? How did data from photoelectric experiments change our understanding of the atom?

27. How did Albert Einstein explain the photoelectric effect?

28. What is a photon?

29. What is a threshold frequency for the photoelectric effect and when is it reached?

30. Explain the concept of wave-particle duality of an electron.

Section 8.3   Atomic Spectroscopy and the Bohr Model

31. Explain the concept of atomic spectroscopy?

32. Explain what happens when a gas-filled tube has an electric charge passed through it.

33. Fill in the following table:

Contained Gas Excited by Electrical Charge	Color
Hydrogen	
Helium	
Mercury	
Neon	

34. Explain what an emission spectrum is and what it can be used for.

35. Scientists have been analyzing selected stars. How do we know what elements comprise a star?*

36. What is the difference between white light and an emission spectrum of an element?

37. What discovery changed the classical physics view of particles only following Newton's laws of motion? How did the view change?

38. Who was Johannes Rydberg? What did he do to further our knowledge of the atom?

39. Who was Niels Bohr? What did he do to further our knowledge of the atom?

40. What processes are involved when radiation is emitted or absorbed in an atom?

41. What is a flame test? Why can it be used to identify elements?

42. Fill in the following table:

Element	Flame-Test Color
Sodium	
Potassium	
Lithium	
Barium	

43. What is the difference between an absorption spectrum and an emission spectrum? Which spectrum are flame tests based on?

44. What is unique about observations made when electrons change between energy states in an atom? What is true about the energy of the transition? Explain why classical physics could not explain this transition of electrons.

45. What types of transitions produce low-energy radiation? What types produce high-energy radiation?

The Wave Nature of Matter: The de Broglie Wavelength, the Uncertainty Principle, and Indeterminacy

Section 8.4

46. Who was Louis de Broglie? What did he propose about the electron? What experimental evidence supported his claim?

47. Draw a picture showing what happens when a beam of electrons is passed through a slit. How was this different than what scientists at the time expected?

48. How is an electron like Schrödinger's cat?*

49. What is the de Broglie Relation and what can it tell us?

50. What is the relationship between the wavelength of an electron and its momentum?

51. What do you observe when a beam of electrons goes through two narrow slits?

52. Why is it impossible to observe both the wave and particle nature of an electron at the same time? Why are these called complementary properties?

53. How are the complementary properties of an electron related to the Heisenberg Uncertainty Principle?

54. Explain what is meant by *deterministic*. Why are Newton's Laws deterministic?

55. Explain why electrons in atoms are not deterministic but show indeterminacy.

56. What is a probability distribution map? Why does one need them for electrons?

Section 8.5   Quantum Mechanics and the Atom

57. What type of properties are position and energy? What does this mean?

58. How should an electron's position best be described?

59. What is a *wave function*? What does the plot of the wave function squared represent?

60. What is an orbital? How many quantum numbers describe an orbital?

61. Identify each quantum number and its symbol. What information does each quantum number provide?

62. What equation can represent the energy of a principle quantum number?

63. Fill in the following table, identifying the energy of an electron in an orbital of hydrogen: $E_n = -2.18 \times 10 - 18J(1/n2)$

Principle Quantum Number	E_n
1	
2	
3	
4	

64. What quantum number describes the shape of an orbital?*

65. What quantum number describes the orientation of an orbital?*

66. What quantum number describes electron spin? What are the possible values of electron spin?*

67. Sketch a diagram showing orbitals in the first three energy levels and their first three quantum numbers (see page 333 of the text Chemistry A Molecular Approach AP* Edition by Tro).

68. How can the number of sublevels on any principle quantum number be determined?

69. How can you determine how many orbitals are in any sublevel?

70. How can you determine how many orbitals are in any principle quantum level?

71. What does each wavelength in an emission spectrum correspond to?

72. When does an atom emit light?

73. How can the energy of an atomic emission be determined? Include the equation and what all the variables represent.

74. What sign is given to the calculated energy in problem 73 and why?

75. What is the relationship between the wavelength and energy in electron transitions?

76. In the hydrogen atom, what type of transitions produce ultraviolet wavelengths? Visible wavelengths? Infrared wavelengths?

77. Determine the wavelength of light absorbed when an electron in a hydrogen atom makes a transition from an orbital $n = 2$ to $n = 7$. Show all your work.

The Shapes of Atomic Orbitals   Section 8.6

78. What is the shape of an s orbital?

79. Where is the highest probability of finding an electron in an s orbital?

80. What does a radial distribution function indicate?

81. Why is a radial distribution function more useful than a density in representing electron probability?

Note: Students will not make any calculations involving radial distribution functions on the AP Chemistry Exam.

82. What is an orbital node? Include a diagram in your answer.*

83. How many p orbitals are in any principle quantum level starting on $n = 2$?

84. What is the shape of a p orbital? Include a sketch of the p orbitals: p_x, p_y, and p_z. What is the difference between the three?

85. What is the difference in shape between a $2p$ orbital and a $3p$ orbital?

86. How many d orbitals are in any principle quantum number starting with $n = 3$?

87. Sketch the shapes of all the $3d$ orbitals. How do we tell them apart?*

88. How many *f* orbitals are on any principle quantum number starting with $n = 4$?

89. What is meant by the *phase of a wave*?

90. Why are atoms often represented as spheres regardless of the different orbital shapes?

Self-Assessment Answers

1. _____   2. _____   3. _____

4. _____   5. _____   7. _____

8. _____   10. _____

PERIODIC PROPERTIES OF THE ELEMENTS

This chapter explores the reasons for periodicity. A brief history is covered in Section 9.2: The Development of the Periodic Table. Although the history is fascinating, it is not a major concept in the AP Chemistry Curriculum. More important concepts include how to write electron configurations for atoms and ions and understand the trends in outer configurations (valence electrons) and how they relate to periodic trends in size of atoms, ionic radii, ionization energies, and electron affinities. The trends are explained using effective nuclear charge, Coulomb's law, and shielding. Trends can be observed both across the table (periods) or down the table (families or groups). The trends of properties in families can be addressed by looking at electron configurations within families. A good strategy on the AP Exam is to start by writing electron configurations on these type of questions. This chapter addresses several Learning Objectives in the AP Chemistry Curriculum. Although Section 9.9 has excellent data to analyze and examples from the alkali metals, halogens, and the noble gases that need to be reviewed, the most important sections are as follows:

9.3 **Electron Configurations: How Electrons Occupy Orbitals**

9.4 **Electron Configurations, Valence Electrons, and the Periodic Table**

9.6 **Periodic Trends in the Size of Atoms and Effective Nuclear Charge**

9.7 **Ions: Electron Configurations, Magnetic Properties, Ionic Radii, and Ionization Energy**

9.8 **Electron Affinities and Metallic Character**

Specific Learning Objectives Addressed in This Chapter:

SAP-1 Atoms and molecules can be identified by their electron distribution and energy.

SAP-1.A Represent the electron configuration of an element or ions of an element using the Aufbau principle.

SAP-1.B Explain the relationship between the photoelectron spectrum of an atom or ion and the electron configuration of the species, the interactions between the electrons and the nucleus.

SAP-2 The periodic table shows patterns in electronic structure and trends in atomic properties.

SAP-2.A Explain the relationship between trends in atomic properties of elements and electronic structure and periodicity.

SAP-2.B Explain the relationship between trends in the reactivity of elements and periodicity.

Concepts and Vocabulary to Review:

Section 9.2

The Development of the Periodic Table

As more elements were discovered, scientists began to notice recurring properties. These observations lead to the development of the periodic table where elements are organized by periodic properties. Scientists and their contributions to the periodic table:

Johann Döbereriner	Organized elements into triads such as calcium, barium, strontium
John Newlands	Organized table into octaves, noticing properties repeated every 8th element
Dmitri Mendeleev	Organized the elements by increasing mass and repeating properties; predicted germanium and its properties
Henri Mosley	Organized the elements by increasing atomic number and repeating properties

Section 9.3

Electron Configurations: How Electrons Occupy Orbitals

Electrons are important to understand as they are the particles involved in bonding. When all of the electrons in an atom are in their lowest possible energy state, the atom is said to be in its "ground state". Electron configurations are written to show how, according to the quantum model, the electrons occupy orbitals (defined energies and shapes calculated from mathematical models) in the atom. It is the arrangement of electrons that determines the chemical properties of an atom. Although orbitals generally do not exist in the absence of an electron, chemists often talk about them as if they do, using terms like *hold* or *occupy,* or even *unoccupied.* Any single orbital can be occupied by two electrons at the most (they must have opposite spins), but the different types of orbital sublevels can cluster to hold different maximum numbers of electrons. The *s* orbital can hold up to two electrons, the *p* orbital, with three sublevels, can hold up to six electrons (two in each sublevel), the *d* orbital, with five sublevels, can hold up to ten electrons, and the *f* orbital, with seven sublevels, can hold up to fourteen electrons.

Orbital	Number of Sublevels	Maximum Number of Electrons
s	1	2
p	3	6
d	5	10
f	7	14

While the skill of writing an atom's electron configuration and determining the number of valence electrons is important, students need to understand and be able to explain how trends in chemical properties of families and periods can be explained as a result of the changes in configurations.

Electron configurations indicate the energy level and orbital of all the electrons in an atom. For instance, the atom boron has the configuration $1s^2 2s^2 2p^1$ indicating it has two electrons in the first energy level and three electrons in the second energy level. The numbers in front of each orbital designation is the energy level or primary "shell". The orbitals, or *subshells*, are indicated by s, p, d, and f. The number of electrons present in each orbital is indicated by the superscript. If the superscripts are added together, this must equal the total number of electrons. If this is a neutral atom, this number will equal the proton number and hence the atomic number. In the neutral atom of sodium, there are 11 protons and therefore 11 electrons. It has the electron configuration $1s^2 2s^2 2p^6 3s^1$. The superscripts of $2 + 2 + 6 + 1 = 11$.

The Pauli exclusion principle indicates no two electrons can be in the same atom with the same set of four quantum numbers. Essesntially, this means no two electrons can be in the same place at the same time. AP Chemistry students will not be assessed on assigning quantum numbers to electrons. Students do need to understand how the Pauli exclusion principle relates to orbital diagrams and determining if an atom exhibits the property of paramagnetism or diamagnetism. The Pauli exclusion principle states when there are two electrons in the same orbital, they must have opposite spins. Orbital diagrams can be used to indicate if electrons are paired or unpaired in their orbitals. If one electron is in an orbital, it is represented by a half arrow going up in a box. If there are two electrons in an orbital, it is represented by a half arrow going up and a half arrow going down.

H
1s

Electron configuration   Orbital diagram
He $1s^2$
1s

If all electrons are paired, the atom is diamagnetic and will not be attracted to a magnetic field. If there are unpaired electrons, the atom is paramagnetic and will show an attraction to a magnetic field.

Another factor affecting how electrons fill orbitals is Hund's rule regarding sublevel energy splitting. When electrons fill sublevels of orbitals, such as $2p$ ($2p_x$, $2p_y$, and $2p_z$), the electrons will put one electron in each of the three 2*p* orbitals before the second electron of opposite spin is added to each of the orbitals. When looking at orbital diagrams of the atoms of boron, carbon, nitrogen, and oxygen, you can see this—parallel spins in equal energy orbitals are entered before pairing. Why? The electrons can spread out farther from each other reducing the repulsion between electrons. When all the suborbitals have only 1 electron with parallel spins, this is more stable due to the reduced repulsion.

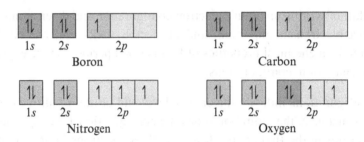

Figure 9.1

If the first electron in an orbital has an up spin, each sublevel of 2*p* has an up spin, then the next electron will be a down spin. Note that "up" and "down" are arbitrary indications, they just have to be opposites but by convention the up spin is entered first.

Coulomb's law states $E = \dfrac{q_1 q_2}{r}$ and this shows how the potential energy of two charged species depends on their charges ($q_1 q_2$) and on the distance between them (r). Note that q_1 and q_2 keep their signs as well as their value. For opposite charges, the potential energy is negative and becomes more negative as the particles get closer together. This means opposite charges attract each other. For like charges, the potential energy is positive and decreases as the electrons inhabit orbitals, on average, farther from the nucleus. This means when comparing two atoms within the same column (family) and with the same charge, the potential energy of the outermost electron decreases as the atoms get larger due to an increase in the average distance of the electron from the nucleus, which contains the protons.

The magnitude of the interaction between charged particles increases as the charge increases. Charges of +2 and −2 are more attracted to each other than charges of +1 and −1. Of course, *r* may not be the same so the value may not increase as much as expected. A + 1 and −2 are also more attracted than a + 1 and −1.

What affects the pull of the positively charged nucleus on the valence (outermost) electrons? Other than the distance described above, an additional factor is shielding. The more inner energy level orbitals between the outer electrons and the nucleus, the less pull from the nucleus will be on the outermost electrons. As you go down a family in the periodic table, the number of outer valence electrons is the same, but the number of lower energy levels between the nucleus and valence electrons increases. The inner core electrons occupy inner space, but also shield the valence electrons that are furthest from the nucleus from nuclear charge. Thus, the nuclear charge the outer electrons experience is reduced, and this is called the *effective nuclear charge* (Z_{eff}). The end result is a general ordering of how electrons fill orbitals by energy (strongest forces—most negative energy first) and this pattern is known as the Aufbau principle.

General Energy Ordering of Orbitals for Multielectron Atoms

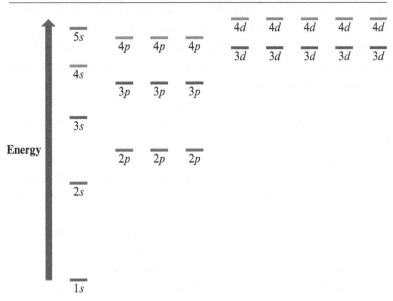

Figure 9.2 General Energy Ordering of Orbitals for Multielectron Atoms.

In general, the order is $1s$ $2s$ $2p$ $3s$ $3p$ $4s$ $3d$ $4p$ $5s$ $4d$ $5p$ $6s$ $4f$ $5d$ $6p$ $7s$ $5f$ $6d$ $7p$. Detailed energy considerations lead to a few irregularities in filling order, but they are not part of the AP curriculum. Students should be able to take an element on the periodic table and indicate its configuration without memorizing the order of filling. Knowing the placement of s, p, d, and f orbitals, a student should be able to follow the table to derive its electron configuration.

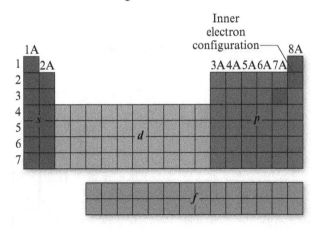

Nitrogen has seven electrons the first two would be in $1s$ then on the next period the next two electrons would be in $2s$ and then 3 electrons in $2p$.

Electron Configurations, Valence Electrons, and the Periodic Table

Section 9.4

There are two ways to write electron configurations. They can be written in the order in which orbitals fill using the Aufbau principle or they can be written by energy level. What is the difference? There is none when looking at atoms without d and f orbitals.

For instance, sodium would have the same configuration either way: $1s^2 2s^2 2p^6 3s^1$. However, if zinc is compared, they are different. In order of filling, zinc's configuration is $1s^2 2s^2 2p^6 3s^2 3p^6 4s^2 3d^{10}$. However, in order of decreasing energy level, the configuration is $1s^2 2s^2 2p^6 3s^2 3p^6 3d^{10} 4s^2$. Why would this be helpful? When electrons are removed from an atom, they are removed from the highest (least bound) energy level first. For zinc this would be the $4s^2$ electrons so the first electron removed from the zinc would be a $4s$ electron not a $3d$ electron. This also helps to identify core and valence electrons easily because the valence electrons are at the end of the configuration. On the AP exam, students should expect to see either method of writing configurations. Also, if students are asked to write a *complete configuration*, electron configurations must start with $1s$. An abbreviated configuration starting with a noble gas such as $[Ar]4s^1$ for potassium is not acceptable as a *complete* electron configuration.

If all elements' electron configurations are put in sequence on the periodic table, patterns of arrangement emerge. Atoms in the same column (family) all have the same number of valence electrons (outer) in the same type of orbital. For instance, all of column one are the alkali metals, which all end in an s^1 configuration. The difference is the energy level, n. When comparing three alkali metal electron configurations, we can observe lithium ends in $2s^1$, sodium ends in $3s^1$, and potassium ends in $4s^1$. It is the electron that gives rise to periodic properties.

Notice on the periodic table the sequence in *s, p, d,* and *f* filling is apparent. From knowing the location of atoms ending in an *s, p, d,* or *f* orbital, a student should be able to determine a complete configuration of any atom by simply following the table. For instance, on the table, the first orbital is $1s$, the next orbital is $2s$, and then

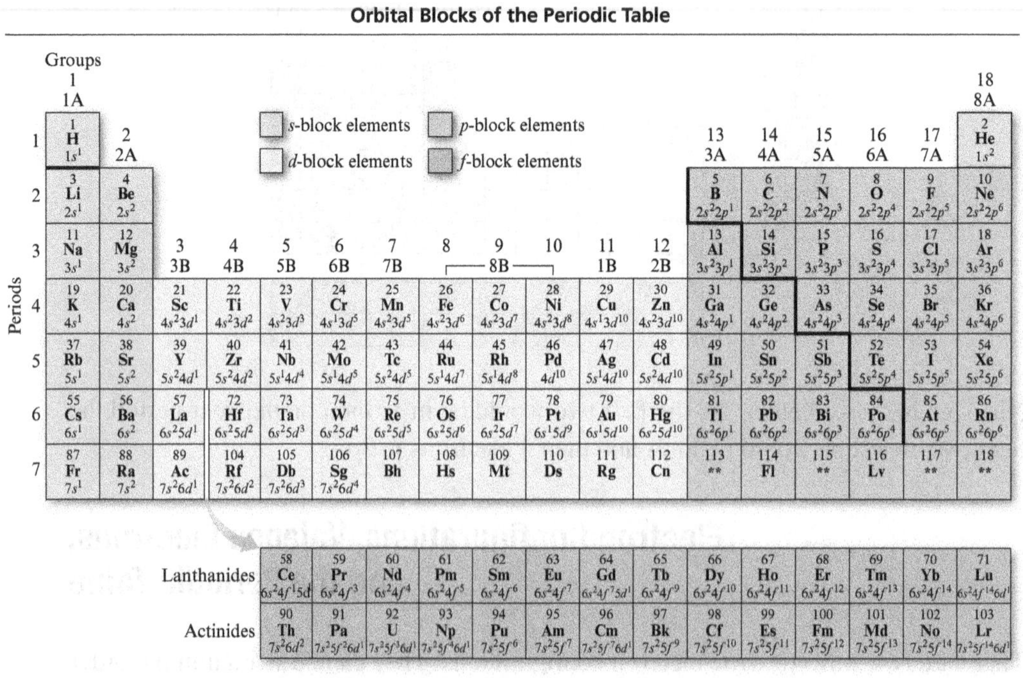

Orbital Blocks of the Periodic Table

Figure 9.3 The *s, p, d,* and *f* Blocks of the Periodic Table.

2p. When considering atoms with d and f orbitals, the d orbital number is one behind the row number and the f orbital number is two behind the row number. Looking at the periodic table, 4s is followed by 3d, 5s is followed by 4d, 6s is followed by 4f, and then 5d, whereas 7s is followed by 5s and then 6d. As noted above, any exceptions in filling, such as chromium and copper, need not be memorized but students may be asked to explain why the exception occurs.

Periodic Trends in the Size of Atoms and Effective Nuclear Charge

Section 9.6

To determine the radius of an atom, the distance between the nuclei of two atoms is measured. Half this distance is the radius. This is called *van der Waals radius*.

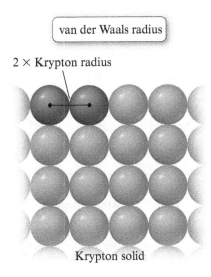

Figure 9.4 The van der Waals radius of an atom is one-half the distance between adjacent nuclei in the atomic solid.

If atoms are chemically bonded, then the radius has a different value and is found to be different in nonmetals and metals. In nonmetals, it is half the distance between the nuclei of the two atoms bonded together, whereas in metals it is half the distance

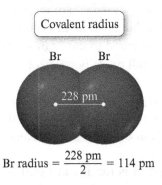

$$\text{Br radius} = \frac{228 \text{ pm}}{2} = 114 \text{ pm}$$

Figure 9.5 The covalent radius of bromine is one-half the distance between two bonded bromine atoms.

between the nuclei of two atoms in a crystal of the metal. When an atom bonds to an-other atom, the radius is always less than the van der Waals radius of the atom. How the radius is determined is not tested by AP.

When comparing atoms in families and periods, trends in the radii can be observed.

Atomic Radii

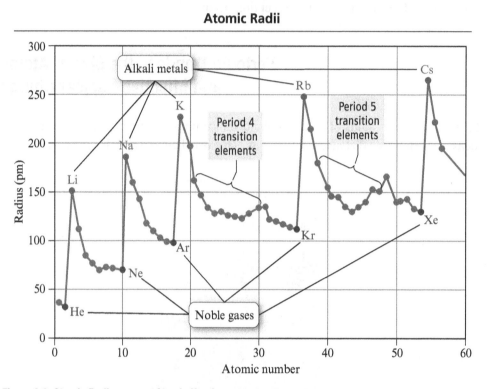

Figure 9.6 Atomic Radius versus Atomic Number   Notice the periodic trend in atomic radius, starting at a peak with each alkali metal and falling to a minimum with each noble gas.

When students are asked to explain these trends, they need to use the concepts of shielding and effective nuclear charge, depending on the atoms being compared. An explanation of why the potassium atom is larger than the sodium atom is NOT the trend is atoms get larger going down a column. This may be the trend, but is NOT the explanation for the trend. To get credit for their answer the student is expected to explain the additional energy level and the further distance from the nucleus of the outer valence electrons in potassium with $1s^2 2s^2 2p^6 3s^2 3p^6 4s^1$ compared to sodium with $1s^2 2s^2 2p^6 3s^1$. An acceptable answer would be: Even though both potassium and sodium end in an s^1 configuration, potassium has an ad-ditional energy level of $4s$ compared to the $3s$ of sodium. The $4s$ is further from the nucleus and has less nuclear pull on its outer electron. This results in a larger atom.

If a test question asks for a comparison, be sure to address both species being asked about and a good start is to begin by writing the electron configuration of both species. Often, the answer will be apparent from similarities or differences in electron configurations.

Effective nuclear charge (Z_{eff}) is the inward pull of the outer valence electrons by the unscreened positive charge of the nucleus. The more tightly an electron is held, the harder it is to remove. Going down a column on the periodic table,

Trends in Atomic Radius

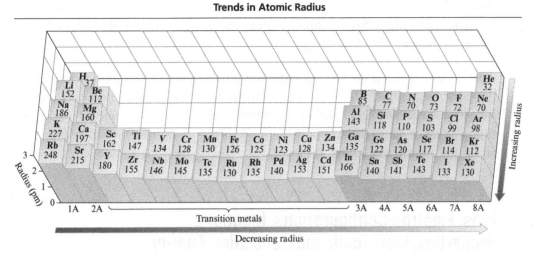

Figure 9.7 Trends in Atomic Radius   In general, atomic radii increase as we move down a column and decrease as we move to the right across a period in the periodic table.

additional orbitals are between the nucleus and the outermost electrons. This increase in shielding of the outer electrons reduces the effective pull of the positive nucleus and therefore nuclear charge. Comparing a $4s^1$ electron to a $5s^1$ electron, the $5s^1$ electron that is further from the nucleus is easier to remove.

The Z_{eff} experienced by an electron is the actual nuclear charge (Z) which is the number of protons minus the number of core electrons (S). $Z_{eff} = Z - S$. In the example for lithium in Figure 9.8, the effective nuclear charge is $3+ - 2 = 1+$.

Effective nuclear charge experienced across a period increases. The amount of shielding remains the same since all electrons are in the same energy level while the number of protons in the nucleus increases giving rise to a greater nuclear

Shielding and Effective Nuclear Charge

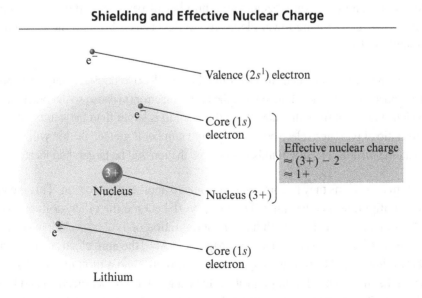

Figure 9.8 Shielding and Effective Nuclear Charge   The valence electron in lithium experiences the 3+ charge of the nucleus through the screen of the 2− charge of the core electrons. The effective nuclear charge acting on the valence electron is approximately 1+.

charge. This increases the attraction between the nucleus and the outer electrons. Comparing beryllium to the lithium example above $Z_{eff} = Z - S$ is $4 + -2 = 2+$ indicating an increased nuclear charge.

Across the transition metals, the radii and effective nuclear charge are relatively the same since inner electrons are being filled and the outer electrons are the s electrons. For instance, in filling $3d$, atoms scandium through zinc, electrons are filling an inner 3d, so the size of the atom does not change very much and in these atoms the outer electrons are $4s$ electrons.

Section 9.7   Ions: Electron Configurations, Magnetic Properties, Ionic Radii, and Ionization Energy

While how to write an electron configuration can be a question by itself on the AP exam, they can be used in answers to explain periodic properties and/or explain trends in atomic properties based on their location on the periodic table. When writing an electron configuration of an ion, it is important to understand the difference between anions and cations. Anions add electrons to form a negatively charged species whereas cations have lost one or more electrons to form a positively charged species. When subtracting electrons, students must understand they are removed from the outermost energy level first, which is not necessarily the last orbital filled in the periodic table sequence which is the case for the nonrepresentative elements. For instance, zinc has the configuration $1s^2 2s^2 2p^6 3s^2 3p^6 4s^2 3d^{10}$, but when the zinc forms its +2 cation, the configuration becomes $1s^2 2s^2 2p^6 3s^2 3p^6 3d^{10}$. The entire $4s$ orbital is not present. This is when it is beneficial to write configurations in order of energy level showing the 4s at the end. $1s^2 2s^2 3s^2 3p^6 3d^{10} 4s^2$ as this shows the $4s$ clearly is the furthest from the nucleus and will be removed first. Cations have smaller radii than their atoms because the number of protons in the nucleus has not changed, however, there are fewer electrons, so the protons have an increased pull on the remaining electrons.

For anions, the additional electrons result in a lower effective nuclear charge because the proton number again has not changed, but the added electron(s) cause so the outer electrons to experience less pull from the nucleus, and the anion is larger than the neutral atom. The key is the ratio of protons to electrons. If the proton number is greater, the ion will be smaller than its atom and if the electron number is greater, the ion will be larger than its atom.

When atoms form ions they become isoelectronic to another atom or ion. This means the electron configuration is the same. They DO NOT become the other atom or ion. Na^+ is isoelectronic to neon. They both have a configuration of $1s^2 2s^2 2p^6$. When comparing Z_{eff} for isoelectronic species such as Na^+, Mg^{2+} and Al^{3+}, the core electrons in each case is 10 but sodium has 11 protons, magnesium 12 protons, and aluminum has 13 protons pulling on the them. The aluminum protons have a greater pull per electron and hence is a smaller ion. See figure 9.9. In contrast, for species such as O^{2-} and F^- which are also isoelectronic to neon with 10 electrons, the oxide ion has 8 protons and the fluoride ion

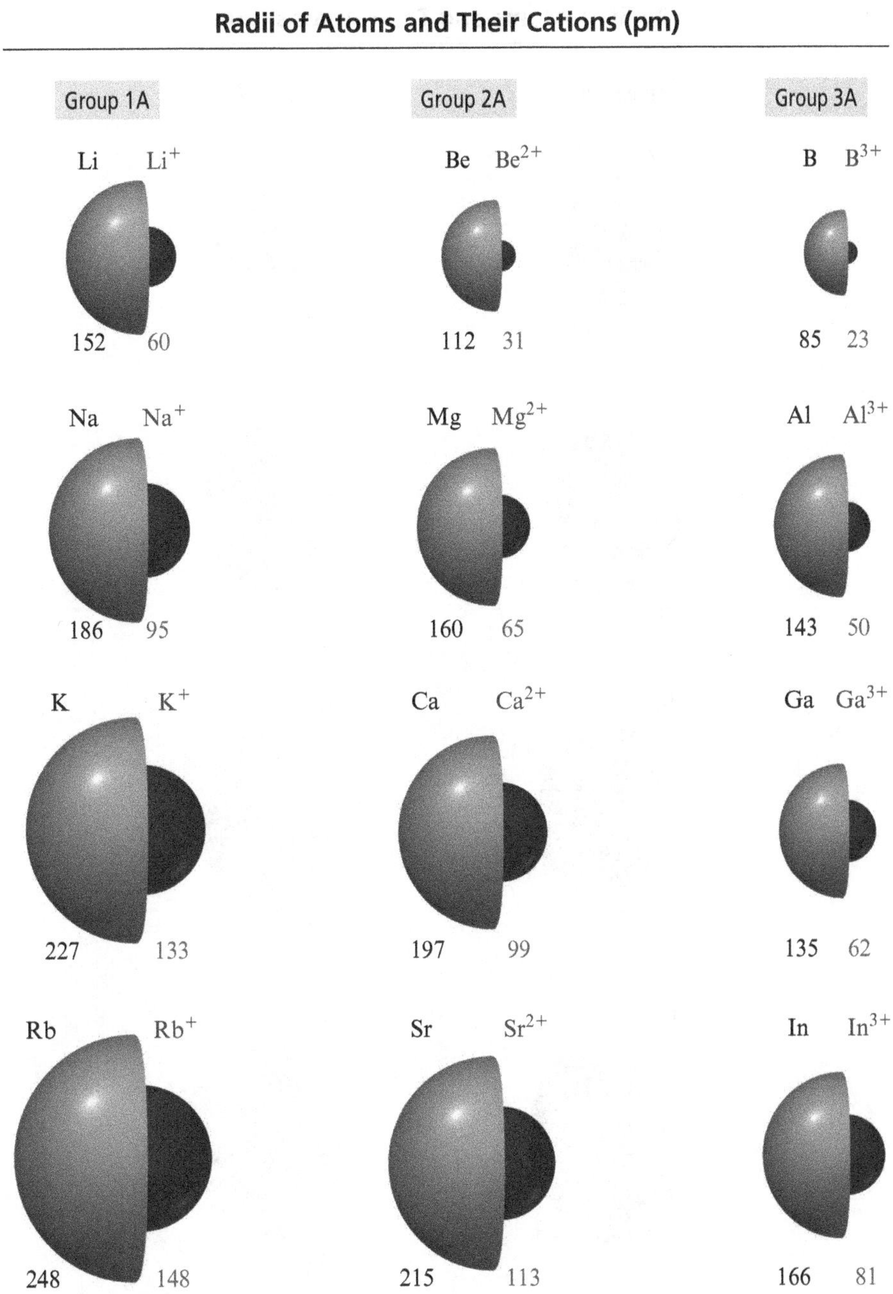

Radii of Atoms and Their Cations (pm)

Group 1A	Group 2A	Group 3A

Li Li$^+$	Be Be^{2+}	B B^{3+}
152 60	112 31	85 23
Na Na$^+$	Mg Mg^{2+}	Al Al^{3+}
186 95	160 65	143 50
K K$^+$	Ca Ca^{2+}	Ga Ga^{3+}
227 133	197 99	135 62
Rb Rb$^+$	Sr Sr^{2+}	In In^{3+}
248 148	215 113	166 81

Figure 9.9 Sizes of Atoms and Their Cations   Atomic and ionic radii (pm) for the first three columns of main-group elements.

has 9 protons. The pull per proton is less for oxide so it is larger than the fluoride ion. See figure 9.10.

When looking at electron configurations of atoms or ions, if the orbital diagram shows unpaired electrons, the species will be paramagnetic. The unpaired electron(s) generates a magnetic field and is attracted to an external magnetic field. If all the electrons in a species are paired, the species will not be attracted to a magnetic field. This is called *diamagnetic*. In general, only the atoms in columns 2A, 2B, and 8A of the periodic table have all electrons paired and are the only diamagnetic elements. This is due to Hund's Rule.

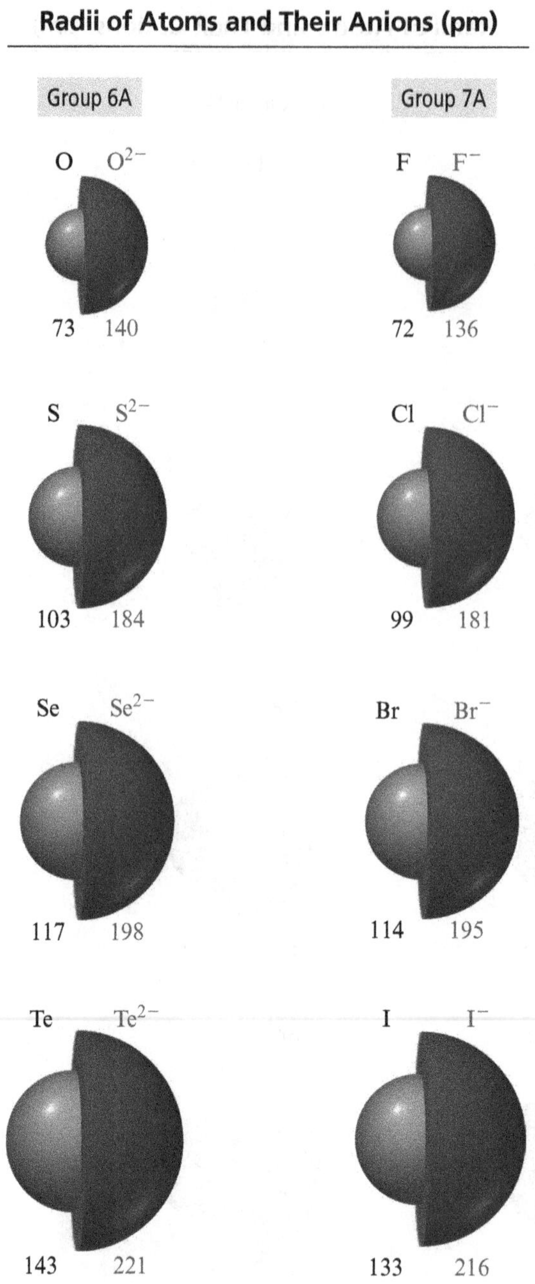

Radii of Atoms and Their Anions (pm)

Group 6A		Group 7A	
O	O^{2-}	F	F$^-$
73	140	72	136
S	S^{2-}	Cl	Cl$^-$
103	184	99	181
Se	Se^{2-}	Br	Br$^-$
117	198	114	195
Te	Te^{2-}	I	I$^-$
143	221	133	216

Figure 9.10 Sizes of Atoms and Their Anions   Atomic and ionic radii for groups 6A and 7A in the periodic table.

Ionization energy (IE) is defined as the energy required to remove an electron from an atom or ion in its gaseous state. The energy required to remove an electron is always defined as positive because an input in energy is required. A sample equation would be $Na(g) \rightarrow Na^+(g) + 1e^-$. The amount of energy needed to remove an outer electron depends upon the force of attraction between the electron and the effective nuclear charge (protons in the nucleus minus screening electrons). When comparing sodium and potassium, the outer electron in potassium is further away from the nucleus in a 4s and therefore not held as tightly and will be easier to remove than the outer electron in sodium which is in a 3s.

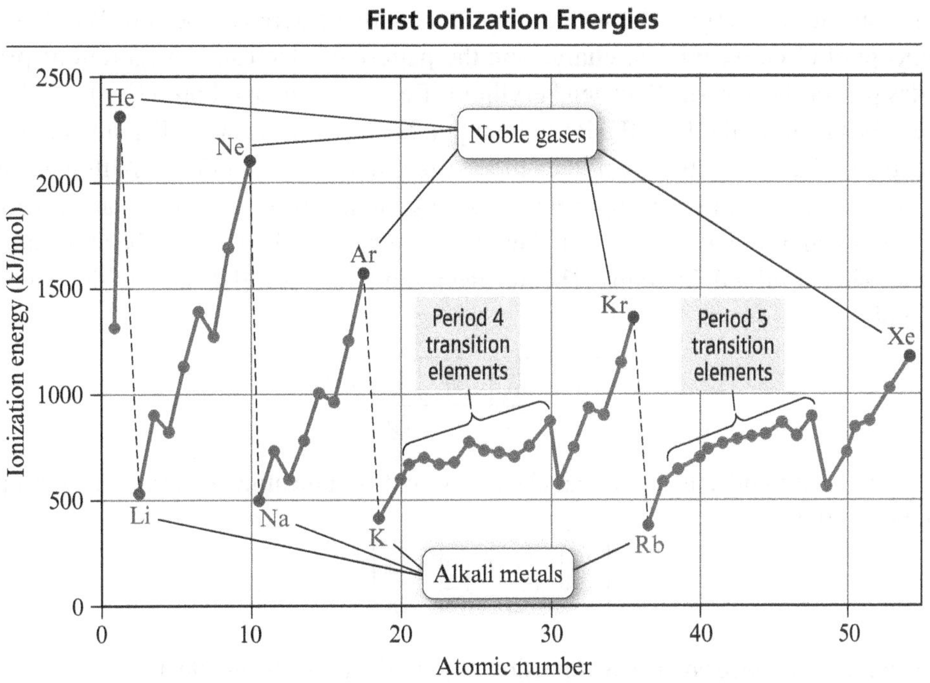

First Ionization Energies

Figure 9.11 First Ionization Energy versus Atomic Number for the Elements through Xenon First ionization energy starts at a minimum with each alkali metal and rises to a peak with each noble gas.

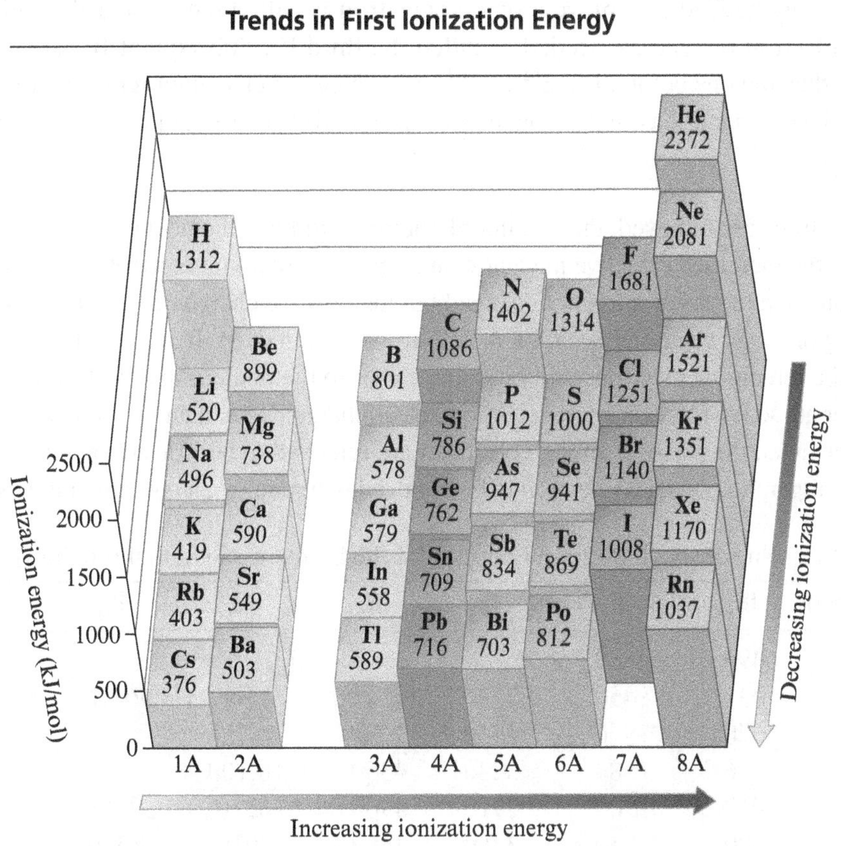

Trends in First Ionization Energy

Figure 9.12 Trends in Ionization Energy   First ionization energy increases as we move to the right across a period and decreases as we move down a column in the periodic table.

The ionization energies do not consistently increase across a period. Why? The concept of effective nuclear charge and the pattern of electron configurations provides part of the answer. Between beryllium (Be) $1s^2 2s^2 2p^1$ and boron (B) $1s^2 2s^2 2p^2$, there is a drop in the first IE. Be is losing a $2s$ electron, whereas B is losing a $2p$ electron. The $2p$ electron is higher in energy and easier to remove. Although the atoms following are also losing p electrons, this still needs more energy than the $2s$ of Be. Between nitrogen and oxygen, there is also a drop in IE. This can be understood by looking at orbital diagrams. The nitrogen family has parallel spins in the outer p orbitals.

In the oxygen family, an additional electron is added, indicating a pairing of electrons in the p_x orbital.

The additional electron causes repulsion among the two pairing electrons, making it easier to remove the electron. When all the outer p orbitals have parallel spins, there is reduced repulsion (Hund's rule) and the species is more stable.

The energy needed to remove a second electron is called the second IE, and for a third electron the energy needed is called the third IE. Subsequent IEs are always larger than the one before, i.e., $3^{rd} > 2^{nd} > 1^{st}$. Note—you cannot remove more electrons than a species has, so hydrogen only has one IE because it only has one electron to remove.

As electrons are removed, the amount of energy to remove the next electron increases due to the increased effective nuclear charge on the remaining electrons. The number of protons in the species has not changed but the positive charge of the nucleus is they pulling on fewer electrons as additional electrons are removed. If an orbital shell is also lost, the remaining electrons will be much closer to the nucleus and will experience a greater attractive force as a result of the nuclear charge. Note, again the nuclear charge has remained the same. If enough electrons are removed to be isoelectronic to a noble gas configuration, the next electron to be removed will require a larger amount in energy

Table 9.1 Successive Ionization Energies for the Elements Sodium through Argon (kJ/mol)

Element	IE$_1$	IE$_2$	IE$_3$	IE$_4$	IE$_5$	IE$_6$	IE$_7$
Na	496	4560					
Mg	738	1450	7730		Core electrons		
Al	578	1820	2750	11,600			
Si	786	1580	3230	4360	16,100		
P	1012	1900	2910	4960	6270	22,200	
S	1000	2250	3360	4560	7010	8500	27,100
Cl	1251	2300	3820	5160	6540	9460	11,000
Ar	1521	2670	3930	5770	7240	8780	12,000

due to the loss of an energy level resulting in the outermost electrons being closer to the nucleus and therefore experiencing greater pull from the protons in the nucleus.

Electron Affinities and Metallic Character   Section 9.8

Electron affinity is the energy change upon the addition of an electron to an atom in its gaseous state. Affinities do not exhibit any definite trends although in general most affinities are negative and when orbitals are full like in the noble gases, it takes energy to add an electron.

Electron Affinities (kJ/mol)

1A							8A
H −73	2A	3A	4A	5A	6A	7A	**He** >0
Li −60	**Be** >0	**B** −27	**C** −122	**N** >0	**O** −141	**F** −328	**Ne** >0
Na −53	**Mg** >0	**Al** −43	**Si** −134	**P** −72	**S** −200	**Cl** −349	**Ar** >0
K −48	**Ca** −2	**Ga** −30	**Ge** −119	**As** −78	**Se** −195	**Br** −325	**Kr** >0
Rb −47	**Sr** −5	**In** −30	**Sn** −107	**Sb** −103	**Te** −190	**I** −295	**Xe** >0

Figure 9.13 Electron Affinities of Selected Main-Group Elements

Metals tend to lose electrons therefore metallic character decreases across a period. The cations are on the left and anions are on the right. Moving down a column, metallic character increases as the electrons are not held as tightly and are easier to remove.

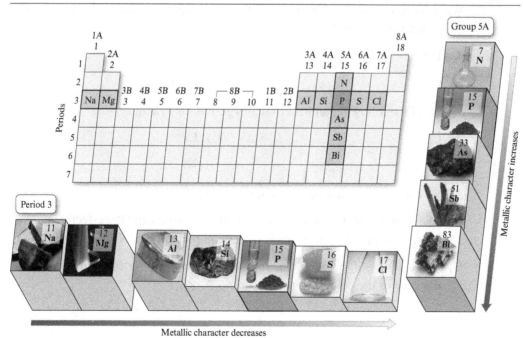

Figure 9.14 Trends in Metallic Character II   As we move down group 5A in the periodic table, metallic character increases. As we move across period 3, metallic character decreases.

Additional Practice

Self-Assessment Quiz Questions Q1, Q2, Q3, Q4, Q6, Q7, Q8, Q9, Q10, Q11, Q12, Q13, Q14, and Q15

Problems:

Review Questions 8, 9, 12, 14, 17, 20, 21, 25, 27, 28, 30, 31, 35, 36, 37, and 38

Electron Configurations 41, 43, 44, 47, and 48

Valence Electrons and Simple Chemical Behavior from the Periodic Table 49–52

Coulomb's Law and Effective Nuclear Charge 53–57

Atomic Radius 61

Ionic Electron Configurations, Ionic Radius, Magnetic Properties, and Ionization Energy 62, 65, 67, and 72

Electron Affinity and Metallic Character 78

Cumulative Problems 85, 87, 88, 89, 90, 91, 105, and 106

Conceptual Problems 125

Data Interpretation and Analysis 133

Practice AP Test Questions

1. An element from Group 2, X, reacts with chlorine gas. What is the formula of the most likely product formed?

    A) XCl

    B) XCl_2

    C) XCl_3

    D) X_2Cl_2

2. When an active metal, M, reacts with water, which substance is always one of the products produced?

    A) H_2O

    B) O_2

    C) H_2

    D) MOH

3. Which of the following atoms has the largest atomic radius?

    A) Ca

    B) V

    C) Cr

    D) Ni

4. A Na^+ cation is smaller than a Na atom because:

    A) The sodium cation has more protons than electrons and the effective nuclear charge on the outer electrons is larger compared to the Na atom.

    B) The distance of the outer electrons to the nucleus is shorter compared to the distance of the outer electron in Na^+.

C) Coulombic forces between the protons in the sodium cation are greater than Coulombic forces between the sodium atom's proton and outer electrons.

D) The sodium cation has one less electron compared to the sodium atom. Fewer electrons in the sodium cation occupy less space compared to the electrons in the sodium atom.

5. Which atom has the largest first ionization energy in units of kJ/mol?

A) Na

B) Rb

C) Mg

D) Sr

6. Which has a lower ionization energy, Na^+ or Mg^+?

A) Na^+ because the second ionization will remove a core electron.

B) Mg^+ because the second ionization will remove a 3s electron.

C) Mg^+ because Mg has a larger nuclear charge than Na.

D) Na^+ because its smaller radius causes a larger nucleus/electron attraction.

7. Which half-equation represents the second ionization energy of magnesium?

A) $Mg\,(g) \rightarrow Mg^+\,(g) + e^-$

B) $Mg^+\,(g) + e^- \rightarrow Mg\,(g)$

C) $Mg^-\,(g) + e^- \rightarrow Mg^{2-}\,(g)$

D) $Mg^+\,(g) \rightarrow Mg^{2+}\,(g) + e^-$

8. Elements having the outermost electron configuration ns^2np^3 are found in which area of the periodic table?

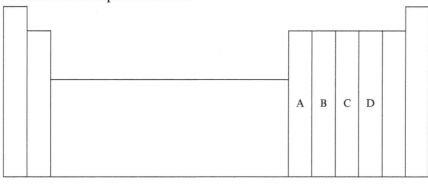

A) A   B) B   C) C   D) D

9. What neutral atom of an element has the ground state electronic configuration $1s^2 2s^2 2p^4$?

   A) Beryllium

   B) Oxygen

   C) Fluorine

   D) Neon

10. Among the alkali metals, cesium reacts more rapidly than sodium. What is one reason for this?

    A) Cesium has a higher nuclear charge.

    B) The valence electron in cesium is at a greater average distance from the nucleus compared to the valence electron in sodium.

    C) Cesium has a higher atomic weight than sodium.

    D) Cesium has more electrons compared to sodium.

Chapter 9 Practice AP Test Questions Answers:

1. B); 2. C); 3. A); 4. C); 5. D); 6. B); 7. D); 8. C); 9. B); 10. B)

Data Interpretation and Analysis Question: Periodic Properties of the Elements Mg^{2+} and ATP

The structure for ATP, adenosine triphosphate, is as follows.

The acidic hydrogens in the phosphate groups react with water to leave the ATP^{4-} ion.

Magnesium 2+ ions are responsible for stabilizing phosphate compounds in the cells. Without sufficient levels of Mg^{2+} ions, the nutrients in food could not be metabolized into energy. Mg^{2+} ions can bind with two or three of the charged phosphate groups.

a) Draw a structure showing a Mg^{2+} ion binding with two phosphate groups in ATP^{4-}.

b) Draw a structure showing a Mg^{2+} ion binding with three phosphate groups in ATP^{4-}. Pay particular attention to keeping the Mg^{2+} to oxygen interactions the same distance. What does this do to the shape of ATP?

c) Although many different types of metal ions are available, ATP^{4-} ions bind preferentially with Mg^{2+} ions. Explain the trend in Group 2A metal ions binding with ATP: $Mg^{2+} > Ca^{2+} > Sr^{2+} > Ba^{2+}$.

d) Group 1A metal cations can also bind with ATP. Arrange the following Group 1A metal cations with respect to preference in binding to ATP^{4-} : Li^+, Na^+, K^+.

e) Would you expect the binding preference to ATP to be greater, less, or the same compared to the binding preference of the Group 2A cations.

Data Interpretation and Analysis Question Answers with Brief Explanations

a) and b)

Modes by which Mg^{2+} provides
stability to ATP.

c) Mg^{2+} is the smallest and has the largest charge density. Ba^{2+} is the largest of the Group 2A ions. It will not polarize the P-O linkages of the phosphate groups as well as Mg^{2+}. Mg^{2+} polarizes the P-O linkages of the phosphate groups the best.

d) Li^+ is the smallest ion of the Group 1A ions, and it has the largest charge density. K^+ is the largest of the Group 1A ions and has a smaller charge density compared to Li^+. Li^+ will have a greater tendency to bind to ATP compared to the other Group 1A cations.

e) The Group 1A cations will have less tendency to bind to ATP compared to the Group 2A ions because their charge density is less and they will not polarize the oxygen to phosphorus bond.

READING GUIDE

Understanding the arrangement of the elements in periodic table is key foundational knowledge in chemistry. The relationships and patterns observed explain trends of the elements. The emphasis in AP Chemistry is the explanation of the concepts not memorizing trends. For example, the size of atoms in Group 1 decreases as you go down a column. This is a trend. However, the explanation of the trend requires a student to know how to apply Coulomb's force law to charge particles and effective nuclear charge. This material is found in the AP Chemistry curriculum in Unit 1. Terms in this chapter not used in the AP curriculum include *oxidizing agent* and *reducing agent*.

Nerve Signal Transmission   Section 9.1

1. What is meant by *ion pumping*? What ion is pumped out of cells? What ion is pumped into cells?*

2. What is a chemical gradient?*

3. Explain what an ion channel is and include an example.*

4. Explain what a periodic property is and provide an example.

The Development of the Periodic Table   Section 9.2

5. How did Johann Döbereiner organize the elements?

6. How did John Newlands arrange the elements?

7. How did Dmitri Mendeleev arrange the elements in the periodic table? What other chemists suggest a similar table? Why did different scientists arrange the elements in different ways? Why has Mendeleev's arrangement of the periodic table survived until today?

8. What elements did Mendeleev predict would be found?

9. What did Henry Mosley add to the way the elements were arranged in the periodic table?

Electron Configurations: How Electrons Occupy Orbitals   Section 9.3

10. What is meant by electron configuration? What does it describe?

11. Define ground state of an atom. Where are electrons generally found?

12. What is electron spin?

13. What is sublevel-energy splitting?

14. What does an orbital drawing indicate? Use a hydrogen atom to explain.

15. What are the two possible spin states of an electron? How are they indicated in an orbital diagram?

16. Explain the Pauli exclusion principle.

17. What are degenerate orbitals? Use phosphorus to help explain why multi electron atoms are not degenerate. In a principle energy level, what is the order of energy in the sublevels?

18. What three concepts need to be understood to put the energy sublevels in correct order?

19. Describe three conclusions that can be made about attractions and repulsions from Coulomb's law.

20. What is shielding in an atom? What does it help explain about atomic properties?

21. What is effective nuclear charge? What does it help explain about atomic properties?

22. What is the difference between shielding and effective nuclear charge? What is orbital penetration? How do these concepts help explain atomic properties?

23. Explain why a $2s$ orbital experiences greater nuclear charge than $2p$ orbitals.

24. Write the order of the orbitals from $1s$ though $4d$ in order of increasing electron energy.

25. What is the aufbau principle?

26. Explain Hund's rule. Why does this occur?

27. Summarize the rules of orbital filling.

28. Explain how to write an electron configuration. Write the electron configurations and make orbital drawings of the following atoms:

   Carbon:

   Oxygen:

   Sodium:

29. Write the inner configuration of sodium.

Section 9.4   Electron Configurations, Valence Electrons, and the Periodic Table

30. Draw an outline of the periodic table and use it to explain how the electrons fill orbitals.

31. What is the difference between core and valence electrons in an atom? Explain using a Period 2 element as an example.

32. In a ground state atom, which electrons considered valence electrons?

33. What is the general outer electron configuration of alkali metals? Alkaline earth metals? Halogens? Noble gases?

34. Where are the inner transition metals located on the periodic table? Why are they called *inner*?

35. Sketch a periodic table. Identify the location of atoms that are filling their last electrons in *s*, *p*, *d*, and *f* orbitals.

36. Why is the *s* block being filled only in two columns in the periodic table?

37. Explain how to look at the periodic table and determine the number of valence electrons in any ground-state atom.

38. What does the configuration $1s^2 2s^2 2p^3$ indicate about the number of orbitals, orbital sublevel splitting, and Hund's rule? Explain how the principle quantum number (energy level) of *f* orbitals compares to its row number on the periodic table?

39. Explain how the principle quantum number (energy level) of *d* orbitals compares to its row number on the periodic table?

Note: For the AP Chemistry Exam, students will not have to assign quantum numbers to electrons. However, students do have to know the quantum mechanical model.

40. Write the electron configurations of chromium and copper and explain why these electron configurations are exceptions to the filling rule.

Note: For the AP Chemistry Exam, students will not have to memorize the exceptions to the Aufbau principle. However, if told certain elements are exceptions, students should be able to provide reasons based on theory for the exception.

The Explanatory Power of the Quantum Mechanical Model

Section 9.5

41. How do the electron configurations of the elements in a column of the periodic table correspond to the properties of the elements in the column?

42. Explain why noble gases are the most chemically stable elements? Why are they less stable going down the column from He to Xe?

43. Which metals are the most reactive? Explain why. Include an electron configuration in your explanation.

44. Which group of nonmetals are the most reactive? Explain why.

Section 9.6

Periodic Trends in the Size of Atoms and Effective Nuclear Charge

45. How is the nonbonding atomic radius of an atom determined?

46. What is another term for the nonbonding atomic radius?

47. Explain how to determine the bonding radius in metals and in nonmetals.

48. What is another name for the bonding radius?

49. Define atomic radius. Include a drawing in your answer.

50. Describe what is observed when comparing atomic radii as one goes down a column on the periodic table. Explain the reason for the observed trend. Include a graph with your explanation.

51. Describe what is observed when comparing atomic radii as one goes across a period of the representative elements on the periodic table. Explain the reason for the observed trend. Include a graph with your explanation.

52. What is effective nuclear charge? How is effective nuclear charge of an atom determined? Include an equation in your answer. Explain why it takes more energy to remove an electron from He than H.

53. Explain how core electrons affect effective nuclear charge. Explain how valence electrons affect effective nuclear charge.

54. Across a period, how does an increased nuclear charge affect atom size? Explain.

55. Identify and explain why some elements are called transition metals. What is observed in the atomic radii of transition metals while moving across a period on the periodic table? Why does this occur?

Section 9.7

Ions: Electron Configurations, Magnetic Properties, Ionic Radii, and Ionization Energy

56. Explain how to determine the number of electrons in an anion. How do you write the electron configuration of an anion? Provide an example.

57. Explain how to determine the number of electrons in a cation. How do you determine the electron configuration of a cation? Provide an example.

58. Explain why the last electron orbital to be occupied in the neutral atom is not always the first electron to be removed when the atom forms a cation. Use scandium, Sc, as an example in your explanation.

59. Define paramagnetic. How can paramagnetism be predicted for an atom from its electron-filled orbital diagram? Provide an example of an atom or molecule that exhibits paramagnetic behavior.

60. Define diamagnetic. How can diamagnetism be predicted for an atom from its filled electron orbital diagram? Provide an example of an atom or molecule that exhibits diamagnetic behavior.

61. Explain what happens to an atomic radius when a cation forms. Explain why this occurs.

62. Explain what happens to an atomic radius when an anion forms. Explain why this occurs.

63. Define isoelectronic and include an example of three isoelectronic species in your answer.

64. Define ionization energy. Write an equation representing the process of ionization energy.

65. Is ionization energy defined as positive or negative value? Explain why.

66. Explain the difference between IE_1, IE_2, and IE_3 using lithium as an example.

67. Explain what is observed in the trend of first ionization energies in the period from Li to Ne. Use a diagram to support your answer.

68. Explain the trend in ionization energy between Be and B. Explain why it occurs.

69. Explain the trend in ionization energy between N and O. Explain why it occurs.

70. How does the second ionization energy of an element compare to its third ionization energy? Explain why.

71. When comparing successive ionization energies of elements in the periodic table, when would a large increase in the ionization energy of an atom be expected to be observed?

Electron Affinities and Metallic Character   Section 9.8

72. What is electron affinity? Write an equation representing the process of electron affinity.

73. Explain the electron affinity trends in the main group elements across a period and down a column.

74. Explain why the trend in electron affinity occurs.

75. Explain metallic character and identify typical trends of metallic character across a period and down a column.

76. Explain why metals have the following properties but non-metals do not have these properties.

Conductivity:

Malleability:

Ductility:

77. Explain why metallic character trends occur.

Section 9.9   **Periodic Trends Summary**

78. Which trends decrease down a column and why?

79. Which trends increase across a period and why? Which trends decrease across a row and why?

Self-Assessment Answers

1. _____   2. _____   3. _____

4. _____   5. _____   6. _____

7. _____   8. _____   9. _____

10. _____   11. _____   12. _____

13. _____   14. _____   15. _____

CHAPTER

10

CHEMICAL BONDING I: THE LEWIS MODEL

The majority of this chapter is covered in the AP Chemistry curriculum. However, it is important to note the AP focus is on understanding the principles, not on memorizing details such as electronegativity of carbon. These details should only be studied as examples of how to explain/demonstrate principles, and not as a set of facts to be memorized. Students are expected to understand Lewis, Valence Shell Electron Pair Repulsion, and Molecular Orbital theories of bonding. The Lewis theory is covered in this chapter and the other two theories are covered in Chapter 11. Understanding this chapter is crucial to several aspects of chemistry. One must understand not only Lewis structures, but also what those structures indicate in terms of molecule characteristic properties. The sections of the chapter to study include:

10.2 **Types of Chemical Bonds**

10.3 **Representing Valence Electrons with Dots**

10.4 **Ionic Bonding: Lewis Symbols and Lattice Energies**

10.5 **Covalent Bonding: Lewis Structures**

10.6 **Electronegativity and Bond Polarity**

10.7 **Lewis Structures of Molecular Compounds and Polyatomic Ions**

10.8 **Resonance and Formal Charge**

10.9 **Exceptions to the Octet Rule: Odd-Electron Species, Incomplete Octets, and Expanded Octets**

10.10 **Bond Energies and Bond Lengths**

10.11 **Bonding in Metals: The Electron Sea Model**

Specific Learning Objectives Addressed in This Chapter:

SAP-3 Atoms or ions bond due to interactions between them, forming molecules.

SAP-3.A Explain the relationship between the type of bonding and the properties of the elements participating in the bond.

SAP-3.B Represent the relationship between potential energy and the distance between atoms, based on factors that influence the interaction strength.

SAP-4 Molecular compounds are arranged based on Lewis diagrams and Valence Shell Electron Pair Repulsion (VSEPR) theory.

SAP-4.A Represent a molecule with a Lewis diagram.

SAP-4.B Represent a molecule with a Lewis diagram that accounts for resonance between equivalent structures or that uses formal charge to select between nonequivalent structures.

SAP-4.C Based on the relationship between Lewis diagrams, VSEPR theory, bond orders, and bond polarities:

- Explain structural properties of molecules.

- Explain electron properties of molecules.

Concepts and Vocabulary to Review:

Section 10.1   **Bonding Models and AIDS Drugs**

X-ray crystallography is a technique in which X-rays are scattered when directed at a crystal. The resulting pattern can be studied and the data gathered can be used to determine the structure of a substance. Models of the structures can be used to predict properties. One model is Lewis dot structures. In this model, the basic position of atoms (or ions) can be observed.

Section 10.2   **Types of Chemical Bonds**

All chemical bonds involve the overlap of electron density between two (or more) positively charged nuclei, in one form or another. It is the coulomb force of attraction between species of opposite charge that provides the net energy gain. If the "sharing" arrangement is not energetically more stable than the isolated atoms, the chemical bonds will not form. When formed, ionic, covalent, and metallic bonds lower the potential energy between atoms within the resulting species. The transfer of electrons from the metal with low ionization energy to the nonmetal with high electron affinity in an ionic bond, creates oppositely charged ions attracted to each other. In covalent compounds, some electrons are primarily shared. In metallic bonds, metals have low ionization energies and lose electrons easily. These electrons are pooled among all the positively charged metal atoms and are called an *electron sea*. The valence electrons are delocalized, which means they do not belong to one particular atom. Students should be able to look at what makes up a species and determine if the bonding is ionic, covalent, or metallic, using available evidence about the individual components.

Table 10.1

Types of Atoms	Type of Bond	Characteristic of Bond
Metal and nonmetal	Ionic	Electrons transferred
Nonmetal and nonmetal	Covalent	Electrons shared
Metal and metal	Metallic	Electrons pooled

Representing Valence Electrons with Dots   Section 10.3

In a Lewis symbol the valence electrons are represented as dots around the symbol of the element. This visual model along with the concept of the octet rule (filling ion until it holds eight electrons) has allowed for a simple way to approach the drawing of molecules. The following drawings are representatives of their columns.

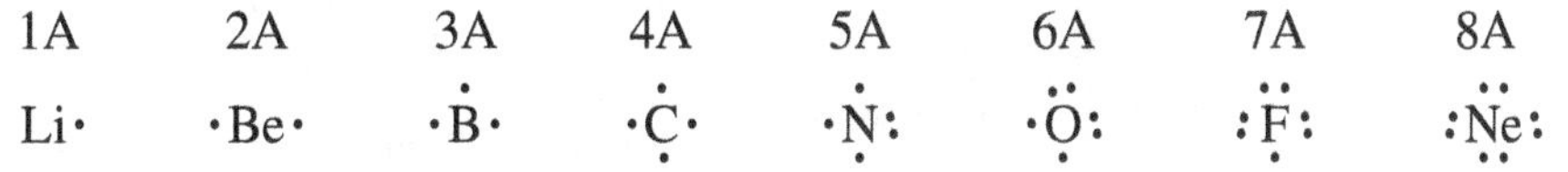

1A	2A	3A	4A	5A	6A	7A	8A
Li·	·Be·	·B·	·C·	·N:	·O:	:F:	:Ne:

Figure 10.1 Period 2 Lewis Structures

Ionic Bonding: Lewis Symbols and Lattice Energies   Section 10.4

The Lewis model can be used to write ionic equations, showing the transfer of electrons.

$$K· + :\ddot{C}l: \longrightarrow K^+ \left[:\ddot{C}l:\right]^-$$

The K atom starts with one valence electron and loses it to form K^+ which is isoelectronic to argon. Cl has seven valence electrons and gains the electron forming Cl^- which is also isolectronic to argon. The bracket around the Cl^- dot structure with the charge superscripted outside the bracket indicates an ion structure. The above example shows the transfer of one valence electron from potassium to chorine. In the example, the equation shows separate atoms as reactants and the Lewis structures for the ions as products. On the AP test, when students are asked to write an equation for an ionic compound, it is not required to use this format unless they are asked specifically to write the Lewis structures. They should recognize it is ionic and, as a solid, will form a stable lattice. In this case, a 1+ and 1− indicate a 1:1 ratio of cation to anion in the lattice that is formed. Lattice energy is the energy associated with the formation of the crystalline lattice of alternating cations and anions from gaseous atoms. This energy is calculated by using the Born-Haber cycle shown below on the next page. Some of the steps are endothermic and some are exothermic. Look at the diagram of the Born-Haber cycle while going through the steps in the next paragraph.

Step 1 is an endothermic step as it takes energy to sublime into a gas, step 2 is endothermic as it takes energy to break the bonds in chlorine gas and change them into chlorine atoms, step 3 is endothermic as it takes energy to remove an electron from a sodium atom to form an ion of sodium (ionization energy), step 4 is exothermic as energy is released when a chlorine atom accepts an electron (electron affinity), and step 5 is exothermic as energy is released as the lattice forms. The energy of step 5 is the lattice energy.

When comparing a group of compounds such as alkali metal chlorides, a trend in lattice energy emerges.

Born–Haber Cycle for Production of NaCl from Na(s) and Cl$_2$(g)

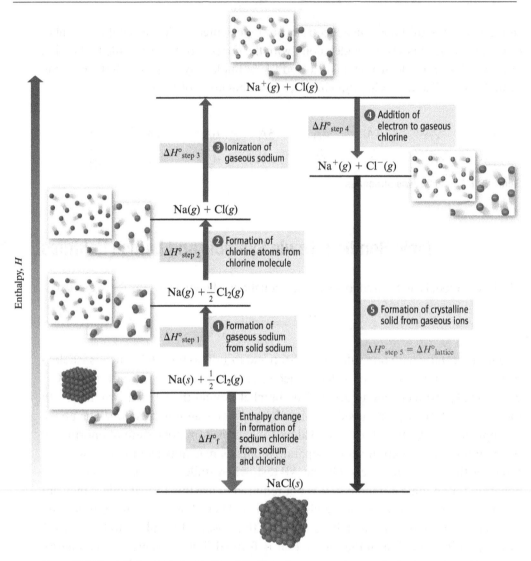

Figure 10.2 Born–Haber Cycle for Sodium Chloride   The sum of the steps is the formation of NaCl from elemental Na and Cl$_2$. The enthalpy change of the last step (step 5) is the lattice energy.

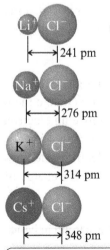

Metal Chloride	Lattice Energy (kJ/mol)
LiCl	−834
NaCl	−788
KCl	−701
CsCl	−657

The trend shown above in the metal chlorides is the smaller the alkali metal cation, the larger the lattice energy.

Remember Coulomb's law is $E = \dfrac{q_1 q_2}{r}$, and in each case, the q_1 and q_2 are $+1$ and -1. In this example, the decrease in lattice energy can be explained by the increase in the ionic radii. Going down the column in the bond length diagram above, it is apparent the radii are increasing, and the positive and negative charges are further away from each other. The metal cations increase in size due to increased shielding by the addition of number of energy levels. And the outer electrons are further from the positively charged nucleus. This results in less energy being released when the lattice forms.

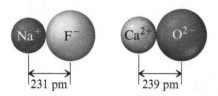

Figure 10.3

Table 10.2

Compound	Lattice Energy (kJ/mol)
NaF	−910
CaO	−3414

So why is the lattice energy of CaO so much greater than NaF when NaF has a shorter radius? Going back to the equation $E = \dfrac{q_1 q_2}{r}$, the reason is found in q_1 and q_2. Although both compounds have a 1:1 ratio of atoms, the CaO has q_1 and q_2 values of $+2$ and -2, whereas NaF has $+1$ and -1. The greater charge difference of $q_1 q_2$ is $2 \times (-2)$ versus $1 \times (-1)$, giving CaO approximately four times greater attraction, although the radius of CaO is slightly larger compared to NaF.

How can this data be summarized? Lattice energies become more exothermic (release more heat) as the ions get closer together (the radius of the ions decreases) and as the magnitude of ionic charge increases. The most important factor of the two is the magnitude of ionic charge.

So why are ionic compounds nonconductors in the solid state, but conduct when liquid or when dissolved in water? In the solid form, the ions are localized and held tightly in a lattice and no free electrons are available to conduct an electrical charge. When ionic compounds melt, the ions are free to move around and act as charge carriers. When they dissolve, they form ions in solution (sometimes surrounded by attracted water molecules); these can move freely to conduct an electrical charge.

Ionic compounds also have high melting points because the oppositely charged ions are attracted to each other in every direction in the lattice. Additionally, these forces are cumulatively strong and must be overcome to melt.

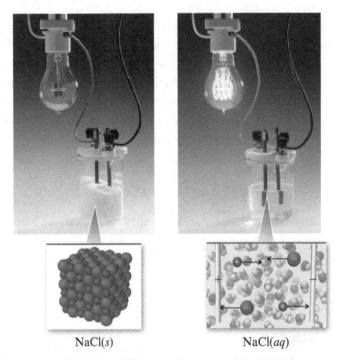

Figure 10.4 Solid sodium chloride does not conduct electricity. Aqueous sodium chloride conducts electricity.

Can ionic compounds have covalent bonds? Yes. If the ionic compound contains a polyatomic ion, the polyatomic ion contains one or more covalent bonds. The compound is still ionic because the cation and anion are held together by electrostatic charge. An example of a polyatomic ion with covalent bonds is NO_3^-. The nitrate ion has three N—O covalent bonds. When nitrate combines with the potassium ion, an ionic bond is present between the two ions, resulting in the formula unit KNO_3. In the lattice one K^+ alternates with a NO_3^-.

Section 10.5 Covalent Bonding: Lewis Structures

G. N. Lewis found two electrons are shared when single covalent bonds form. The two electrons are called a *bonding pair*. Any nonbonding pairs of electrons on an atom are called *lone pairs*. When four electrons are shared in a bond, a double bond forms. This is stronger than a single bond and will be shorter in length. If six electrons are shared, such as in the nitrogen molecule, N_2, a triple bond forms. See figure 10.5. It is stronger and shorter than a double bond. In general, the ranking of these bonds is single $<$ double $<$ triple in strength and a single $>$ double $>$ triple in length. On the AP Exam, data to support these concepts will be provided and the student will be expected to analyze and explain how the data supports the provided evidence.

:C̤̈l:C̤̈l: *or* :C̤̈l—C̤̈l:

:Ö::Ö: *or* :Ö=Ö:

:N:::N: *or* :N≡N:

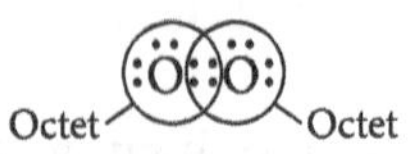

Figure 10.5

Lewis structures can be used to explain why a molecule or compound has a certain formula. When looking at properties of covalent compounds, it is important to note covalent bonds are directional. Although there may be a strong bond within a covalently bonded molecule (intramolecular forces), the forces between two different molecules (intermolecular forces) are weaker, leading to a low melting point. Students need to be able to describe the difference in factors affecting the melting points of covalent molecules and ionic compounds.

Molecular Compound

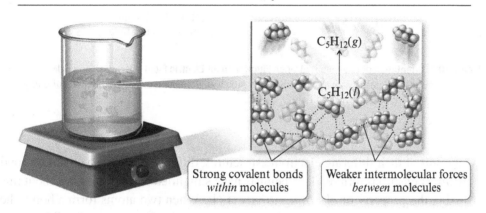

Figure 10.6 Intermolecular and Intramolecular Forces The covalent bonds between atoms of a molecule are much stronger than the interactions between molecules. To boil a molecular substance, we simply have to overcome the relatively weak intermolecular forces, so molecular compounds generally have low boiling points.

Electronegativity and Bond Polarity   Section 10.6

Covalent bonds share electrons, however, the sharing may not be equal. Similar to a tug-of-war, the nucleus in each atom's bond is pulling on the electrons. If the pull is equal, the bond is said to be *nonpolar* and electrons are being equally shared. When the pull is not equal, the sharing is not equal, and one side will have a slight positive charge as the electron density moves away and the other a slight negative charge due to an increase in electron density. The atom whose side the electrons have the stronger pull toward possess the slight partial negative charge, indicated by δ^-, and the other atom is left with a slight partial positive charge, indicated by a δ^+. This is also indicated by an arrow over the compound, showing the direction the electrons are being pulled. The two diagrams below show this representation. Technically, the "pull" will be unequal any time the atoms in the bond are not the same element (i.e., when it is not a homonuclear diatomic molecule), though sometimes the difference can be quite small for atoms of different elements.

$$\overset{\longmapsto}{\text{H}-\text{F}} \quad or \quad \overset{\delta^+ \quad \delta^-}{\text{H}-\text{F}}$$

These bonds are given the special name *polar covalent*. In an electric field, you can tell the difference between polar covalent and nonpolar covalent molecules. The nonpolar does not align to the field, whereas polar covalent molecules align the partial charges toward the opposite pole, as seen in the following figure.

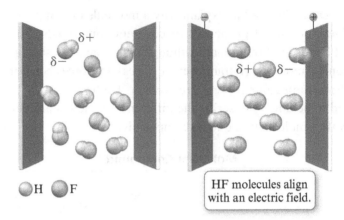

Figure 10.7 Orientation of Gaseous Hydrogen Fluoride in an Electric Field   Because one side of the HF molecule has a slight positive charge and the other side a slight negative charge, the molecules align themselves with an external electric field.

As a result of their differing electronic structures, different atoms in a chemical bond will attract electrons differently. Chemists have simplified current thinking about this by using the property of *electronegativity* (EN). When two atoms form a bond, the more electronegative atom will pull the electrons in its direction and will have the higher electron density $\left(\overset{+\longrightarrow}{H-F}\right)$. We can determine this by looking at electronegativity values. Over time, several different schemes have been devised to compute electronegativity values. The most common scheme is used in this text. The table of electronegativities is in Figure 10.8 uses the most common values.

The most electronegative element is fluorine and the least is francium. This is an inverse relationship to atomic size. The smaller the atom is, the less the positive nucleus is shielded, and therefore, the greater the atom's ability to attract electrons in a bond. The differences in electronegativity can be generalized into a continuum to aid in predicting if a bond is nonpolar, polar, or ionic.

When electrons are shared equally, the difference in electronegativities will be 0 although up to a difference in 0.4 is considered by most texts to be a nonpolar bond. Polar covalent bonds in general are when the difference in electronegativities is between 0.4 and 2.0 while ionic bonds are above a difference of 2.0. See figure 10.9. The O-H bond in water is (O)3.5 – 2.1(H) for a difference of 1.4. The greater electron density is around the more electronegative oxygen pulling the H toward it and the bond is polar covalent $\left(\overset{+\longrightarrow}{H-O}\right)$.

The magnitude of a bond's polarity is indicated by a dipole moment (μ) and is expressed in the unit of *debye* (D). In the AP curriculum, students are not expected to calculate the dipole moment, but they should understand the concept of a dipole. The smaller the difference in EN, the smaller the dipole moment will be. The dipole moment can also be used to determine percent ionic character.

$$\text{Percent ionic character} = \frac{\text{measured dipole moment}}{\text{dipole moment if fully transferred}} \times 100\%$$

Trends in Electronegativity

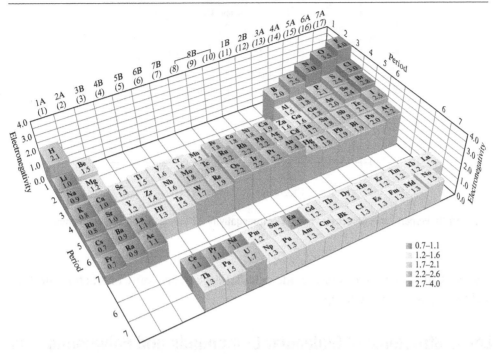

Figure 10.8 Electronegativities of the Elements   Electronegativity generally increases as we move across a row in the periodic table and decreases as we move down a column.

The Continuum of Bond Types

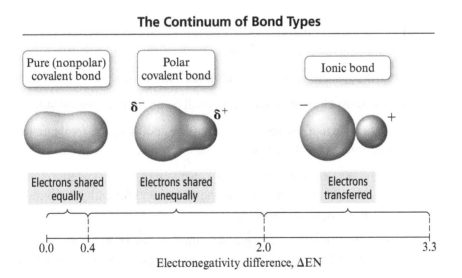

Figure 10.9 Electronegativity Difference (ΔEN) and Bond Type

The percent ionic character indicates the degree to which an electron is actually transferred. If the electron was fully transferred in the ionic bond, this would be 100%. In reality, ionic bonds never achieve 100% transfer; a bond with greater than 50% ionic character is considered to be ionic.

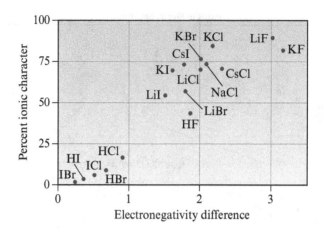

Figure 10.10 Percent Ionic Character versus Electronegativity Difference for Some Compounds

The AP Curriculum does not include calculating percent ionic character, but does include explaining the concept.

Section 10.7   Lewis Structures of Molecular Compounds and Polyatomic Ions

Students are expected to draw simple Lewis structures. For more complex molecules, the basic structures are given and students are asked to explain and predict properties based on the structures. There are several general rules to writing a Lewis structure.

1. Draw a basic structure by positioning the atoms as symmetrically as possible around the central atom

    a. Hydrogen atoms are always terminal and can only have two electrons.

    b. The most electronegative atoms will be around the central atom.

2. Calculate the total number of electrons by adding up the total number of valence electrons of each atom in the molecule.

    a. If the species is an ion, the ion's charge must be considered. For anions, add electrons equal to the charge and for cations subtract electrons equal to the charge.

    b. Ion structures should be placed within square brackets and the charge of the ion placed on the outside upper right of the bracket.

3. Distribute the electrons around the atoms, filling octets around atoms except for hydrogen which is filled with two electrons. Some other exceptions include lithium, beryllium, and boron.

    a. After placing two electrons in each bond, electrons should be distributed to terminal atoms first.

    b. See Section 10.9 Boron does not fill an octet of electrons, but fills with six electrons. Some atoms will expand and take more than an octet of electrons. Generally, this occurs with nonmetals P, S, Cl and below in their columns and Kr and Xe in the noble gases. Current research indicates this is not due to d hybridization and knowing hybridization in these cases will not be tested on the AP exam.

4. If atoms lack octets, form double or triple bonds with the central atoms.

   a. If two bonding atoms lack two electrons to complete the octets, a double bond will be needed. If the atoms lack four electrons, either two double bonds or a triple bond will be needed.

Example: Writing Lewis Structures

Write the Lewis Structure for CO_2.

Solution

Because carbon is the less electronegative atom, put it in the central position.

$$O C O$$

Total number of electrons for Lewis structure $=$

$$\begin{pmatrix} \text{number of} \\ \text{valence} \\ \text{e}^- \text{ for C} \end{pmatrix} + 2 \begin{pmatrix} \text{number of} \\ \text{valence} \\ \text{e}^- \text{ for O} \end{pmatrix}$$

$$= 4 + 2(6) = 16$$

Bonding electrons are first.

$$O:C:O$$

(4 of 16 electrons used)

Lone pairs on terminal atoms are next.

$$:\ddot{O}:C:\ddot{O}:$$

(16 of 16 electrons used)

Since carbon lacks an octet, move lone pairs from the oxygen atoms to bonding regions to form double bonds.

$$:\ddot{O}:C:\ddot{O}:$$
$$\downarrow$$
$$:\ddot{O}=\ddot{C}=\ddot{O}:$$

For Practice

Draw the Lewis structure for CO.

Resonance and Formal Charge   Section 10.8

The concept of resonance is used when two or more possible Lewis structures can be drawn for the same substance. Neither structure is actually correct as the actual structure is an average of the possible structures. The different structures are drawn with a double-headed arrow between them to indicate this.

$$:\ddot{O}=\ddot{O}-\ddot{\underset{..}{O}}: \quad \longleftrightarrow \quad :\ddot{\underset{..}{O}}-\ddot{O}=\ddot{O}:$$

The resonance structures indicate the delocalization of electrons contributes to the stability of the molecule.

The formal charge of an atom in a Lewis structure is the charge it would have if all the bonding electrons were shared between the bonded atoms. Formal charge can be used to distinguish between different resonance structures and help determine which is the best model. The calculation of formal charge is done on each atom in a structure.

Formal charge = number of valence electrons − (number of nonbonding electrons + $\frac{1}{2}$ number of bonding electrons).

When assigned, comparing the formal charges in competing structures four rules generally apply:

1. The sum of all formal charges in a neutral molecule is zero.

2. The sum of all formal charges in an ion must equal the charge of the ion.

3. Small (or zero) formal charges on individual atoms are better than large ones.

4. If formal charges cannot be avoided, the most negative charge whould reside on the most electronegative atom.

$[OCN]^-$ has three resonance structures. The calculation of formal charge is shown below.

Example: Assigning Formal Charges

Assign formal charges to each atom in the resonance structures of the cyanate ion (OCN^-). Which resonance structure is likely to contribute most to the correct structure of OCN^-?

$$\overset{A}{[:\ddot{\underset{..}{O}}-C\equiv N:]^-} \quad \overset{B}{[:\ddot{O}=C=\ddot{N}:]^-} \quad \overset{C}{[:O\equiv C-\ddot{\underset{..}{N}}:]^-}$$

Solution

Calculate the formal charge on each atom by finding the number of valence electrons and subtracting the number of nonbonding electrons and one-half the number of bonding electrons.

	A			B			C		
	$[:\ddot{O}—C≡N:]^-$			$[:\ddot{O}=C=\ddot{N}:]^-$			$[:O≡C—\ddot{N}:]^-$		
Number of valence e⁻	6	4	5	6	4	5	6	4	5
−number of nonbonding e⁻	−6	−0	−2	−4	−0	−4	−2	−0	−6
−$\frac{1}{2}$(number of bond e⁻)	−1	−4	−3	−2	−4	−2	−3	−4	−1
Formal charge	**−1**	**0**	**0**	**0**	**0**	**−1**	**+1**	**0**	**−2**

The sum of all formal charges for each structure is −1, as it should be for a 1− ion. Structures A and B have the fewest non-zero formal charges and are preferred over structure C. Structure A is preferable to B because it has the negative formal charge on the more electronegative atom. You would therefore expect structure A to make the biggest contribution to the resonance forms of the cyanate ion.

For Practice 10.8

Assign formal charges to each atom in the resonance structures of N_2O. Which resonance structure is likely to contribute most to the correct structure of N_2O?

$$\begin{array}{ccc} A & B & C \\ :\ddot{N}=N=\ddot{O}: & :N≡N—\ddot{O}: & :\ddot{N}—N≡O: \end{array}$$

Answer: B

Section 10.9

Exceptions to the Octet Rule: Odd-Electron Species, Incomplete Octets, and Expanded Octets

Some Lewis structures do not follow the octet rule. These include odd-electron species, incomplete octets, and expanded octets.

Odd-electron species are called free radicals and have an odd number of electrons. One electron will be always left unpaired in its orbital. An example is nitrogen dioxide with 17 electrons.

Certain elements form incomplete octets with fewer than eight electrons around an atom. Examples include H, Be, and B. B for instance has three electrons and when all three are paired in bonding, it will have six electrons instead of eight. Figure 10.11 shows an example of the Lewis dot structure of BF_3.

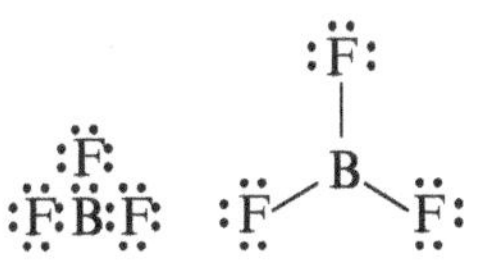

Figure 10.11

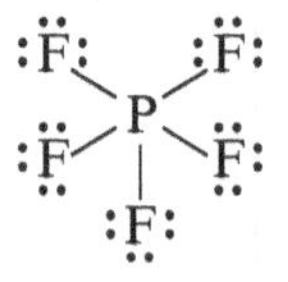

Figure 10.12

A few elements can expand and have more than eight electrons. For instance, phosphorus has five valence electrons. It can bond with three additional electrons forming PH_3 to gain the octet of electrons but it can also form 5 bonds and have ten electrons around it as in PF_5, as shown in Figure 10.12. The possibility of expansion occurs in P, S, Cl, Ar and the elements below them in their column. Noble gases can form bonds since molecules such as XeF_4 exist.

The shapes of these substances will be addressed in the next chapter.

Section 10.10   Bond Energies and Bond Lengths

Bond energy is the amount of energy required to break one mole of the bonds in the gas phase molecules. Bond energies are always positive because they require the addition of energy to break a bond. The stronger the bond, the more energy that is required to break it. Generally, the stronger the bond the shorter the bond length will be.

Table 10.3   Average Bond Energies

Bond	Bond Energy (kJ/mol)	Bond	Bond Energy (kJ/mol)	Bond	Bond Energy (kJ/mol)
H—H	436	N—N	163	Br—F	237
H—C	414	N=N	418	Br—Cl	218
H—N	389	N≡N	946	Br—Br	193
H—O	464	N—O	222	I—Cl	208
H—S	368	N=O	590	I—Br	175
H—F	565	N—F	272	I—I	151
H—Cl	431	N—Cl	200	Si—H	323
H—Br	364	N—Br	243	Si—Si	226
H—I	297	N—I	159	Si—C	301
C—C	347	O—O	142	S—O	265
C=C	611	O=O	498	Si=O	368
C≡C	837	O—F	190	S=O	523
C—N	305	O—Cl	203	Si—Cl	464
C=N	615	O—I	234	S=S	418
C≡N	891	F—F	159	S—F	327
C—O	360	Cl—F	253	S—Cl	253
C=O	736*	Cl—Cl	243	S—Br	218
C≡O	1072			S—S	266
C—Cl	339				

*799 in CO_2.

It is possible to determine the enthalpy of a reaction from known bond energies of reactants and products. A balanced equation and the bond energy of every bond present are needed. Drawing a Lewis structure of each molecule is helpful to identify and count all types of bonds in the reactants and products. The energy of bonds broken is always positive as energy is added to break bonds while energy of bonds forming is always negative as energy is released.

$$\Delta H_{rxn} = \Sigma(\Delta H \text{ all bonds broken}) + \Sigma(\Delta H \text{ all bonds formed})$$

On the AP test, this equation is written with a minus sign between bonds broken and bonds formed so values listed in the table can be used in the equation.

$$\Delta H_{rxn} = \Sigma(\Delta H \text{ all bonds broken}) - \Sigma(\Delta H \text{ all bonds formed})$$

For the reaction $2H_2 + O_2 \rightarrow 2H_2O$ there is 1 H—H bond per H_2, 1 O=O) in the reactants and 2 H—O bonds per water in the products. $[2(436) + 498] - [2(464)] = 442$ kJ/mol.

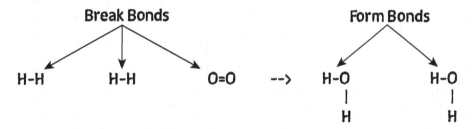

Energy is released when bonds form. The overall enthalpy of a reaction depends on the relationship between the values of bonds broken (+) and bonds forming (−). Reactions are *exothermic* when weak bonds break and strong bonds form and are *endothermic* when strong bonds break and weak bonds form. A diagram showing this relationship is in the following figure.

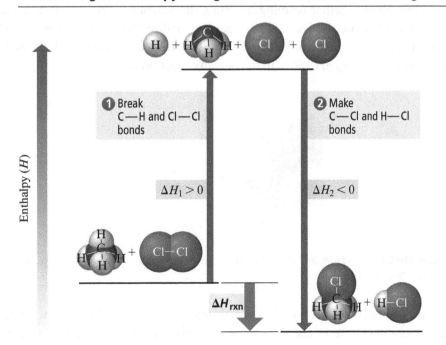

Estimating the Enthalpy Change of a Reaction from Bond Energies

Figure 10.13 Estimating ΔH_{rxn} from Bond Energies We can approximate the enthalpy change of a reaction by summing up the enthalpy changes involved in breaking old bonds and forming new ones. This reaction is exothermic because the energy needed to break bonds in not as much as the energy given off in the formation of the bonds formed as shown in figure 10.13. If the energy needed to break the bonds is more than the energy released in the formation of the new bonds, the reaction will be endothermic.

In general, stronger bonds are shorter than weaker bonds. Comparing single bonds between carbons, double bonds and triple bonds, the triple bond, the strongest bond, is the shortest. Remember bonds within a molecule are intramolecular and are based on electronegativity differences. when compared, H–O, H–C, H–N, H–O has the greatest difference, will be the most polar bond, and will be the shortest as the O is pulling the H in tighter than the N or C.

Table 10.4   Average Bond Lengths

Bond	Bond Length (pm)	Bond	Bond Length (pm)	Bond	Bond Length (pm)
H—H	74	C—C	154	N—N	145
H—C	110	C=C	134	N=N	123
H—N	100	C≡C	120	N≡N	110
H—O	97	C—N	147	N—O	136
H—S	132	C=N	128	N=O	120
H—F	92	C≡N	116	O—O	145
H—Cl	127	C—O	143	O=O	121
H—Br	141	C=O	120	F—F	143
H—I	161	C—Cl	178	Cl—Cl	199
				Br—Br	228
				I—I	266

Section 10.11   Bonding in Metals: The Electron Sea Model

When metals bond together forming an array, the valence electrons of the metal atoms form an electron sea. The electrons are not localized on a single atom, but are delocalized and can move among atoms, hence the term *sea*. In this model, the metal exists as positively charged cations in the negative electron sea.

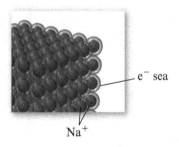

Figure 10.14 The Electron Sea Model for Sodium   In this model of metallic bonding, Na^+ ions are immersed in a "sea" of electrons.

Because the electrons are free to move, metals tend to readily conduct electric charge and heat. Since the electrons can slide past one another, metals can generally be hammered into sheets (malleability) and drawn into wires (ductility).

Additional Practice

Self-Assessment Quiz Questions Q1, Q2, Q3, Q4, Q5, Q6, Q7, Q8, Q9, Q10, Q11, Q12, Q13, Q14, and Q15

Problems:

Review Questions 3, 6, 11, 12, 13, 14, 15, 19, 20, 21, 22, 26, 27, 28, 31, 32, 33, and 34

Valence Electrons and Dot Structures 35, and 37

Ionic Lewis Symbols and Lattice Energy 39, 43, 45, and 48

Simple Covalent Lewis structures, Electronegativity, and Bond Polarity 49, 50, 51, 52, 53, 54, 55, 56, and 57

Covalent Lewis Structures, Resonance, and Formal Charge 59, 60, 63, 64, 65, and 72

Odd-Electron Species, Incomplete Octets, and Expanded Octets 75, 78, and 82
Cumulative Problems 85, 86, 87, 91, 98, 99, 106, 109, and 114

Challenge Problems 119, and 121

Conceptual Problems 126, 127, and 128

Data Interpretation and Analysis 135

Equations to know:

Formal charge = number of valence electrons − (number of nonbonding electrons + 1/2 number of shared electrons)

$$\Delta H_{rxn} = \Sigma \left(\Delta H \text{ all bonds broken} \right) - \Sigma \left(\Delta H \text{ all bonds formed} \right)$$

Practice AP Test Questions

1. Given a table of electronegativity values of elements, arrange the following X—Cl bonds in the following compounds in order of increasing ionic character: BCl_3, PCl_3, $ScCl_3$, and $LaCl_3$

Element	Electronegativity
B	2.0
La	1.1
P	2.1
Sc	1.3
Cl	3.0

   A) B—Cl, P—Cl, Sc—Cl, La—Cl

   B) Sc—Cl, La—Cl, B—Cl, P—Cl

   C) La—Cl, P—Cl, Sc—Cl,B—Cl

   D) P—Cl, B—Cl, Sc—Cl, La—Cl

2. Of the bonds C—N, C=N, and C≡N, the C≡N bond is:

   A) Weakest/longest

   B) Strongest/longest

   C) Weakest/shortest

   D) Strongest/shortest

3. A valid Lewis structure, obeying the Octet Rule, can be drawn for all of the following compounds except:

   A) $CaCl_2$

   B) NCl_3

   C) CCl_4

   D) ICl_5

4. How many contributing resonance structures can be drawn for the SO_3 molecule? Note that the Octet Rule for the sulfur atom applies.

   A) Two

   B) Three

   C) Four

   D) Five

5. Given the information in a table of bond dissociation energies, calculate the change in enthalpy, ΔH, in units of kJ, for the following gas-phase reaction:

   $$H_2C=CH_2 + H—Br \rightarrow CH_3CH_2Br$$

Bond	D (kJ/mol)
C—C	348
C=C	614
C—H	413
H—Br	141
C—Br	194

   A) +148

   B) −148

   C) +200

   D) −200

6. Give the complete electronic configuration for Ca^{2+}.

    A) $1s^2 2s^2 2p^6 3s^2 4p^6$

    B) $1s^2 2s^2 2p^6 3s^2 3p^6$

    C) $1s^2 2s^2 2p^6 3s^2 3p^5$

    D) $1s^2 2s^2 3s^2 4s^2 5s^2$

7. Which of the following statements best describes lattice energy?

    A) A negative sign for lattice energy refers to the amount of energy required to form the lattice.

    B) An ionic crystal lattice becomes stronger as the charge on the cation and anion increases.

    C) Lattice energy describes the energy associated with forming only ionic compounds.

    D) An ionic crystal lattice becomes stronger as the cation size increases.

8. Place the following compounds in order of **increasing** magnitude of lattice energy.

    CaO   MgO   BaO

    A) MgO < CaO < BaO

    B) BaO < MgO < CaO

    C) BaO < CaO < MgO

    D) CaO < MgO < BaO

    E) CaO < BaO < MgO

9. Which of the following reactions is associated with the lattice energy of CaO $(\Delta H°_{lattice})$?

    A) $Ca(s) + (1/2)O_2(g) \rightarrow CaO(s)$

    B) $CaO(s) \rightarrow Ca(s) + (1/2)O_2 (g)$

    C) $Ca^{2+}(aq) + O^{2-}(aq) \rightarrow CaO(s)$

    D) $Ca^{2+}(g) + O^{2-}(g) \rightarrow CaO(s)$

10. Use the data given below to construct a Born–Haber cycle and to estimate the lattice energy of CaO(s).

	ΔH°(kJ)
$Ca(s) \rightarrow Ca(g)$	193
$Ca(g) \rightarrow Ca^{+}(g) + e^{-}$	590
$Ca^{+}(g) \rightarrow Ca^{2+}(g) + e^{-}$	1010
$2\,O(g) \rightarrow O_2(g)$	−498
$O(g) + e^{-} \rightarrow O^{-}(g)$	−141
$O^{-}(g) + e^{-} \rightarrow O^{2-}(g)$	878
$Ca(s) + \frac{1}{2}O_2(g) \rightarrow CaO(s)$	−635

A) −3400 kJ

B) −2700 kJ

C) +1400 kJ

D) +3400 kJ

Chapter 10 Practice AP Test Questions Answers:

1. D); 2. C); 3. D); 4. A); 5. D); 6. B); 7. B); 8. C); 9. D); 10. A)

Data Interpretation and Analysis Question: Diazomethane

Diazomethane, CH_2N_2, is a shock-sensitive explosive gas at room temperature. It can be used to add $-CH_2-$ groups to double bonds.

a) Write a Lewis structure for diazomethane in which all atoms obey the octet rule and carbon has four bonds. How many valence electrons are present?

b) Write three resonance structures for diazomethane. All three structures will have the C—N—N structure.

c) Show the formal charge on each atom in your resonance structures.

d) Use formal charge rules to determine which two structures are plausible.

e) When heated, diazomethane decomposes to form N_2 and CH_2. Write a balanced equation for this reaction and draw a Lewis structure for CH_2. What is the formal charge of the CH_2 group? This CH_2 group will react with *cis*-2-butene to produce 1,2-dimethyl cyclopropane. Draw a Lewis structure for *cis*-2-butene and draw a Lewis structure for 1,2-dimethyl cyclopropane.

Data Interpretation and Analysis Question Answers with Brief Explanations

a)

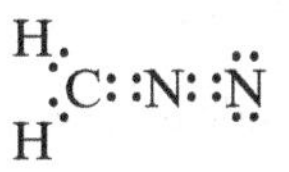

Valence electrons
$2N = 2 \times 5 = 10$
$1C = 1 \times 4 = 4$
$2M = 2 \times 1 = \underline{2}$
16

b) and c)

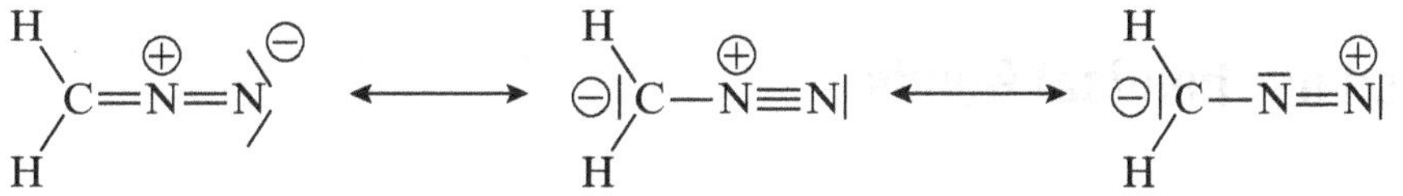

d) The first and second structures are most plausible.

e)

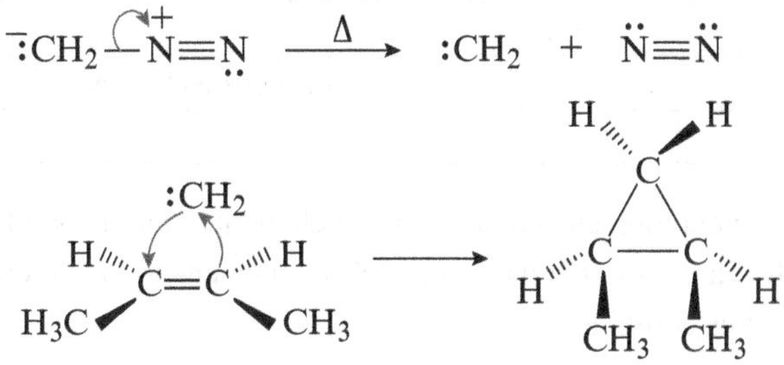

READING GUIDE

Many of the concepts introduced in this chapter on chemical bonding are found in Unit 2 and Unit 3 covering the structure and rearrangement of atoms, ions, molecules and the forces between them. Also covered are sections of Unit 6 on energy. Concepts in the chapter not in the AP Chemistry curriculum include using formal charge to explain why certain molecules do not obey the octet rule and defending Lewis models based on the limitations of the model.

1. What are the three models of bonding? Is one of the models "right"? Explain your answer.

Section 10.1 **Bonding Models and AIDS Drugs**

2. What technique was used to find the structure of HIV-1 protease?*

3. What is the function of compounds acting as inhibitors? Include an example in your answer.

4. What is the Lewis model? What are Lewis structures used for?

Section 10.2 **Types of Chemical Bonds**

5. Why do bonds form? What forces are involved in forming a bond?

6. Fill in the following table:

Types of Atoms	Type of Bond	Characteristic of Bond
	Ionic	
		Electrons Shared
Metal and Metal		

7. When a metal element combines with a nonmetal element, an ionic bond is usually formed. How are these bonds formed? What happens to the potential energy when the atoms combine?

8. Explain how two nonmetal atoms usually combine to form covalent bonds. Explain how the bond holds the molecule together. What happens to the potential energy when the atoms combine?

9. Explain how metal atoms combine to form metallic bonds. What happens to the potential energy when the atoms combine?

Representing Valence Electrons with Dots   Section 10.3

10. Which electrons in an electron configuration are used in a Lewis Dot symbol? Draw the Lewis dot symbols for each of the following atoms: Li, Be, B, C, N, O, F, and Ne.

11. Why are hydrogen and helium two exceptions to the octet rule?

12. What is the octet rule? What is it used for and what are its limitations?

Ionic Bonding: Lewis Symbols and Lattice Energies   Section 10.4

13. Using K and Cl, use Lewis diagrams to show how the ionic compound KCl forms. Draw a two dimensional diagram of a 4 × 4 lattice structure of KCl(s).

14. When solid ionic compounds form, what type of structure is made? Is the reaction to make this structure endothermic or exothermic? Justify your answer.

15. Fill in the following table, using Na and Cl_2 forming NaCl as an example:

Step of Born–Haber Cycle	Source of ΔH for the Step	Is the Value Positive or Negative?

16. What law is demonstrated by the Born–Haber cycle energies adding up to the lattice energy?

17. Explain why lattice energies decrease down a column in the periodic table. In your response, use the alkali metal chlorides from LiCl to CsCl as your example.

Metal Chloride	Lattice Energy kJ/mol
LiCl	−834
NaCl	−788
KCl	−701
CsCl	−657

18. The lattice energies of NaF and CaO are $-910\,kJ/mol$ and $-3414\,kJ/mol$ respectively. Explain the reason for this difference using Coulomb's law.

19. Explain why ionic compounds have high melting points, are nonconductors as solids, and are conductors when liquid or dissolved in water. Include a diagram in your answer.

20. Give an example of an ionic compound containing a covalent bond. Explain this example is considered an ionic compound.

Section 10.5   Covalent Bonding: Lewis Structures

21. What is meant by a *lone pair* of electrons? How is this different than a non-bonding pair?

22. Draw molecules of O_2, N_2, and F_2 and circle the bonding electrons. Indicate if the bond is a single, double, or triple bond and explain why.

23. Explain the differences in strength and bond length of single, double, and triple bonds. For each type of bond, cite one example of a species that contains the bond.

24. Draw the Lewis structure of the hydronium ion. Why is this structure stable?

25. What does it mean when ionic bonds are said to be nondirectional, whereas covalent bonds are said to be directional?

26. Using a diagram, explain the difference between ionic compounds and covalent molecules when they melt to form a liquid. What forces are involved? Explain.

Section 10.6   Electronegativity and Bond Polarity

27. Using HF as an example, describe a limitation of the Lewis Model.

28. Write two different ways of showing charge separation on a molecule of HF. How are the two ways different?

29. If charge separation occurs in some molecules, why do these molecules not have an ionic bond?

30. What evidence supports the claim that HF is polar?

31. Explain what a polar covalent bond is and how to know if one is present in a compound.

32. Define electronegativity. What data was used to assign electronegativity values to atoms?

33. Explain why electronegativity increases across a period and decreases down a family.

34. What is the general relationship between size of the atom and electronegativity?

35. Draw a number line from 0 to 4 and indicate how the difference in electronegativity values between two atoms affects bond type.

Note: Using the difference in electronegativity values between two atoms to classify bonds is at best an approximation, a useful tool.

36. How are nonpolar and polar covalent bonds different? How would you know which is present in a molecule?

37. What is a dipole moment, what is its symbol, and what is its unit of measurement?

38. What is percent ionic character and how is it calculated?

39. How many bonds are 100% ionic? What percentage are generally ionic? What does this mean?

40. In general, what percent ionic character is classified as an ionic bond?

Lewis Structures of Molecular Compounds and Polyatomic Ions   Section 10.7

41. What are the 4 steps for writing a Lewis structure?

42. Why are hydrogen atoms considered terminal and where are they placed in a Lewis structure?

43. When drawing a simple Lewis structure, is the most electronegative atom or least electronegative atom most likely to be the central atom? Explain.

44. When drawing a Lewis structure for an ion, what additional steps are needed? How is the structure of an ion drawn? Include an example.

Resonance and Formal Charge   Section 10.8

45. What is resonance? How is resonance indicated in Lewis structures?

46. Why do chemists use resonance structures to represent certain anions and molecules? What is a resonance hybrid? Include in your explanation a short discussion of a comparison of bond length and bond strength. Provide an example of an anion or molecule needing to be represented by resonance structures. What are delocalized electrons? How does this concept apply to resonance structures?

47. Draw the three Lewis resonance structures for SO_2.

48. What is formal charge, the four rules used in calculating formal charge, and how is it calculated? Provide an example showing how to calculate the formal charge in each atom of the molecule.

49. Why are formal charges useful when comparing different possible Lewis structures?* If there are multiple possible structures, how could formal charge help you decide which was the most correct?

Section 10.9   Exceptions to the Octet Rule: Odd Electron Species, Incomplete Octets, and Expanded Octets

50. Identify three exceptions to the octet rule?

51. What are free radicals?*

52. What radical is called the *atmospheric vacuum cleaner*? Why is it called this?*

53. What elements tend to form compounds with incomplete octets?

54. What is a coordinate covalent bond? Draw the Lewis structures for each species involved in the following reaction: $BF_3 + NH_3 \rightarrow F_3BNH_3$. Indicate the location of the coordinate covalent bond.

55. Identify four elements which tend to have expanded octets when forming compounds. Explain why.

Section 10.10   Bond Energies and Bond Lengths

56. Define bond energy. Provide two examples of chemical bonds, one with a high value for bond energy and one with a low value for bond energy. Explain how to use bond energies to determine the enthalpy of a reaction. Provide an example showing the steps to do the calculation.

57. Are bond energies considered to be positive or negative? Why?

58. What is the relationship between the bond energies of the reactants and products in an exothermic reaction? Endothermic?

59. Explain why it is incorrect to say energy is stored in bonds.

60. What is the general relationship found between bond strength and bond length? Explain why this trend occurs.

Section 10.11   Bonding in Metals: The Electron Sea Model

61. What is an electron sea? Include a diagram in your answer.

62. Explain why solid metals can conduct an electric charge (electricity).

63. Metals can conduct heat, and are malleable and ductile. Using the electron sea model, explain why.

64. Draw the Lewis structure of ozone. (This is in the inserted section. Keep in mind ozone does not have a metallic bond.) Why is ozone an important molecule in the stratosphere?

Self-Assessment Answers

1. _____   2. _____   3. _____

4. _____   5. _____   6. _____

7. _____   8. _____   9. _____

10. _____   11. _____   12. _____

13. _____   14. _____   15. _____

CHEMICAL BONDING II: MOLECULAR SHAPES, VALENCE BOND THEORY, AND MOLECULAR ORBITAL THEORY

Additional theories in predicting shapes and properties of molecules are explored in this chapter. The first model is the Valence Shell Electron Pair Repulsion (VSEPR) model. This model is used in conjunction with Lewis structures from the last chapter. Additional theories are valence bond theory and molecular orbital theory. These models are more complex than the Lewis model but these models can explain properties and molecular shape. Most of this chapter is in the AP Curriculum. However, AP only expects an understanding of orbital theory basics, focusing on how molecular properties (e.g., strength of bonds and shapes of molecules) can be explained by models or theories, without in-depth details. Teachers should focus on student mastery of the basic ideas. Mastery of the names of molecular geometries, as well as explanation (using VSEPR) of why molecules have a particular geometry is required. Information in this chapter is tested every year although electron groups are called electron domains in the AP curriculum.

Specific Learning Objectives Addressed in This Chapter:

SAP-3 Atoms or ions bond due to interactions between them, forming molecules.

SAP-3.A Explain the relationship between the type of bonding and the properties of the elements participating in the bond.

SAP-3.B Represent the relationship between potential energy and the distance between atoms, based on factors that influence the interaction strength.

SAP-3.C Represent an ionic solid with a particulate model that is consistent with Coulomb's law and the properties of the constituent ions.

SAP-3.D Represent a metallic solid and/or alloy using a model to show essential characteristics of the structure and interactions present in the substance.

SAP-4 Molecular compounds are arranged based on Lewis diagrams and Valence Shell Electron Pair Repulsion (VSEPR) theory.

SAP-4.A Represent a molecule with a Lewis diagram.

SAP-4.B Represent a molecule with a Lewis diagram that accounts for resonance between equivalent structures or that uses formal charge to select between nonequivalent structures.

SAP-4.C Based on the relationship between Lewis diagrams, VSEPR theory, bond orders, and bond polarities:

- Explain structural properties of molecules.
- Explain electron properties of molecules.

Concepts and Vocabulary to Review:

VSEPR Theory: The Five Basic Shapes   Section 11.2

VSEPR stands for Valence Shell Electron Pair Repulsion. This is a model with considerable success in predicting/explaining shapes of simple molecules made from atoms covalently bonded together. This model makes a single assumption: The shape of a molecule is based on the number of electron groups on the central atom. Electron groups are usually pairs of electrons in single bonds, double bonds, triple bonds, or nonbonded pairs called lone pairs; in rare cases, they are single electrons. The electron groups will repel each other as much as possible in three-dimensional space. The number of electron groups surrounding a central atom result in the five basic shapes of molecules. When two electron groups are present such as in CO_2, they repulse to opposite sides of the central atom forming a linear shape. The angle formed between the electron groups surrounding the central atom is known as the *bond angle*, in this case, with 180° bond angles. In this section, basic shapes with only bonding pairs are discussed. In Section 11.3, the effect of lone pairs on molecular shape and bond angles will be explored.

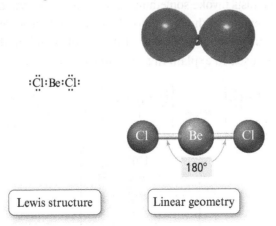

Figure 11.1 Representing Electron Geometry with Balloons   The bulkiness of balloons causes them to assume a linear arrangement when two of them are tied together. Similarly, the repulsion between two electron groups produces a linear geometry.

Shapes with three electron domains:

When three electron groups (domains) are present, the maximum angle is 120° from each other in a flat plane (two dimensional). This arrangement is called *trigonal planar*. *Trigonal* means *three* and *planar* indicates they will be *in the same plane*.

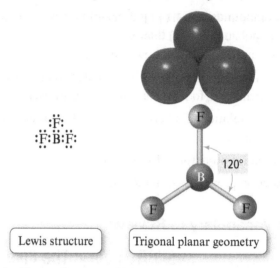

Lewis structure   Trigonal planar geometry

Figure 11.2 Representing Electron Geometry with Balloons   Like three balloons tied together, three electron groups adopt a trigonal planar geometry.

Bond angles will only be exact and the resulting molecular shape will only be completely symmetrical when fully equivalent bonds are present. An example is BF_3, the boron atom is pulled equally by the three fluorine atoms and form a trigonal planar shape with 120° angles. This means having only one type of bond and atom joined to a central atom. In Figure 11.3, CH_2O has three electron groups, but the angles are not 120° because the bonds are not equal. The double bond between the carbon and oxygen atoms involves two electron pairs. These additional electrons result in a greater electron density and increased repulsion resulting in bond angles that are actually 121.9° (H—C—O) and 116.2° (H—C—H). Similarly, BF_3 will be symmetrical, but substituting an F with a less electronegative Cl forming BF_2Cl will not.

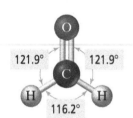

Figure 11.3

However, some molecules show symmetry even when the simple bonding model suggests otherwise. Chemists invoke something called *resonance structures* to explain such a phenomenon. For example, the nitrate ion NO_3^- is symmetric, even though VSEPR predicts an asymmetric geometry because of the double bond. In this case, three resonance structures are used to explain this. The unfortunate use of the term *resonance*

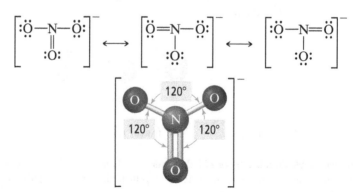

Figure 11.4 Nitrate Ion Resonance Structures

originally was used because chemists thought the structures "resonated" between one another. We now know that the different structures are never observed and the actual structure is a true "blend" of the three. However, the name persists. The arrows between structures are used to indicate resonance. All of bonds in the nitrate ion are equivalent. The bonds have the same bond length and bond strength. The bond order is 1.33 or one and a third. There are no single bonds or double bonds in the nitrate ion.

Shapes with four electron domains

When four electron groups are present, the groups move into three-dimensional (3-D) space and form a tetrahedral shape. For symmetric tetrahedrons, the bonds will be 109.5°. A common error students make is thinking the angles are 90° because this is how a Lewis structure is drawn on flat paper. It is vital that students build 3-D models to assure they understand this difference, and practice properly representing these on flat paper as 3-D structures. How to draw 3-D structures is fully explained in Section 11.4. By looking at the ball and stick model and the 3-D structure, you can determine what the pattern is.

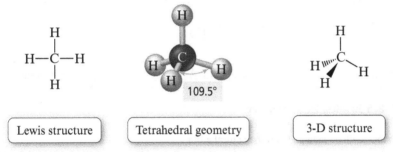

| Lewis structure | Tetrahedral geometry | 3-D structure |

Figure 11.5 Methane Structure Representations

Shapes with five electron domains

When five electron groups are present, there has to be two different bond angles. Three of the electron groups form a trigonal planar shape with 120° angles, whereas the remaining two groups are arranged vertically with one atom above and one atom below the central atom. (However, note that the terms *above* and *below* mean nothing as molecules can be rotated in space.) This is only the way we represent it on a piece of paper. The vertical electron groups will be 90° from the electron groups in the plane. Be sure students convince themselves this must be the case by looking at a physical model. Although not reported as a bond angle, the two electron groups

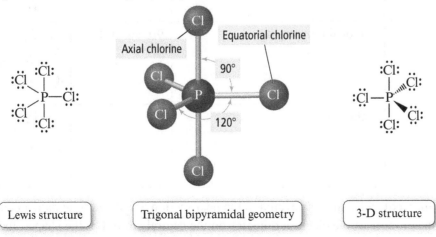

| Lewis structure | Trigonal bipyramidal geometry | 3-D structure |

Figure 11.6 Phosphorus Pentachloride Structure Representations

above and below the axis are 180° away from each other. Only adjacent atoms form angles referred to as *bond angles*. An equatorial Cl—P—equatorial Cl bond angle is 120° and an axial Cl—P—equatorial Cl bond angle is 90°.

Shapes with six electron domains

Six electron groups form an octahedral geometry. All angles are 90°. Four of the groups are in a plane and take the shape of a square around the central atom and are called equatorial. The other two pairs are above and below the plane at maximum distance from each other and are called axial.

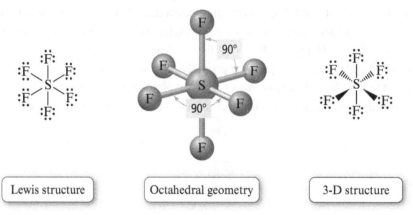

| Lewis structure | Octahedral geometry | 3-D structure |

Figure 11.7 SF6 Structure Representations

Summary Table of the Five Basic Shapes with no lone pairs on the central atom

Number of Electron Groups	Example(s)	Name of Shape (electron geometry and molecular geometry)	Bond Angles	Drawing
2	$BeCl_2$ CO_2	Linear	180°	$\ddot{O}=C=\ddot{O}$
3	BF_3 CH_2O	Trigonal planar	120° if bonds are equal	:F̈: | :F̈—B—F̈:
4	CH_4	Tetrahedral	109.5° if bonds are equal	H | H—C—H | H
5	PCl_5	Trigonal bipyramidal	90° and 120°	:C̈l: :C̈l: \ | :C̈l ⟩P—C̈l: / | :C̈l: :C̈l:
6	SF_6	Octahedral	90°	:F̈: :F̈. | .F̈: \ | / :F̈. S .F̈: / | \ :F̈:

All other molecular shapes covered in the next section are due to lone pairs occupying one or more of the electron domains on the central atom. For the shapes above, the electron geometry and molecular geometry are the same due to no lone pairs.

VSEPR Theory: The Effect of Lone Pairs   Section 11.3

A *lone electron pair* refers to a pair of valence electrons on the central atom that are not used to covalently bond the central atom to another atom. When lone pairs

Four electron groups with lone pairs:

3 bonds and 1 lone pair on the central atom:

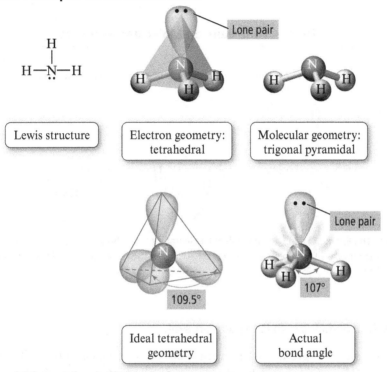

| Lewis structure | Electron geometry: tetrahedral | Molecular geometry: trigonal pyramidal |

| Ideal tetrahedral geometry | Actual bond angle |

2 bonds and 2 lone pairs on the central atom:

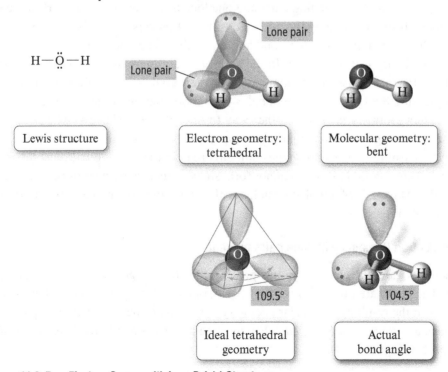

| Lewis structure | Electron geometry: tetrahedral | Molecular geometry: bent |

| Ideal tetrahedral geometry | Actual bond angle |

Figure 11.8 Four Electron Groups with Lone Pair(s) Structures

of electrons are present in the electron groups, there are usually unequal repulsions between the lone pair domain and a domain with a bond with the lone pair having a greater repulsion. When lone pairs are present on the central atom, the electron geometry and molecular geometry are not the same.

In general, if additional lone pairs are located on the central atom, the smaller the bond angles will be.

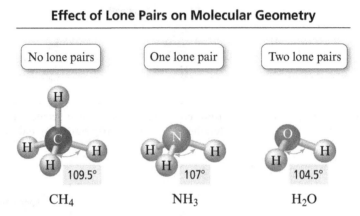

Effect of Lone Pairs on Molecular Geometry

No lone pairs   One lone pair   Two lone pairs

CH₄   NH₃   H₂O

109.5°   107°   104.5°

Figure 11.9 The Effect of Lone Pairs on Molecular Geometry The bond angles get progressively smaller as the number of lone pairs on the central atom increases from zero in CH_4 to one in NH_3 to two in H_2O.

Four Electron Domains with lone pairs present:

When four electron groups are present there are two possibilities: Three bonding pairs and one lone pair or two bonding groups and two lone pairs. In the case of ammonia, there are three bonding pairs and one lone pair. The lone pair exerts a greater repulsive force on the neighboring electrons and pushes on the N—H bond electrons slightly compressing the bond angle together. The geometry of the resulting molecule is trigonal pyramidal. In the case of water, there are two bonding groups and two lone pairs. Two lone pairs have a greater repulsive force than one lone pair, compressing the H—O—H bond angles even more than in ammonia. The resulting molecular geometry is *bent*. Another way to form the bent shape is when there are three electron groups, two bonding groups, and one lone pair, such as in SO_2. Be sure in learning names and shapes students realize there is logical reason for the names. Three atom molecules cannot form shapes other than linear or bent. Looking at built 3-D models of a molecule helps with determining the name of the molecular shape. See Figure 11.8.

Five electron Domains with lone pairs present:

When there are five electron groups present, the electron geometry is trigonal bipyramidal. There are possibilities of one, two, or three lone pairs. When there is one lone pair, the resulting molecular geometry is *seesaw*. If there are two lone pairs, the molecular geometry is *T-shaped*, whereas three lone pairs result in a linear molecular shape. See Figure 11.10.

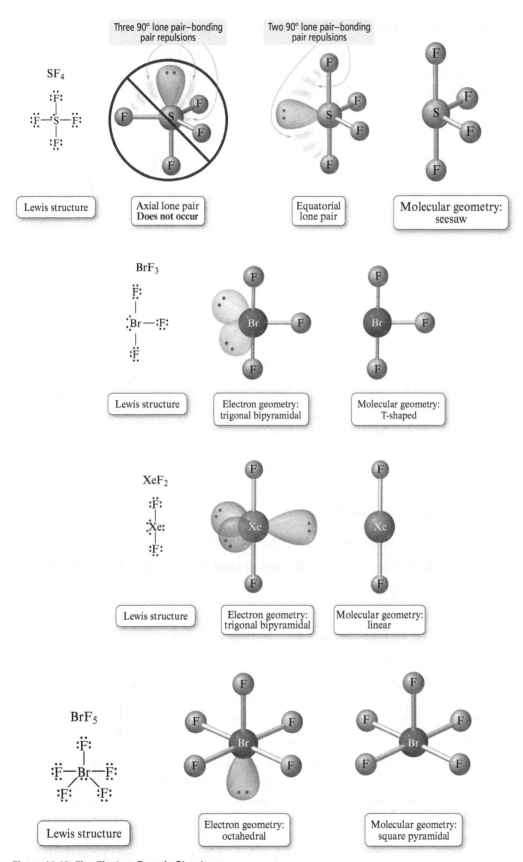

Figure 11.10 Five Electron Domain Structures

Six electron domains with lone pairs present:

When there are six electron groups there are possibilities of one or two lone pairs. If there is one lone pair, the molecular geometry is *square pyramidal* while two lone pairs results in a *square planar* molecular geometry.

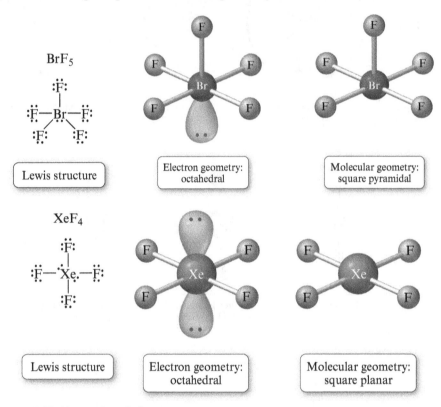

Figure 11.11 Six Electron Domain Structures

Table 11.1   Table of Electron Groups with Geometry and Molecular Shape

Number of Electron Groups	Electron Geometry	Number of Lone Pairs	Name of Molecular Shape
4	Tetrahedral	1	Trigonal pyramidal
4	Tetrahedral	2	Bent
5	Trigonal bipyramidal	1	Seesaw
5	Trigonal bipyramidal	2	T shape
5	Trigonal bipyramidal	3	Linear
6	Octahedral	1	Square pyramidal
6	Octahedral	2	Square planar

This is summarized in the following table. Note students do not need to memorize this table, but they must understand why each shape forms and as well as the properties, electron repulsions, and intermolecular forces associated with each of these shapes. Remember: (1) Electron geometries are the same as molecular geometries only when there are no lone pairs of electrons on the central atom. (2) Lone pairs of electrons will exhibit greater repulsions pushing bond angles closer together. (3) If more than one structure can be drawn, the molecule has resonance.

Table 11.2 3-D shapes of Basic Structures, Electron and Molecular Geometries

Electron Groups*	Bonding Groups	Lone Pairs	Electron Geometry	Molecular Geometry	Approximate Bond Angles		Example
2	2	0	Linear	Linear	180°	$\ddot{O}=C=\ddot{O}$	
3	3	0	Trigonal planar	Trigonal planar	120°		
3	2	1	Trigonal planar	Bent	<120°	$\ddot{O}=\ddot{S}-\ddot{O}$	
4	4	0	Tetrahedral	Tetrahedral	109.5°		
4	3	1	Tetrahedral	Trigonal pyramidal	<109.5°		
4	2	2	Tetrahedral	Bent	<109.5°	$H-\ddot{O}-H$	
5	5	0	Trigonal bipyramidal	Trigonal bipyramidal	120° (equatorial) 90° (axial)		
5	4	1	Trigonal bipyramidal	Seesaw	<120° (equatorial) <90° (axial)		
5	3	2	Trigonal bipyramidal	T-shaped	<90°		
5	2	3	Trigonal bipyramidal	Linear	180°		
6	6	0	Octahedral	Octahedral	90°		
6	5	1	Octahedral	Square pyramidal	<90°		
6	4	2	Octahedral	Square planar	90°		

*Count only electron groups around the central atom. Each of the following is considered one electron group: a lone pair, a single bond, a double bond, a triple bond, or a single electron.

Section 11.4   **VSEPR Theory: Predicting Molecular Geometries**

When drawing structures on paper, there are ways to indicate the shape in 3-D depending on whether the bond is going into the page (a hatched wedge) or coming out of the page (solid wedge). After drawing a Lewis structure, determine the geometry, and build a model. This will help with drawing 3-D shapes. An atom behind is indicated by the hatched wedge and an atom in front is indicated by the solid wedge. The following diagrams show how to draw several 3-D shapes.

Straight line	Hatched wedge	Solid wedge
Bond in plane of paper	Bond going into the page	Bond coming out of the page

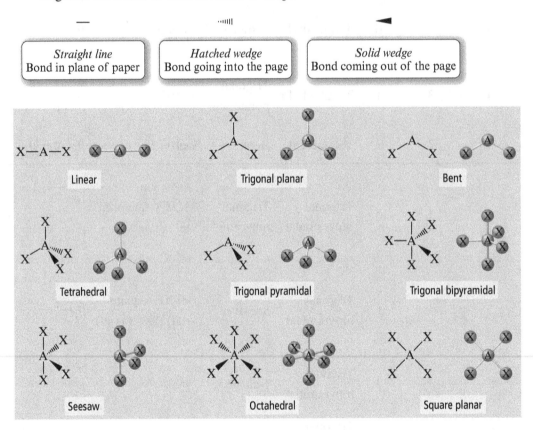

Figure 11.12

In larger molecules, with more than one central atom, there will be combinations of shapes, such as in methanol, in which a tetrahedral shape is around the carbon atom, whereas a bent shape is around the oxygen atom. Only one central atom is focused on at a time. On the AP test, the specific atom the geometry is asked for will be identified.

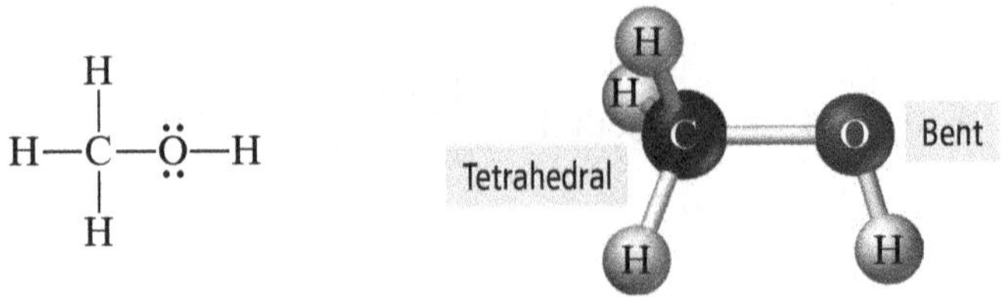

Figure 11.13 Methanol Structure

On the AP Exam, students will need to be able to interpret structures as well draw them.

Molecular Shape and Polarity   Section 11.5

Many properties of molecules are due to the polarity of the molecule. Molecular polarity depends on *both* molecular shape *and* molecular polarity. Do not confuse this with bond polarity. It is possible to have polar bonds and be a nonpolar molecule. It all depends on the shape of the molecule and whether or not there is a resulting net dipole. The molecule will be polar if the shape and bond polarity results in a *net* dipole greater than zero. For instance, in carbon dioxide, subtracting electronegativities 3.5 – 2.5, the C—O bonds subtract to 1.0 and are polar, but because the two bonds are equal and on opposite sides of the molecule, with a bond angle of EXACTLY 180°, the two opposite dipole moments cancel each other, resulting in a net dipole of zero. Thus, CO_2 is nonpolar as a molecule. If there is even a slight deviation from exact angular cancellation, the net dipole will not be zero and the molecule will be slightly polar.

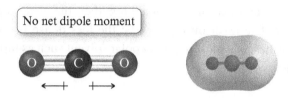

Figure 11.14 Carbon Dioxide Structure

Water also has polar bonds with an electronegativity difference between the oxygen and hydrogen atoms of 3.5 – 2.1 resulting in a difference of 1.4 just like the C—O bonds in carbon dioxide, but a tetrahedral electron geometry and bent shape. The orientation of the two H—O water has bonds and the two lone electron pairs results in a net dipole, therefore water is a polar molecule.

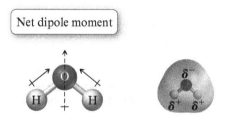

Figure 11.15 Water Structure

Students are not expected to add vectors, but if they have an understanding of vectors from physics and mathematics, it helps them understand net dipole moments. There is a review of vector addition on page 452 in the text book. By looking at each general molecular shape, the general presence of a dipole can be predicted. We use *generally* here because it depends on the atoms in the bonds as well as the angles. A tetrahedral shape can be polar or nonpolar. If a central atom has all the same types of atoms attached, it will assume a tetrahedral shape, and it will be nonpolar. An example would be CCl_4. Different bond polarities among the bonded atoms of a symmetric shape can also result in a polar molecule. An example would be CH_3Cl. Students should be able to look at shapes and determine

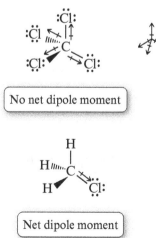

Figure 11.16 Tetrahedral Structure   **Figure 11.17 Trigonal Pyramidal Structure**

polarity; they should be capable of explaining why it is present or why it is not present. Molecular polarity is important because several molecular properties depend on the degree of polarity present. For instance, molecules with similar polar properties can dissolve in each other and form solutions. Water is polar and hence other polar molecules will dissolve in it, but nonpolar molecules such as oil will not. When water and oil are mixed together, the water layer stays separate from the oil layer. The layer on top will be the less dense layer. When cleaning oil-based paintbrushes, one must use a nonpolar solvent such as turpentine or mineral oil instead of water.

Figure 11.18 Oil and water do not mix because water molecules are polar and the molecules that compose oil are nonpolar. The intermolecular forces in a sample of liquid oil are different than the intermolecular forces in a sample of liquid water. Hence, oil and water are not miscible.

An interesting question arises when you consider washing oil from your hands using soap and water. How does soap work if water and oil do not mix? Soap is a unique type of molecule having a polar end attracted to water and a nonpolar end attracted to oil. The soap acts as a link between the two, so you can clean oil off your clothes, skin, or dishes.

Section 11.6   Valence Bond Theory: Orbital Overlap as a Chemical Bond

Another model used to explain how atoms form bonds is called valence bond theory. In this theory, when the nuclei of two atoms approach each other, a lone electron in an atomic orbital overlaps another lone electron in its atomic orbital. The interaction brings the electrons closer together. The optimum distance is where overlap occurs without too much repulsion between nuclei. The result is a blend of two or more atomic orbitals and the geometry of the overlap will determine the shape of the molecule. This is shown using H_2 in the following diagram.

Interaction Energy of Two Hydrogen Atoms

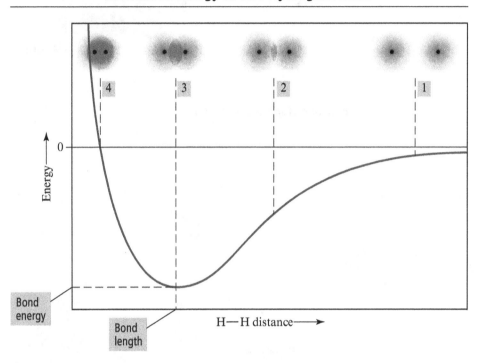

Figure 11.19 Interaction Energy Diagram for H_2   The potential energy of two hydrogen atoms is lowest when they are separated by a distance that allows their 1s orbitals a substantial degree of overlap without too much repulsion between their nuclei. This distance, at which the system is most stable, is the bond length of the H_2 molecule (labeled 3 on this graph).

Valence Bond Theory: Hybridization of Atomic Orbitals   Section 11.7

Simple overlaps cannot adequately explain all bonding and resulting molecular shapes. Hybridization theory is used to explain these examples. In this theory, when atomic orbitals combine, the new orbitals can be hybrids of the original orbitals. Hybrid orbitals minimize the energy of the molecule by maximizing the orbital overlap in a bond. The number of atomic orbitals shown in the hybrid notation always equals the number of hybrid orbitals formed. The shape of the molecule depends on the number of these hybrid orbitals formed. For example, the tetrahedral shape results from sp^3 hybridization. One *s* and three *p* atomic orbitals hybridize to form four equivalent sp^3 hybrid orbitals. All four sp^3 hybrid orbitals are exactly equal.

H₂S bond formation

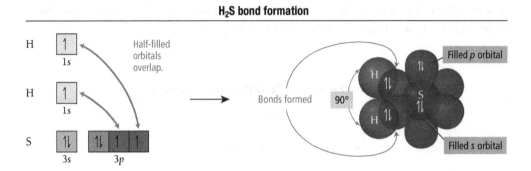

Formation of sp^3 Hybrid Orbitals

One s orbital and three p orbitals combine to form four sp^3 orbitals.

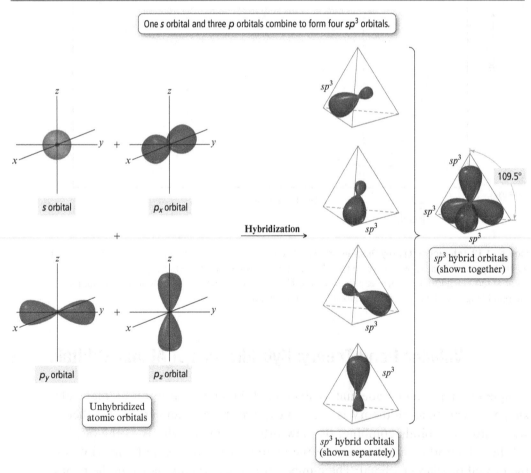

Figure 11.20 sp^3 Hybridization   One *s* orbital and three *p* orbitals combine to form four sp^3 hybrid orbitals.

In sp^2 hybridization, three equal sp^2 orbitals form resulting in a trigonal planar geometry.

Another concept in molecular bonding that uses atomic orbital overlap theory is the formation of sigma and pi bonds. Straight end-to-end overlap bonds are called *sigma bonds*. These overlaps can involve either *s* or *p* orbitals. *Pi bonds* are formed from side-to-side overlap of *p* orbitals. Figure 11.22 illustrates both sigma and pi bonds as well as the resulting Lewis structure.

Formation of *sp*^{2} Hybrid Orbitals

One *s* orbital and two *p* orbitals combine to form three *sp*^{2} orbitals.

s orbital $+$ *p*$_x$ orbital $+$ *p*$_y$ orbital   Hybridization $\rightarrow$ *sp*^{2} hybrid orbitals (shown separately)   *sp*^{2} hybrid orbitals (shown together)

Unhybridized atomic orbitals

Figure 11.21 *sp*^{2} Hybridization   One *s* orbital and two *p* orbitals combine to form three *sp*^{2} hybrid orbitals. One *p* orbital (not shown) remains unhybridized.

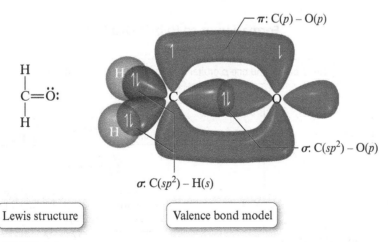

$$\text{H}-\overset{\text{H}}{\underset{\text{H}}{\text{C}}}=\ddot{\text{O}}:$$

π: C(*p*) – O(*p*)

σ: C(*sp*^{2}) – O(*p*)

σ: C(*sp*^{2}) – H(*s*)

Lewis structure   Valence bond model

Figure 11.22 CH$_2$O Structure

When a sigma and pi bond form between two atoms, a double bond is produced. A triple bond forms from a sigma and two pi bonds. Generally, pi bonds are weaker than sigma bonds. However, the combination of sigma and pi bonds in a double bond is stronger than a single sigma bond. A triple bond is even stronger, explaining why N$_2$

which has a triple bond is relatively nonreactive. This model also explains why the rotation in a double bond is limited due to the side-to-side overlap of the pi bonds. The sigma bonding in single bonds does not limit bond rotation. This rotation around a bond is very important in organic chemistry. When a double bond forms between two carbon atoms there is the possibility of an arrangement of atoms to form isomers of *cis* and *trans*. In a *cis* formation, the atoms on each side of the bond stay on the same side. In a *trans* formation, the two atoms on each side will be on opposite sides of the bond. This can be thought of as one atom *up* and the other atom *down*. Molecules that have the same formula, but different shapes are called isomers. Two isomers could have the same formula while one is *cis* and the other *trans*.

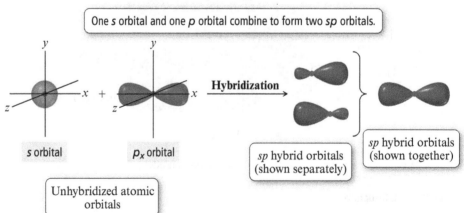

Figure 11.23 Formation of *cis*- and *trans*- Structures

In the *cis*- isomer the chlorine atoms are both on the bottom while in the *trans*- the chlorine atoms are diagonally across from each other.

Another type of hybridization is *sp*. An example is acetylene (ethyne) in which a triple bond forms between the carbon atoms. The *sp* hybrid on each C atom is only involved in the sigma bond formation, leaving two *p* orbitals on each C to form the two pi bonds.

Formation of *sp* Hybrid Orbitals

One *s* orbital and one *p* orbital combine to form two *sp* orbitals.

s orbital p_x orbital   **Hybridization**   *sp* hybrid orbitals (shown separately)   *sp* hybrid orbitals (shown together)

Unhybridized atomic orbitals

Figure 11.24 *sp* Hybridization   One *s* orbital and one *p* orbital combine to form two *sp* hybrid orbitals. Two *p* orbitals (not shown) remain unhybridized.

In the AP curriculum, only *sp*, sp^2, and sp^3 hybridizations are covered.

Molecular Orbital Theory: Electron Delocalization   Section 11.8

Another theory of bonding is molecular orbital theory. In this theory, orbitals are delocalized, whereas in the valence bond theory, they are attributed to a particular atom. Students do not need to know how to solve mathematically the wave functions of these orbitals, nor do they need to know the order of filling. However, students should understand Hund's rule is still followed. Bonding orbitals are lower in energy than the atomic orbitals from which they were formed.

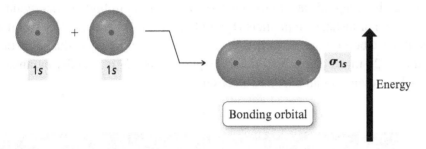

Figure 11.25 Formation of 1s Bonding Orbital

Some electrons fill antibonding orbital's, which have higher energies than the atomic orbitals from which they were formed.

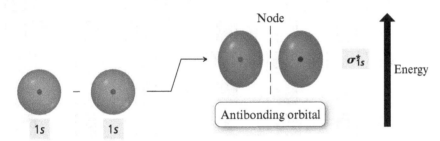

Figure 11.26 Formation 1s Antibonding Orbital

The bonding orbitals have a greater electron density compared to the antibonding orbitals.

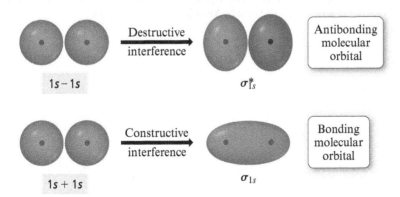

Figure 11.27 Formation of Bonding and Antibonding Orbitals   Constructive interference between two atomic orbitals gives rise to a molecular orbital that is lower in energy than the atomic orbitals. This is the bonding orbital. Destructive interference between two atomic orbitals gives rise to a molecular orbital that is higher in energy than the atomic orbitals. This is the antibonding orbital.

Molecular orbital theory can predict the bond order and whether certain bonds will form. The equation used is:

$$\text{Bond order} = \frac{(\text{number of electrons in bonding MO's}) - (\text{number of electrons in antibonding MO's})}{2}.$$

Stable bonds require a positive bond order, which can even be ½. Although the order of filling bonding and antibonding orbitals will not be tested on the AP Exam, students should practice filling the orbitals and determining the bond order. The stability and strength of the bond is determined by the relationship of the number of electrons in lower energy bonding orbitals to the number of electrons in higher energy antibonding orbitals. For instance, it predicts H_2 will have a single bond and He_2 will not form since it has a bond order of zero. Lewis structures predict O_2 is diamagnetic, but in Figure 11.28 molecular orbital theory explains why O_2 is actually paramagnetic due to the presence of an unpaired electron.

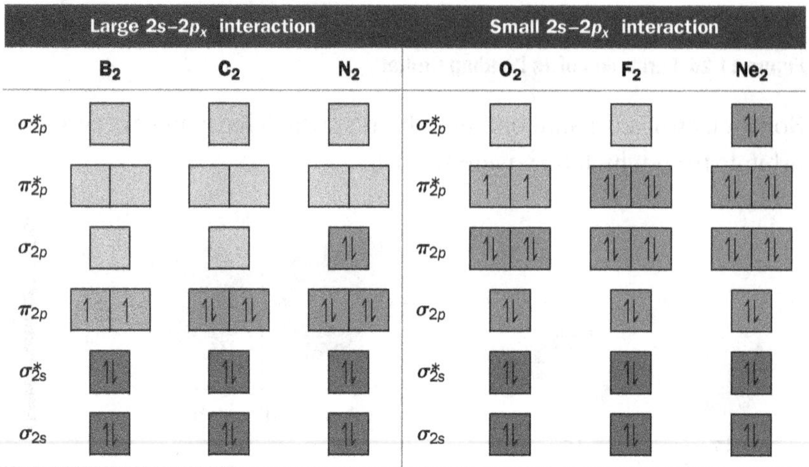

	Large 2s–2px interaction				Small 2s–2px interaction		
	B₂	C₂	N₂		O₂	F₂	Ne₂
Bond order	1	2	3		2	1	0
Bond energy (kJ/mol)	290	620	946		498	159	—
Bond length (pm)	159	131	110		121	143	—

Figure 11.28 Molecular Orbital Energy Diagrams for second-row *p*-block Homonuclear Diatomic Molecules The MO energy diagrams can explain properties not explained by Lewis structures. Oxygen gas is paramagnetic and is predicted by MO but not Lewis structures.

Looking at the MO in Figure 11.29 diagram for NO we can see an unpaired electron making it paramagnetic.

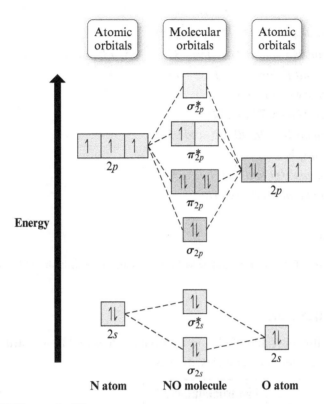

Figure 11.29 MO Diagram for NO

All of these bonding theories can help us predict the properties of molecules. They can be used to determine bond order, paramagnetic or diamagnetic properties, polarity of bonds, bond angles, hybridization, polarity of molecules, and molecular shapes.

Additional Practice

Self-Assessment Quiz Questions Q1, Q2, Q3, Q4, Q5, Q6, Q7, Q8, Q9, Q10, Q11, Q12, Q13, Q14, and Q15

Problems:
Review Questions 3, 4, 5, 7, 15, 17, 27 and 30
VSEPR Theory and Molecular Geometry 33, 34, 35, 43, and 44
Molecular Shape and Polarity 47, 48, 51, and 52
Valence Bond Theory 67 and 68
Molecular Orbital Theory 77 and 80
Cumulative Problems 87, 89, 90, 92, and 95
Challenge Problems 99
Conceptual Problems 109 and 111
Data Interpretation and Analysis 118

Equations to know:

$$\text{Bond order} = \frac{(\text{number of electrons in bonding MOs}) - (\text{number of electrons in antibonding MOs})}{2}$$

Practice AP Test Questions

1. Given the following table of electronegativity values and Lewis structure, the PCl_3 molecule overall can be classified as:

Element	Electronegativity
B	2.0
La	1.1
P	2.1
Sc	1.3
Cl	3.0

   A) a nonpolar molecule

   B) a polar molecule

   C) an ionic compound

   D) a coordinate covalent compound

2. The Cl—C—Cl bond angle in CCl_4 is closest to:

   A) 60°

   B) 90°

   C) 109°

   D) 120°

3. What is the molecular geometry of the $AsCl_3$ molecule?

   A) Trignonal pyramidal

   B) Trignonal planar

   C) Tetrahedral

   D) Trigonal bipyramidal

4. What is the molecular geometry of the ICl_4^- ion?

   A) Trignonal pyramidal

   B) Octahedral

   C) Tetrahedral

   D) Square planar

5. The orbital hybridization on the carbon atom in CH_2O is:

   A) sp

   B) sp^2

   C) sp^3

   D) sp^4

6. The best Lewis structure for CH_2Cl_2 is as given below:

   A) 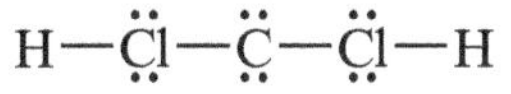 H—C̈l—C̈—C̈l—H

   B)
   $$\begin{array}{c} H \\ | \\ :\ddot{C}l-C-\ddot{C}l: \\ | \\ H \end{array}$$

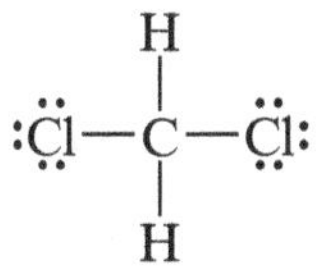

   C) H—H—C̈—C̈l—C̈l:

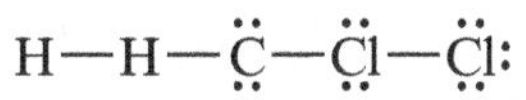

   D) 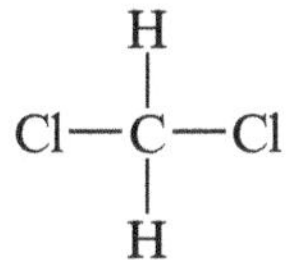
   $$\begin{array}{c} H \\ | \\ Cl-C-Cl \\ | \\ H \end{array}$$

7. Which one of the following molecules is classified as nonpolar?

   A) CH_2Cl_2

   B) $N_2H_2Cl_2$

   C) C_2Cl_4

   D) NCl_3

8. Using Lewis structures and formal charge rules, identify which of the following ions is most stable.

   OCN^- ONC^- NOC^-

   A) OCN^-

   B) ONC^-

   C) NOC^-

   D) All of these compounds are equally stable according to Lewis theory and formal charge rules.

9. Draw the Lewis structure for NO_2^- including any valid resonance structures. Which of the following statements is TRUE?

   A) The nitrite ion contains one N—O single bond and one N=O double bond.

   B) The nitrite ion contains two N—O bonds that are equivalent to $1\frac{1}{2}$ bonds.

   C) The nitrite ion contains two N=O double bonds.

   D) The nitrite ion contains two N—O single bonds.

10. The O—N—O bond angle of the nitrite ion, NO_2^- is as given below:

    A) Less than 90°

    B) About 90°C

    C) Greater than 90° but less than 120°

    D) About 120°

Chapter 11 Practice AP Test Questions Answers:

1. B); 2. B); 3. A); 4. D); 5. B); 6. B); 7. C); 8. A); 9. B); 10. C)

Data Interpretation and Analysis Question: Azobenzene and Solar Energy

Azobenzene, a photochromic T-type system, exhibits a reversible isomerisation process between its *trans* and *cis* isomers of different stability. Figure 1 illustrates the Lewis structures for the *cis* and *trans* isomers. In this process, a photoreaction causes the rearrangement of the molecule. The reverse *cis*-to-*trans* conversion can occur in the dark when heat is applied.

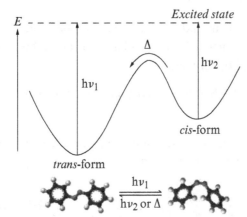

trans-azobenzene   *cis*-azobenzene

Figure 1

Figure 2 plots an energy level-diagram for the photo switching isomerization process of azeobenzene.

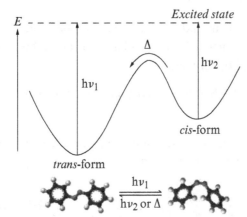

Figure 2
Source: Beilstein J. Org. Chem. **2012,** *8,* 1003–1017.

Hydrazobenzene $(C_6H_5)HNNH(C_6H_5)$ has a similar structure to azobenzene.

a) Hydrazobenzene does not exhibit isomerization when exposed to light. Can hydrazobenzene have *cis* and *trans* isomers? Draw the Lewis structure for hydrazobenzene.

b) What is the hybridization of N atom in each substance, azeobenzene and hydrazobenzene?

c) What is the N—N—C bond angle in each substance?

d) What is the shape of the molecule around the N atom of each substance?

e) How many σ bonds and π bonds are in each substance?

f) *trans*-azeobenzene has greater delocalization of the p electrons compared to hydrazobenzene. Explain why this is true. Draw resonance structures to show the extent of delocalization of the π electrons.

g) Which isomer of azeobenzene is more stable? Explain.

h) Which substance, azeobenzene or hydrazobenzene, would be the better choice for a solar energy conversion device? Explain.

Data Interpretation and Analysis Question Answers with Brief Explanations

a) The N–N bond in hydrazobenzene is a single bond. The N atoms are free to rotate about his bond. Therefore, *cis* and *trans* isomers of hydrazobenzene are not possible.

b) The N atoms in azeobenzene are sp^2 hybridized. The N atoms in hydrazobenzene are sp^3 hybridized.

c) The N–N–C bond in azeobenzene is about 118 °C. The N–N–C bond in hydrazobenzene is about 107.5 °C.

d) The molecular shape around the N atom in azeobenzene is trigonal planar for the *cis* and *trans* isomers. The molecular shape around the N atom in hydrazobenzene is trigonal pyramidal.

e) Azeobenzene has 7 π bonds and 9 σ bonds. Hydrazobenzene has 6 π bonds and 11 σ bonds.

f) The *p* orbitals in *trans*-azobeneze are in a plane and can overlap. The *p* orbitals in *cis*-azobenezene are not in a plane and cannot overlap.

g) The *trans*-azobenzene isomer is more stable compared to the *cis* isomer because it has resonance structures. The ability to undergo resonance makes the molecule more stable.

h) Azobenzene can switch between two isomers when exposed to sunlight and heat; therefore, it is the best choice for a solar energy device.

READING GUIDE

This chapter goes into the structure of molecules and the reasons behind the geometries of the structures. These concepts are part of Units 2, 3, and 4 in the AP Chemistry curriculum. Concepts not in the curriculum include orbital hybridizations with *d* orbitals and memorizing molecular orbital filling order.

Morhine: A Medical Imposter   Section 11.1

1. What is morphine? What is it derived from? How does morphine work on nerves?

2. What is an endorphin? How is morphine a medical imposter?

VSEPR Theory: The Five Basic Shapes   Section 11.2

3. What does VSEPR stand for and what is this theory based on?

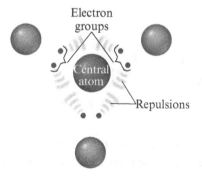

4. Using the figure above, explain what determines the geometry of a molecule.

5. Fill in the following table:

Number of Electron Groups on Central Atom	Example Molecule	Basic Name of the Shape	Bond Angle(s)	Basic Drawing of the Shape
2				
3				
4				
5				
6				

6. Explain why the bond angles in formaldehyde are not the predicted 120° for a trigonal planar structure.

7. Draw the Lewis structure for methane. Using methane as an example, explain why the Lewis structure gives an incomplete picture of the geometric structure of the molecule. Include a 3-D diagram of methane, showing its geometrical shape, in your answer.

Section 11.3   VSEPR Theory: The Effect of Lone Pairs

Use the following diagram in answering questions 8–10.

Effect of Lone Pairs on Molecular Geometry

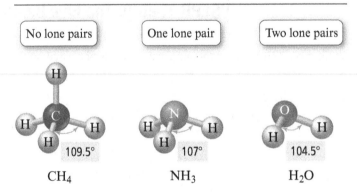

8. When lone electron pairs are present on a central atom in a simple molecule, why are the electron geometries different from the molecular geometries?

9. Explain why a tetrahedral electron geometry with one lone pair on the central atom does not show 109.5° angles. Use a 3-D drawing in your answer.

10. Explain why a tetrahedral electron geometry with two lone pairs on the central atom does not show 109.5° angles. Use a 3-D drawing in your answer.

11. Explain how the electron geometries with five electron groups form molecular shapes with the following numbers of lone pairs. Use diagrams in your answers.

   1 lone pair:

   2 lone pairs:

   3 lone pairs:

12. Explain how the electron geometries with six electron groups form molecular shapes with the following numbers of lone pairs. Use diagrams in your answers.

   1 lone pair:

   2 lone pairs:

13. Fill in the table below:

Number of Electron Groups	Number of Bonding Groups	Number of Lone Pairs on Central Atom	Name of Electron Geometry	Name of Molecular Geometry	Example	Drawing
4		1				
4		2				
5		1				
5		2				
5		3				
6		1				
6		2				

14. In general, summarize electron group repulsions and how they affect bond angles. Justify your answer.

VSEPR Theory: Predicting Molecular Geometries   Section 11.4

15. In a three-dimensional (3-D) model how do you indicate (i) a bond in a plane of the paper, (ii) a bond going into the page, and (iii) a bond coming out of the page? Include a diagram in your answer.

16. Using a 3-D model, draw the basic model of each of the following:

Shape	3-D General Model
Linear	
Trigonal Planar	
Bent	
Tetrahedral	
Trigonal Pyramidal	
Trigonal Bipyramidal	
Seesaw	
Octahedral	
Square Planar	

17. Explain how to predict the shape of larger molecules.

Section 11.5   Molecular Shape and Polarity

18. What is a net dipole moment? How is it indicated in a drawing? Can dipole moments cancel each other? Explain using a diagram.

19. Compare CCl_4 to CH_2Cl_2. Explain how to determine if a molecule is polar or not.

20. How can a molecule have polar bonds and be nonpolar? Justify your answer using an example.

21. Explain how phosphine, PH_3, can have nonpolar P-H bonds and be a polar molecule? Include a diagram in your answer.

22. Why is it important to be able to determine the polarity of a molecule? What properties does polarity explain?

23. In one, two, and three dimensions, explain how to do vector addition. Include diagrams in your answer.

24. What are the unique properties of soap that allow it to clean off oil in a water environment?

25. On the following diagram indicate which end will dissolve in water and which end will in dissolve fats and oils.

Valence Bond Theory: Orbital Overlap as a Chemical Bond   Section 11.6

26. What is valence bond theory? What is a hybridized orbital?

27. Explain how the Lewis model and the valence bond theory differ in their description of a chemical bond.

28. In valence bond theory, what determines the shape of the molecule?

29. Explain how to interpret this diagram of how two hydrogen atoms interact.

Interaction Energy of Two Hydrogen Atoms

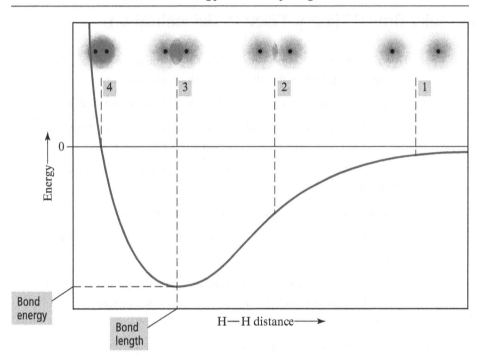

Valence Bond Theory: Hybridization of Atomic Orbitals   Section 11.7

30. How do hybrid orbitals differ from atomic orbitals?

31. How is the number of hybrid orbitals determined?

32. Using a diagram, explain why a central atom such as carbon in CCl_4 is sp^3 hybridized and the molecule forms a tetrahedral shape.

33. Using a diagram, explain why a central atom with sp^2 hybridization forms a trigonal planar shape.

34. What types of orbitals and hybrid orbitals compose a double bond? A triple bond? Why is rotation in a double bond restricted?

35. Draw the Lewis structure and the valence bond diagram of CO_2, show the location of sigma bonds and pi bonds. Explain the difference between a sigma bond and a pi bond.

36. Draw the two possible structures of 1,2-dichloroethane. Name each structure. Why are these molecules called isomers?

37. Using a diagram, explain why acetylene, C_2H_2, *sp* hybridization is linear in shape. Using diagrams, explain how AsF_5, SF_6, and ClF_3 can form using hybridization. What is the geometry of each?

Note: AP will not have questions with d orbital hybridization.

Section 11.8

Molecular Orbital Theory: Electron Delocalization

38. How does molecular orbital theory differ from valence bond theory? What can MO theory explain that the other models can't explain?

39. What is the difference between bonding and anti-bonding orbitals?

40. Explain how to determine bond order in a simple molecule. What does a positive bond order indicate? A negative bond order?

41. Explain how to determine if a molecule is paramagnetic or diamagnetic using MO theory.

42. What does it indicate if MO theory predicts a bond order of zero?

Note: For the AP Chemistry Exam students will not have to complete molecular orbital diagrams.

43. Using an oxygen molecule as an example, show how the Lewis theory, valence bond theory, and MO theory differ. Include diagrams with your answer.

44. Is oxygen paramagnetic or diamagnetic? Justify your answer.

Self-Assessment Answers

1. _____   2. _____   3. _____

4. _____   5. _____   6. _____

7. _____   8. _____   9. _____

10. _____   11. _____   12. _____

13. _____   14. _____   15. _____

LIQUIDS, SOLIDS, AND INTERMOLECULAR FORCES

The state of matter of a substance reflects the structure of the particles composing the substance. Topics will include the energy of state change from solid to liquid to gas and the reverse; attractive forces between molecules that have to be overcome to melt or vaporize the substance; and properties such as surface tension due to the forces between molecules. This chapter has many concepts students answer incorrectly on the AP exam due to common misconceptions. Section 12.8 on phase diagrams will not be tested on the AP exam, but students should understand these concepts since they are considered to be prior knowledge. In this chapter, the main AP curriculum is as follows:

12.2 **Solids, Liquids, and Gases: A Molecular Comparison**

12.3 **Intermolecular Forces: The Forces That Hold Condensed States Together**

12.4 **Intermolecular Forces in Action: Surface Tension, Viscosity, and Capillary Action**

12.5 **Vaporization and Vapor Pressure**

12.6 **Sublimation and Fusion**

12.7 **Heating Curve for Water**

12.9 **Water: An Extraordinary Substance**

Specific Learning Objectives Addressed in This Chapter:

SAP-5 Intermolecular Forces can explain the physical properties of a material.

SAP-5.A Explain the relationship between the chemical structures of molecules and the relative strength of their intermolecular forces when:
- The molecules are of the same chemical species.
- The molecules are of two different chemical species.

SAP-5.B Explain the relationship among the macroscopic properties of a substance, the particulate-level structure of the substance, and the interactions between these particles.

SAP-6 Matter exists in three states: solid, liquid, and gas, and their differences are influenced by variances in spacing and motion of molecules.

SAP-6.A Represent the differences among solid, liquid, and gas phase using a particulate-level model.

ENE-2 Changes in a substance's properties or change into a different substance requires an exchange of energy.

ENE-2.A Explain the relationship between experimental observations and energy changes associated with a chemical or physical transformation.

ENE-2.B Represent a chemical or physical transformation with an energy diagram.

Concepts and Vocabulary to Review:

Section 12.2 Solids, Liquids, and Gases: A Molecular Comparison

This section should be review for most students, but it is fundamental to understanding Section 12.3, which is an important section of the AP curriculum, especially the particle view of each state of matter. Students should be able to look at a particle diagram and determine if the substance is a gas, a liquid, or a solid by the arrangement of particles.

Table 12.1 The Three Physical States of Water

Phase	Temperature (°C)	Density (g/cm³, at 1 atm)	Molar Volume	Molecular View
Gas (steam) molecules are far apart and are at a high speed	105	5.90×10^{-4}	30.5 L	
Liquid (water) jumbled molecules but sliding over each other	20	0.998	18.0 mL	
Solid (ice) structured rigid arrangement and molecules are vibrating	−5.0	0.917	19.6 mL	

Most substances increase in density when they solidify because the molecules move closer together when they go from the liquid to solid state. Water is an unusual, but very important, exception because liquid water is denser than ice. This is due to the structure water adopts when freezing into its crystal—the molecules are organized so that they actually get further apart.

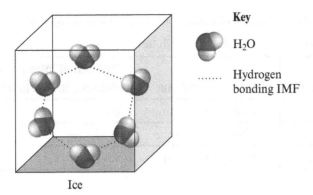

Key

H_2O

...... Hydrogen bonding IMF

Ice

In gases, molecules are far apart and move rapidly and randomly throughout the entire volume of the container. The relatively large distance between individual molecules allows gases to be easily compressed thus demonstrating one of their unique properties.

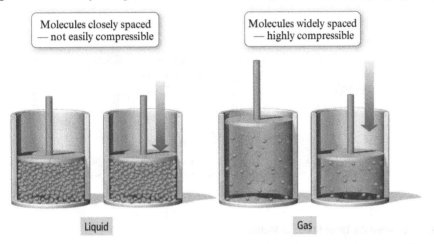

Molecules closely spaced — not easily compressible

Molecules widely spaced — highly compressible

Liquid

Gas

Figure 12.1 Gases Are Compressible   Molecules in a liquid are closely spaced and are not easily compressed. Molecules in a gas have a great deal of space between them, making gases compressible.

In liquids, molecules are in close contact but move relatively freely. The degree of this freedom of motion depends on the amount of attractive forces between the molecules. This freedom of motion explains why we can pour liquids. Liquids assume the shape of the container they are in, but interact somewhat with their container, such as when forming a meniscus at the surface, or climbing in a capillary tube.

In solids, the atoms are essentially locked into a position and do not move freely around each other. They do vibrate in position. Some solids may be crystalline where a very ordered structure exists or they may be amorphous where no long-range order exists.

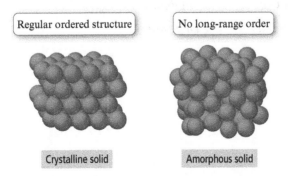

Regular ordered structure

No long-range order

Crystalline solid

Amorphous solid

Figure 12.2 Crystalline and Amorphous Solids   In a crystalline solid, the arrangement of the particles displays long-range order. In an amorphous solid, the arrangement of the particles has no long-range order.

A summary of the properties of each state is in the following table.

Table 12.2   Properties of the States of Matter

State	Density	Shape	Volume	Strength of Intermolecular Forces (Relative to Thermal Energy)
Gas	Low	Indefinite	Indefinite	Weak
Liquid	High	Indefinite	Definite	Moderate
Solid	High	Definite	Definite	Strong

To change from one state to another requires an exchange of energy. This can occur through a change in temperature, pressure, or both. When the state changes, this is known as a *phase change*.

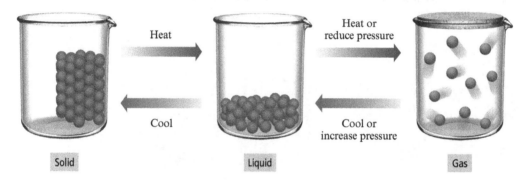

Figure 12.3   Transitions between the Three States of Matter

Gases can be changed noticeably by small variations in either temperature and/or pressure. Liquids will be changed only slightly and solids even less so in response to temperature and pressure changes. Common terms used in describing these phase (state) transitions are:

Solid → Liquid	*Melting*
Liquid → Gas	*Evaporating*
Gas → Liquid	*Condensing*
Liquid → Solid	*Freezing*
Solid → Gas	*Subliming*
Gas → Solid	*Depositing*

Intermolecular Forces: The Forces That Hold Condensed States Together

The structure of matter is influenced by interactions or attractive forces holding a group of molecules together. These interactions are called *intermolecular forces*. Strong forces of attraction tend to result in the substance being a solid or liquid, except at high temperatures. Weak forces of attractions tend to result in substances being in the gas phase at room temperature.

Students should understand the forces of attraction between molecules are not bonds within the molecule. Interfering with intermolecular forces between molecules does not change the bonding within the substance and does not result in new substances. Adding energy to boiling water does not break the O—H bonds within H—O—H to form hydrogen and oxygen gas, but rather the forces between neighboring H_2O molecules are overcome and water molecules are able to pull away from each other and enter the vapor phase.

The strength of a substance's intermolecular forces is reflected in its boiling points. The types of these forces **between molecules** are dispersion forces, dipole–dipole forces, and hydrogen bonding. Although the forces are separately classified according to their origins, they can all be present at the same time. An additional type, ion–dipole force, is present in aqueous solutions involving salts and in some other mixtures.

Dispersion forces, also called London forces (after Fritz London, the scientist who first explained them) are due to the lack of homogeneity of the electron distribution within each molecule. Nonpolar molecules have only dispersion forces between molecules. The greater the number of electrons, the greater the dispersion force because the electrons are less strongly attracted to the positively charged nucleus, and their electron orbital-distribution is easier to distort or become asymmetrical. A dipole moment is created when electrons become unevenly distributed around the positive nucleus. This creates uneven distributions of charge where one side of the molecule has a partial negative charge and the other side has a partial positive charge called

Dispersion Force

An instantaneous dipole on any one helium atom induces instantaneous dipoles on neighboring atoms, which then attract one another.

$\delta-$ $\delta+\cdots\delta-$ $\delta+\cdots\delta-$ $\delta+$

Figure 12.4 Dispersion Interactions   The temporary dipole in one helium atom induces a temporary dipole in its neighbor. The resulting attraction between the positive and negative charges creates the dispersion force.

instantaneous dipoles. (If this uneven distribution of charge is temporary, an instantaneous dipole moment forms. These are also called *temporary dipoles*). These temporary dipoles result in forces of attraction between molecules called *dispersion forces*. The stronger the total number of dispersion forces acting on a species, the higher the boiling point. (Remember: Boiling is adding enough thermal energy to the molecules to overcome the attractive forces holding liquid molecules together.)

The shape of the molecule will also affect the boiling point since shape affects the number of possible interactions. Molecules whose shape allows for them to "fit together" will have a greater area of interaction and higher boiling points. This concept explains why different isomers, especially non-polar organic isomers, have different boiling points.

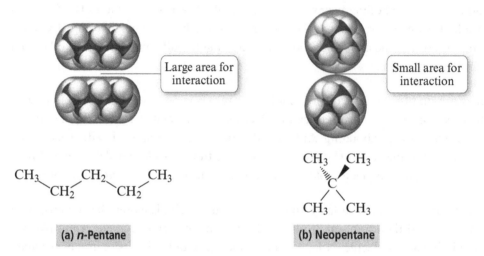

(a) *n*-Pentane   (b) Neopentane

Figure 12.5 Dispersion Force and Molecular Shape   (a) The straight shape of *n*-pentane molecules allows them to interact with one another along the entire length of the molecules. (b) The nearly spherical shape of neopentane molecules allows for only a small area of interaction. Thus, dispersion forces are weaker in neopentane than in *n*-pentane, resulting in a lower boiling point.

When comparing boiling points within a group such as the n-alkanes, the longer the chain, the stronger the dispersion forces and the greater the area for interaction.

Polar molecules have dipole–dipole forces as well as dispersion forces acting between them. These permanent dipoles contain areas of electrostatic charge in the polar molecules and are attracted to the oppositely charged area in another molecule. Dispersion forces are not "switched off" in these molecules, but have additional attractive forces. The dipole interactions and the dispersion forces act together to total the forces of attraction.

When comparing liquid samples of molecules of similar mass and similar numbers of electrons, molecules exhibiting dispersion and dipole–dipole intermolecular forces among molecules will have a higher boiling point compared to molecules having just dispersion intermolecular forces. For instance, ethane (C_2H_6) with a molar mass of 30.0 g/mol has only dispersion forces and a boiling point of -88 °C, whereas formaldehyde (CH_2O), also with a molar mass of 30.0 g/mol, has dispersion forces and dipole–dipole forces between molecules and has a boiling point of -19.5 °C.

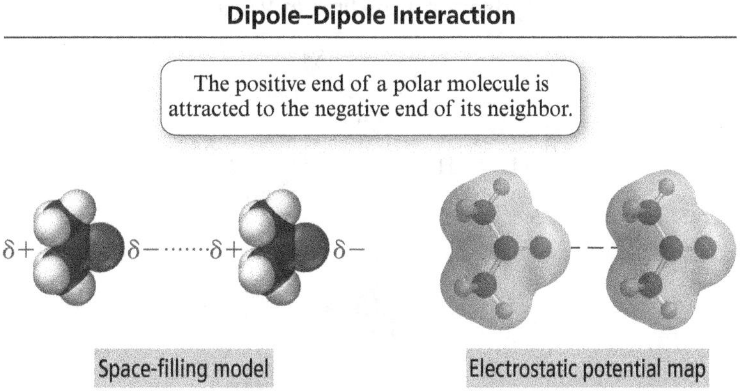

Dipole–Dipole Interaction

The positive end of a polar molecule is attracted to the negative end of its neighbor.

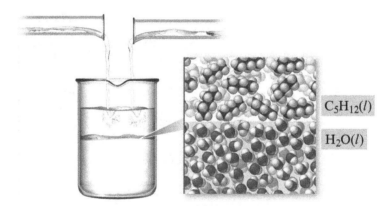

$\delta+$ ⋯⋯ $\delta-$ ⋯⋯⋯ $\delta+$ ⋯⋯ $\delta-$

Space-filling model   Electrostatic potential map

Figure 12.6 Dipole–Dipole Interaction   Molecules with permanent dipoles, such as acetone, are attracted to one another via dipole–dipole interactions.

The polarity of two different molecules affects their *miscibility*—the ability to mix two liquids without the liquids separating out as two liquids, like oil and water. Water and ethanol are miscible while oil and water are not. In oil and water, the intermolecular forces between the polar water molecules are too strong for its molecules to disperse among the nonpolar oil molecules.

$C_5H_{12}(l)$

$H_2O(l)$

Figure 12.7 Polar and Nonpolar Substances   Water and pentane do not mix because water molecules are polar and pentane molecules are nonpolar. A sample of liquid water has hydrogen bonding IMFs and dispersion IMFs, while a sample of liquid pentane has dispersion IMFs only.

An extreme version of a dipole–dipole interaction is hydrogen bonding. This occurs when molecules with hydrogen atoms are bonded to very small highly electronegative atoms, like fluorine, oxygen, or nitrogen, and interact with other similar molecules. The hydrogen bond is not inside the molecule, but it is a strong attraction between molecules and is a type of intermolecular force. In diagrams, this force between molecules is represented with a dashed line. See Figure 12.8.

Examples of hydrogen bonding include the interactions between HF molecules, NH_3 molecules, and/or H_2O molecules. When comparing families of molecules, molecules with hydrogen bonding have higher boiling points. In the following diagram, water has a much higher boiling point than the rest of the molecules in its family. This is explained given the increased intermolecular forces resulting from hydrogen bonding. See Figure 12.9.

Hydrogen Bonding in Water

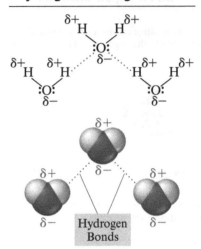

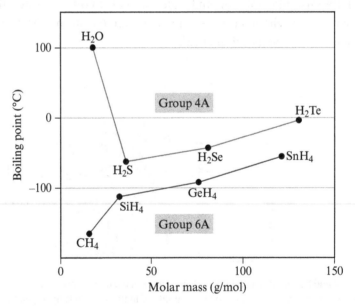

Figure 12.8 Hydrogen Bonding in Water

Figure 12.9 Boiling Points of Group 4A and 6A Compounds   Because of hydrogen bonding, the boiling point of water is anomalous compared to the boiling points of other hydrogen-containing compounds in its family of H_2S, H_2Se, and H_2Te.

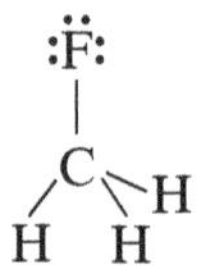

Keep in mind, a compound can have hydrogen atoms and small highly electronegative atoms in it and not exhibit hydrogen bonding. An example is fluoromethane. It contains both H and F atoms, however, they are not bonded to each other, but are both bonded to the central carbon atom. A sample of fluoromethane exhibits dispersion forces and dipole–dipole forces.

**Figure 12.10
Fluoromethane Structure**

Ion–dipole forces result when soluble ionic compounds are mixed with a polar compound. An example is NaCl in water. The positive poles of the water molecules are attracted to the negatively charged chloride ion, whereas the negative poles of the water molecules are attracted to the positively charged sodium ion. Hence, polar water can dissolve a variety of ionic compounds. See Figure 12.11.

Ion–Dipole Forces

The positively charged end of a polar molecule such as H_2O is attracted to negative ions, and the negatively charged end of the molecule is attracted to positive ions.

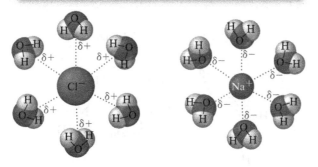

Figure 12.11 Ion–Dipole Forces   Ion–dipole forces exist between Na^+ and the partial negative ends of H_2O molecules and between Cl^- and the partial positive ends of H_2O molecules.

The types of intermolecular forces are summed up in the following table. Remember intermolecular forces are not exclusive, and some can be present simultaneously.

Table 12.3   Types of Intermolecular Forces

Type	Present In	Molecular Perspective	Strength
Dispersion*	All molecules and atoms	$\delta-$ $\delta+$ ···· $\delta-$ $\delta+$	0.05–20+ kJ/mol
Dipole–dipole	Polar molecules	$\delta+$ $\delta-$ ····· $\delta+$ $\delta-$	3–20+ kJ/mol
Hydrogen bonding	Molecules containing H bonded to F, O, or N	$\delta+$ $\delta+$ ··· $\delta-$ ··· $\delta+$ $\delta-$ $\delta-$	10–40 kJ/mol
Ion–dipole	Mixtures of ionic compounds and polar compounds	$\delta-$: $\delta-$ $\delta-$: + : $\delta-$ $\delta-$: $\delta-$	30–100+ kJ/mol

*The dispersion force can become very strong (as strong and even stronger than the others) for molecules of high molar mass.

An interesting cross-domain occurrence vital to biology is that the bases in DNA are held together by hydrogen bonding. Additionally, the helix structures of both proteins and nucleic acids (e.g., DNA and RNA) are due to hydrogen bonding between one part of these (very long) molecules and another part of the *same* molecule.

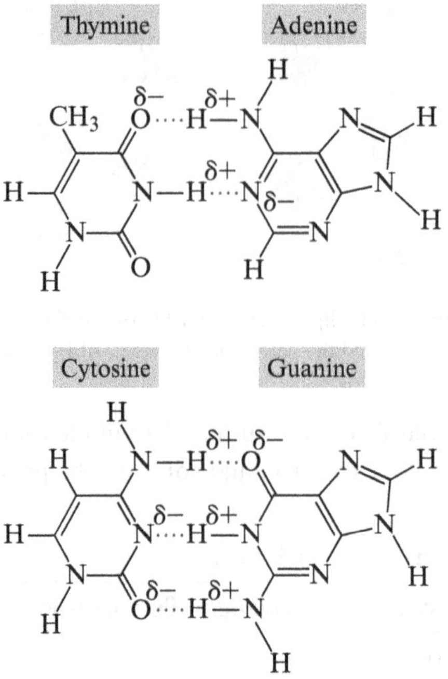

Figure 12.12 Complementary Base Pairing via Hydrogen Bonds   The individual bases in DNA interact with one another via specific hydrogen bonds that form between A and T and between C and G.

Section 12.4   Intermolecular Forces in Action: Surface Tension, Viscosity, and Capillary Action

Three observable consequences of intermolecular forces in liquids are surface tension, viscosity, and capillary action. *Surface tension* results from the molecules on the surface interacting only with the molecules to either side of them and below them, whereas a molecule in the center of the liquid interacts with molecules in all directions. Thus, there is a net force in toward the body of the liquid forming a "skin" of tightly bonded surface molecules. See Figure 12.13.

The stronger the intermolecular forces, the stronger the surface tension. The surface tension creates a film on the surface of the liquid resisting penetration. Water has hydrogen bonds, dipole interactions, and dispersion forces between water molecules resulting in a high surface tension. Hence, water skippers appear to walk on water and paper clips can float on the surface of water. In contrast, benzene has only dispersion forces resulting in a much lower surface tension, and paper clips cannot float on liquid benzene.

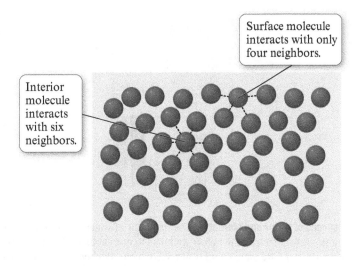

Figure 12.13 The Origin of Surface Tension   Molecules at the liquid surface have a higher potential energy than those in the interior. As a result, a liquid tends to minimize its surface area; its surface behaves like a "skin."

Figure 12.14 Surface Tension in Action   A paper clip floats on water because of surface tension.

Viscosity is a measure of a liquid's resistance to flow. Temperature affects viscosity as most liquids flow more freely at a higher temperature. More viscous liquids have stronger intermolecular forces. Molasses is more viscous than water. Motor oil developers take this into consideration when trying to produce formulas for oil that will flow well and lubricate effectively at high and low temperatures.

Capillary action is the phenomenon of a liquid rising or depressing in a narrow tube against gravity. Two forces are actually involved—adhesion and cohesion. *Adhesion* is the attraction of molecules to different materials such as the surface of the tube and *cohesion* is the attraction of the molecules to themselves. If the adhesive forces between glass and a liquid are stronger than the cohesive forces within the liquid, the level of liquid will rise in a tube of glass until the force of gravity on the column is balanced. The thinner the tube, the higher the liquid will rise. The balance between the adhesive and cohesive forces can also be observed in the shape of the meniscus in the tube or a graduated cylinder. Water has a concave meniscus because the adhesive forces are stronger than the cohesive forces. The meniscus of liquid mercury is convex because the cohesive forces are greater than the adhesive forces. See Figure 12.15.

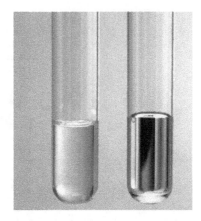

Figure 12.15 Meniscuses of Water and Mercury   The meniscus of water is concave because water molecules are more strongly attracted to the glass wall than to one another. The meniscus of mercury is convex because mercury atoms are more strongly attracted to one another than to the glass walls.

Section 12.5

Vaporization and Vapor Pressure

In order for a liquid to change to a vapor, it must overcome the forces of attraction holding its molecules together in the liquid. As some liquid molecules escape as vapor, the vapor is now a gas creating pressure over the liquid. When a liquid is placed in a closed container, some of the liquid might change to a gas. If a dynamic equilibrium is reached, then there are liquid molecules escaping as vapor at the same the rate vapor molecules are condensing back into liquid. The partial pressure that develops in the closed container when the liquid is in equilibrium with its own vapor is called *vapor pressure*. We can use the term *pressure exerted by the vapor* to describe the behavior of the vapor in the container. We can also refer to the vapor pressure of a liquid as the liquid's ability to vaporize at a given temperature. If not in a closed system, this pressure is not constant, but in a closed system, it reaches an equilibrium vapor pressure, depending only on the chemical nature of the liquid and the temperature. This is the principle used in raising the boiling point of water by using a pressure cooker. Increasing the pressure in the closed system of the pressure cooker, results in the boiling point of the liquid increasing, making the liquid hotter than 100 °C.

Kinetic molecular theory provides an explanation for why the vapor pressure of a liquid depends on the temperature. When the temperature of a liquid is raised, the *average* kinetic energy of the molecules increases. Remember in a liquid, there is a range of kinetic energies. The molecules with the higher kinetic energy may have enough energy to overcome the attractive intermolecular forces and vaporize.

In Figure 12.16 you can see that there are more molecules at the higher temperature with the energy to overcome the intermolecular forces and vaporize. If the surface area of the liquid is increased, a greater number of molecules have the ability to escape the surface. However, the relative number at equilibrium will be independent of the surface area. A substance whose molecules vaporize easily is called *volatile* and those that tend not to vaporize are called *nonvolatile*.

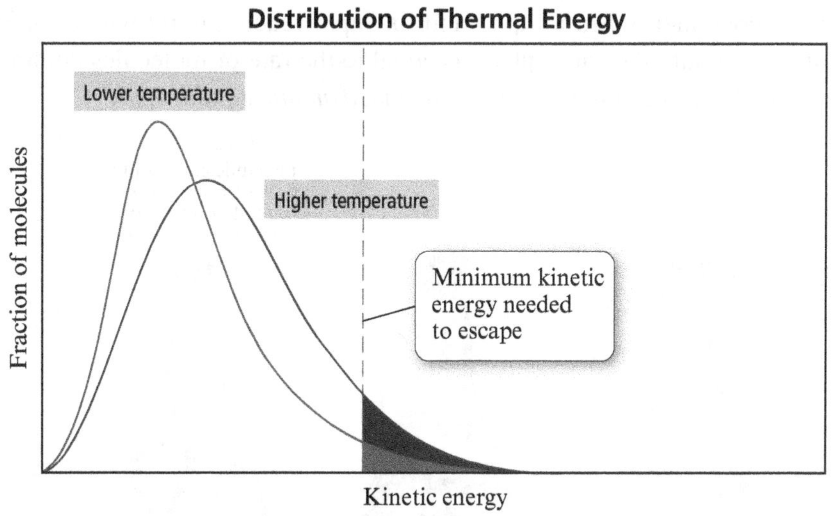

Distribution of Thermal Energy

Fraction of molecules

Lower temperature

Higher temperature

Minimum kinetic energy needed to escape

Kinetic energy

Figure 12.16 Distribution of Thermal Energy   The thermal energies of the molecules in a liquid are distributed over a range. The peak energy increases with increasing temperature.

A phase change from liquid to gas requires the addition of energy. This is an endothermic process.

$$\text{Liquid} \rightarrow \text{gas} \quad \textit{Evaporating} \quad +\Delta H_{\text{vap}} \quad \text{Endothermic}$$

Going to a more condensed phase requires the removal of the same amount of energy needed to change the phase in the opposite direction. Condensation is an exothermic process, the sign is opposite, but has the same numerical value of ΔH_{vap}.

$$\text{Gas} \rightarrow \text{liquid} \quad \textit{Condensing} \quad -\Delta H_{\text{vap}} \quad \text{Exothermic}$$

We use a combination of these processes to keep our bodies cool. When we get hot from exercising, we sweat. When sweat evaporates from our skin (endothermic), heat is absorbed by the liquid water in sweat. We, in turn, are cooled down due to this loss of heat. The amount is 40.7 kJ per mole of water in sweat at 100 °C. This is also affected by the surrounding conditions. If there is high humidity or lots of moisture in the air, vaporization will occur more slowly; and if the air is dry, vaporization will occur more quickly. The total cooling will be the same, but the rate of cooling will be different.

Figure 12.17 When we sweat, water evaporates from the skin. Since evaporation is endothermic, the result is a cooling effect.

In a sealed container, when a liquid and its vapor reach a point where the rate of molecules going into the vapor phase is equal to the rate of molecules coming back to the liquid phase, the system is said to be in a *dynamic equilibrium*.

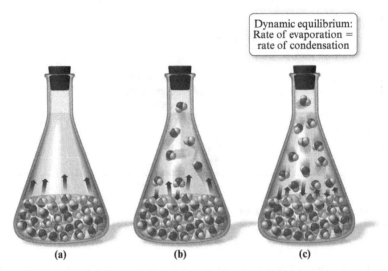

Dynamic equilibrium:
Rate of evaporation =
rate of condensation

(a)   (b)   (c)

Figure 12.18 Vaporization in a Sealed Flask   **(a)** When water is in a sealed container, water molecules begin to vaporize. **(b)** As water molecules build up in the gas state, they begin to recondense into the liquid. **(c)** When the rate of evaporation equals the rate of condensation, dynamic equilibrium is reached.

It is important to understand that the amount of vapor pressure is a reflection of the magnitude of the intermolecular forces present between molecules. If a lot of vapor is present, the attraction between molecules in the liquid is relatively weak.

If something disturbs the dynamic equilibrium, the system will react to restore the equilibrium.

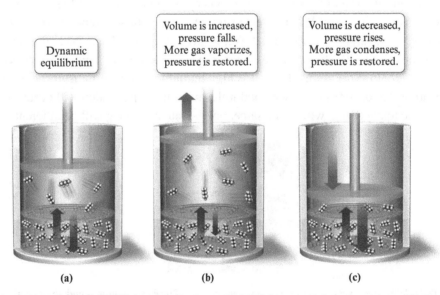

Dynamic
equilibrium

Volume is increased,
pressure falls.
More gas vaporizes,
pressure is restored.

Volume is decreased,
pressure rises.
More gas condenses,
pressure is restored.

(a)   (b)   (c)

Figure 12.19 Dynamic Equilibrium in *n*-Pentane   **(a)** Liquid *n*-pentane is in dynamic equilibrium with its vapor. **(b)** When the volume is increased, the pressure drops and some liquid converts to gas to bring the pressure back up. **(c)** When the volume is decreased, the pressure increases and some gas converts to liquid to bring the pressure back down.

A substance boils at the temperature at which the liquid's vapor pressure equals the external pressure. 100 °C is considered the normal boiling point of water. What is a *normal boiling point*? It is the boiling temperature at 1 atmosphere of pressure or 760 mmHg. These are the temperatures published in manuals as standard.

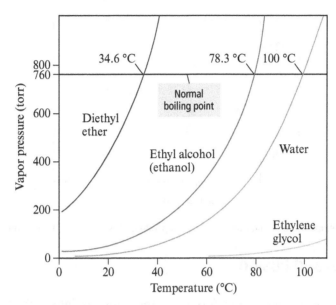

Figure 12.20 Vapor Pressure of Several Liquids at Different Temperatures   At higher temperatures, more molecules have enough thermal energy to escape into the gas state, so vapor pressure increases with increasing temperature.

What if the pressure is not at 1 atmosphere? At any temperature when the vapor pressure equals the external pressure, the liquid will boil. This explains why, when water is boiled at a higher altitude where the pressure is less than 1 atmosphere, the boiling point will be lower. The external pressure changes, and therefore the vapor pressure required to equal it changes. For example, the boiling points at higher elevations (lower atmospheric pressure) will be lower than at sea level.

Table 12.4   Boiling Points of Water at Several Locations of Varied Altitudes

Location	Elevation (ft)	Approximate Pressure (atm)*	Approximate Boiling Point of Water (°C)
Mount Everest, Tibet (highest mountain peak on Earth)	29,035	0.32	78
Mount McKinley (Denali), Alaska (highest mountain peak in North America)	20,320	0.46	83
Mount Whitney, California (highest mountain peak in 48 contiguous U.S. states)	14,495	0.60	87
Denver, Colorado (mile high city)	5,280	0.83	94
Boston, Massachusetts (sea level)	20	1.0	100

*The atmospheric pressure in each of these locations is subject to weather conditions and can vary significantly from these values.

As long as some liquid is present and is in contact with the gas, the temperature will not rise above the boiling point.

Knowing this, one can look at a graph and determine the boiling point by seeing where the temperature remains constant between the liquid and gas phases.

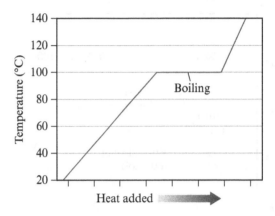

Figure 12.21 The Temperature during Boiling   The temperature of water during boiling remains at 100 °C.

Section 12.6   ## Sublimation and Fusion

Sublimation is the process of transforming a solid directly into a gas. Solid carbon dioxide, also called dry ice, does this at normal conditions of temperature and pressure. At the surface of the solid substance, the molecules are vibrating faster, are not bound as tightly by the intermolecular forces as they are within the body of the material, and when they have enough energy to overcome the intermolecular forces, they can escape as a gas.

Figure 12.22 Dry ice (solid CO_2) sublimes but does not melt at atmospheric pressure.

Ice also does this at temperatures below freezing. This explains why frozen foods kept in a freezer develop ice crystals and the food dries out. The ice (water) within the food sublimes and is then deposited on the outside as fresh ice often called freezer burn.

Solid $\rightarrow$ gas   *Subliming* $+\Delta H_{sub}$ Endothermic

Gas $\rightarrow$ solid   *Depositing* $-\Delta H_{sub}$ Exothermic

When the rate of the gas being formed is equal to the rate of the gas being deposited, the phase change is at dynamic equilibrium. The pressure at dynamic equilibrium is the vapor pressure of the solid. The enthalpies of these changes are all state functions since only differences from the beginning to the end matter.

Most substances change from a solid into a liquid when heat is added and then back into a solid when cooled.

Solid $\rightarrow$ liquid   *Melting* $+\Delta H_{fus}$ Endothermic

Liquid $\rightarrow$ solid   *Freezing* $-\Delta H_{fus}$ Exothermic

When the temperature during heating and cooling is graphed, the temperature remains constant at the point where the transition between states occurs (see Figure 12.23). Students need to read these graphs and identify melting points and freezing points. As with boiling and condensing, the amount of energy absorbed during melting, which is an endothermic process, is the same amount of energy removed for freezing, which is an exothermic process. Thus, one graph represents the transitions in either direction. If the graph is transitioning downward, heat is being removed (lost by the system) indicating a cooling curve and in a transition moving upward heat is being added to the system which indicates a heating curve.

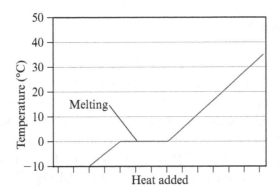

Figure 12.23 Temperature during Melting   The temperature of water during melting remains at 0.0 °C as long as both solid and liquid water remain.

Comparing the heat of vaporization and the heat of fusion for the same substance, we find that the heat of vaporization is a higher value as more forces need to be overcome to fully separate the molecules.

Heating Curve for Water   Section 12.7

When the graphs for melting and boiling are added together, both the transitions between solid and liquid and liquid to gas can be identified.

There are two different kinds of overall change represented in such a curve: the change within a state such as heating liquid water and the change of state called a phase change such as changing solid ice to liquid water. The calculation of the

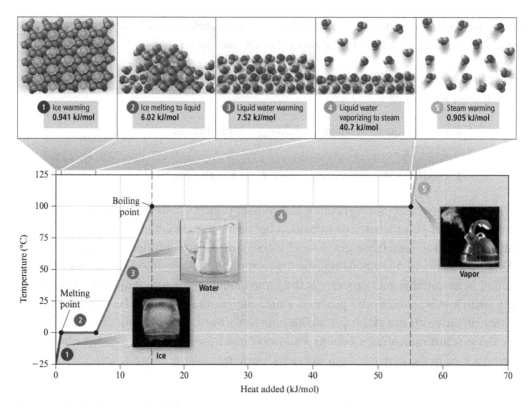

Figure 12.24 Heating Curve for Water

amount of energy involved in each type of change has to be done separately. In the stages where the substance is heating and not changing state, such as heating the solid, heating the liquid, or heating the gas, a specific heat equation is used. Each state has its own value for specific heat (*c*); $q = mc\Delta T$ (remember: the equation used for specific heat on the AP test is slightly different than the equation in the text). The specific heat of ice is 2.09 J/g·°C, the specific heat of water (liquid) is 4.18 J/g·°C, and the specific heat of water vapor is 2.01 J/g·°C.

During each state transition or phase change, the equations used are similar, but each uses different constants; $q = n\Delta H_{fus}$ and $q = n\Delta H_{vap}$. Notice on the in Figure 12.24, evidence of the temperature of a phase change is not observing a temperature change. The ΔH_{fus} is 6.02 kJ/mol and ΔH_{vap} is 40.7 kJ/mol. A common mistake in these calculations where a mass of substance is given is forgetting to convert mass to moles of substance.

The total enthalpy change, ΔH, through any series of steps is simply the sum of the ΔH values for each step, provided that the amount of substance remains constant.

$$\Delta H_1 + \Delta H_2 + \Delta H_3 + \Delta H_4 + \Delta H_5 = q$$

These can be written as one long problem, or each amount of energy can be calculated from each step and then added. Another major error is not converting to similar units so the values can be added.

A sample problem might be how much energy is required to raise the 100.0 g of ice at −10 °C to steam at 120 °C. First, draw a quick sketch to see all the phases—this will go through all five steps with 1. changing from −10 °C to 0 °C, 2. changing from 0 °C as a solid to 0 °C as a liquid, 3. changing from 0 °C as a liquid to 100 °C as a liquid, 4. changing from 100 °C as a liquid to 100 °C as a gas, and 5. changing from 100 °C as a gas to 120 °C as a gas. Writing this as one problem would be [(100.0 g ice × 10 °C × 2.09 J/g · °C) × 1 kJ/1000 J] + (100.0 g ice/18.01 g/mol × 6.02 kJ/mol) + [(100.0 g water × 100 °C × 4.18 J/g · °C) × 1 kJ/1000 J] + (100.0 g water/18.01 g/mol × 40.7 kJ/mol) + [(100.0 g steam × 20 °C × 2.01 J/g · °C) × 1 kJ/1000 J] = q or $q = 3.1 × 10^2$ kJ.

Water: An Extraordinary Substance   Section 12.9

Why is water extraordinary?

It is a liquid at room temperature due to the dipole interactions, dispersion forces, and hydrogen bond attractions between the molecules. Other compounds with a similar molar mass such as methane are gases at room temperature. For its molar mass, water has a high boiling point.

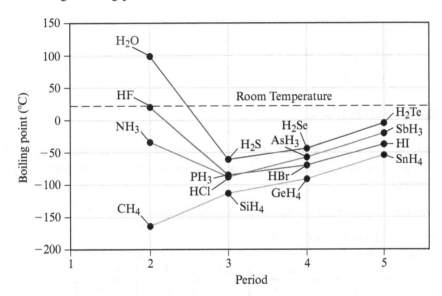

Figure 12.25 Boiling Points of Main-Group Hydrides   Water is the only common main-group hydride that is a liquid at room temperature.

Due to water's polarity, it can dissolve a good variety of polar and ionic substances. This can be a problem when contaminates get into the water supply, but is a great advantage to living cells where many substances are needed to be in solution.

When water freezes, it forms a less dense state, so its solid floats on its liquid. This is an important feature for life on earth. Ice forms on the tops of lakes, and fish and other life forms can continue to live in the water below. A disadvantage of this property is that when water freezes, the expansion of the solid causes water delivery pipes to break or living cells to burst (e.g., frostbite). What is flash freezing? Flash freezing is done so quickly the water molecules do not have time to arrange themselves in a regular pattern, which prevents the cells in food from bursting.

The high specific heat of water relative to land keeps coastal areas and islands at fairly constant temperatures.

Additional Practice

Self-Assessment Quiz Questions Q1, Q2, Q3, Q4, Q5, Q6, Q7, Q8, and Q9

Problems:
Review Questions 9, 10, 11, 12, 13, 15, 16, 17, 19, 22, 23, 29, 31, and 32
Intermolecular Forces 35, 37, 39, 41, 43, and 45
Surface Tension, Viscosity, and Capillary Action 48, 49, and 51
Vaporization and Vapor Pressure 53, 54, 60, and 62
Sublimation and Fusion 67, 68, 71, and 72
Uniqueness of Water 79, 80, 81, and 82
Cumulative Problems 84, 91, and 94
Conceptual Problems 105 and 108
Data Interpretation and Analysis 117

Equations to know:

$$\text{In } P_{vap} = \frac{-\Delta H_{vap}}{RT} + \text{In } \beta \text{ (β is a constant)}$$

$$\text{In } \frac{P_2}{P_1} = \frac{-\Delta H_{vap}}{R} \left(\frac{1}{T_2} - \frac{1}{T_1} \right)$$

Practice AP Test Questions

1. Solid KBr dissolves in water to form a solution of potassium bromide, KBr(*aq*). The predominat intermolecular force between the bromide ions and water molecules is:

    A) Ion–ion   B) Ion–dipole   C) Hydrogen bond   D) Dipole–dipole

2. Given the following information:

	CH_4	SiH_4	GeH_4	SnH_4
MW (g/mol)	16	32	76	122
Boiling Point (°C)	−162	−112	−88	−52

    Which statement *best* explains the increase in boiling point of the four compounds from CH_4 to SnH_4.

    A) The strength of London dispersion forces increases due to an increased number of electrons making the electron cloud more polarizable. The increase in the strength of the London dispersion forces between molecules requires an increase in energy to separate the molecules.

    B) When the molecular weight increases, an increase in energy is needed to get the heavier molecules moving faster.

    C) The strength of London dispersion forces and dipole–dipole interactions increases thus requiring more energy to separate the molecules.

    D) The strength of London dispersion forces increases and the molecular weight increases. Both factors are required to explain the increase in the boiling point.

3. Diethyl ether has a boiling point of 34.5 °C and 1-butanol has a boiling point of 117 °C. Both compounds have the same molecular weight and same molecular formula ($C_4H_{10}O$). Which statement best explains the difference in boiling points?

$H_3C-CH_2-CH_2-CH_2-\overset{..}{\underset{..}{O}}-H$

1-butanol

$H_3C-CH_2-\overset{..}{\underset{..}{O}}-CH_2-CH_3$

Diethyl ether

A) The strength of London dispersion forces is greater in 1-butanol.

B) Oxygen is toward the end of the structure in 1-butanol and in the middle of the structure in Diethyl ether.

C) The 1-butanol molecules can form strong hydrogen bonds with other 1-butanol molecules. Diethyl ether forms dipole–dipole intermolecular forces, which are not as strong as hydrogen bonds.

D) The Diethyl ether molecules have more hydrogen atoms in place to form strong hydrogen bonds with other Diethyl ether molecules. 1-butanol also forms hydrogen bonds, but not as many as Diethyl ether.

4. Which drawing best indicates where hydrogen bonding occurs in methylamine, CH_3NH_2?

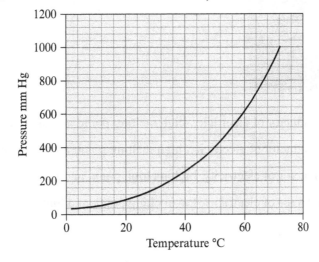

A)   B)   C)   D)

5. Graph 1 below plots the vapor pressure of methanol as a function of temperature. Estimate the normal boiling point of methanol.

A) 20 °C   C) 62 °C

B) 50 °C   D) 72 °C

Graph 1

6. In which of the following groups are the compounds arranged correctly in order of increasing melting point?

Low m.p. → High m.p.

A) NaCl, $MgCl_2$, $AlCl_3$, $SiCl_4$

B) LiCl, $BeCl_2$, BCl_3, CCl_4

C) $SiCl_4$, $AlCl_3$, $MgCl_2$, NaCl

D) $AlCl_3$, CCl_4, $SiCl_4$, BCl_3

7. Based on molecular weight, molecular structure, and intermolecular forces, which liquid sample when placed in its own closed rigid container would develop the highest vapor pressure at room temperature?

A) diethyl ether

B) 1,4-butanediol

C) n-butanol

D) 1,2-dimethoxyethane

8. Given the following representation of the structure of a solid compound, what properties will this compound most likely exhibit at room temperature?

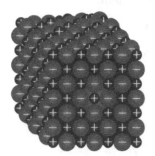

A) Good conductor of electricity, high melting point, and high vapor pressure

B) Good conductor of electricity, high melting point, and low vapor pressure

C) Nonconductor of electricity, high melting point, and low vapor pressure

D) Nonconductor of electricity, low melting point, and high vapor pressure

9. The Lewis structures of propanoic acid and isopropanol are provided below. Based on molecular weight, molecular structure, and intermolecular forces, which liquid sample will have the higher boiling point at 1 atm pressure and for what reason?

propanoic acid

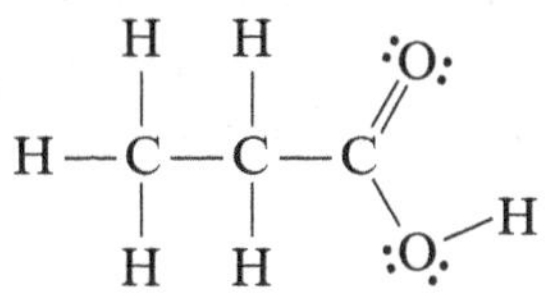

Isopropanol

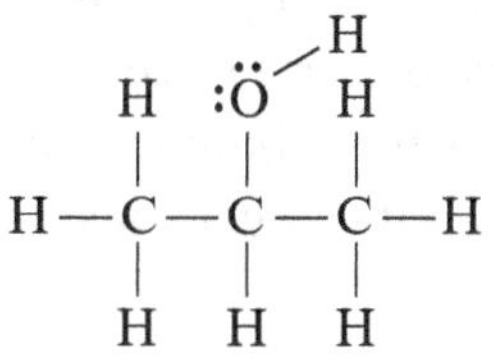

A) Isopropanol will have the higher boiling point because it has more electrons thus a larger electron cloud that can be distorted, creating more points of London dispersion forces.

B) Propanoic acid will have the higher boiling point because it can form two hydrogen bonds with another propanoic acid molecule.

C) Isopropanol will have the higher boing point because it can form both hydrogen bonds and London dispersion forces with other isopropanol molecules.

D) Propanoic acid will have the higher boiling point because it has more electrons, and it can form London dispersion forces. Also, the molecule can form a hydrogen bond with another propanoic acid molecule.

10. Which of the following describes how intermolecular forces influence physical properties of matter.

I) Intermolecular forces are primarily responsible for the input energy required to separate molecules in order for boiling to occur.

II. Intermolecular forces are primarily responsible for the attractive forces that determine the solubility of solids and liquids in water.

III. Intermolecular forces are not responsible for keeping large molecules like polymers and surfactants in the liquid state.

A) I only

B) II only

C) III only

D) I and II

Chapter 12 Practice AP Test Questions Answers:

1. B); 2. D); 3. C); 4. D); 5. C); 6. C); 7. B); 8. C); 9. B); 10. D)

Data Interpretation and Analysis: Intermolecular Forces

Physical properties of pure covalent substances are correlated with the strength of the total intermolecular forces of attraction between molecules. The boiling point of dibromomethane is about 2.5 times larger than the boiling point of dichloromethane. Since both substances have dipole–dipole intermolecular forces and dispersion inter-molecular forces, one of these forces of attraction has a larger contribution compared to the other. Table 1 lists the boiling point, dipole moment, polarizability, and van der Waals volume of several halogen containing molecules.

Table 1

Compound	Boiling Point (°C)	μ (D)	Polarizability (cm³)	Van der Waals Volume (L/mol)
CH_2F_2	−52.0	1.98		0.06268
CH_2Cl_2	39.6	1.60	7.21×10^{-24}	0.08689
CH_2Br_2	96.9	1.43	9.32×10^{-24}	0.1065
CF_4	−129	0.00	3.84×10^{-24}	0.06325
CCl_4	76.5	0.00	10.5×10^{-24}	0.1281
CBr_4	189.5	0.00		0.1718

a) Explain how the listed measurements for the dipole moment (μ) and polarizability of the compounds are related to the terms dipole–dipole intermolecular force and dispersion intermolecular force.

b) CH_2Br_2 and CBr_4 have polar covalent bonds. Explain why CH_2Br_2 has a dipole moment while CBr_4 does not have a dipole moment. Draw a 3-D structure for each compound to support your explanation.

c) Draw 3-D Lewis structures, including, including partial charges, for three neigh-boring molecules of dibromomethane in a sample of $CH_2Br_2(l)$ and indicate where two different intermolecular forces, dipole-dipole and dispersion, are operating.

d) Which intermolecular force, dipole–dipole or dispersion, plays a larger role in determining the higher boiling point of dibromomethane compared to the boiling point of dichloromethane? Explain.

e) Which intermolecular force, dipole–dipole or dispersion, best accounts for the trend in boiling points of the compounds listed in Table 1? Explain.

f) Does the molar mass by itself account for the trend in boiling points of the compounds listed in Table 1? Explain.

g) There seems to be a correlation between polarizability and van der Waals volume. Explain.

h) Estimate the value of polarizability for CH_2F_2 and CBr_4. Justify your prediction.

i) A student proposes that a plot of dipole moment versus van der Waals volume is useful to estimate the extent to which a compound is soluble in water. Graph 2 shows a plot of dipole moment versus van der Waals volume.

Graph 2

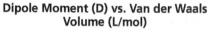

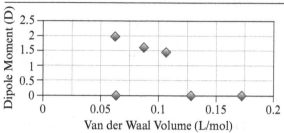

Does this graph provide enough information to estimate the extent of water solubility of a compound? Explain.

Data Interpretation and Analysis Question Answers with Brief Explanations

a) Dipole moment and polarizability are each a measurement of a unique physical property of a compound made on a sample of a substance. The terms dipole-dipole intermolecular force and dispersion intermolecular force are types of intermolecular forces of attraction acting between molecules. One does not directly measure dipole-dipole intermolecular force or dispersion intermolecular forces. One infers the strength of the IMFs operating between molecules by comparing physical properties such as boiling point and melting point.

b) Both in CBr_4 and CH_2Br_2 are in a tetrahedral arrangement. Bromine is more electronegative compared to carbon. Therefore, all of the C-Br bonds are polar covalent with the partial negative charge on bromine and the partial positive charge on carbon. The four C-Br bonds in CBr_4 are symmetrical with the vector dipoles pointing away from each other in a tetrahedral arrangement, thus cancelling each other. CBr_4 has a net dipole moment of zero. CH_2Br_2 has two C-Br bonds each pointing away from each other. These two vector dipoles do not cancel each other, they add to form a net dipole moment.

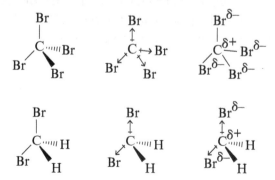

c)

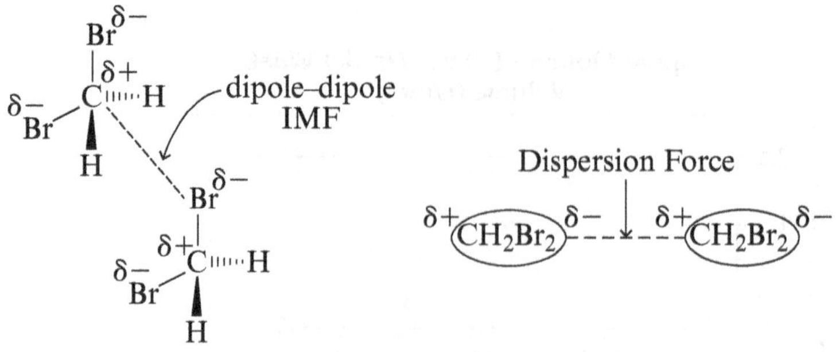

d) The dipole moment for CH_2Cl_2 is larger compared to the dipole moment for CH_2Br_2 dispersion. Based on just this information one would expect CH_2Cl_2 to a have a higher boiling point, but this is not so. The polarization for CH_2Br_2 is larger compared to the polarization for CH_2Cl_2, therefore dispersion forces are the predominate intermolecular forces.

e) Dispersion forces, as indicated by polarization values, best account for the trend in boiling points of the compounds listed in Table 1 because there is a correlation between the two.

f) Molar mass by itself does not account for the trend in boiling points of the compounds listed in Table 1 because there is no correlation.

g) There is a correlation between polarizability and van der Waals volume because polarization is a measure of the degree to which the molecule's electron cloud can be distorted to form temporary dipole moments. The more electrons a molecule has, the greater the likelihood of distortion of the electron cloud.

h) The estimated value of polarizability for CH_2F_2 is 5.2×10^{-24} cm^3 and CBr_4 is 12×10^{-24} cm^3. CH_2F_2 has fewer electrons compared to CH_2Cl_2 so we would expect the polarization of CH_2F_2 to be less than CH_2Cl_2 and the polarization of $CHBr_4$ to be greater than CCl_4.

i) The information in the graph could be somewhat useful. Water is a polar substance and has a net dipole moment, CF_4, CCl_4 and CBr_4 are all insoluble in water and all have a net dipole moment of zero. CH_2F_2, CH_2F_2 and CH_2Br_4 all have a net dipole moment and all are water soluble.

This chapter is a mixture of AP and non AP Chemistry curriculum. Concepts are primarily part of Unit 3 in the curriculum and the energy of phase changes are part of Unit 6. The AP Chemistry curriculum does not directly test on phase diagrams, although the concepts are considered prior knowledge.

Water, No Gravity   Section 12.1

1. Why does water form a sphere?

2. When the thermal energy of a substance is high relative to its intermolecular forces, what state of matter tends to exist?

3. What state of matter tends to exist when the thermal energy of a substance is low in comparison to its intermolecular forces?

Solids, Liquids, and Gases: A Molecular Comparison   Section 12.2

4. Using diagrams at the particulate level, explain the difference among solids, liquids, and gases.

5. Discuss two physical properties of each state of matter. Explain the difference between a crystalline solid and an amorphous solid.

6. Explain how molecules are moving in each beaker. Explain what is occurring between each arrow in the following diagram:

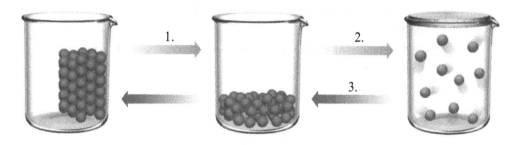

Section 12.3   **Intermolecular Forces: The Forces That Hold Condensed States Together**

7. Where do intermolecular forces originate from? For each of the following intermolecular forces, state the types of substances likely to have the force. Also explain where it occurs, what creates the force, how to determine if the force is present, and indicate how it is reflected in melting points. Also include a drawing of the force from a molecular perspective of the following intermolecular forces.

    Dispersion forces:

    Dipole–dipole forces:

    Hydrogen bonding:

    Ion–dipole forces:

8. Compare and contrast a permanent dipole with an instantaneous dipole. What does the term polarizability refer to?

9. Are intermolecular forces stronger or weaker than bonding forces within molecules? Justify your answer.

10. What is miscibility? What factors affect miscibility?

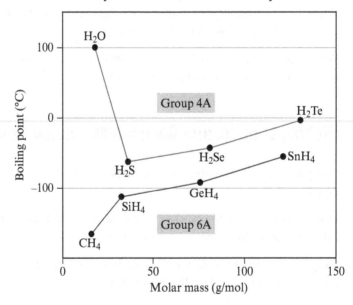

11. Using the figure above, explain the reasons for the observed trends in boiling points.

12. Make a table with the types of intermolecular forces and what types of substances they occur in.

Intermolecular Forces in Action: Surface Tension, Viscosity, and Capillary Action

Section 12.4

13. Using intermolecular forces, explain the concepts of surface tension, viscosity, and capillary action.

14. Using the terms adhesion and cohesion, explain what is occurring and why in the following picture:

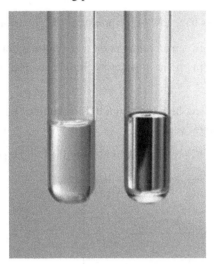

Vaporization and Vapor Pressure

Section 12.5

15. Which process, endothermic or exothermic, is associated with vaporization? With condensation? Explain why in each case.

16. Explain how the human body uses vaporization to keep cool.

17. What is the difference between a volatile and a nonvolatile substance?

18. Explain what a distribution of thermal energy for liquid molecules indicates.

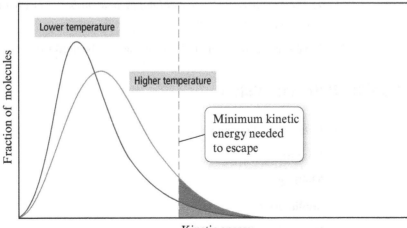

Distribution of Thermal Energy

19. Explain which volume of water will completely evaporate first at the same temperature and pressure and why: a 250-mL beaker with 100 mL of water or a 100-mL volumetric flask with 100 mL of water.

20. What is the definition of the enthalpy of vaporization for a substance?

21. Under what conditions do a liquid and its vapor reach a dynamic equilibrium? Use Le Chatelier's principle to explain what happens when a system in dynamic equilibrium is disturbed.

22. What types of substances have low vapor pressures? High vapor pressures?

23. What is the difference between a boiling point and a normal boiling point? What happens to the boiling point of water as altitude changes and explain why?

24. When water is being heated, how can you tell if the bubbles forming are air bubbles or bubbles of water vapor?

25. Using the following graph, explain how to identify the boiling point:

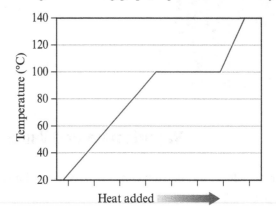

26. Explain how to use the Clausius–Clapeyron equation and a graph to find the heat of vaporization in a laboratory setting.

27. When does a critical transition point occur? What is a critical temperature? What is a critical pressure? Why are these points important?

Note: The AP Chemistry Exam will not include problems involving the Clausius–Clapeyron equation.

28. What is a supercritical fluid? What can they be used for?

Section 12.6   Sublimation and Fusion

29. Define the following terms:

    Fusion:

    Melting:

    Sublimation:

    Deposition:

30. What is freezer burn and what causes it?

31. Explain how to determine the melting point on the following graph.

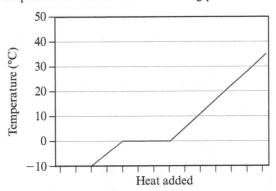

32. Why does the temperature of a drink with ice in it remain constant until all the ice has melted?

33. Identify each of the following processes as exothermic or endothermic: freezing, melting, subliming, and depositing.

34. What two enthalpy values are added to determine the heat of sublimation? Why is the heat of sublimation a state function?

Heating Curve for Water   Section 12.7

35. On the following diagram, write the equation to determine the amount of energy needed to heat water:

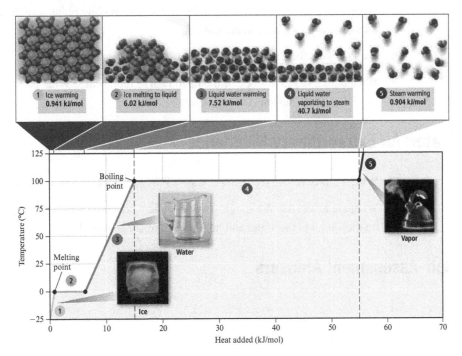

36. Show all steps used to determine the amount of energy required to raise 100.0 grams of ice from a temperature of −10.00 °C to water vapor at 110.0 °C.

Section 12.8   Phase Diagrams

Note: The AP Chemistry Exam will not include questions involving phase diagrams.

Phase Diagram for Water

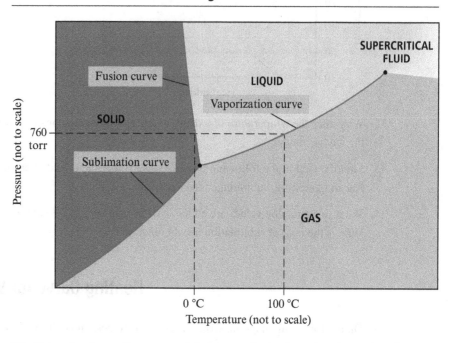

37. Using the above diagram, explain how to determine a freezing point, the normal freezing point, a boiling point, the normal boiling point, a sublimation point, the triple point, and critical point.*

38. Explain what the triple point and the critical point each represent.*

39. What does a negative slope of the fusion curve represent?* What does a positive slope of the fusion curve represent?

Section 12.9   Water: An Extraordinary Substance

40. What are three unique properties of water? Why are they important to life on Earth?

41. What are examples of biological and chemical contaminants in water? How do they get into the water and how is each of them treated?*

Self-Assessment Answers

1. _____   2. _____

3. _____   4. _____

5. _____   6. _____

7. _____   8. _____

9. _____   10. _____

SOLIDS AND MODERN MATERIALS

This chapter covers the various types of solids and provides many examples of modern uses of these solids. Many-cross domain examples are provided. While students are not tested on the AP exam on the specific crystal structures such as the face-centered cubic, understanding unit cells and packing structures will help them understand why certain compounds have a particular structure. Students do need to know the different types of solids, their properties, and be able to compare and contrast the different solids from each other.

Specific Learning Objectives Addressed in This Chapter:

SAP-5 Intermolecular Forces can explain the physical properties of a material.

SAP-5.A Explain the relationship between the chemical structures of molecules and the relative strength of their intermolecular forces when:

- The molecules are of the same chemical species.
- The molecules are of two different chemical species.

SAP-5.B Explain the relationship among the macroscopic properties of a substance, the particulate-level structure of the substance, and the interactions between these particles.

SAP-6 Matter exists in three states: solid, liquid, and gas, and their differences are influenced by variances in spacing and motion of molecules.

SAP-6.A Represent the differences among solid, liquid, and gas phases using a particulate-level model.

SAP-3 Atoms or ions bond due to interactions between them, forming molecules.

SAP-3.A Explain the relationship between the type of bonding and the properties of the elements participating in the bond.

SAP-3.C Represent an ionic solid with a particulate model that is consistent with Coulomb's law and the properties of the constituent ions.

SAP-3.D Represent a metallic solid and/or alloy using a model to show essential characteristics of the structure and interactions present in the substance.

Concepts and Vocabulary to Review:

Section 13.1   **Friday Night Experiments: The Discovery of Graphene**

Graphene is one form of carbon. It is only one atom thick. When you write with a graphite pencil, some flakes of graphene may be present.

Section 13.2   **X-Ray Crystallography**

One method of determining structures of solids is through a technique called X-ray crystallography. X-rays are shot through a crystal, and a pattern of diffraction will result. The patterns from different angles can be studied to determine the structure.

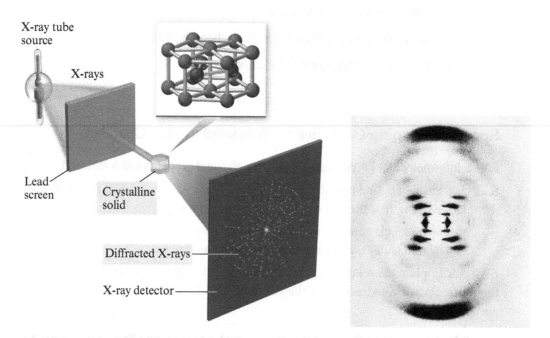

Figure 13.1 X-Ray Diffraction Analysis   In X-ray crystallography, an X-ray beam is passed through a sample, which is rotated to allow diffraction from different crystalline planes. The resulting patterns, representing constructive interference from various planes, are analyzed to determine crystalline structure.

This technique was instrumental in determining the structure of DNA. Knowledge of structures can help in the development of drugs to combat certain diseases.

Unit Cells and Basic Structures   Section 13.3

Crystals have a regular arrangement of atoms that build a lattice. The smallest repeating unit of the lattice is called a unit cell. Within the unit cell, the number of atoms each atom is in direct contact with is called its coordination number.

Cubic Cell Name	Atoms per Unit Cell	Structure	Coordination Number	Edge Length in terms of r	Packing Efficiency (fraction of volume occupied)
Simple Cubic	1		6	$2r$	52%
Body-Centered Cubic	2		8	$\dfrac{4r}{\sqrt{3}}$	68%
Face-Centered Cubic	4		12	$2\sqrt{2}r$	74%

Figure 13.2 Cubic Crystalline Lattices   The different colors used for the atoms in this figure are for clarity only. All atoms within each structure are identical. Unit cells, such as the cubic ones shown here, are customarily portrayed with "whole" atoms, even though only a part of the whole atom may actually be in the unit cell.

How the layers of the lattice pack on top of each other determines how close the atoms can get to each other and is called packing structure. The figure above shows that the lattice, no matter how it is packed, still contains empty space.

The Fundamental Types of Crystalline Solids   Section 13.4

Crystalline solids can be classified into three groups based on the individual units in the solid. They are molecular solids, ionic solids, and atomic solids. Students need to be able to distinguish and explain each type of solid and relate its properties to its structure.

Molecular solids have molecules held together by intermolecular forces. Those forces can include dispersion forces, dipole–dipole forces, and hydrogen bonding.

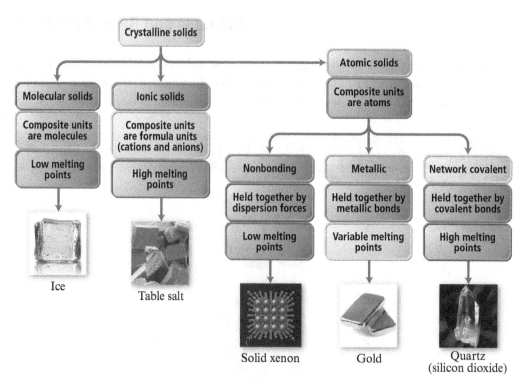

Figure 13.3 Types of Crystalline Solids

Examples of molecular solids are ice and dry ice. In general, molecular solids have low melting points.

Some solids have polymorphs, different crystal forms of the same substance. Chocolate is an example of a polymorph.

Ionic solids are composed of ions held together by coulombic attractions between the cations and anions in the lattice. Coulombic attractions are generally much stronger than intermolecular forces, which explains why ionic solids having higher melting points than molecular solids.

Atomic solids are divided into three categories: nonbonding atomic solids, metallic atomic solids, and network covalent solids.

Nonbonding atomic solids are represented by the noble gases, such as neon and helium. They only have dispersion forces and have very low melting points, hence are gases at room temperature.

Metallic atomic solids have metallic bonds involving metal cations with a delocalized sea of electrons. See Figure 13.4 for a diagram of the electron sea. The electron sea allows for the conduction of electricity in metals. The strength of metallic bonds varies, so there are a wide range of melting points. The stronger the metallic bond, the higher the melting point is. The only elemental metal that is a liquid at room temperature is mercury.

Network covalent solids have very strong covalent bonds. Examples include diamond, graphite, and silicon dioxide. A diamond is a giant molecule made of carbon atoms bonding to four other carbon atoms with covalent bonds. The electrons are held in position and are not free to flow; therefore, they do no not conduct electricity. This strong covalently bonded network has a melting point of about 3800 °C.

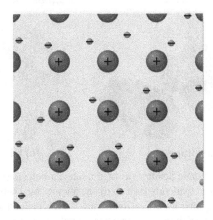

Figure 13.4 The Electron Sea Model   In the electron sea model for metals, the metal cations exist in a "sea" of electrons.

The Structures of Ionic Solids   Section 13.5

Cation and anion attractions are what hold ionic solids together. The closer the ions are to each other, the stronger the attraction. How solids pack into the solid form is a function of the size of the ions. If the ions are approximately the same size, they will pack differently than if one of the ions is large and the other is small. The ratio of ions in the formula unit also effects how the lattice is occupied.

Network Covalent Atomic Solids: Carbon and Silicates   Section 13.6

Graphite is another solid form of pure carbon where atoms are covalently bonded to each other. In graphite, however, only two, not four, bonds are formed, and only in the horizontal plane. Between each plane, or "sheet," are delocalized sigma and pi bonds allowing some electrons to move throughout the material. Thus, graphite can conduct an electrical charge. The weak dispersion forces between the layers of graphite allow the sheets to move past one another. This ability to slide over another layer explains why graphite is a good lubricant.

(a) Graphite   (b) Diamond

Figure 13.5 Network Covalent Atomic Solids   (a) In graphite, carbon atoms are arranged in sheets. Within each sheet, the atoms are covalently bonded to one another by a network of sigma and pi bonds. Neighboring sheets are held together by dispersion forces. (b) In diamond, each carbon atom forms four covalent bonds to four other carbon atoms in a tetrahedral geometry.

Some other forms of carbon are buckminsterfullerene, nanotubes, and graphene. Depending on the forces, the structure and bonding, the same element can have many forms with different properties.

Silicon dioxide and the silicates are also network covalent solids. The networked structure is held together by covalent bonds. Various forms are also observed, such as diamond-like SiO_2 network in quartz and graphite-like network in mica.

In order for network covalent solids to melt, the covalent bonds must be broken. This results in these substances having some of the highest melting points known.

Section 13.7   Ceramics, Cement, and Glass

There are many types of ceramics. The properties of different ceramics depends on whether or not it is a silicate ceramic, oxide ceramic, or nonoxide ceramic. Silicate ceramics are clay based and often used in fine china. Oxide ceramics are used in cutting tools and nonoxide ceramics include Boron nitride (BN) forms structures similar to diamond, and silicon nitride (Si_3N_4) that forms layers like mica.

Cement is a mixture mostly of calcium carbonate and silica. If sand and pebbles are added, it becomes concrete.

If molten silica is cooled quickly, it forms amorphous glass. Amorphous means it lacks a distinct pattern of crystalline structure. There are many types of glass. Each has different characteristics based on what is added to the silica.

Semiconductors and Band Theory   Section 13.8

The electron sea model explains the conductivity of metals and semimetals. The band theory is another way of explaining conduction properties. Band theory is associated with molecular orbital theory as discussed in Chapter 10. The energy gap between the bonding orbitals and the antibonding orbitals is the conduction band. If the gap between them is very large, the substance will have insulating properties because no electrons are promoted into the gap; if there is no gap, the substance will have conducting properties as mobile electrons move. If there is a small gap, a semiconductor exists. If heated, more electrons are promoted into the conduction band for greater conductivity.

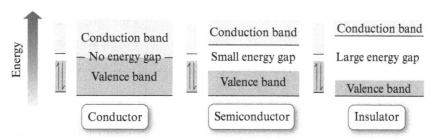

Figure 13.6 Band Gap   In a conductor, there is no energy gap between the valence band and the conduction band. In semiconductors there is a small energy gap, and in insulators there is a large energy gap.

Doping can improve the conduction ability of a semiconductor. Doping can be performed by adding impurities that are negative charge carriers (n-type) or positive charge carriers (p-type). When semiconductors are doped with phosphorus, extra electrons are added since phosphorus has five valence electrons compared to four silicon electrons. The extra electron with a negative charge is an n-type semiconductor. If doped with gallium instead, the result is a p-type semiconductor. Gallium has three valence electrons, one less than silicon, resulting in a positive charge carrier. Many electronic devices have diodes. These diodes have p-n junctions, some are p-type on one side and n-type on the other.

Polymers and Plastics   Section 13.9

Long chainlike molecules made of repeating units are called polymers. The repeating units are monomers. Some polymers include starch, protein, and DNA. In combining the monomers, if they simply combine without losing any atoms they are called addition polymers. If an atom is eliminated when the monomers combine, a condensation polymer forms. Some of the many types of polymers are listed in the accompanying table. AP Chemistry students can expect to see polymer structures on the AP Chemistry Exam. The product formed in a reaction of two monomers is called a dimer. An example is nylon.

Table 13.1   Polymers of Commercial Importance

Polymer	Structure	Uses
Addition Polymers Polyethylene	$-(CH_2-CH_2)_n$	Films, packaging, bottles
Polypropylene	$\begin{bmatrix} CH_2-CH_2 \\ \quad\quad\; CH_3 \end{bmatrix}_n$	Kitchenware, fibers, appliances
Polystyrene	$\begin{bmatrix} CH_2-CH \\ \quad\; C_6H_5 \end{bmatrix}_n$	Packaging, disposable food containers, insulation
Polyvinyl chloride	$\begin{bmatrix} CH_2-CH \\ \quad\;\; Cl \end{bmatrix}_n$	Pipe fittings, clear film for meat packaging
Condensation Polymers Polyurethane	$\begin{bmatrix} C-NH-R-NH-C-O-R'-O \\ \parallel \quad\quad\quad\quad\quad\;\; \parallel \\ O \quad\quad\quad\quad\quad\quad\; O \end{bmatrix}_n$ R, R' = $-CH_2-CH_2-$ (for example)	"Foam" furniture stuffing, spray-on insulation, automotive parts, footwear, water-protective coatings
Polyethylene tere-phthalate (a polyester)	$\begin{bmatrix} O-CH_2-CH_2-O-C-\bigcirc-C \\ \quad\quad\quad\quad\quad\quad\;\; \parallel \quad\quad\;\; \parallel \\ \quad\quad\quad\quad\quad\quad\; O \quad\quad\;\; O \end{bmatrix}_n$	Tire cord, magnetic tape, apparel, soda bottles
Nylon 6, 6	$\begin{bmatrix} NH-(CH_2)_6-NH-C-(CH_2)_4-C \\ \quad\quad\quad\quad\quad\quad\quad\quad \parallel \quad\quad\quad\quad\;\; \parallel \\ \quad\quad\quad\quad\quad\quad\quad\quad O \quad\quad\quad\quad\; O \end{bmatrix}_n$	Home furnishings, apparel, carpet fibers, fish line, polymer blends

Additional Practice

Self-Assessment Quiz Questions Q7, Q8, Q10, and Q12
Problems:
Review Questions 3, 7, 8, 9, 11, 14, 19, 23, and 25
Types of solids and their structures 39, 41, 42, 43, and 44
Semiconductors and Band Theory 65 and 66
Conceptual Problems 95, 96, and 99

Practice AP Test Questions

1. Ge is a(n) _____ because _____.

    A) conductor; all the lower-energy band orbitals are filled and the gap between the lower- and higher-energy bands is large.

B) insulator; because all the lower-energy band orbitals are filled and the gap between the lower- and higher-energy bands is large.

C) semiconductor, the gap between the filled lower- and empty higher-energy bands is small.

D) semiconductor, the gap between the filled lower- and empty higher-energy bands is large.

2. Inorganic compounds that are semiconductors have an average of _____ valence electron(s).

A) one   B) two

C) three   D) four

3. Polyethylene terephthalate has what as its two monomers?

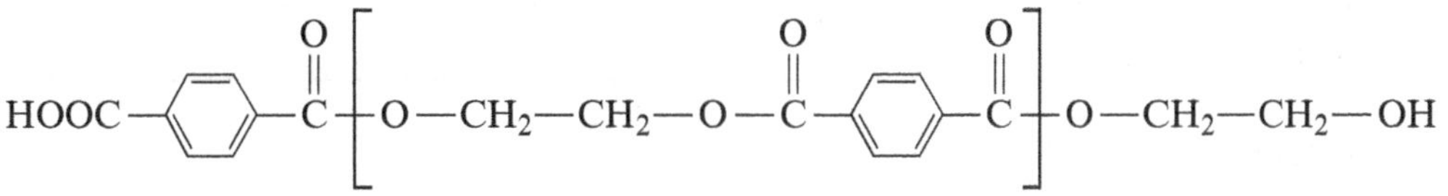

Polyester A

A) Benzoic acid and n-propanol

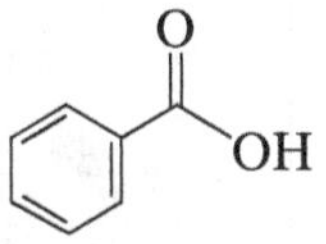

Benzoic acid 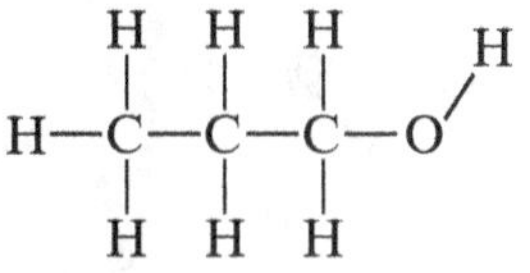   n-propanol

B) Benzene-1, 4-dicarboxylic acid and ethylene glycol

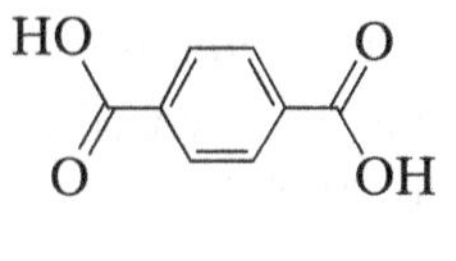

Benzene-1, 4-dicarboxylic acid 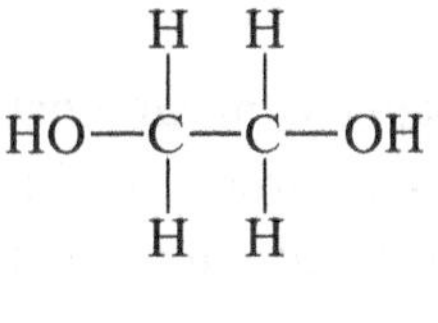   ethylene glycol

acid   alcohol

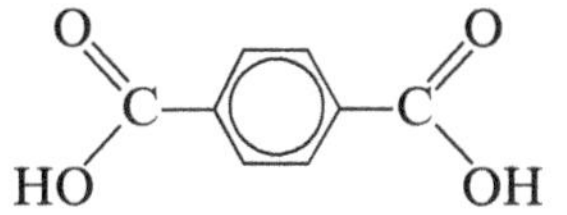

$$HO-CH_2-CH_2-OH$$

Benzene-1, 4-dicarboxylic acid   ethane-1, 2-diol
(terephthalic acid)   (ethylene glycol)

C) Benzoic acid and ethanol

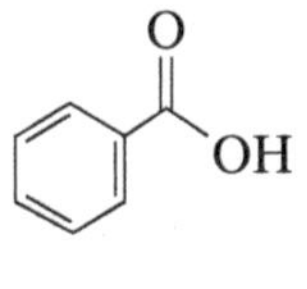

Benzoic acid 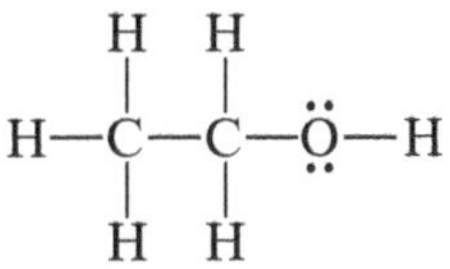   ethanol

D) Benzene-1, 4-dicarboxylic acid and ethanol

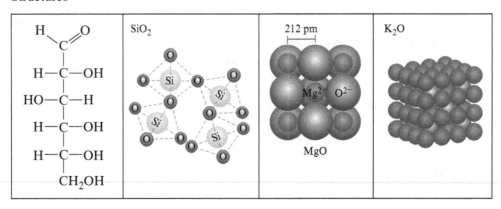

Benzene-1, 4-dicarboxylic acid   ethanol

The following information may be useful to help you answer Questions 4–10.

	Solubility in Water at 25 °C	Melting Point	Boiling Point	Dipole Moment
MgO	Not soluble	2,852 °C	3,600 °C	6.2 D
CO_2	1.45 g/L	-----	−78.5 °C	0.0 D
$C_6H_{12}O_6$ glucose	909 g/l	146 °C	150 °C	8.68 D

Structures

4. When solid magnesium carbonate is heated to 350 °C, it decomposes to magnesium oxide and carbon dioxide. What physical state is the released carbon dioxide and the magnesium oxide in when they cool to 90 °C?

	CO_2	Magnesium oxide
A)	Gas	gas
B)	Solid	solid
C)	Gas	solid
D)	Solid	liquid

5. Which of the following is expected to have the lowest value enthalpy of formation?

A) MgO

B) CO_2

C) $C_6H_{12}O_6$

D) SiO_2

6. Which of the following is an ionic solid?

    A) MgO

    B) CO_2

    C) $C_6H_{12}O_6$

    D) SiO_2

7. Which of the following when dissolved in water at 50°C in a closed ridged container, forms a nonconducting aqueous solution with a low vapor pressure?

    A) MgO

    B) CO_2

    C) $C_6H_{12}O_6$

    D) SiO_2

8. Which solid is held together primarily by strong covalent network bonding?

    A) MgO

    B) CO_2

    C) $C_6H_{12}O_6$

    D) SiO_2

9. Which solid has the higher melting point?

    A) MgO

    B) CO_2

    C) K_2O

    D) SiO_2

10. Which solid is likely to dissolve in water to produce an acidic solution?

    A) MgO

    B) CO_2

    C) K_2O

    D) SiO_2

1. C); 2. D); 3. B); 4. C); 5. B); 6. A); 7. C); 8. C); 9. A); 10. B)

Chapter 13 Practice AP Test Questions Answers:

Data Interpretation and Analysis Question: Polymers

A student observes 10 cm × 10 cm samples of two different polymers and records the following observations about each sample.

	Soluble	Weight	Texture	Transparency	Looks like	Strength
Sample A	Does not dissolve in water	Heavy, sinks in water	Rough, thick	Cannot see through, opaque	Rough fabric	Can stop a speeding bullet
Sample B	Does not dissolve in water	Light, initially floats on water	Smooth, thin	Yes, can see through	Clear wrap	Can easily cut with scissors

The chemical structures of the two samples are represented by the diagrams below. Each diagram shows a single segment of the polymer.

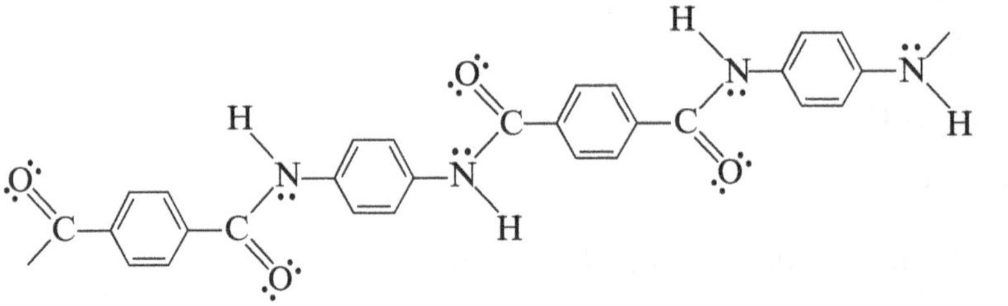

Sample A

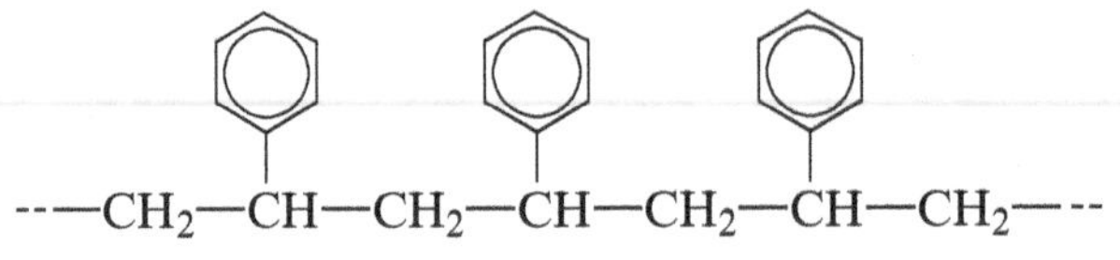

Sample B

When two monomers react to make polymer A, the reaction also has hydrogen chloride, HCl as one of the products.

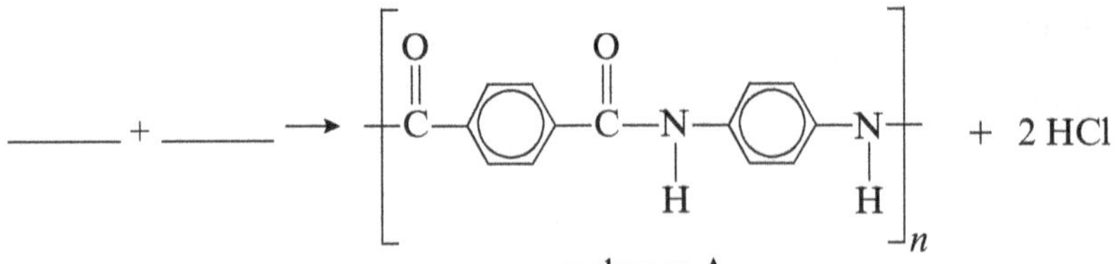

polymer A

When one type of monomer reacts to make polymer B, there are no additional products.

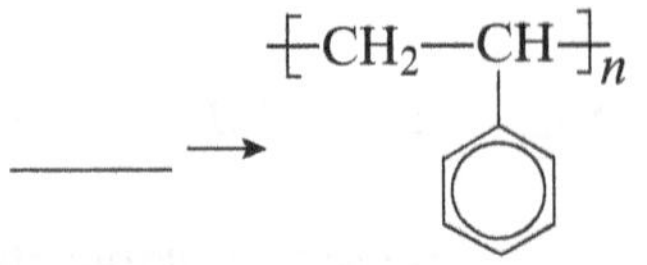

polymer B

a) Draw Lewis structures representing the two monomers of Sample A.

b) Draw a Lewis structure representing the monomer of Sample B.

c) Sample A is much stronger compared to Sample B. Account for this difference in terms of the types and strengths of intermolecular forces present in each sample.

d) Starting with a segment of Sample A, draw another segment of Sample A next to this one and show the location of the predominant intermolecular force, by using dotted lines, responsible for the unusual high strength of Sample A.

e) Starting with a segment of Sample B, draw another segment of Sample B next to this one and show the location of the intermolecular force by using dotted lines, responsible for keeping Sample B together as a solid.

Data Interpretation and Analysis Question Answers with Brief Explanations

a) Two monomers for Sample A

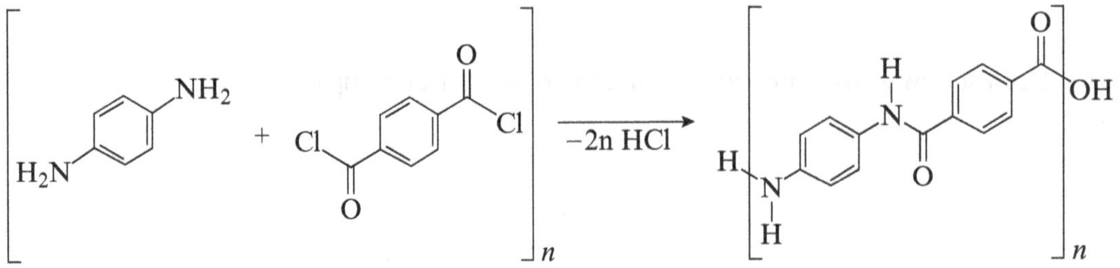

b) Monomer for Sample B

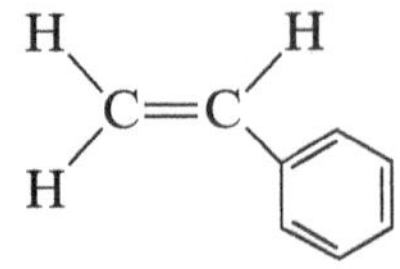

c) Sample A has hydrogen bonding as the predominant type of intermolecular force. Because there are numerous hydrogen bonding IMFs between segments of all the strands of Sample A, hydrogen bonding accounts for the unusually high strength of Sample A. Sample A also has London dispersion forces. Sample B does not have hydrogen bonding; it does not have any polar covalent bonds. It has London dispersion forces as the predominant type of intermolecular force.

d) Two segments of Sample A polymer with the dotted lines representing hydrogen bonding between the two segments.

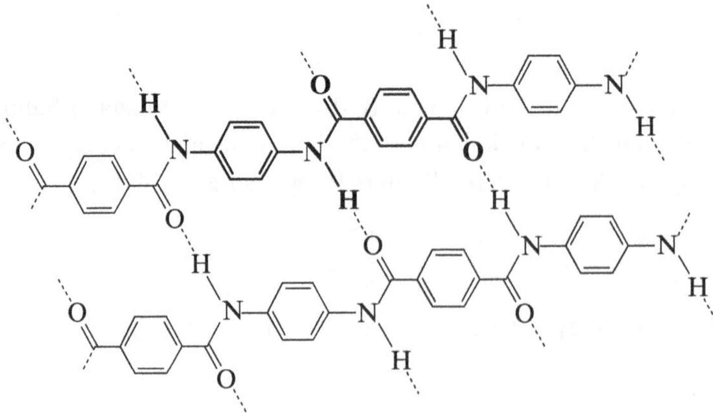

e) Two segments of Sample B with the dotted lines representing London dispersion forces between the two segments.

$$-CH_2-CH-CH_2-CH-CH_2-CH-CH_2-CH-CH_2-CH-CH_2-CH-$$

$$-CH_2-CH-CH_2-CH-CH_2-CH-CH_2-CH-CH_2-CH-CH_2-CH-$$

READING GUIDE

This chapter is a mixture of AP and non AP Chemistry curriculum. Concepts are primarily part of Unit 2 in the curriculum. Not in the AP Chemistry curriculum are crystal shapes, packing structures, and use of the Clausius–Clapeyron equation.

Section 13.1

Friday Night Experiments: The Discovery of Graphene

1. Who discovered graphene? How was it discovered? What are the properties of graphene?

Section 13.2

X-Ray Crystallography

2. Explain how X-ray crystallography is used to determine the structure of crystals. What is a diffraction pattern? What does the pattern indicate? Identify two structures that were discovered by X-ray crystallography.

Section 13.3

Unit Cells and Basic Structures

Note: The AP Chemistry Exam will not include questions or problems involving specific varieties of crystal lattices for ionic compounds.

3. What is a unit cell?* What is a coordination number? What is the relationship between a coordination number and packing efficiency?

4. Fill in the following table for each type of unit cell and its properties:*

Cubic Cell Name	Atoms per Unit Cell	Structure	Coordination Number	Edge Length in Terms of r	Packing Efficiency (fraction of volume occupied)
Simple Cubic					
Body-Centered Cubic					
Face-Centered Cubic					

5. Using diagrams, explain the concepts of hexagonal closest packing and cubic closest packing.*

The Fundamental Types of Crystalline Solids   Section 13.4

6. Fill in the diagram below showing the different categories of crystalline solids with the composition of each type of solid, the relative melting point, and an example of each.

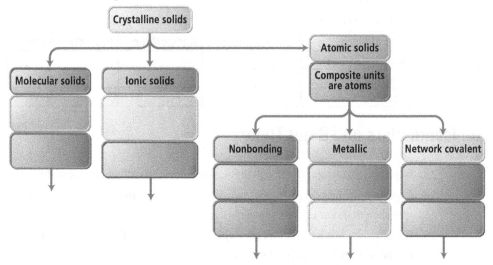

7. What forces hold molecular solids together? What are the properties of molecular solids?

8. What is a polymorph? Give an example of a polymorph.

9. Explain the process of tempering in chocolate formation.

10. Explain the composition and properties of ionic solids.

11. Explain the differences between the different types of atomic solids. Include examples of each, the forces holding them together, and their properties.

12. Explain the electron sea model of metallic bonding. Include a diagram in your answer. Why does being delocalized allow for the conduction of electricity?

The Structures of Ionic Solids   Section 13.5

13. Explain how the size of a cation and anion affect the ionic lattice.

14. What does a coordination number of 8 indicate?

Network Covent Atomic Solids: Carbon and Silicates   Section 13.6

15. Carbon composes both graphite and diamond. What are the properties of each? Why do they have different properties? Include diagrams in your answer. What forces hold layers of graphite together? What holds diamonds together? What is needed to turn graphite into diamonds?

16. Explain the composition and structure of buckminsterfullerenes, buckyballs, nanotubes, and graphene.

17. What are silicates? Explain what holds silicates together? What percentage of the earth's crust is thought to be silicates?

18. What is silica?

Section 13.7   # Ceramics, Cement, and Glass

19. Define ceramics. What are the three types, their composition, and properties?

20. What is the difference between cement and concrete?

21. What is glass composed of?

22. Fill in the following table.

Type of Glass	Common Name	Composition	Property	Use
Soda-lime glass				
Borosilicate glass				
Leaded glass				

Section 13.8   # Semiconductors and Band Theory

23. Explain the concept of delocalization. How does this affect conductivity?

24. Explain how the size of energy gap affects the ability to be a semiconductor. Include a diagram in your answer.

25. Explain how semiconductors are doped. Explain the difference between p-type and n-type semiconductors.

26. What are p-n junctions? What are they used for?

Section 13.9   # Polymers and Plastics

27. What are polymers made of? What are the characteristics of polymers? What holds polymers together?

Name	Formula	Use	Type polymer
Polyethylene			
Polypropylene			
Polystyrene			
Polyvinyl chloride			
Polyurethane			
Polyester			
Nylon			

28. Explain the difference between addition polymers and condensation polymers and their uses.

29. What is a dimer? Include an example in your answer.

30. What is Kevlar? What is it used for?

Self-Assessment Answers

1. _____   2. _____   3. _____

4. _____   5. _____   6. _____

7. _____   8. _____   9. _____

10. _____   11. _____   12. _____

13. _____

SOLUTIONS

Solutions are all around us. Normally, we only think of solutions as aqueous, but the air we breathe is a solution of mostly oxygen in nitrogen. In this chapter, properties of solutions will be addressed. Parts of this chapter are not in the AP curriculum but should have been addressed in an earlier course, including molality and colligative properties. The primary sections pertaining to AP material are:

14.1 **Thirsty Solutions: Why You Shouldn't Drink Seawater**

14.2 **Types of Solutions and Solubility**

14.3 **Energetics of Solution Formation**

14.4 **Solution Equilibrium and Factors Affecting Solubility**

14.5 **Expressing Solution Concentration**

14.8 **Colloids**

Specific Learning Objectives Addressed in This Chapter:

TRA-1.A Identify evidence of chemical and physical changes in matter.

TRA-1.B Represent changes in matter with a balanced chemical or net ionic equation:

- For physical changes.
- For given information about the identity of the reactants and/or product.
- For ions in a given chemical reaction.

TRA-1.C Represent a given chemical reaction or physical process with a consistent particulate model.

TRA-1.D Explain the relationship between macroscopic characteristics and bond interactions for:

- Chemical processes.
- Physical processes.

SAP-5.A Explain the relationship between the chemical structures of molecules and the relative strength of their intermolecular forces when:

- The molecules are of the same chemical species.
- The molecules are of two different chemical species.

SAP-5.B Explain the relationship among the macroscopic properties of a substance, the particulate-level structure of the substance, and the interactions between these particles.

SAP-6.A Represent the differences among solid, liquid, and gas phase using a particulate-level model.

SPQ-3.A Calculate the number of solute particles, volume, or molarity of solutions.

SPQ-3.B Using particulate models for mixtures:

- Represent interactions between components.

- Represent concentrations of components.

SPQ-3.C Explain the relationship between the solubility of ionic and molecular compounds in aqueous and nonaqueous solvents, and the intermolecular interactions between particles.

*SPQ-3.C2 Substances with similar intermolecular interactions tend to be miscible or soluble in one another.

TRA-6.A Explain the relationship between the occurrence of a reversible chemical or physical process, and the establishment of equilibrium, to experimental observations.

TRA-6.B Explain the relationship between the direction in which a reversible reaction proceeds and the relative rates of the forward and reverse reactions.

TRA-7.F Represent a system undergoing a reversible reaction with a particle model.

SPQ-5.D Explain the relationship between the solubility of a salt and changes in the enthalpy and entropy that occur in the dissolution process.

ENE-4.A Identify the sign and relative magnitude of the entropy change associated with chemical or physical processes.

ENE-2.A Explain the relationship between experimental observations and energy changes associated with a chemical or physical transformation.

ENE-2.F Calculate the heat q absorbed or released by a system undergoing a chemical reaction in relationship to the amount of reacting substance in moles and the molar enthalpy of reaction.

ENE-3.B Calculate the enthalpy change for a chemical or physical process based on the standard enthalpies of formation.

Concepts and Vocabulary to Review:

Section 14.1   **Thirsty Solutions: Why You Shouldn't Drink Seawater**

Solutions are homogeneous mixtures of two or more substances. Some basic vocabulary of solutions includes the terms *solute* and *solvent*. These terms apply to any type of solution, although most think of solutions as aqueous. *Solute* is the substance in the minority component being dissolved (often but not necessarily a solid), and the *solvent* is in the majority component doing the dissolving. For instance, in salt water, water is the solvent and salt is the solute. If two substances are soluble in each other, they will naturally start to mix when they are put together until they are uniformly distributed in each other. An example of a liquid in liquid solution is alcohol in water.

Types of Solutions and Solubility   Section 14.2

For an aqueous solution the solvent is water, but for other solutions the solute can be a solid, liquid, or gas. In the air we breathe, nitrogen is the solvent and oxygen and carbon dioxide are solutes. The gases in the air mix due to the molecule's random motions and *entropy*, which is a measure of the energy randomization in a system. Each of the components and kinetic energy will disperse or spread out over the largest possible volume. This tendency explains why kinetic energy will disperse from a hot object to a cold object.

Table 14.1   Common Types of Solutions

Solution Phase	Solute Phase	Solvent Phase	Example
Gaseous solution	Gas	Gas	Air (mainly oxygen and nitrogen)
Liquid solution	Gas Liquid Solid	Liquid Liquid Liquid	Club soda (CO_2 and water) Vodka (ethanol and water) Seawater (salt and water)
Solid solution	Solid	Solid	Brass (copper and zinc) and other alloys

When a solute does dissolve in a solvent, it is said to be *soluble*; if a substance does not dissolve, it is said to be *insoluble*. This is not a strict definition, as a tiny amount will dissolve even for "insoluble" substances. The amount of the solute dissolving depends mostly on the interaction of intermolecular forces between the substances. A solute may be soluble in one solvent but not in another due to the intermolecular forces. Oil is not soluble in a water solvent but is soluble in turpentine. This is why paint brushes with oil-based paints are cleaned in turpentine and not water. There are several types of intermolecular forces whose interactions are reviewed in the diagram below.

Intermolecular Forces

These forces may contribute to or oppose the formation of a solution.

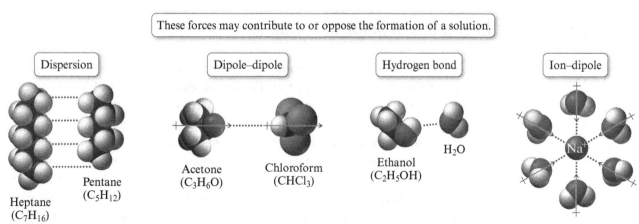

| Dispersion | Dipole–dipole | Hydrogen bond | Ion–dipole |

Heptane (C_7H_{16})   Pentane (C_5H_{12})

Acetone (C_3H_6O)   Chloroform ($CHCl_3$)

Ethanol (C_2H_5OH) H_2O

Na⁺

Figure 14.1 Intermolecular Forces Involved in Solutions

The interactions between the solute and solvent molecules determine if a solution forms. If the interactions between the solute and solvent are greater than or equal to the interaction of the solvent with itself or the solute with itself, a solution will form. For instance, water is a polar molecule and has hydrogen-bonding interactions with other water molecules. Ammonia is a polar molecule and has hydrogen-bonding interactions with other ammonia molecules as well. Ammonia and water will also form hydrogen bonding with each other and ammonia will therefore dissolve in each other. When all three interactions are the same (e.g., water–water; ammonia–ammonia; ammonia–water), the substances are called *miscible*. Oil added to water does not form a solution because the dispersion forces in the oil are not enough to overcome the solvent attractions to itself (water hydrogen bonding to other water molecules).

Table 14.2   Relative Interactions and Solution Formation

Solvent–solute interactions	>	Solvent–solvent and solute–solute interactions	Solution forms
Solvent–solute interactions	=	Solvent–solvent and solute–solute interactions	Solution forms
Solvent–solute interactions	<	Solvent–solvent and solute–solute interactions	Solution may or may not form, depending on relative disparity of interactions.

In the case of water and hexane, water forms hydrogen bonds with other water molecules, and hexane molecules are attracted to other hexane molecules by dispersion forces. The water does not form hydrogen bonds with the hexane and the amount of energy needed to pull the water molecules away from each other to form a solution is too great. A solution does not form. In contrast, hexane with dispersion forces will dissolve in heptane, which also has dispersion forces. Be careful of using the phrase "like dissolves like," because it is never accepted on the AP test as a complete enough explanation for why two substances dissolve in each other. The interactions must be fully described as in the examples above. Although students will say water is the universal solvent, and it is very powerful solvent, it does not dissolve everything.

Section 14.3   **Energetics of Solution Formation**

This section is crucial to understanding the thermodynamics of solutions. When solutions form, the process can be exothermic or endothermic. It depends on the relationship of the energy required to pull the solute particles apart from each other, the energy required to pull the solvent particles apart from each other, and the energy released when the solute and solvent interact to make the solution. Pulling the solute (ΔH_{solute}) and solvent ($\Delta H_{solvent}$) particles apart always requires energy, whereas the bonding of the solute and solvent always releases energy. See Figure 14.2. Both Step 1 and 2 are endothermic and Step 3 is exothermic. The overall result is the difference between Step 1 and 2 compared to Step 3. The amount of energy required to pull particles apart from each other depends on the forces holding them together. The weaker the force, the less energy is required. In an endothermic enthalpy of solution

Energetics of Solution Formation

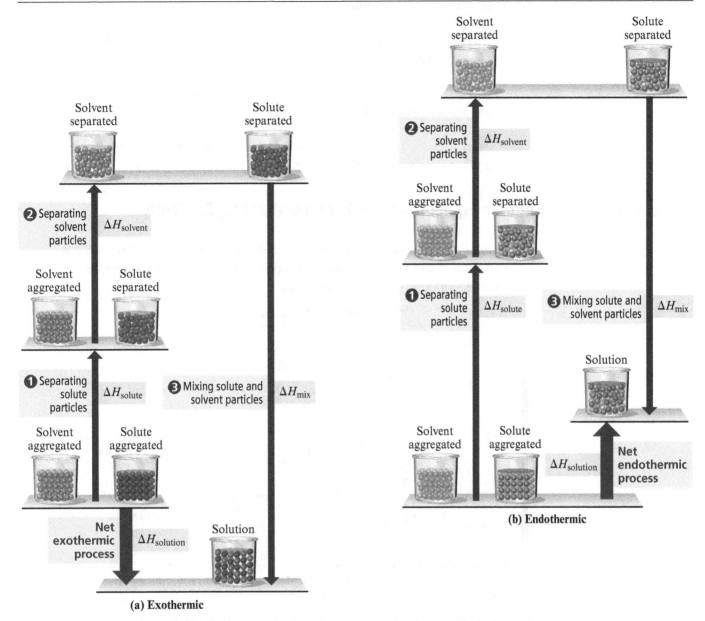

Figure 14.2 Energetics of the Solution Process   (a) When ΔH_{mix} is greater in magnitude than the sum of ΔH_{solute} and $\Delta H_{solvent}$, the heat of solution is negative (exothermic). (b) When ΔH_{mix} is smaller in magnitude than the sum of ΔH_{solute} and $\Delta H_{solvent}$, the heat of solution is positive (endothermic).

(ΔH_{soln}), the energy released is less than the magnitude of the energy needed to pull apart the solute (ΔH_{solute}) and solvent ($\Delta H_{solvent}$). In an exothermic enthalpy of solution, the energy released is greater than the magnitude of solute (ΔH_{solute}) and solvent ($\Delta H_{solvent}$). If the energy released is equal to the magnitude of solute (ΔH_{solute}) and solvent ($\Delta H_{solvent}$), and a solution forms, the gain in entropy will drive the mixing of the solution.

Heat of hydration is the energy change when one mole of gaseous solute ions is dissolved in water. Using heat of hydration, we can write the solution process as

$\Delta H_{soln} = \Delta H_{solute} + \Delta H_{hydration}$. The ΔH_{solute} is always endothermic (positive) and the $\Delta H_{hydration}$ is always exothermic (negative).

$|\Delta H_{solute}| < |\Delta H_{hydration}|$ results in an exothermic enthalpy of solution and the temperature of the solution will increase.

$|\Delta H_{solute}| > |\Delta H_{hydration}|$ results in an endothermic enthalpy of solution and the temperature of the solution will decrease.

$|\Delta H_{solute}| \approx |\Delta H_{hydration}|$ results in an isothermic enthalpy of solution and the temperature of the solution does not noticeably change.

Section 14.4   Solution Equilibrium and Factors Affecting Solubility

As a salt dissolves, eventually some ions will start to re-form the salt. Every salt has a different point at which this will start to happen. For ionic compounds, the energy needed to pull apart a crystal lattice is $\Delta H_{(solute)}$.

Heat of Hydration

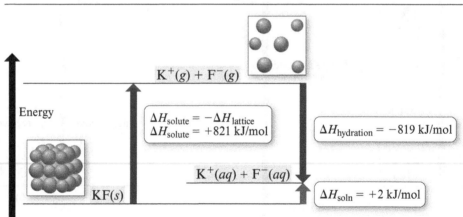

$K^+(g) + F^-(g)$

Energy

$\Delta H_{solute} = -\Delta H_{lattice}$
$\Delta H_{solute} = +821$ kJ/mol

$\Delta H_{hydration} = -819$ kJ/mol

$K^+(aq) + F^-(aq)$

$\Delta H_{soln} = +2$ kJ/mol

$KF(s)$

Figure 14.3 Heat of Hydration and Heat of Solution   The heat of hydration is the heat emitted when 1 mol of gaseous solute ions is dissolved in water. The sum of the negative of the lattice energy (which is ΔH_{solute}) and the heat of hydration is the heat of solution.

The solvation process can eventually reach equilibrium. To reach this state, there needs to be both undissolved solute and dissolved solute. When the rate of dissolving of the solute equals the rate of recrystallization of the solute, the system has reached dynamic equilibrium. In an equation, a double arrow is used to indicate the equilibrium state.

$$NaCl(s) \rightleftharpoons Na^+(aq) + Cl^-(aq)$$

Solutions with the maximum amount of dissolved particles are called *saturated*. If additional solute is added to a saturated solution no *net* dissolving will occur since the system is in dynamic equilibrium. Unsaturated solutions do not have the maximum amount of solute dissolved so when additional solute is added, it will dissolve.

Supersaturated solutions contain more than the maximum amount of dissolved solute. These are normally formed by slowly cooling a saturated solution. These solutions are not in a state of dynamic equilibrium (no excess solute can be present), are thus unstable and if disturbed, some solute will crystallize out, or in the case of a liquid solute, form a separate layer.

One important process used to purify a solid is recrystallization. A saturated solution is formed at a higher temperature and as the solution cools, the excess crystal comes out as a more pure sample of crystal.

The amount of solute dissolved in a saturated solution is affected by temperature. For most solids, the amount that can dissolve will increase with increasing temperature. See Figure 14.5, only 1 solid decreases with temperature. For gases, the opposite is true; less gas dissolves as the temperature increases. This is easily seen in soda pop. As a soda warms, the soda releases more of the dissolved carbon dioxide and eventually goes flat.

Solution Equilibrium

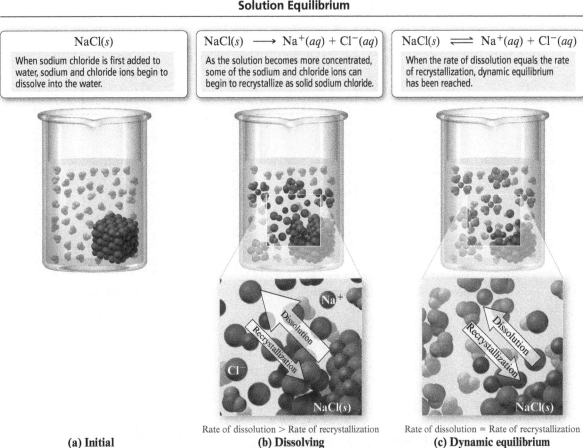

NaCl(s)

When sodium chloride is first added to water, sodium and chloride ions begin to dissolve into the water.

NaCl(s) $\longrightarrow$ Na$^+$(aq) + Cl$^-$(aq)

As the solution becomes more concentrated, some of the sodium and chloride ions can begin to recrystallize as solid sodium chloride.

NaCl(s) $\rightleftharpoons$ Na$^+$(aq) + Cl$^-$(aq)

When the rate of dissolution equals the rate of recrystallization, dynamic equilibrium has been reached.

Rate of dissolution > Rate of recrystallization

Rate of dissolution = Rate of recrystallization

(a) Initial   (b) Dissolving   (c) Dynamic equilibrium

Figure 14.4 Dissolution of NaCl (a) When sodium chloride is first added to water, sodium and chloride ions dissolve into the water. (b) As the solution becomes more concentrated, some of the sodium and chloride ions recrystallize as solid sodium chloride. (c) When the rate of dissolution equals the rate of recrystallization, dynamic equilibrium is reached.

Pressure also changes the solubility of gases in solution. The greater the pressure of the gas above the solution, the greater the amount of gas dissolved. When a soda-pop can is opened, the pressure of the CO_2 on the liquid in the can of soda immediately decreases and in response, some of the CO_2 comes out of the solution. This relationship is known as Henry's law.

Figure 14.5 Precipitation from a Supersaturated Solution   When a small piece of solid sodium acetate is added to a supersaturated sodium acetate solution, the excess solid precipitates out of the solution.

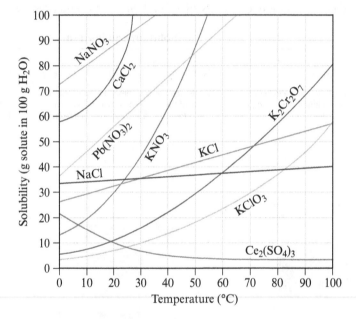

Figure 14.6 Solubility and Temperature   The solubility of most solids increases with increasing temperature.

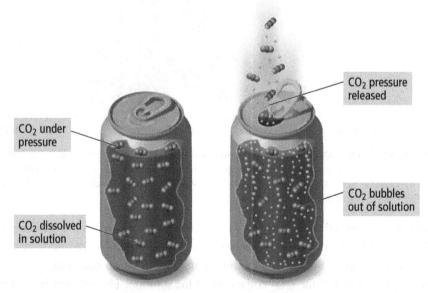

Figure 14.7 Soda Fizz   The bubbling that occurs when a can of soda is opened results from the reduced pressure of carbon dioxide over the liquid. At lower pressure, the carbon dioxide is less soluble and bubbles out of solution.

Expressing Solution Concentration   Section 14.5

The AP curriculum emphasizes molarity as a concentration unit. *Molarity (M)* is the number of moles of solute per liter of solution. $M = \dfrac{\text{moles solute}}{\text{liters of solution}}$. Students must explain in writing how to make a solution of any amount and any concentration. See Figure 14.8 to review the correct steps in making a solution.

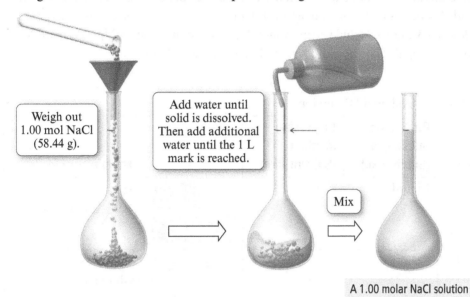

Weigh out 1.00 mol NaCl (58.44 g).

Add water until solid is dissolved. Then add additional water until the 1 L mark is reached.

Mix

A 1.00 molar NaCl solution

Figure 14.8 Preparing a Solution of Known Concentration   To make a 1 M NaCl solution, we add 1 mol of the solid to a 1.0 L volumetric flask and dilute with water to the mark to make 1 L of solution.

Two important terms used about solutions are *dilute* and *concentrated. Dilute solutions* have very little solute and *concentrated solutions* have large amounts of solute in relative to the amount of solution. Obviously, these are relative terms and do not have exact definitions in chemistry. AP questions usually give actual concentration values, for example, 0.1 M for a dilute solution and greater than 1 M for a concentrated solution. Molarity is temperature dependent. Different temperatures can vary the volume of solution that would affect the concentration calculation.

How would you prepare 100.0 mL of a 0.250 M aqueous solution of KNO_3?

Solution: From the molarity and volume, determine the number of moles of KNO_3, then determine the mass of KNO_3 needed.

$0.1000\ L \times 0.250\ \text{mole}/L = 0.0250\ \text{mole}\ KNO_3$

The molar mass of KNO_3 is 101.1 grams/mole

$0.0250\ \text{mole}\ KNO_3 \times 101.1\ g/\text{mole} = 2.53\ \text{grams}\ KNO_3$

Obtain a 100.0 mL volumetric flask. Place about 20 mL of deionized water in the flask. Carefully add the solid KNO_3 to the water in the flask. Stir. Use a water bottle to wash the sides of the flask to ensure all of the solid is in solution. Add more water and swirl. Place a top on the volumetric flask and invert 10 times. Open the top and add water until the bottom of meniscus of the solution aligns with 100.0 mL mark on the flask.

Section 14.8   Colloids

Some mixtures are not true solutions. Colloidal dispersions are an example. Finely divided particles between 1 nm and 1000 nm, which are dispersed in the medium, are *colloids*. Examples include soapy water, fog, smoke in the air, whipped cream, milk, blood, and opal. The AP exam has rarely addressed colloids.

Table 14.2   Types of Colloidal Dispersions

Classification	Dispersing Substance (Solute-like)	Dispersing Medium (Solvent-like)	Example
Aerosol	Liquid	Gas	Fog (water droplets in air)
Solid aerosol	Solid	Gas	Smoke (ash in air)
Foam	Gas	Liquid	Whipped cream (air bubbles in butterfat)
Emulsion	Liquid	Liquid	Milk (milk fat globules in water)
Solid emulsion	Liquid	Solid	Opal (water in silica glass)

Brownian motion is the random motion of particles by particles suspended in a medium. This motion is caused by collisions between the particles and molecules of the medium.

Colloids can be identified by the Tyndall effect. If a light beam passes through a colloidal suspension, light is scattered. When light comes through a window and you see dust in the air, this is the Tyndall effect. In contrast, true solutions do not scatter light in this way. Instead, the light will pass directly through the solution.

Figure 14.9 The Tyndall Effect   When a light beam passes through a colloidal suspension (left), it is visible because the colloid particles scatter some of the light. The beam is not visible in a noncolloidal solution (right), nor would it be visible in pure water.

A soap molecule is a bridge between a polar substance such as water and a nonpolar substance such as oil or dirt. It is a bridge because the polar end of the soap will link to the polar water while the nonpolar end of the soap links to the nonpolar oil.

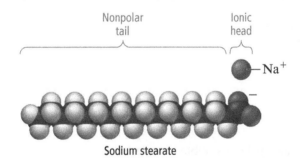

Sodium stearate

Figure 14.10 Soap Molecule Structure   A soap molecule has a charged ionic head and a long nonpolar hydrocarbon tail.

Additional Practice

Self-Assessment Quiz Questions Q1, Q2, Q3, Q4, Q8, Q12, Q14, and Q15
Problems:
Review Questions 5, 7, 10, 11, 12, 13, 14, and 26
Solubility 29, 33, and 34
Energetics of Solution Formation 35, 36, 37, and 40
Solution Equilibrium and Factors Affecting Solubility 41, 43, 45, 46, and 48
Concentrations of Solutions 53, 54, 55, and 61a
Vapor Pressure of Solutions 69 and 70
Conceptual Problems 134, 135, 136, and 138

Equations to know:

$M = \text{mol solute}/\text{L of Solution}$

Practice AP Test Questions

1. A laboratory procedure requires 0.270 mole of methanol, CH_3OH, to be added as a solvent. What volume of 1.50 M CH_3OH is needed to attain this number of moles?

   A) 5.55 mL

   B) 45.0 mL

   C) 405 mL

   D) 180 mL

2. Which substance is least soluble in water?

   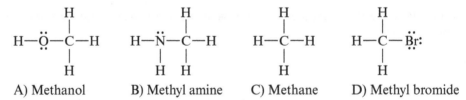

   A) Methanol   B) Methyl amine   C) Methane   D) Methyl bromide

3. The reason for your choice in Test Question #2 is:

   A) Methanol forms the strongest hydrogen bonding with the water molecules.

   B) Methyl amine forms the strongest hydrogen bonding with the water molecules.

   C) Methane exhibits London dispersion forces with water molecules.

   D) Methyl bromide has the highest molar mass.

Questions 4–9 refer to the following statement. When solid ammonium chloride dissolves in water, the temperature of the resultant solution decreases.

4. For such a process, which statement best describes the reason why dissolving occurs spontaneously?

   A) Enthalpy decreases.

   B) Enthalpy increases.

   C) Vapor pressure decreases.

   D) Entropy increases.

5. When 5.00 grams of ammonium chloride (MM = 53.49), initially at 21.00 °C, dissolves in 45.00 mL of water initially at 21.00°C, the temperature of resultant solution is 12.64 °C. Calculate $\Delta H_{solution}$.

   A) −18.7 kJ/mol

   B) +18.7 kJ/mol

   C) −1.87 kJ/mol

   D) +1.87 kJ/mol

6. Which arrow in the following two diagrams represents the change in enthalpy of solution, $\Delta H_{solution}$, for ammonium chloride? The lengths of the arrows are somewhat proportional to enthalpy changes involved when a solid dissolves to form a solution.

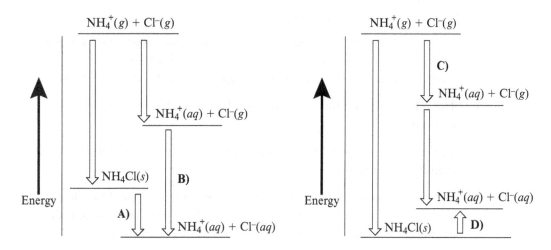

   A) A

   B) B

   C) C

   D) D

7. Given the following information, determine the change in enthalpy of solution per mole of NH_4Cl. Calculate the enthalpy of solution for NH_4Cl, $\Delta H_{solution}$, in units of kJ per mole.

NH_4Cl	Enthalpy Change
Lattice energy NH_4Cl (s)	-705 kJ/mol
Enthalpy of hydration, NH_4^+ (g)	-307 kJ/mol
Enthalpy of hydration, Cl^- (g)	-381 kJ/mol

A) -17 kJ/mol

B) $+17$ kJ/mol

C) $+74$ kJ/mol

D) -74 kJ/mol

8. Which equation represents the change in enthalpy of solution for the ionic compound NH_4Cl?

A) $NH_4^+(g) + Cl^-(g) \rightarrow NH_4Cl(s)$

B) $NH_4^+(aq) + Cl^-(aq) \rightarrow NH_4Cl(s)$

C) $NH_4Cl(s) \xrightarrow{H_2O(l)} NH_4^+(aq) + Cl^-(aq)$

D) $NH_4Cl(s) + H_2O(l) \rightarrow NH_4^+(aq) + Cl^-(aq) + H_3O^+(aq)$

9. Which of the following is a plausible explanation of how ions in NH_4Cl interact with water in the dissolving process?

A) The NH_4^+ ions form an ion–dipole intermolecular force with the partial positive ends of water molecules and the Cl^- ions form an ion–dipole intermolecular force with the partial negative ends of water molecules.

B) The NH_4^+ ions and the Cl^- ions form hydrogen bonds to available water molecules.

C) The NH_4^+ ions and the Cl^- ions form London dispersion forces with the available water molecules.

D) The NH_4^+ ions form an ion–dipole intermolecular force with the partial negative end of water molecules and the Cl^- ions form an ion–dipole intermolecular force with the partial positive ends of water molecules.

10. Aqueous solutions of $NiSO_4$ have a green color. Five nickel(II) sulfate solutions of known concentrations were prepared. Each solution was transferred to its own small, rectangular cuvette and placed into a Colorimeter (or Spectrometer). A maximum wavelength of 656 nm was selected and the absorbance of each solution was measured and recorded.

Concentration (Molarity)	Absorbance
0.400	0.713
0.320	0.546
0.240	0.411
0.160	0.277
0.080	0.131

Determine the concentration, in units of molarity, of a $NiSO_4$ solution that has an absorbance of 0.356.

A) 0.21 M

B) 0.20 M

C) 0.19 M

D) 0.18 M

Chapter 14 Practice AP Test Questions Answers:

1. B); 2. C); 3. C); 4. D); 5. B); 6. D); 7. B); 8. C); 9. D); 10. A)

Data Interpretation and Analysis Question: Energy Exchanged When Ionic Salts Dissolve in Water

Use the data displayed in Tables 1 and 2 to help answer the questions associated with this problem.

Table 1

Compound	Lattice Energy (kJ/mol)	ΔH_{soln} (kJ/mol)
KBr	−672	+19.8
LiBr	−807	−48.3
KI	−632	+20.3
LiI	−730	−63.3

Table 2

Ion	Ionic Radius (pm)	ΔH_{hydr} (kJ/mol)
Li^+	76	−520
Na^+	102	−410
K^+	138	−336
Cl^-	181	−378
Br^-	196	−284
I^-	220	−247

a) Write an equation representing dissolving KBr(s) in water.

b) Is dissolving solid KBr in water an endothermic or exothermic process?

c) When 5.00 grams of solid KBr dissolves in 100.0 mL of water, does the resultant solution of KBr(aq) become hotter or cooler, or does it remain at the same temperature?

d) In the box below, complete a particle representation diagram for showing how water molecules interact with the K^+ ion in an aqueous solution of KBr to represent the heat of hydration process. Include four water molecules with proper orientation to the cation in your diagram.

e) Is dissolving solid LiBr in water an endothermic or exothermic process?

f) Complete a sketch of two qualitative energy diagrams comparing the difference in the dissolving processes of KBr and LiBr. Explain what makes the difference in the change in enthalpy of solution for the two dissolving processes.

g) Explain why the heat of hydration is always exothermic for cations and anions.

h) Explain why the heat of hydration trend decreases as the cation or anion ionic radius decreases.

i) Which cation, lithium or potassium, has stronger ion–dipole interactions with water? Explain.

j) Calculate the amount of heat exchanged in units of kJ and display the proper sign of this heat exchange when 5.00 grams of solid LiBr completely dissolves in water. Is your answer consistent with your answer in e)?

Data Interpretation and Analysis Question Answers with Brief Explanations

a) $KBr(s) \xrightarrow{H_2O(l)} K^+(aq) + Br^-(aq)$

b) The dissolving process is slightly endothermic.

c) The resultant solution of KBr(aq) becomes slightly cooler.

d)

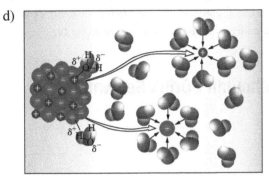

e) The dissolving process is exothermic.

f) For an exothermic dissolving process, when the solid particles and solvent particles mix, there is excess energy released. For an endothermic process, when the solid particles and solvent particles mix, there is energy released by not as much as was taken in to separate the particles. Hence, net energy is absorbed from the surroundings.

g) Intermolecular ion–dipole forces of attraction are formed. When IMF form, energy is released.

h) Smaller ions having the same charge as large ions have a larger charge density.

i) The lithium cation has stronger ion–dipole interactions with water compared to the potassium cation because smaller ions having the same charge as large ions have a larger charge density.

j) 5.0 g LiBr × 1 mol LiBr/86.8 grams × (−48.3 kJ/mol) = −2.78 kJ

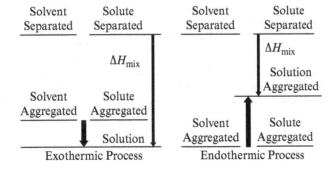

READING GUIDE

The focus of this chapter is solutions, their properties, and the interaction of intermolecular forces forming solutions. Evidence of intermolecular forces through species interactions for different types of solutions is part of Unit 3. Solution equilibrium is also part of Unit 3. Not covered in the AP Chemistry curriculum are colligative properties such as freezing point depressions and boiling point elevations and concentration units other than molarity.

Section 14.1   Thirsty Solutions: Why You Shouldn't Drink Seawater

1. Definitions:

   Solute:

   Solvent:

   Solution:

2. Which way does nature tend to mix solutions? Why is seawater considered "thirsty"?

Section 14.2   Types of Solutions and Solubility

3. Give examples of all the types of solutions provided below:

   Table 14.1   Common Types of Solutions

Solution Phase	Solute Phase	Solvent Phase	Example
Gaseous solution	Gas	Gas	
Liquid solution	Gas Liquid Solid	Liquid Liquid Liquid	
Solid solution	Solid	Solid	

4. Explain what is occurring in the below figure:

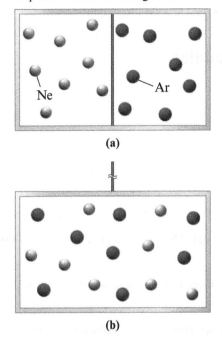

(a)

(b)

5. Define the following vocabulary: Include an example in each definition.

   Aqueous solution:

   Soluble:

   Insoluble:

   Entropy:

   Miscible:

6. What is entropy and how does it affect solution formation?

7. Use the following figure to explain the effect intermolecular forces have on the formation of a solution:

Intermolecular Forces

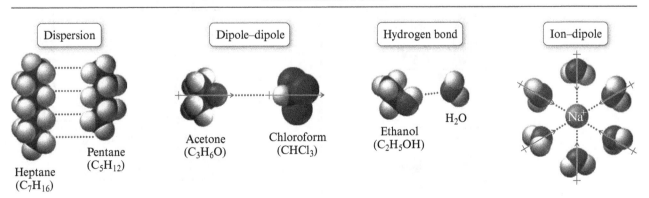

8. Explain the types of interactions that lead to solution formation and the types of interactions that do not lead to solution formation.

Section 14.3   Energetics of Solution Formation

9. Vocabulary:

   Enthalpy of solution:

   Exothermic:

   Endothermic:

   Heat of hydration:

10. What are the three steps needed for a solution to form? For each step, include the general ΔH.

11. Using the three steps in Question 10, explain how the solution process can be exothermic or endothermic.

12. Draw a graph showing what would happen to the temperature of the solution when: a) an exothermic solution forms and b) an endothermic solution forms.

13. Identify the steps leading to the formation of an exothermic and an endothermic solution on the following figures:

Energetics of Solution Formation

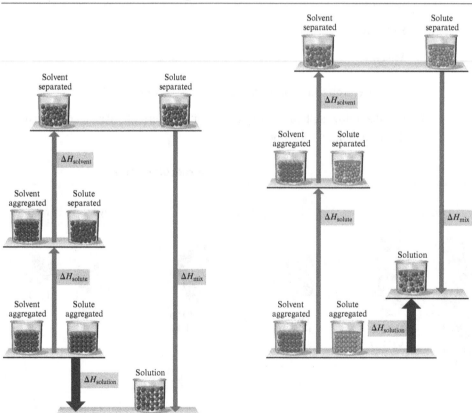

14. What two terms combine to yield the heat of solution?

15. Explain what is occurring in each of these diagrams:

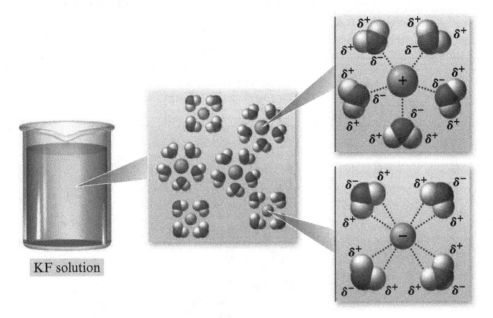

KF solution

16. What is the relationship between the enthalpy of solute and the enthalpy of hydration in an exothermic solution? In an endothermic solution? When is the enthalpy of solute is approximately equal to the enthalpy of hydration? Include an example for each relationship.

Section 14.4   Solution Equilibrium and Factors Affecting Solubility

17. Use the following pictures to explain how a dynamic equilibrium of a solution is reached.

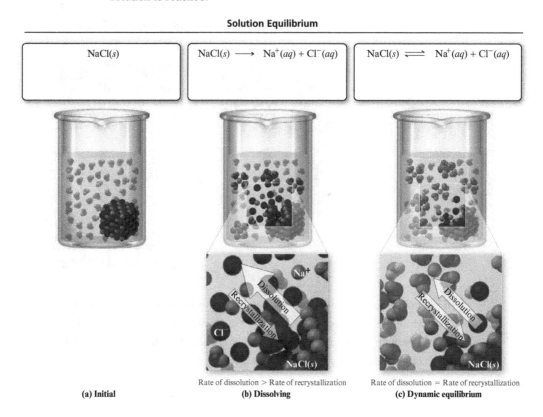

Solution Equilibrium

NaCl(s)   NaCl(s) ⟶ Na⁺(aq) + Cl⁻(aq)   NaCl(s) ⇌ Na⁺(aq) + Cl⁻(aq)

Rate of dissolution > Rate of recrystallization   Rate of dissolution = Rate of recrystallization

(a) Initial   **(b) Dissolving**   **(c) Dynamic equilibrium**

18. Define the following vocabulary terms:

Saturated solution:

Unsaturated solution:

Supersaturated solution:

19. How can you determine if a solution is saturated or unsaturated?

20. Explain how temperature in general affects the solubility of solids. What technique is used to purify a solid? Explain how it purifies a sample.

21. Explain how temperature affects the solubility of gases. What type of relationship is this?

22. Explain why fish tend to prefer cold water.

23. Using a can of soda as an example, explain how pressure affects the solubility of gases in the following diagram. Why does an opened can of soda pop go "flat"?

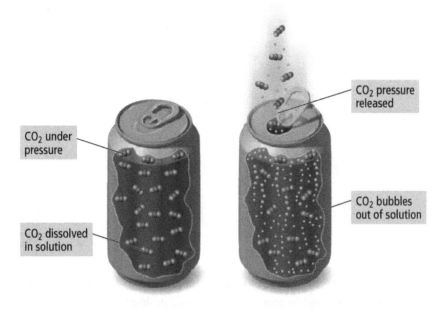

CO$_2$ under pressure

CO$_2$ dissolved in solution

CO$_2$ pressure released

CO$_2$ bubbles out of solution

24. What is Henry's law and how does it apply to solutions?

Expressing Solution Concentration   Section 14.5

25. What is the difference between a dilute solution and a concentrated solution?

26. How is each of the following units of concentration calculated? Include the accepted units of each.

Note: several units and their calculations will not be assessed on the AP Exam. They are notated with a*

   Molarity:

   Molality:*

   Mole fraction:

   Mole percent:

   Percent by volume:*

   Percent by mass:*

27. Explain how to make a molar solution using the following diagram.

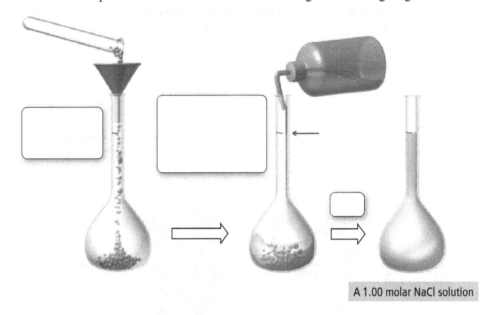

A 1.00 molar NaCl solution

28. What is a POP? (see the dirty dozen on page 590) Why are they hazardous?*
    What is bioamplification and why is this a problem?

Section 14.6*   Colligative Properties: Vapor Pressure Lowering, Freezing Point Depression, Boiling Point Elevation, and Osmotic Pressure* Note: Colligative properties, Sections 14.6 and 14.7, are not assessed on the AP Chemistry Exam.

29. What are colligative properties? Explain how each of the following is affected
    by colligative properties and why.* Include formulas with your answers.

    Vapor pressure:

    Freezing point:

    Boiling point:

    Osmotic pressure:

30. Explain Raoult's law.*

31. What is an ideal solution?* How does one determine if a solution is ideal?

Section 14.7*   Colligative Properties of Strong Electrolyte Solutions

32. What are strong electrolytes?

33. What is the van't Hoff factor? Why is it important in determining colligative
    properties?* How does the van't Hoff factor change the equations for boiling
    point elevation, freezing point depression, and osmotic pressure?

34. What are hyperosmotic, hyposmotic, and isosmotic solutions? Why are these important in medicine?*

Colloids   Section 14.8

35. What are colloids? Why are they not considered true solutions? How can you determine if something is a colloid or true solution?

36. In the following table, give an example of each type of colloid.

Types of Colloidal Dispersions

Classification	Dispersing Substance (Solute-like)	Dispersing Medium (Solvent-like)	Example
Aerosol	Liquid	Gas	
Solid aerosol	Solid	Gas	
Foam	Gas	Liquid	
Emulsion	Liquid	Liquid	
Solid emulsion	Liquid	Solid	

37. Explain how soap is used to clean.

38. What is Brownian motion? Include a diagram in your answer.

39. What is the Tyndall effect? Include a diagram in your answer.

Self-Assessment Answers

1. _____   2. _____   3. _____

4. _____   5. _____   6. _____

7. _____   8. _____   9. _____

10. _____   11. _____   12. _____

13. _____   14. _____   15. _____

CHEMICAL KINETICS

This chapter has many places for students to interpret data and analyze graphs which are addressed in the science practices and learning objectives associated with this chapter. This whole chapter addresses Unit 5 on rates of reactions. Pay particular attention to analyzing graphs and data to support a claim such as a rate law. To go along with this chapter, students should do a lab experiment determining rate laws. Laboratory experiments involving Beer's law and laboratory experiments using colorimetry are useful for developing a better understanding of kinetics. The sections of the most importance in the textbook are below:

15.2 **The Rate of a Chemical Reaction**

15.3 **The Rate Law: The Effect of Concentration on Reaction Rate**

15.4 **The Integrated Rate Law: The Dependence of Concentration on Time**

15.5 **The Effect of Temperature on Reaction Rate**

15.6 **Reaction Mechanisms**

15.7 **Catalysis**

Specific Learning Objectives Addressed in This Chapter:

TRA-3 Some reactions happen quickly, while others happen more slowly and depend on reactant concentrations and temperature.

TRA-3.A Explain the relationship between the rate of a chemical reaction and experimental parameters.

TRA-3.B Represent experimental data with a consistent rate law expression.

TRA-3.C Identify the rate law expression of a chemical reaction using data that show how the concentrations of reaction species change over time.

TRA-4 There is a relationship between the speed of a reaction and the collision frequency of particle collisions.

TRA-4.A Represent an elementary reaction as a rate law expression using stoichiometry.

TRA-4.B Explain the relationship between the rate of an elementary reaction and the frequency, energy, and orientation of molecular collisions.

TRA-4.C Represent the activation energy and overall energy change in an elementary reaction using a reaction energy profile.

TRA-5 Many chemical reactions occur through a series of elementary reactions when combined form a chemical equation.

TRA-5.A Identify the components of a reaction mechanism.

TRA-5.B Identify the rate law for a reaction from a mechanism in which the first step is rate limiting.

TRA-5.C Identify the rate law for a reaction from a mechanism in which the first step is not rate limiting.

TRA-5.D Represent the activation energy and overall energy change in a multistep reaction with a reaction energy profile.

ENE-1 The speed at which a reaction occurs can be influenced by a catalyst.

ENE-1.A Explain the relationship between the effect of a catalyst on a reaction and changes in the reaction mechanism.

Concepts and Vocabulary to Review:

The Rate of a Chemical Reaction   Section 15.2

Chemical reactions can be slow or fast. Rates are measured using changes in concentration such as molarity over the change in time. Molarity per second can be represented as M/s, Ms^{-1}, or $molL^{-1}s^{-1}$. The rate is dependent on several factors, which are the focus of this chapter. Reactants decrease as products increase, although this depends on the direction the equation is written relative to the initial concentrations of reactants and products. When calculating rates for reactants a negative sign is in front of the ratio of the change in concentration with change in time indicating a loss of reactants and for products the sign is positive indicating a gain in the amount of products. The chemical equation coefficients show how each substance changes in relationship to each other.

Generally, we can relate the measure rates for different species using:

$$aA + bB \rightarrow cC + dD$$

$$\text{Rate} = -\frac{1}{a}\frac{\Delta[A]}{\Delta t} = -\frac{1}{b}\frac{\Delta[B]}{\Delta t} = +\frac{1}{c}\frac{\Delta[C]}{\Delta t} = +\frac{1}{d}\frac{\Delta[D]}{\Delta t}$$

Notice the − signs in front of reactants indicating a loss and a + sign in front of products indicating a gain. In a reaction if the rate of change of one species is known, using stoichiometry, the rate of change of all other species can be determined.

Instantaneous rates of change are determined from a graph by drawing a tangent line to the curve of concentration with time at a certain point and then finding the slope of the line.

The graph in Figure 15.1, shows an upward curve representing a product species starting at zero, although products do not always start at zero in every reaction, and increase with time whereas the reactants start with higher and decrease concentration with time, forming a downward curve on a typical concentration against time graph. On the graph of concentration versus time the exact rate, called an instantaneous rate, can be determined at any point by drawing a tangent line through the point and then determining the slope of the tangent line. By contrast, an average rate is determined by the rate of change over a time interval. It is similar to saying you average 50 km/hr (average rate) or saying at this moment we are going 65 km/hr (instantaneous rate).

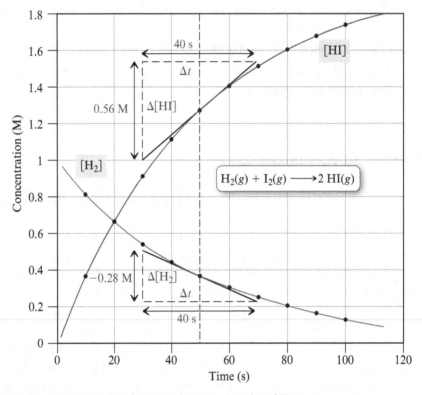

Figure 15.1 Reactant and Product Concentrations as a Function of Time   The graph shows the concentration of one of the reactants (H_2) and the product (HI) as a function of time. The other reactant (I_2) is omitted for clarity.

Measuring reaction rates when either a reactant or a product is a colored solution is often done with spectroscopy. The reaction can be monitored by measuring the change in intensity of the light absorbed. A variety of methods can be used to determine the concentration by taking samples at intervals. See Appendix 1 for details on using this method with colored solutions. When using either a colorimeter or spectrometer, poor sample readings can occur if fingerprints are on the cuvette. This error will reflect more light, resulting in a concentration reading that is too high.

Gas chromatography, mass spectrometry, or titrations are some techniques that can be used as long as the measurement does not take a significant amount of time relative to the reaction time. The following two figures show the use of a spectrometer and gas chromatograph.

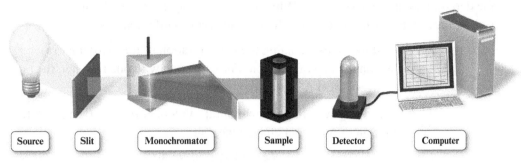

Figure 15.2 The Spectrometer   In a spectrometer, light of a specific wavelength is passed through the sample, and the intensity of the transmitted light—which depends on how much light is absorbed by the sample—is measured and recorded.

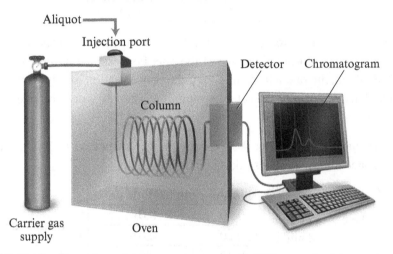

Figure 15.3 The Gas Chromatograph   In a gas chromatograph (GC), a sample of the reaction mixture, or aliquot, is injected into a specially constructed column. Because of their characteristic physical and chemical properties, different components of the mixture pass through the column at different rates and thus exit at different times. As each component leaves the column, it is detected electronically and a chromatogram is recorded. The area under each peak in the chromatogram is proportional to the amount of one particular component in the sample mixture.

The Rate Law: The Effect of Concentration on Reaction Rate

Section 15.3

An equation representing the rate of the reaction as it relates to the concentration of reactants(s) is called the rate law. The rate law is determined experimentally and is different for different reactions although it has the basic formula, rate $= k[\,A\,]^n$, where k is called the rate constant, A is a reactant species, and n is the order of reaction.

Before k can be calculated, the value(s) of n must be determined. Experimental evidence where a reactant concentration is changed while other reactant concentrations remain unchanged allows for the determination of the effect of each reactant on the rate, through the order, n. If there are several reactants, a whole series of reaction rate determinations must be carried out. The evidence of the change of rate allows for the determination of the order (n). While there are many orders, including fractional orders, the AP test focus is on zero-, first-, and second-order reactions.

- If n is zero, it indicates changing the concentration of this particular reactant has no effect on the rate of reaction. For a reaction with one reactant, the rate law would be rate $= k[A]^0$ or rate $= k$.

  - If the following was the experimental evidence, $n = 0$. Changing the concentration of A did not change the rate.

Zero Order ($n = 0$)

the concentration doubles

[A](M)	Initial Rate (M/s)
0.10	0.015
0.20	0.015
0.40	0.015

no rate change

- If n is one, it indicates a change in concentration of this reactant will result in a proportional change of the rate. For instance, if the concentration is doubled, the rate will double, or if the concentration is halved, the reaction rate halves. For a one-reactant system, the rate law would be rate $= k[A]^1$ or rate $= k[A]$.

  - If the following was the experimental evidence, $n = 1$. Doubling the concentration of A also doubled the rate.

the concentration doubles

[A](M)	Initial Rate (M/s)
0.10	0.015
0.20	0.030
0.40	0.060

the rate doubles

- If n is two, it indicates a change in concentration of this reactant will result in the rate changing with a square function. If the concentration is doubled, the rate will increase by 2^2 or a factor of 4. If the concentration is tripled, the rate will increase by 3^2 or a factor of 9. For a one-reactant system, the rate law would be rate $= k[A]^2$.

  - If the following was the experimental evidence, $n = 2$. Doubling the concentration of A squares the rate or 2^2

Second Order ($n = 2$)

the concentration doubles

[A](M)	Initial Rate (M/s)
0.10	0.015
0.20	0.060
0.40	0.240

the rate quadruples

These orders can also be determined graphically assuming a system with a 1:1 stoichiometry, A → P. If the chemical equation is not a 1:1 stoichiometry, mathematical adjustments will need to be made to the equations in order to determine the rate constant, k, from the slope of the line. In a zero order reaction, the concentration changes as the rate changes therefore, a plot of concentration versus

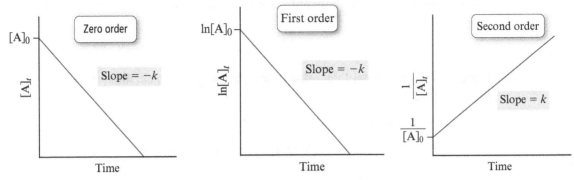

A plot of reactant concentration as a function of time yields a straight line.

A plot of the natural log of the reactant as a function of time yields a straight line.

A plot of the inverse of the reactant concentration versus time yields a straight line.

Figure 15.4 Zero, first, and second order graphs to determine an order for a reaction with 1:1 stoichiometry

time results in a linear relationship as shown in Figure 15.4. The slope of the line is equal to $-k$, where k is the rate constant. In a first order reaction, the plot to get a straight line is ln[A] versus time. In this case, the slope of the line is again equal to $-k$ (this is the way usually shown on the AP test for first order reactions). When graphing a second order reaction, the plot to get the linear relationship is $1/[A]$ versus time. The line will have positive slope, therefore the slope $= k$.

When there is more than one reactant, then each reactant must have its order determined from experimental evidence. For the reaction $a\text{A} + b\text{B} \rightarrow c\text{C} + d\text{D}$ the rate law would be Rate $= k[\text{A}]^m[\text{B}]^n$.

The total reaction order is the sum of all the reactant orders. If there are two reactants A and B, and each has an order of 1, the total order would be 2. The units of k vary depending on the total order. For zero-order reactions, the units of k are equal to the rate units. In first-order reactions, the units of k are time^{-1}, and in second-order reactions, the units are M^{-1}time^{-1}.

The Integrated Rate Law: The Dependence of Concentration on Time

Section 15.4

As a reaction proceeds, we can determine a concentration at a certain time if the rate law is known. The integrated rate law is on the AP Exam, which is also called the differential rate law in the Tro text, and is dependent on the order of the reaction.

In a first order reaction, for $\text{A} \rightarrow \text{P}$, remember the rate is proportional to the concentration as shown in $-\dfrac{\Delta[\text{A}]}{\Delta t} = k[\text{A}]$. To find a concentration at time t, the equation can be rearranged to $\dfrac{\ln([\text{A}]_t)}{[\text{A}]_0} = -kt$ or $\ln[\text{A}]_t = -kt + \ln[\text{A}]_0$. The subscript 0 is for original or beginning time. Taking data and making a graph to determine k also allows you to determine concentrations at other times as well as the order for that species.

Example: The First-Order Integrated Rate Law: Using Graphical Analysis of Reaction Data

Consider the equation for the decomposition of SO_2Cl_2:

$$SO_2Cl_2(g) \rightarrow SO_2(g) + Cl_2(g)$$

The concentration of SO_2Cl_2 was monitored at a fixed temperature as a function of time during the decomposition reaction, and the following data were tabulated:

Time (s)	[SO$_2$ Cl$_2$] (M)	Time (s)	[SO$_2$ Cl$_2$] (M)
0	0.100	800	0.0793
100	0.0971	900	0.0770
200	0.0944	1000	0.0748
300	0.0917	1100	0.0727
400	0.0890	1200	0.0706
500	0.0865	1300	0.0686
600	0.0840	1400	0.0666
700	0.0816	1500	0.0647

Show that the reaction is first order, and determine the rate constant for the reaction.

Solution

In order to show that the reaction is first order, prepare a graph of $\ln\left[SO_2Cl_2\right]$ versus time as shown.

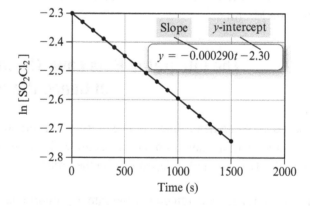

The plot is linear, confirming that the reaction is indeed first order. To obtain the rate constant, determine the slope of the line. Since the stoichiometry is 1:1, the slope of the line will be equal to $-k$. Since the slope of the best fitting line is $-2.90 \times 10^{-4}\ s^{-1}$, the rate constant is $+2.90 \times 10^{-4}\ s^{-1}$.

For reactions with 1:1 stoichiometry, the general format is shown in the graph below.

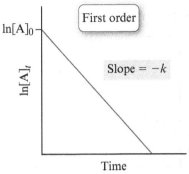

Figure 15.5 First-Order Integrated Rate Law For a first-order reaction with 1:1 stoichiometry, a plot of the natural log of the reactant concentration as a function of time yields a straight line. The slope of the line is equal to $-k$ and the y-intercept is $\ln[A]_0$.

At any point of time on the graph, the natural log of the concentration can be used to calculate the concentration. Plotting data on other types of graphs using linear or exponential scales may provide useful information.

For a second order reaction, the concentration time equation is different: $\frac{1}{[A]_t} = kt + \frac{1}{[A]_0}$. Again, using data to make a graph is an important skill and is shown in the example below.

Example: The Second-Order Integrated Rate Law: Using Graphical Analysis of Reaction Data for a Reaction with 1:1 Stoichiometry

Consider the equation for the decomposition of NO_2:

$$NO_2(g) \rightarrow NO(g) + O(g)$$

The concentration of NO_2 is monitored at a fixed temperature as a function of time during the decomposition reaction and the data tabulated in the margin at right. Show by graphical analysis that the reaction is not first order and that it is second order. Determine the rate constant for the reaction.

Solution

In order to show that the reaction is *not* first order, prepare a graph of $[NO_2]$ versus time as shown:

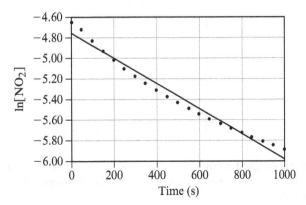

The plot is *not* linear (the straight line does not fit the data points), confirming that the reaction is not first order. In order to show that the reaction is second order, prepare a graph of $1/[NO_2]$ versus time as shown:

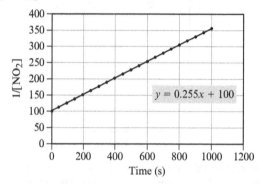

This graph is linear (the data points fit well to a straight line), confirming that the reaction is indeed second order. To obtain the rate constant, determine the slope of the best-fitting line. The slope is $0.255 \, M^{-1} \cdot s^{-1}$; therefore, since this reaction has 1:1 stoichiometry the rate constant is $0.255 \, M^{-1} \cdot s^{-1}$.

For reactions with 1:1 stoichiometry, the second-order reaction then can be summarized to look like the graph below.

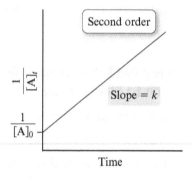

Figure 15.6 Second-Order Integrated Rate Law   For a second-order reaction with 1:1 stoichiometry, a plot of the inverse of the reactant concentration as a function of time yields a straight line. The slope of the line is equal to k and the y-intercept is $1/[A]_0$.

For a zero-order reaction where the rate law is rate $= k$, the integrated rate law is $[A]_t = [A]_0 - kt$. From data a graph would have the appearance of the figure below.

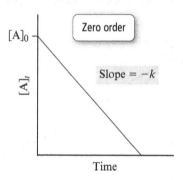

Figure 15.7 Zero-Order Integrated Rate Law   For a zero-order reaction with 1:1 stoichiometry, a plot of the reactant concentration as a function of time yields a straight line. The slope of the line is equal to $-k$ and the y-intercept is $[A]_0$.

The negative slope of the line indicates the *slope* $= -k$. In a problem, you may have to take data and try several graphs to determine which gives a linear relationship to determine the order, write an appropriate rate law, and determine the value of k (with correct units!). Remember to consider the stoichiometry when using the slope to find the rate constant.

The half-life of a reaction occurs when half of the initial amount of reactant reacts. The concentration time equation can be used but if it is known to be at the half-life $(t_{1/2})$, then the half-life equation can be used. The most common equation used is for first-order reaction since all nuclear reactions are first order. For first order, graphically, it is observed that the length of each half-life for a first-order reaction is constant and independent of the concentration. Only the first order half-life equation $t_{1/2} = 0.693/k$ appears on the equation pages provided on the AP exam. Concentration does not enter into this equation so has no effect on the length of the half-life.

Half-Life for a First-Order Reaction

At t_0

For a first-order reaction, the half-life is constant and independent of concentration.

After 1 half-life

After 2 half-lives

After 3 half-lives

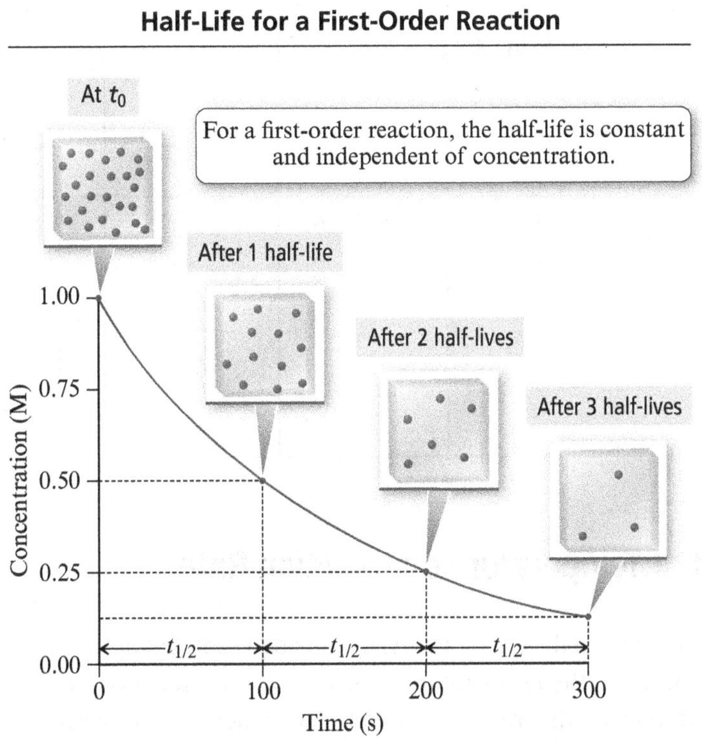

Figure 15 .8 Half-Life: Concentration versus Time for a First-Order Reaction   For this reaction, the concentration decreases by one-half every 100 seconds ($t_{1/2} = 100$ s). The dark spheres represent reactant molecules (the products are omitted for clarity).

For zero order and second order, the length of the half-life is dependent on concentration. Looking at the two equations in the following table for half-life, concentration has a different affect in each half-life. In zero order, the higher the concentration, the longer the half-life, but in second order, since the higher concentration would be in the denominator, indicating the higher the concentration the shorter the half-life.

The following table summarizes the equations and relationships for reactions with 1:1 stoichiometry $A \rightarrow P$:

Order of reaction and rate law	Units of k (time unit is in seconds)	Concentration time equation	Relationship slope and k	Half-life equation	Graph
0 rate $= k$	M/s or Ms^{-1}	$[A]_t = -kt + [A]_0$	slope $= -k$	$t_{1/2} = \dfrac{[A]_0}{2k}$	*y*-intercept $= [A]_0$, Slope $= -k$, [A]$_t$ vs Time t
1 rate $= k[A]$	s^{-1}	$\dfrac{\ln([A]t)}{[A]_0} = -kt$ or $\ln[A]_t = -kt + \ln[A]_0$	slope $= -k$	$t_{1/2} = \dfrac{0.693}{k}$	*y*-intercept $= \ln[A]_0$, Slope $= -k$, ln[A]$_t$ vs Time t
2 rate $= [A]^2$	$M^{-1}s^{-1}$	$\dfrac{1}{[A]_t} = kt + \dfrac{1}{[A]_0}$	slope $= k$	$t_{1/2} = \dfrac{1}{k[A]_0}$	Slope $= k$, *y*-intercept $= 1/[A]_0$, 1/[A]$_t$ vs Time t

Section 15.5   The Effect of Temperature on Reaction Rate

Students are not expected to solve the Arrhenius equation but are expected to understand how it indicates the temperature dependence for a reaction and the activation energy needed to reach the transition state for the reaction to proceed.

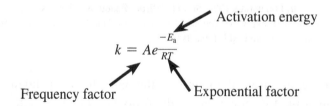

$$k = Ae^{\frac{-E_a}{RT}}$$

Activation energy

Frequency factor

Exponential factor

In the equation E_a is the activation energy and T is temperature.

Activation Energy

$$2 H_2(g) + O_2(g) \rightleftharpoons 2 H_2O(g)$$

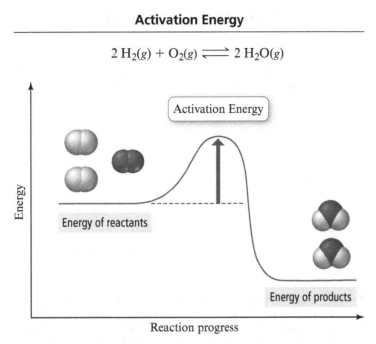

Figure 15.9 The Activation Energy Barrier   Even though the reaction is energetically favorable (the energy of the products is lower than that of the reactants), an input of energy is needed for the reaction to take place.

In the figure above, the number of molecules that can reach the activation energy and proceed to product formation depends on their energy, which is temperature dependent. When the reactants reach the top of the activation energy barrier, they are in a transition state which has a higher energy than either the reactants or products. The higher the activation energy, the slower the reaction is.

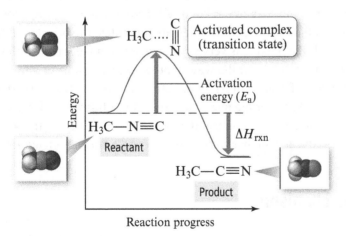

Figure 15.10 The Activated Complex   The reaction pathway includes a transitional state—the activated complex—that has a higher energy than either the reactant or the product.

As the temperature increases, the number of reactant species with the energy needed to reach the activation energy increases.

Thermal Energy Distribution

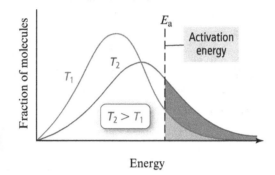

As temperature increases, the fraction of molecules with enough energy to surmount the activation energy barrier also increases.

Figure 15.11 Thermal Energy Distribution   At any given temperature, the atoms or molecules in a gas sample have a range of energies. The higher the temperature, the wider the energy distribution and the greater the average energy. The fraction of molecules with enough energy to surmount the activation energy barrier and react (shaded regions) increases sharply as the temperature rises.

Notice Figure 15.11 is not a temperature graph but the fraction of molecules with the energy needed. T_2 is the higher temperature as there is a greater fraction of reactant species with the activation energy. This data supports the claim that a reaction rate will proceed faster at a higher temperature.

Not only do reactants need to reach the activation energy, they also need to collide with each other and in the correct orientation. If the reactants are individual atoms, the orientation does not matter but when molecules are reacting orientation does matter. The parts of each reactant where the bond will form need to collide. How often the reactants actually collide with the right orientation is called the orientation factor. This factor is a fraction. If the fraction is very small, the reaction will proceed slowly. A way to visualize this is to think of all the ways a puzzle piece can fit in, only one way of fitting it in will work. If 1 in 5 collisions are effective, the fraction is 0.20, if it is 1 in 4 then the fraction is 0.25. For the puzzle analogy, it is a faster rate if it takes 5 tries to get the puzzle piece in correctly compared to taking 50 tries. If a reaction is proceeding slowly, usually it is due to a high activation energy and a small orientation factor.

Section 15.6   Reaction Mechanisms

Even though we write chemical equations that show reactants going directly to products, many reactions actually occur in a series of steps. In these steps, intermediate products are formed which also have to collide with the right orientation. Intermediates are products formed but are then used in another step. These steps are called the mechanism of a reaction. Each step is called an elementary step. By analyzing the steps in a reaction mechanism, the rate law and balanced equation can be determined. To determine the balanced equation, all the elementary steps are added together. Intermediates will cancel out of the balanced equation as they will be found as both reactant and product. For example,

$$\text{Step 1} \quad A_2 + BC \rightarrow AB + AC$$
$$\text{Step 2} \quad AB + BC \rightarrow AC + B_2$$

$$\text{Total} \quad A_2 + 2BC \rightarrow 2AC + B_2$$

Notice AB is a product in the first reaction and a reactant in the second reaction. AB is an intermediate which will cancel in the overall reaction. In each of the two elementary steps in this example species need to collide. These steps are then called bimolecular. If there is a reaction such as $A_2 \rightarrow 2A$, this reaction is unimolecular since there is only one reactant molecule, but two product molecules. A rate law can be written for each step of the mechanism because a step in a mechanism represents what the molecules are doing.

Within a mechanism, one of the steps will be much slower than the other(s). This step is called the rate-determining step and determines the overall rate law of the reaction. When looking at an energy diagram comparing each step in a two-step mechanism, the slow step will have a higher activation energy. Another possible contributing factor to a slow step in a reaction mechanism is the orientation or the alignment of the molecules for a favorable collision.

Energy Diagram for a Two-Step Mechanism

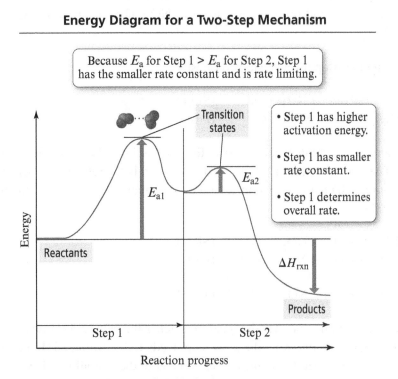

Figure 15.12 Energy Diagram for a Two-Step Mechanism

The rate law of the slow step will be the rate law of the whole reaction.

Table 15.1   Rate Laws for Elementary Steps

Elementary Step	Molecularity	Rate Law
A → products	1	Rate = $k[A]$
A + A → products	2	Rate = $k[A]^2$
A + B → products	2	Rate = $k[A][B]$
A + A + A → products	3 (rare)	Rate = $k[A]^3$
A + A + B → products	3 (rare)	Rate = $k[A]^2[B]$
A + B + C → products	3 (rare)	Rate = $k[A][B][C]$

Students will not be expected to propose a mechanism but will be asked to evaluate the rate law for a plausible mechanism from provided data and justify their choice.

Mechanisms with a Slow Initial Step

The following reaction between nitrogen dioxide and carbon monoxide occurs at low temperatures:

$$NO_2(g) + CO(g) \rightarrow NO(g) + CO_2(g)$$

By doing experiments, it is determined that this reaction is zero order with respect to CO and second order with respect to NO_2. The experimental rate law is rate = $k[NO_2]^2$.

The following two-step mechanism is proposed:

Step 1: $NO_2 + NO_2 \rightarrow NO_3 + NO$ (Slow)
Step 2: $NO_3 + CO \rightarrow NO_2 + CO_2$ (Fast)

The mechanism represents what occurs at the particle level. Each step is an elementary step. There are two questions we need to answer. Is the rate law associated with the proposed mechanism consistent with the experimental rate law? Is this mechanism plausible?

Step 1: $NO_2 + NO_2 \rightarrow NO_3 + NO$ (Slow)
Step 2: $NO_3 + CO \rightarrow NO_2 + CO_2$ (Fast)
_____
    $NO_2 + CO \rightarrow NO + CO_2$ Overall

When the two steps add, the overall equation matches the balanced chemical reaction so it may be plausible and now the slow step needs to be evaluated. Intermediates cannot appear in the overall chemical equation and in the overall rate law. Note that this overall chemical equation is not a third step in the mechanism. We cannot write a rate law from the overall chemical equation. Step 1 involves a bimolecular collision between two NO_2 molecules and this bimolecular collision is represented in the rate law for Step 1. Step 2 is faster compared to Step 1 and the rate constant k_2 for Step 2 is larger compared to the rate constant for Step 1, k_1. The intermediate, NO_3, is slowly generated in Step 1, but it reacts quickly in Step 2. The rate of the overall reaction cannot go faster than the rate at which NO_3 is generated in Step 1. Since Step 1 is the slow step, it is the rate determining step and a rate law for this step can be written, rate $= k_1[NO_2][NO_2]$, which we can rewrite as rate $= k[NO_2]^2$. The rate law associated with the mechanism for this reaction is consistent with the experimental rate law. This means that the proposed mechanism is plausible. We can write a rate law directly from the slow step of a reaction mechanism because the steps of a mechanism represent elementary reactions—what the particles are doing. We cannot prove that a mechanism is the way the particles react, but we can disprove a mechanism.

Mechanisms with a Fast Initial Step

The following reaction between nitric oxide and chlorine occurs at moderate temperatures:

$$2NO(g) + Cl_2(g) \rightarrow 2NOCl(g)$$

By doing experiments, it is determined that this reaction is first order with respect to Cl_2 and second order with respect to NO. The experimental rate law is, rate $= k[NO]^2[Cl_2]$. It is a coincident that stoichiometric coefficients in the balanced chemical equation match the exponents in the rate law. We note that it is highly unlikely that the mechanism would involve only one step, namely a simultaneous collision of three molecules, two NO molecules and one Cl_2 molecule. The following two-step mechanism is proposed:

Step 1: $NO + Cl_2 \rightleftharpoons NOCl_2$ (Fast)
Step 2: $NOCl_2 + NO \rightarrow 2NOCl$ (Slow)

Is the rate law associated with the proposed mechanism consistent with the experimental rate law? Is this mechanism plausible?

Does the sum of the elementary reactions sum to the overall balanced chemical equation?

Step 1: $NO + Cl_2 \rightleftharpoons NOCl_2$ (Fast)
Step 2: $NOCl_2 + NO \rightarrow 2NOCl$ (Slow)
_____
$2NO + Cl_2 \rightarrow 2NOCl$ Overall

Yes, the sum of the elementary reactions add up to the overall balanced chemical equation so it may be plausible and now the slow step has to be evaluated.

Since Step 2 is the slow step, this is the rate-determining step. Because Step 2 is an elementary step and is a bimolecular collision between one $NOCl_2$ molecule and one NO molecule, we can write the rate law for Step 2 as:

$$\text{rate} = k_2[NOCl_2][NO]$$

However, since we cannot measure the concentration of intermediates and this rate law includes the intermediate $NOCl_2$, we cannot include this intermediate in the rate law. In order to determine if the proposed rate law is plausible, we need to derive a rate law which involves only the reactants from the overall balanced chemical equation.

Step 1 involves a fast equilibrium system for which the rate of the forward reaction equals the rate of the reverse reaction:

$$\text{Rate}_{forward} = k_1[NO][Cl_2] \quad \text{and} \quad \text{Rate}_{reverse} = k_{-1}[NOCl_2]$$

where k_1 is the rate constant for the forward reaction in Step 1 and k_{-1} is the rate constant for the reverse reaction in Step 1.

Since the two rates are equal, we write $[k_1[NO][Cl_2]] = k_{-1}[NOCl_2]$

Rearranging, we obtain:

$$\frac{k_1}{k_{-1}}[NO][Cl_2] = [NOCl_2]$$

We substitute the expression for $[NOCl_2]$ in the rate law rate $= k_2[NOCl_2][NO]$ and obtain:

$$\text{rate} = \frac{k_2 k_1}{k_{-1}}[NO][Cl_2][NO] = k[NO]^2[Cl_2]$$

where k is equal to $\frac{k_2 k_1}{k_{-1}}$

This rate law associated with the proposed mechanism is consistent with the experimental rate law. The proposed mechanism is plausible.

Section 15.7   **Catalysis**

Reaction rates and mechanisms can be altered by catalysts. A catalyst is a chemical species that is added and is not consumed in the reaction. In the following example,

A + 2B + C → AB + BC
BC + D → BD + C
A + 2B + D → AB + BD

C is a catalyst as it is first a reactant and then is reformed as a product. C is not in the final equation along with the intermediate BC, which is formed and then consumed. A catalyst speeds up a reaction by providing an alternate mechanism or pathway. The alternate mechanism has a lower activation energy than the original pathway of the reaction. See Figure 15.13.

**Energy Diagram for Catalyzed and
Uncatalyzed Pathways**

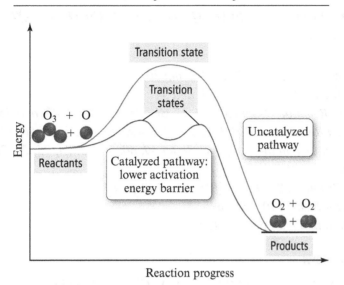

Figure 15.13 Catalyzed and Uncatalyzed Decomposition of Ozone   In the catalytic destruction of ozone (red), the activation barrier for the rate-limiting step is much lower than in the uncatalyzed process (blue). Notice the reactants for both reactions start in the same place and end in the same place but the pathways are different.

Homogeneous catalysts are in the same phase as the reactants, for example, both solids whereas heterogeneous catalysts are in a different phase, such as a solid and a gas. Catalysts can be destructive to the environment such as the destruction of the ozone layer in the stratosphere by chlorine catalysts from chlorofluorocarbons or they can be advantageous such as in a catalytic converter in a car which contains solid catalysts like platinum and converts pollutants in the automobile exhaust into less harmful substances. An important group of catalysts are biological enzymes. These enzymes are large complex proteins which are very specific and which often only affect one reaction. For instance, there are several digestive enzymes and each breaks down a particular food into its constituent parts.

Figure 15.14 Chymotrypsin, a Digestive Enzyme   This model of chymotrypsin shows a section of a protein substrate (light grey) in the active site.

Additional Practice

Self-Assessment Quiz Questions Q1, Q2, Q3, Q4, Q5, Q6, Q7, Q8, Q9, Q10, Q11, Q12, Q13, Q14, and Q15

Problems:
Review Questions 4, 5, 6, 9, 12, 15, 16, and 20
Reaction Rates 25, 27, 29, 31, 32, 33, and 34
Rate Law and Reaction Orders 35, 36, 37, 38, 39, 40, 41, 42, 43, and 45
The Integrated Rate Law and Half-Life 47, 48, 49, 50, 51, 53, 55, 56, 57, and 58
Effect Temperature and the Collision Model 59, 60, 69, 73, 74, 75, 76, 77, and 78
Catalysis 80
Cumulative Problems 83, 95, 96, 105, 106, 108, and 109
Conceptual Problems 120, 121, and 122
Data Interpretation and Analysis 125

Equations to know:

$$\text{Rate} = -\frac{1}{a}\frac{\Delta[A]}{\Delta t} = -\frac{1}{b}\frac{\Delta[B]}{\Delta t} = +\frac{1}{c}\frac{\Delta[C]}{\Delta t} = +\frac{1}{d}\frac{\Delta[D]}{\Delta t}$$

$$\text{rate} = k[A]^n,$$

$$\text{Rate} = k[A]^m[B]^n.$$

Order of reaction and rate law	Units of k (time unit is in seconds)	Concentration time equation	Relationship slope and k	Half-life equation	Graph
0 rate $= k$	M/s or Ms^{-1}	$[A]_t = -kt + [A]_0$	slope $= -k$	$t_{1/2} = \dfrac{[A]_0}{2k}$	
1 rate $= k[A]$	s^{-1}	$\dfrac{\ln([A]t)}{[A]_0} = -kt$ or $\ln[A]_t = -kt + \ln[A]_0$	slope $= -k$	$t_{1/2} = \dfrac{0.693}{k}$	
2 rate $= [A]^2$	$M^{-1}s^{-1}$	$\dfrac{1}{[A]_t} = kt + \dfrac{1}{[A]_0}$	slope $= k$	$t_{1/2} = \dfrac{1}{k[A]_0}$	

Practice AP Test Questions

Use the following information to help answer Questions 1 and 2.

For the following, data were collected during a method of initial rates experiment for the gas phase reaction

$$BF_3(g) + NH_3(g) \rightarrow F_3BNH_3(g)$$

Experiment	$[BF_3]$	$[NH_3]$	Initial rate M/sec
1	0.350	0.350	0.418
2	0.150	0.350	0.179
3	0.350	0.233	0.278
4	0.700	0.700	

1. The rate equation for the reaction is

   A) rate $= k[BF_3]^2 [NH_3]^2$

   B) rate $= k[BF_3]^{2.33} [NH_3]^{1.50}$

   C) rate $= k[BF_3] [NH_3]$

   D) rate $= k[BF_3]^2 [NH_3]$

2. The initial rate of the reaction, in units of M/s, for Experiment 4 is

   A) 0.818

   B) 0.836

   C) 0.868

   D) 1.67

Use the following information to help answer Questions 3 and 4.

3. The following particulate diagrams represent mixtures of $H_2(g)$ and $NO(g)$ at the molecular level at the beginning of a reaction. Two open circles joined together represent a H_2 molecule, whereas a filled-in circle and a triangle joined together represent a NO molecule. The diagrams show a small portion of the reaction mixture using the same volume. The two substances react as follows:

$$2H_2(g) + 2NO(g) \rightarrow N_2(g) + 2H_2O(g)$$

Experimentally, the rate is first order with respect to H_2 and second order with respect to NO. Based on this fact, which of the following mixtures will have the fastest initial rate?

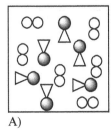
A)

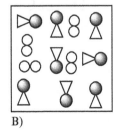
B)

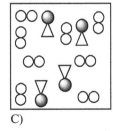
C)

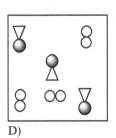
D)

4. If the rate of consumption for NO is 0.44 M/s, what is the rate of formation of nitrogen, in units of M/s?

A) 0.11

B) 0.22

C) 0.88

D) 1.76

5. The reaction $2Mn(CO)_5 \rightarrow Mn_2(CO)_{10}$ is second order. At 25 °C the rate constant for this reaction is $3.0 \times 10^9 \, M^{-1}s^{-1}$. A series of experiments to track the rate of consumption of the reactants were conducted. The initial concentration of the reactant in Experiment #1 was 1.0×10^{-5} M. The initial concentration of the reactant in Experiment #2 was 2.0×10^{-5} M. How long will it take for 90% of the reactants to be consumed in Experiment #1 and Experiment #2?

A) 3.0×10^{-4} s : 6.0×10^{-4} s

B) 3.0×10^{-4} s : 1.5×10^{-4} s

C) 6.0×10^{-4} s : 3.0×10^{-4} s

D) 1.5×10^{-4} s : 3.0×10^{-4} s

Use the following information to help answer Questions 6–10.

The iodination of acetone is acid-catalyzed:

$$CH_3COCH_3 + I_2 \xrightarrow{\text{H}^+} CH_3COCH_2I + H^+ + I^-$$

The rate of consumption of iodine was determined by measuring the concentration of the reactants and the concentration of HI, the catalyst, as a function of time. This reaction is known to be zero order with respect to iodine and first order with respect to H^+.

The rate of disappearance of iodine was determined for the several different concentrations of acetone, keeping the concentration of I_2 and HI constant at a specific temperature.

Trial	$[CH_3COCH_3]$ (M)	$[I_2]$ (M)	HI(M)	Initial Rate of Consumption of I_2 (M/min)
1	1.00	1.30×10^{-3}	0.250	3.35×10^{-4}
2	2.00	1.30×10^{-3}	0.250	7.30×10^{-4}
3	0.500	1.30×10^{-3}	0.250	1.67×10^{-4}

6. What is the experimental rate law for this reaction?

   A) rate = $k[CH_3COCH_3][I_2]$

   B) rate = $k[CH_3COCH_3][HI]$

   C) rate = $k[CH_3COCH_2I][I^-][H^+]$

   D) rate = $k[CH_3COCH_3][H^+][I_2]$

The following three-step mechanism has been proposed for the iodination of acetone:

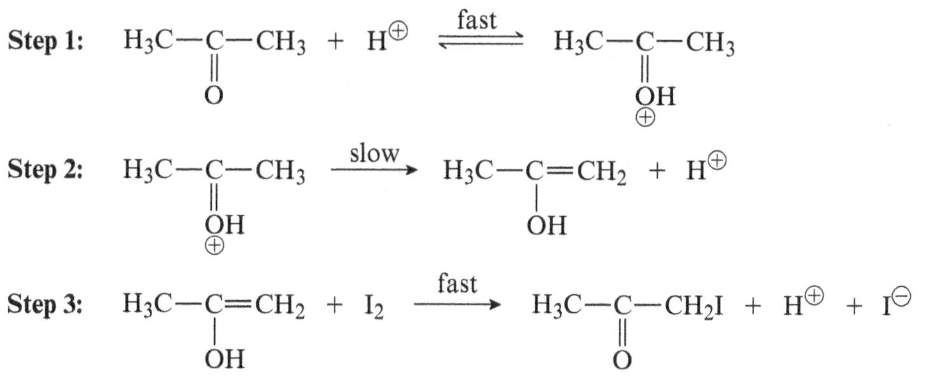

Step 1: $H_3C-\underset{\underset{O}{\|}}{C}-CH_3 + H^{\oplus} \xrightleftharpoons{\text{fast}} H_3C-\underset{\underset{\underset{\oplus}{OH}}{\|}}{C}-CH_3$

Step 2: $H_3C-\underset{\underset{\underset{\oplus}{OH}}{\|}}{C}-CH_3 \xrightarrow{\text{slow}} H_3C-\underset{\underset{OH}{|}}{C}{=}CH_2 + H^{\oplus}$

Step 3: $H_3C-\underset{\underset{OH}{|}}{C}{=}CH_2 + I_2 \xrightarrow{\text{fast}} H_3C-\underset{\underset{O}{\|}}{C}-CH_2I + H^{\oplus} + I^{\ominus}$

7. Do the steps of the mechanism sum to the overall balanced chemical equation?

   A) Yes

   B) No

   C) Perhaps

   D) Not enough information is provided.

8. What is the rate law for this mechanism?

   A) rate = $k[CH_3COCH_3H^+][H^+]$

   B) rate = $k[CH_3COCH_2]$

   C) rate = $k[CH_3COCH_3][H^+]$

   D) rate = $k[CH_3COCH_2][I_2]$

9. Is this proposed mechanism plausible?

   A) Yes

   B) No

   C) Perhaps

   D) Not enough information is provided.

The following four-step mechanism has been proposed for the iodination of acetone:

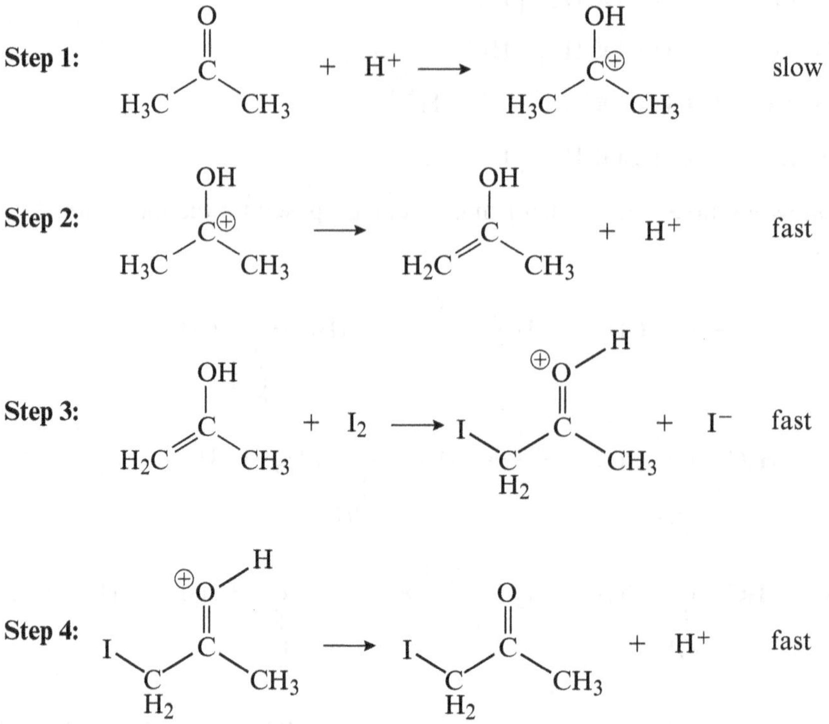

Step 1: H_3C–C(=O)–CH_3 + H⁺ ⟶ H_3C–C⁺(OH)–CH_3 slow

Step 2: H_3C–C⁺(OH)–CH_3 ⟶ H_2C=C(OH)–CH_3 + H⁺   fast

Step 3: H_2C=C(OH)–CH_3 + I_2 ⟶ I–CH_2–C(=O⁺H)–CH_3 + I⁻   fast

Step 4:   I–CH_2–C(=O⁺H)–CH_3 ⟶ I–CH_2–C(=O)–CH_3 + H⁺   fast

10. Is this proposed mechanism plausible?

   A) Yes

   B) No

   C) Perhaps

   D) Not enough information is provided.

Data Interpretation and Analysis Question: Rates of Decomposition of Ethanol Using Two Different Catalysts

At some elevated temperature, when a sample of ethanol gas and a copper catalyst are placed in a sealed rigid empty 1.00 L container the ethanol decomposes according to the chemical equation below

$$CH_3CH_2OH(g) \xrightarrow{Cu} CH_3CHO(g) + H_2(g)$$

In a kinetics experiment, the temperature is held constant, the initial concentration of ethanol gas is 0.0200 M, the concentration of ethanol was measured as a function of time and the following data were recorded:

Time (s)	Concentration (M)
0.0	0.0200
400.0	0.0180
800.00	0.0160
1200.0	0.0140
1600.0	0.0120
2000.0	0.0100

In a second kinetics experiment, the same temperature in the first experiment is used and it is held constant, the initial concentration of ethanol gas is 0.0200 M, an alloy catalyst comprised of 1% copper and 99% silver was used and the concentration of ethanol was measured as a function of time and the following data were recorded:

$$CH_3CH_2OH(g) \xrightarrow{1\% \text{ Cu } 99\%\text{Ag}} CH_3CHO(g) + H_2(g)$$

Time (s)	Concentration (M)
0.0	0.0200
400.0	0.0170
800.00	0.0140
1200.0	0.0110
1600.0	0.0080
2000.0	0.0050

Use the information provided in the two data tables to respond to the following:

a) Determine the order of the reaction with respect to ethanol. Justify your answer.

b) Write the rate law for the decomposition of ethanol in the presence of a metal catalyst.

c) For the first kinetics experiment, determine the rate constant for the reaction and include units. Determine the average rate of reaction for the first kinetics experiment.

d) Estimate the concentration of ethanol in the first experiment after 2100.0 s.

e) For the second kinetics experiment, determine the rate constant for the reaction and include units. Determine the average rate of reaction for the second kinetics experiment.

f) Compare your answers in parts c) and d). Are the two rate constants the same or different? Explain. Take into account the fact that both experiments were performed at the same temperature and started with the same initial concentration.

g) Compare the average rate of reaction of the two experiments. What effect did the alloy catalyst have upon the average rate of reaction compared to the copper catalyst?

h) Identify the dependent and independent variables when comparing the first and second experiments.

i) How would you design two additional kinetics experiments to provide data indicating the alloy catalyst is truly serving as a catalyst? What variables would you control and what variables would you manipulate? What would you predict should happen to the average rate of reaction in your two experiments?

j) If the ethanol completely decomposes in both experiments, is the final pressure in the first experiment more, the same or less compared to the final pressure in the second experiment? Explain.

Data Interpretation and Analysis Question Answers with Brief Explanations

a) A graph of the concentration of ethanol versus time yields a straight line for both experiments. The order of reaction with respect to ethanol is zero order.

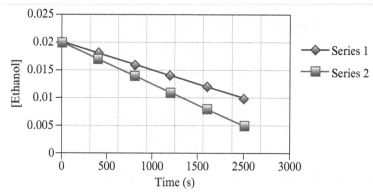

b) rate law rate $= k$ for a zero order reaction.

c) Rate $= k = -\dfrac{\Delta[\text{Ethanol}]}{\Delta \text{Time}} = -\dfrac{[0.0100\ \text{M} - 0.0200\ \text{M}]}{2000.0\ \text{s} - 0.000\ \text{s}} = -\dfrac{[-0.0100\ \text{M}]}{2000.0\ \text{s}}$

   Average Rate $= 5.00 \times 10^{-6}\ \text{Ms}^{-1}$

d) $100.0\ \text{s} \times (-500 \times 10^{-6}\ \text{Ms}^{-1}) = -0.000500\ \text{M}$

   $0.0100\ \text{M} - 0.000500\ \text{M} = 0.00950\ \text{M}$

e) $\text{Rate} = k = -\dfrac{\Delta[\text{Ethanol}]}{\Delta \text{Time}} = -\dfrac{[0.0050\ \text{M} - 0.0200\ \text{M}]}{2000.0\ \text{s} - 0.000\ \text{s}} = -\dfrac{[-0.0150\ \text{M}]}{2000.0\ \text{s}}$

$\text{Average Rate} = 7.50 \times 10^{-6}\ \text{Ms}^{-1}$

f) The rate constant for experiment two is 1.5 times as larger compared to the rate constant in experiment one. Catalysts can speed up the rate of a reaction by altering the reaction mechanism and lowering the activation energy of a reaction.

g) The alloy catalyst increased the rate of reaction 1.5 times as fast compared to the copper metal catalyst.

h) Comparing experiment one to experiment two, we see that the dependent variable is the type of catalyst and the independent variable is time.

i) One experiment should be run at the same temperature and the same initial concentration of ethanol, but using no catalyst. One would expect the average rate of reaction to be slower compared to the average rate of reaction in experiment one. Another experiment should be run at the same temperature and the same initial concentration of ethanol, but twice as much alloy catalyst. One would expect the average rate of reaction to be the same compared to the average rate of reaction in experiment two.

j) The final pressure in the first experiment will be the same compared to the final pressure in the second experiment. Both experiments start with the same amount of ethanol at the same temperature and the same volume. The same chemical reaction occurs, producing twice as many moles of gas at the end compared to the beginning, but the total number of moles of gas produced in each experiment is the same.

READING GUIDE

Chemical kinetics is the focus of Unit 5 in the AP Chemistry curriculum. Determining orders from experimental data, writing rate laws, and understanding mechanisms are skills needed to be mastered. In particular, the AP Chemistry Curriculum places some degree of emphasis on mechanisms.

Section 15.1   Catching Lizards

1. What reaction was first measured for its rate of reaction? What did the collected data show?

Section 15.2   The Rate of a Chemical Reaction

2. For a reaction with enough reactant, what does it mean if the reaction is slow or fast? How is a rate measured for a chemical reaction? What are the usual units for a rate of a reaction?

3. Why does the reaction rate for a reactant have a negative sign and a product have a positive sign?

4. Write the general rate for each reactant and product in the following reaction:

$$2\,H_2(g) \;+\; O_2(g) \rightarrow 2\,H_2O(g)$$

5. Explain how to determine the instantaneous rate for H_2 and HI at 80 seconds. Use the graph below to calculate each rate:

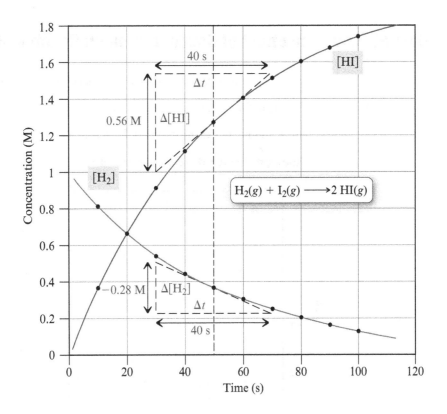

6. Using the same graph from problem 5, calculate the rate of reaction for I_2 at 80 seconds, knowing the chemical equation for the reaction in Question #5 is $H_2(g) + I_2(g) \rightarrow 2\, HI$.

7. For the reaction $aA + bB \rightarrow cC + dD$, write how to determine the reaction rate of each species.

8. What is the difference between an average rate and an instantaneous rate?

9. What types of reactions can use spectroscopy to measure the rate of reaction as a reaction proceeds? Give an example.

10. How does spectroscopy measure rates of reactions? Use the following diagram in your answer:

11. What is an aliquot?

12. What are two other ways of measuring a rate of reaction? Explain how they work.

Section 15.3 The Rate Law: The Effect of Concentration on Reaction Rate

13. What is the general form of the rate law? Indicate what each variable represents.

14. What does it mean if $n = 0, n = 1$, and $n = 2$?

15. Explain why this graph represents a zero order reaction.

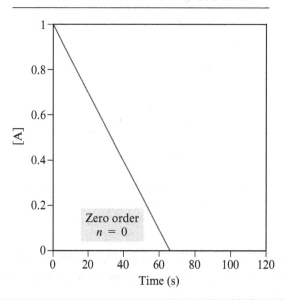

Reactant Concentration versus Time

16. Explain which line represents zero order kinetics and which line represents first order kinetics. Justify your answers.

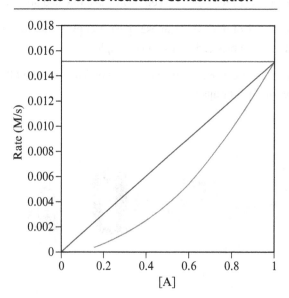

Rate versus Reactant Concentration

17. What is the only way to determine a reaction order?

18. When comparing experimental evidence, what changes will be observed in the change of reaction rate for a zero order reaction? First order? Second order?

19. What are the units of the rate constant for a zero order reaction? First order? Second order?

20. How do you write a general rate law when there are multiple reactants?

21. How do you determine the overall order?

The Integrated Rate Law: The Dependence of Concentration on Time   Section 15.4

22. What is an integrated rate law?

23. What is the integrated rate law of a first order reaction?

24. What order of reaction does the graphical data presented below represent? What does the slope of the line represent in reactions with 1:1 stoichiometry? Explain why. What does the y-intercept represent?

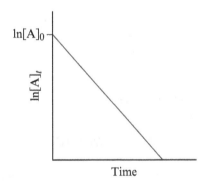

25. What order of reaction does the graphical data presented below represent? What does the slope of the line represent in reactions with 1:1 stoichiometry? Explain why. What does the y-intercept represent?

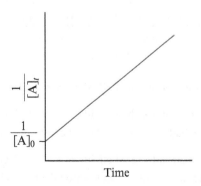

26. What is the second order integrated rate law?

27. What is the zero order integrated rate law?

28. What order of reaction does the graphical data presented below represent? What does the slope of the line represent in reactions with 1:1 stoichiometry? Explain why. What does the y-intercept represent?

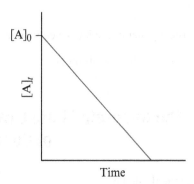

29. What is a half-life of a reaction?

30. Explain how this graph of half-lives provides evidence this is a first order reaction.

Half-Life for a First-Order Reaction

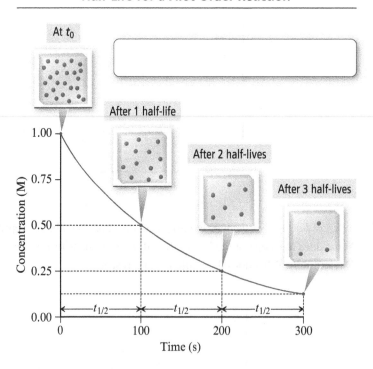

31. What is the equation for the half-life reaction of a first-order reaction?

32. What is the equation for the half-life of a second order reaction? What happens to the half-life time as the concentration decreases?

33. What is the equation for the half-life of a zero order reaction? What happens to the half-life time as the concentration decreases?

The Effect of Temperature on Reaction Rate   Section 15.5

34. Explain how the Arrhenius equation indicates that the rate constant is dependent on the temperature.

35. Identify the activation energy on the graph and explain why this represents an exothermic reaction.

Activation Energy

$$2\ H_2(g) + O_2(g) \rightleftharpoons 2\ H_2O(g)$$

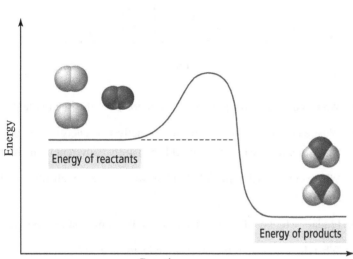

Energy

Energy of reactants

Energy of products

Reaction progress

36. What is an activated complex? When do they form?

37. What is a frequency factor?

38. What is the relationship between the activation energy and the rate of reaction?

39. What is the exponential factor? Why is the exponential factor dependent on both temperature and the size of the activation energy barrier?

40. What does it mean if the exponential factor is 1? Under what conditions will the factor possibly be 1?

41. The graph below illustrates the relationship among T_1, T_2, and the fraction of molecules with enough energy to meet the activation energy barrier. How are the fraction of molecules with sufficient activation energy affected by temperature?

Thermal Energy Distribution

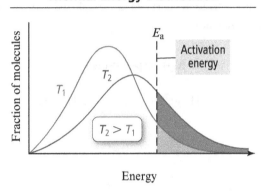

42. What is an Arrhenius plot? What equation does the line in the plot represent?

43. What equation is used to solve for the activation energy of a reaction using data from the rate constants established at two different temperatures?*

44. What is the collision model? Explain what makes an effective collision. What are p and z?

45. Explain why not all collisions result in the formation of product.

46. What does it mean if the orientation factor is 0.32?

47. What is a harpooning mechanism? Include an example in your answer.

Section 15.6   Reaction Mechanisms

48. Explain the difference between a balanced chemical reaction and a reaction mechanism.

49. What do elementary steps represent?

50. What is a reaction intermediate? How is one identified in a reaction mechanism?

51. What is the difference among unimolecular, bimolecular, and termolecular steps? Why are termolecular steps rare?

52. Explain how to deduce the rate-law of an elementary step. From the elementary step rate laws, explain how to deduce the overall rate law of the reaction.

53. Fill in the molecularity and rate law of each of the following elementary steps. What is the relationship between the molecularity and the overall order of the step?

Rate Laws for Elementary Steps

Elementary Step	Molecularity	Rate Law
A $\longrightarrow$ products		
A + A $\longrightarrow$ products		
A + B $\longrightarrow$ products		
A + A + A $\longrightarrow$ products		
A + A + B $\longrightarrow$ products		
A + B + C $\longrightarrow$ products		

54. What is a rate-determining step? How is one determined?

55. What two conditions must be met for a reaction mechanism to be valid?

56. What evidence in the diagram below supports that this reaction has a two step mechanism?

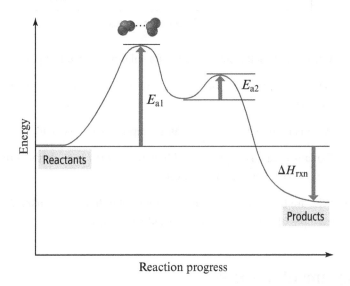

57. If the mechanism begins with a fast intermediate step before the slow step, how can the rate law be determined? How is a fast equilibrium indicated in an equation?

58. How are the concentrations of intermediates from a fast equilibrium expressed in the overall reaction? Include an example in your answer.

Section 15.7   **Catalysis**

59. What does a catalyst do?

60. On the figure below, draw how a catalyst affects the activation energy:

**Energy Diagram for Catalyzed and
Uncatalyzed Pathways**

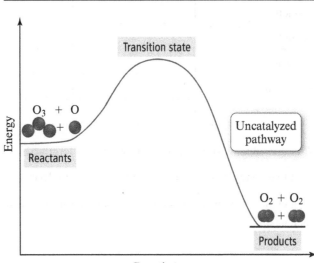

61. What role does the surface area of a solid phase catalyst play?

62. What is the difference between a homogeneous catalyst and a heterogeneous catalyst?

63. What is hydrogenation? Give an example of catalysis with hydrogenation.

64. Explain what an enzyme is and how they work? Include the terms active site and substrate in your answer.

65. Why are biological enzymes so important to living organisms? Give an example of a biological enzyme and what it does.

Self-Assessment Answers

1. _____   2. _____   3. _____

4. _____   5. _____   6. _____

7. _____   8. _____   9. _____

10. _____   11. _____   12. _____

13. _____   14. _____   15. _____

CHAPTER

16

CHEMICAL EQUILIBRIUM

This chapter is the main focus of Unit 7. All sections of this chapter except Section 16.1 need to be mastered. This chapter is foundational to understanding the chapters on acid–base and solubility product equilibria. Although it is important to know how to do the calculations in the chapter, understanding what the calculations mean is much more essential. The important sections are as follows.

16.2 **The Concept of Dynamic Equilibrium**

16.3 **The Equilibrium Constant (*K*)**

16.4 **Expressing the Equilibrium Constant in Terms of Pressure**

16.5 **Heterogeneous Equilibria: Reactions Involving Solids and Liquids**

16.6 **Calculating the Equilibrium Constant from Measured Equilibrium Concentrations**

16.7 **The Reaction Quotient: Predicting the Direction of Change**

16.8 **Finding Equilibrium Concentrations**

16.9 **Le Châtelier's Principle: How a System at Equilibrium Responds to Disturbances**

Specific Learning Objectives Addressed in This Chapter:

TRA-6 Some reactions can occur in both forward and reverse directions, sometimes proceeding in each direction simultaneously.

TRA-6.A Explain the relationship between the occurrence of a reversible chemical or physical process, and the establishment of equilibrium, to experimental observations.

TRA-6.B Explain the relationship between the direction in which a reversible reaction proceeds and the relative rates of the forward and reverse reactions.

TRA-7 A system at equilibrium depends on the relationships between concentrations, partial pressures of chemical species, and the equilibrium constant *K*.

TRA-7.A Represent the reaction quotient Q_c or Q_p, for a reversible reaction, and the corresponding equilibrium expressions $K_c = Q_c$ or $K_p = Q_p$.

TRA-7.B Calculate K_c or K_p based on experimental observations of concentrations or pressures at equilibrium.

TRA-7.C Explain the relationship between very large or very small values of K and the relative concentrations of chemical species at equilibrium.

TRA-7.D Represent a multistep process with an overall equilibrium expression, using the constituent K expressions for each individual reaction.

TRA-7.E Identify the concentrations or partial pressures of chemical species at equilibrium based on the initial conditions and the equilibrium constant.

TRA-7.F Represent a system undergoing a reversible reaction with a particle model.

TRA-8 Systems at equilibrium respond to external stresses to offset the effect of the stress.

TRA-8.A Identify the response of a system at equilibrium to an external stress, using Le Châtelier's principle.

TRA-8.B Explain the relationships between Q, K, and the direction in which a reversible reaction will proceed to reach equilibrium.

Concepts and Vocabulary to Review:

Section 16.2

The Concept of Dynamic Equilibrium

When a reaction begins, the reactant concentrations are high and the product concentrations are low. As the reaction proceeds, the reactant concentrations decrease and the product concentrations increase. In many reactions, as the products start to form, the reaction begins to reverse and product will begin to make reactant. This reversal moves the reaction toward an equilibrium where eventually the rate of reactants making product will equal the rate of the product making reactant. When the two rates are equal, the reaction has reached dynamic equilibrium. The reaction is still going on, but there will be no apparent change in concentrations. The reaction moving from reactant to product is called the forward reaction, and the reaction moving from product to reactant is called the reverse or backward reaction.

$$A \rightleftharpoons B$$

When observing particulate drawings in Figure 16.1, comparing the amount of reactant to product, you can see in (a) that only the reactant is present, so the reaction is just beginning. In (b) product is forming. In (c) and (d), the reactant and product concentrations are remaining the same, indicating the reaction has reached equilibrium. In a graph of concentration versus time for a simple equilibrium system, when the concentrations of both A and B flatten out, this indicates the concentrations of A and B are remaining constant. This is the data needed to indicate the reaction has reached equilibrium. Keep in mind this does NOT necessarily mean the concentrations are the same.

Dynamic Equilibrium

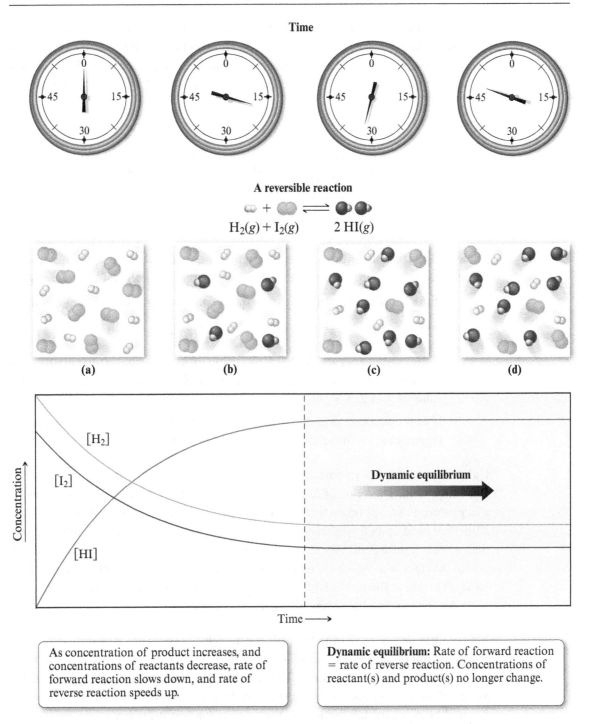

Figure 16.1 Dynamic Equilibrium   Equilibrium is reached in a chemical reaction when the concentrations of the reactants and products no longer change. The molecular images depict the progress of the reaction $H_2(g) + I_2(g) \rightleftharpoons 2HI(g)$. The graph shows the concentrations of H_2, I_2, and HI as a function of time. When the reaction reaches equilibrium, both the forward and reverse reactions continue, but at equal rates, so the concentrations of the reactants and products remain constant.

Section 16.3   **The Equilibrium Constant (K)**

At equilibrium, the concentrations of reactant and products remain constant. The ratio of product raised to the power of their coefficients divided by the concentrations of the reactants raised to their coefficients is called the mass action ratio. This ratio is the equilibrium constant. For the reaction aA + bB $\rightleftharpoons$ cC + dD, the ratio is

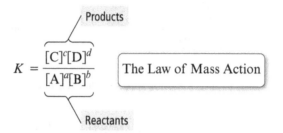

$$K = \frac{[C]^c [D]^d}{[A]^a [B]^b}$$ The Law of Mass Action

Since the coefficients of the balanced equation are part of the mass action ratio, the balanced equation is important. If the equation changes, then the ratio also changes.

- If the equation is reversed, the products and reactants change positions in the ratio, causing the value of K to be the inverse, $\frac{1}{K}$.

- If the coefficients are doubled, the value of K is squared. If the coefficients are tripled, the value of K is cubed. When the coefficients change (n), the value of K is then K^n.

- If two equations are added together, the value of the K's are multiplied together to determine the overall K. $K_{overall} = K_1 K_2$

Calculations of K are important, but understanding what the value of K means is more important. The value of K indicates how far the forward reaction moves toward completion. If a lot of product forms (numerator) and most of the reactants (denominator) are used up before equilibrium is reached, the ratio will be a number greater than 1. This indicates that the reaction is favoring product formation. Since products are on the right in a chemical equation, the reaction favoring products is said to have its equilibrium to the right and the forward reaction is favored. A very large K value indicates the reaction has essentially gone to completion.

If very little product is formed before equilibrium is reached, the ratio will have a small amount of product on top in the ratio (numerator) and a large amount of reactant (denominator) on the bottom. The result will be a small number less than 1, but greater than zero. In this case, reactants are favored and the reaction is said to have its equilibrium to the left, indicating the reverse reaction is favored.

If K is close to 1, the ratio of mass action products and reactants is about the same. This reaction will have progressed approximately half way.

It is important to recognize that the value of K does NOT indicate anything about the rate or speed of the reaction.

Expressing the Equilibrium Constant in Terms of Pressure   Section 16.4

There are different forms of K. When using concentration values, the molarity is indicated by the use of brackets. For example, the concentration of A would be [A]. In this case, the constant is called K_c. The subscript c stands for concentration. For the reaction

$2SO_3(g) \rightleftharpoons 2SO_2(g) + O_2(g)$, the K_c would be written as $K_c = \dfrac{[SO_2]^2[O_2]}{[SO_3]^2}$.

When calculating with pressures, the brackets are not used. Parentheses may be used but are not required, and P is used to indicate pressure. The same reaction written as

a K_p expression would be $K = \dfrac{P(SO_2)^2 PO_2}{P(SO_3)^2}$. Gases must be present to calculate a K_p.

If only a reactant is a gas, the numerator is 1, and if only a product is a gas, the denominator is 1. It is possible to convert from K_p and K_c using $K_p = K_c(RT)^{\Delta n}$. Since gases are creating pressure, R is the gas constant 0.0821 L·atm/K·mol, T is temperature in Kelvin, and Δn is the moles of gaseous product minus the number of moles of gaseous reactant. Δn can be determined by using the coefficients in the balanced equation. In the equation above, there are 3 moles of product $(2SO_2(g) + O_2(g))$ and 2 moles of gas reactant $(2SO_3(g))$. $3 - 2 = 1$. If the moles of gas reactant and moles of gas product are equal, $\Delta n = 0$, then K_p will equal K_c.

Even though K_c uses molarity units in its calculation and K_p uses units of atmospheres, the ratio values of K_c and K_p are considered unitless.

Heterogeneous Equilibria: Reactions Involving Solids and Liquids   Section 16.5

Not all reactions have all reactants and products in the same state of matter or phase, these are called heterogeneous. There are a few special circumstances to remember

A Heterogeneous Equilibrium

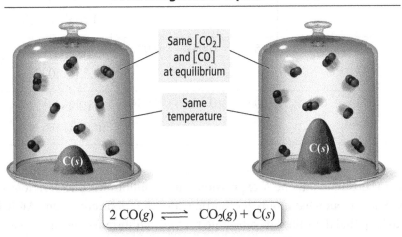

$$2\,CO(g) \rightleftharpoons CO_2(g) + C(s)$$

Figure 16.2 Heterogeneous Equilibrium   The concentration of solid carbon (the number of atoms per unit volume) is constant as long as some solid carbon is present. The same is true for pure liquids. For this reason, the concentrations of solids and pure liquids are not included in equilibrium constant expressions.

about equilibrium expressions. Solids do not change concentration as their concentration is their density, and the same is true of pure liquids. For this reason, solids and pure liquids are not included in equilibrium expressions. The states of matter must be taken into account to write the different K expressions. K_c only has concentrations in molarity, and solids and pure liquids are not included. K_p only has pressures so only gases from the balanced equation are used. A common mistake in problems is to ignore the states of matter. If the reaction involving a solid and an aqueous solution is at equilibrium, even though solids are not put in the expression as long as both solution and solid are present, the reaction will still be at K.

Section 16.6   Calculating the Equilibrium Constant from Measured Equilibrium Concentrations

The value of K for a given reaction is always the same at a given temperature regardless of the starting concentrations. This is shown in the following example.

Table 16.1   Initial and Equilibrium Concentrations for the Reaction
$H_2(g) + I_2(g) \rightleftharpoons 2\,HI(g)$ at 445 °C

Initial Concentrations			Equilibrium Concentrations			Equilibrium Constant
$[H_2]$	$[I_2]$	$[HI]$	$[H_2]$	$[I_2]$	$[HI]$	$K_c = \dfrac{[HI^2]}{[H_2][I_2]}$
0.50	0.50	0.0	0.11	0.11	0.78	$\dfrac{(0.78)^2}{(0.11)(0.11)} = 50$
0.0	0.0	0.50	0.055	0.055	0.39	$\dfrac{(0.39)^2}{(0.055)(0.055)} = 50$
0.50	0.50	0.50	0.165	0.165	1.17	$\dfrac{(1.17)^2}{(0.165)(0.165)} = 50$
1.0	0.50	0.0	0.53	0.033	0.934	$\dfrac{(0.934)^2}{(0.53)(0.033)} = 50$
0.50	1.0	0.0	0.033	0.53	0.934	$\dfrac{(0.934)^2}{(0.033)(0.53)} = 50$

It is easy to substitute into the K expression if the equilibrium concentrations or pressures are known, but what if only the starting concentrations are given? An ICE table is used to help find the values to substitute for the equilibrium concentrations into the K expression. Making an ICE table is a crucial skill to master. (I stands for initial, C for change, and E stands for equilibrium.) For the reaction $A(g) \rightleftharpoons 2B(g)$, at the beginning of the reaction no product is present. If the starting concentration of A is 1.00 M for whatever amount A loses, B gains twice that amount since the coefficients are 1:2. If the amount lost is x, then the amount gained is $2x$.

ICE TABLE	[A]	[B]
I	1.00	0
C	$-x$	$+2x$
E	$1.00 - x$	$2x$

If the amount of change is known, the values can be determined and K solved for. If the amount of change is 0.30, then using the table [A] is 0.70 and [B] is 0.60.

The K expression is $K = \dfrac{[B]^2}{[A]}$. When substituted into the expression, this would be

$K = \dfrac{[0.60]^2}{[0.70]}$, which equals 0.51.

The Reaction Quotient: Predicting the Direction of Change   Section 16.7

If a reaction is not at equilibrium, the ratio of reactant and products is called the reaction quotient, Q_c for concentrations and Q_p for pressures. The calculation is the same, but the end result is used to indicate in what direction the reaction will proceed to reach equilibrium unless the value of Q is the same as K, indicating the reaction is at equilibrium.

- If $Q = K$, the reaction is at equilibrium.
- If $Q > K$, the numerator (product) is too large, and to reach K, the reactant value will need to increase, indicating the reaction will proceed to the left.
- If $Q < K$, the denominator (reactant) is too large, and to reach K, the product value will need to increase, indicating the reaction will proceed to the right.

The following figure shows a graphical example of predicting the direction of change.

Q, K, and the Direction of a Reaction

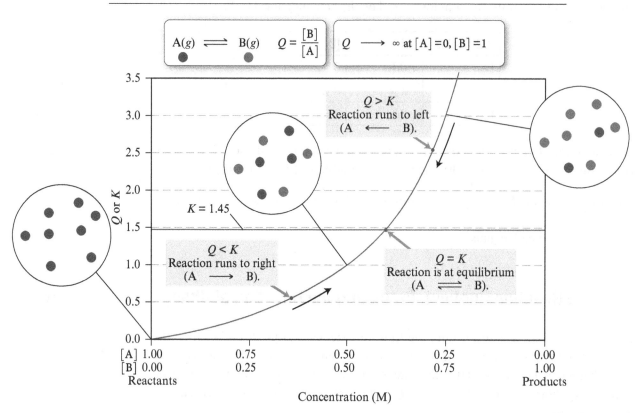

Figure 16.3 Q, K, and the Direction of a Reaction   The graph shows a plot of Q as a function of the concentrations of the reactants and products in a simple reaction A $\rightleftharpoons$ B, in which $K = 1.45$ and the sum of the reactant and product concentrations is 1 M. The far left of the graph represents pure reactant and the far right represents pure product. The midpoint of the graph represents an equal mixture of A and B. When Q is less than K, the reaction moves in the forward direction (A → B). When Q is greater than K, the reaction moves in the reverse direction (A ← B). When Q is equal to K, the reaction is at equilibrium.

Section 16.8   Finding Equilibrium Concentrations

If K is known, then the values in the ICE tables can be substituted and the values of x solved for. Using the reaction A(g) $\rightleftharpoons$ 2B(g) assuming $K = 3.40 \times 10^{-5}$ and the example earlier:

ICE TABLE	[A]	[B]
I	1.00	0
C	$-x$	$+2x$
E	$1.00 - x$	$2x$

and $K = \dfrac{[B]^2}{[A]}$, then $K = \dfrac{[2x]^2}{[1.00 - x]}$. This requires solving the quadratic equation, but many times the value of $-x$ is so small that when subtracted from the original value it does not make a difference. If this is the case, and it is usually case on the AP exam, the equation can be simplified and the quadratic does not need to be solved.

For instance, if $x = 0.0021$ M, then $1.00 - 0.0021 = 0.9979$. When rounded to two places past the decimal point, the answer is 1.00 M and $K = \dfrac{[2x]^2}{[1.00]}$. Assuming K is 3.40×10^{-5}, was it reasonable to ignore the $-x$? $1.00 - 0.00292 = 1.00$, so yes it was. From the ICE table, the value of $3.40 \times 10^{-5} = \dfrac{[2x]^2}{1.00}$ and $x = 0.00292$. B is $2x$, which is 0.0584. To use this approximation method, the difference between the original concentration and x should be less than 5% of the original value. In this case, $\dfrac{0.00292}{1.00} \times 100\% = 0.292\%$, indicating the approximation method was okay to use. In general, the $-x$ values on the AP Exam have been less that 5%. Students still should show the $-x$ value and can then cross it out. To verify, they should check the percent ionization.

Le Châtelier's Principle: How a System at Equilibrium Responds to Disturbances

Section 16.9

For reactions that go to equilibrium, changing concentrations, pressures, or temperatures causes a reaction to adjust to recover equilibrium. Le Châtelier's principle states when a chemical system at equilibrium is disturbed, the system shifts in a direction that will minimize the disturbance. To reestablish equilibrium, the system either shifts to the right forming additional product or shifts to the left forming additional reactant. Analysis of the K value and how the disturbance affects the value is important to predict the direction needed to get back to equilibrium.

Concentration Changes:

If one is adding to a concentration value, the reaction system will move away from the side of the reaction where that species is.

- If the species added is a reactant resulting in $Q < K$, the reaction will shift to the right and make additional product.
- If the species is a product causing $Q > K$, the reaction will shift to the left and make additional reactant.

If a species is subtracted, the system will move to replace that species.

- If the species is a reactant causing $Q > K$, the reaction will shift to the left to make more reactant.
- If the species is a product resulting in $Q < K$, the reaction will move to the right to produce more product.

Le Châtelier's Principle: Changing Concentration

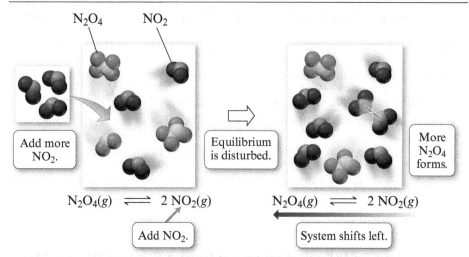

$$N_2O_4(g) \rightleftharpoons 2\,NO_2(g) \qquad N_2O_4(g) \rightleftharpoons 2\,NO_2(g)$$

Figure 16.4 Le Châtelier's Principle: The Effect of a Concentration Change   Adding NO_2 causes the reaction to shift left, consuming some of the added NO_2 and forming more N_2O_4.

Graphically this would look like the following:

Le Châtelier's Principle: Graphical Representation

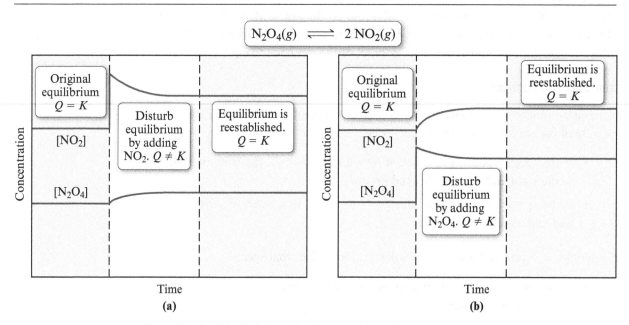

Figure 16.5 Le Châtelier's Principle: Changing Concentration   The graph shows the concentrations of NO_2 and N_2O_4 for the reaction $N_2O_4(g) \rightarrow 2NO_2(g)$ as a function of time in three distinct stages of the reaction: initially at equilibrium (left), upon disturbance of the equilibrium by addition of more NO_2 **(a)** or N_2O_4 **(b)** to the reaction mixture (center), and upon reestablishment of equilibrium (right).

Volume or Pressure Changes:

Volume or pressure changes only affect reactions with gases involved. For reactions involving gases, the balanced equation and states of matter are very important. The reaction must be analyzed to determine which side of the reaction has the most moles of gas.

- If the number of moles of gas on both sides of the equation is the same, changing the pressure or volume will have no effect on the equilibrium.
- Decreasing the volume (or increasing the pressure) causes the reaction to shift to the side of the reaction with the fewest moles of gas.
- Increasing the volume (or reducing the pressure) causes the reaction to shift to the side with the most moles of gas particles.
- Adding an inert gas increases the total pressure, but the partial pressures of the gases in the equilibrium equation do not change, and so it has no effect on the equilibrium.

Le Châtelier's Principle: Changing Pressure

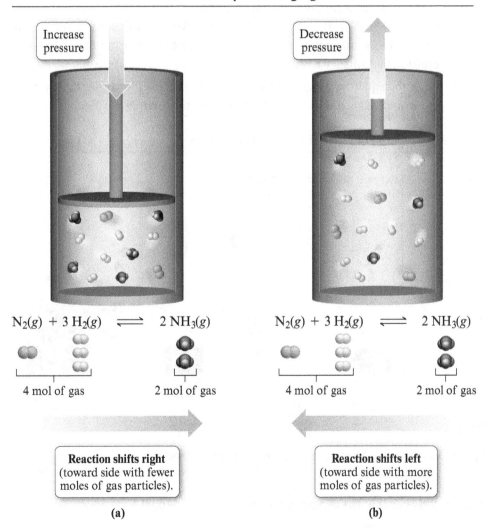

Figure 16.6 Le Châtelier's Principle: The Effect of a Pressure Change (a) Decreasing the volume increases the pressure, causing the reaction to shift to the right (fewer moles of gas, lower pressure). (b) Increasing the volume reduces the pressure, causing the reaction to shift to the left (more moles of gas, higher pressure).

Temperature Changes

Analyzing how temperature change influences a shift in equilibrium requires knowing if a chemical reaction is endothermic or exothermic. Since equilibrium constants are temperature dependent, increasing or decreasing the temperature changes the equilibrium constant.

- If the reaction is endothermic, when heat is being added and the heat can be "treated" as a reactant: For the reaction A + B $\rightleftharpoons$ C + D, the reaction would be A + B + heat $\rightleftharpoons$ C + D. Written this way, one can see increasing the temperature would cause a shift to the products away from the added heat and the value of K would increase due to the increased amount of product in the numerator and a smaller number in the denominator.

- Using the equation above for an endothermic reaction, decreasing the temperature would cause a shift to the left causing the value of K to decrease due to a smaller product value in the numerator and more reactant in the denominator.

- If the reaction is exothermic, when heat is being formed and the heat can be "treated" as a product: For the reaction A + B $\rightleftharpoons$ C + D the reaction would be A + B $\rightleftharpoons$ C + D + heat. Written this way, increasing the temperature would cause a shift to the reactants away from the added heat, resulting in a smaller K value.

- Using the equation for an exothermic reaction above, lowering the temperature would cause a shift to the right, resulting in a larger K value.

Le Châtelier's Principle: Changing Temperature

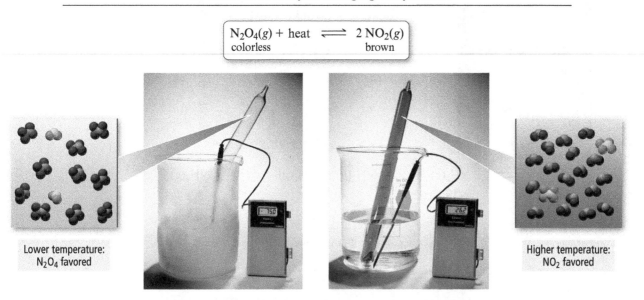

$$N_2O_4(g) + \text{heat} \rightleftharpoons 2\,NO_2(g)$$
colorless   brown

Lower temperature:
N_2O_4 favored

Higher temperature:
NO_2 favored

Figure 16.7 Le Châtelier's Principle: The Effect of a Temperature Change   Because the reaction is endothermic, raising the temperature causes a shift to the right, toward the formation of brown NO_2.

Catalyst: (this is not in the chapter but is required knowledge)

A catalyst has no effect on the equilibrium. A catalyst will increase the rate of reaction so the equilibrium will be reached faster.

Additional Practice

Self-Assessment Quiz Questions Q1, Q2, Q3, Q4, Q5, Q6, Q7, Q8, Q9, Q10, Q11, and Q12

Problems:
Review Questions 3, 4, 5, 6, 7, 9, 12, 14, 17, and 20
Equilibrium and the Equilibrium Constant Expression 21, 22, 23, 24, 25, 27, and 29
K_p, K_c, and Heterogeneous Equilibria 31 and 33
Relating the Equilibrium Constant to Equilibrium Concentration and Equilibrium Partial Pressures 37, 41, 44, and 46
The Reaction Quotient and Reaction Direction 47, 49, and 50
Finding Equilibrium Concentration from Initial Concentration and the Equilibrium Constant 51, 53, 56, 57, and 62
Le Chatelier's Principle 63, 64, 65, 66, 67, 69, 70, 71, and 72
Cumulative Problems 80 and 83
Challenge Problems 97
Conceptual Problems 100, 101, 102, 103, 104, and 105

Equations to know:

Products

$$K = \frac{[C]^c[D]^d}{[A]^a[B]^b}$$ The Law of Mass Action

Reactants

Practice AP Test Questions

Questions 1–3 pertain to the concentration versus time graph below for a hypothetical reaction system A $\rightleftharpoons$ 2B.

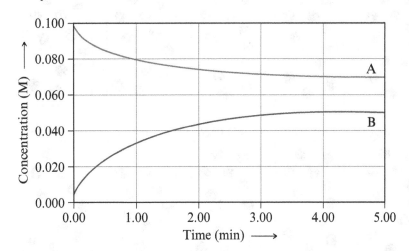

1. Between the start of the reaction and 2.00 minutes, what is true about the relative rates of reaction for A and B?

   A) The rate of consumption of A is twice as fast as the rate of formation of B.

   B) The rate of formation of B is twice as fast as the rate of consumption of A.

   C) The rate of the forward reaction of A is equal to the rate of the reverse reaction of B.

   D) The rate of the forward reaction of B is equal to the rate of the reverse reaction of A.

2. Estimate the value of the equilibrium constant, K_c, for this system.

   A) $K_c < 1$ C) $K_c = 1$

   B) $K_c = 0$ D) $K_c > 1$

The interconversion of A molecules (shaded spheres) and B molecules (unshaded spheres) according to the reaction $A \rightleftharpoons 2B$. Each of the following series of pictures in a set represents a small volume of an experiment as time from left to right progresses. Each choice, A), B), C), D), represents a separate experiment in which time progresses.

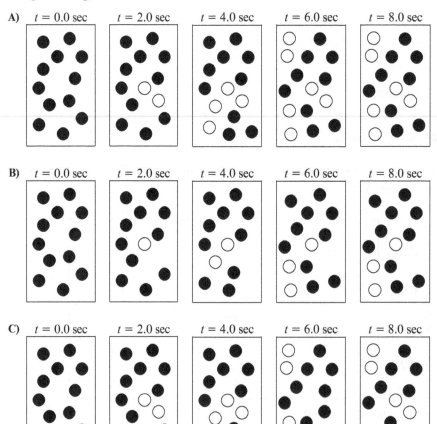

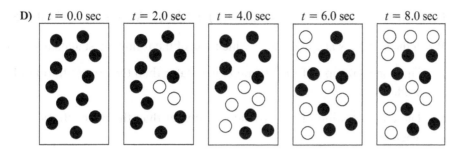

D) $t = 0.0$ sec $t = 2.0$ sec $t = 4.0$ sec $t = 6.0$ sec $t = 8.0$ sec

3. Which of the above sets represents how the reaction system reaches an equilibrium state?

Questions 4–7 pertain to the following situation. Automobile exhaust gases often reach a temperature of 1200 K. At this temperature, carbon dioxide can establish the following equilibrium system $2\,CO_2(g) \rightarrow 2\,CO(g) + O_2(g)$ $\Delta H = -514$ kJ

4. If the system occurs at constant volume, the concentration of $O_2(g)$ at equilibrium will decrease if

   A) CO is added to the system.

   B) CO_2 is added to the system.

   C) $Ar(g)$ is added to the system.

   D) the temperature of the system decreases.

5. An increase in temperature will

   A) increase the partial pressure of $O_2(g)$.

   B) increase the partial pressure of $CO(g)$.

   C) increase the value of K_c.

   D) decrease the value of K_c.

6. An equilibrium mixture contains 0.0020 M CO_2 and 0.0030 M O_2 and $K_c = 1.4 \times 10^2$. Determine the equilibrium concentration of CO.

   A) 9.6×10^{-6} M   C) 1.8×10^{-1} M

   B) 4.3×10^{-1} M   D) 6.2×10^{-1} M

7. At equilibrium, the pressure of CO is 2.6×10^{-6} atm, the pressure of CO_2, and the pressure of O_2 is 5.92×10^{-7} atm. Calculate K_p, the equilibrium constant.

   A) 550   C) 6.2×10^{-12}

   B) 0.056   D) 6.4×10^{-17}

8. For the reaction, $2NOCl(g) \rightleftharpoons 2NO(g) + Cl_2(g)$ $K_c = 1.6 \times 10^{-5}$ at 125 °C.

   When the system is at equilibrium, which one of the following statements is true?

   A) The concentration of the reactants is greater than the concentration of the products.

   B) The concentration of the products is greater than the concentration of the reactants.

   C) The reaction is favored in the forward direction.

   D) The concentration of NOCl is equal to the concentration of NO.

9. At 700 K, carbon tetrachloride decomposes to carbon and chlorine.

$$CCl_4(g) \rightleftharpoons C(s) + 2Cl_2(g)$$

   Just before any reaction occurs, initial amounts of $CCl_4(g)$, $C(s)$, and $Cl_2(g)$ are injected into a rigid reaction container at 700 K. For the first 5 seconds, the concentration of Cl_2 decreases. Which of the following statements describes the relationship between K_c and Q during the first 3 seconds of the reaction?

   A) $K_c < Q$

   B) $K_c = Q$

   C) $K_c > Q$

   D) More information is needed to determine the status of K_c.

10. Ozone can form when an oxygen molecule reacts with a free radical oxygen atom in the presence of nitrogen dioxide.

$$O_2(g) + O(g) \rightleftharpoons O_3(g)$$

   A proposed mechanism for the reverse reaction has two steps:

   Step 1: $NO_2(g) \rightleftharpoons N_2O(g) + O(g)$ $\qquad\qquad$ $K_{eq\,1} = 6.9 \times 10^{-49}$

   Step 2: $O_3(g) + NO(g) \rightleftharpoons NO_2(g) + O_2(aq)$ $\quad$ $K_{eq\,2} = 5.9 \times 10^{-34}$

   Calculate the value of the equilibrium constant for the formation of ozone by the reaction of oxygen molecules with free radical oxygen atoms.

   A) 4.1×10^{-82}

   B) 1.21×10^{-15}

   C) 8.6×10^{14}

   D) 2.6×10^{31}

Data Interpretation and Analysis Question: Decomposition of Ammonium Chloride

When heated solid ammonium chloride decomposes according to the following equation

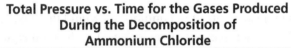

$$NH_4Cl(s) \rightleftharpoons NH_3(g) + HCl(g) \qquad \Delta H = +176 \text{ kJ/mol of rxn}$$

In one experiment, a student places a 10.0 gram sample of solid granular ammonium chloride in a 0.50 L evacuated rigid container. The container and the solid ammonium chloride started at an initial temperature of 298 K and were rapidly heated to 550 K. As the container was heated, the total pressure of the gases in the container was measured as a function of time. The pressure and time data are plotted on the graph below. The student noted solid ammonium chloride was present at all times during the experiment.

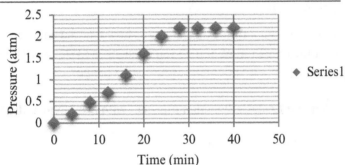

Total Pressure vs. Time for the Gases Produced During the Decomposition of Ammonium Chloride

a) Determine the partial pressure of ammonia gas, $NH_3(g)$, at equilibrium.

b) Write the equilibrium expression for this equilibrium system.

c) Calculate the equilibrium constant, K_p, for this equilibrium system.

In a second experiment involving the same amount of solid granular ammonium chloride in a 0.50 L evacuated rigid container, the temperature of the equilibrium system was increased to 650 K. The student sketched three particle representation diagrams, one at a temperature of 298 K, one at 550 K, and one at 650 K.

d) Which particle representation diagram best depicts the equilibrium system at the higher temperature of 650 K? Justify your answer.

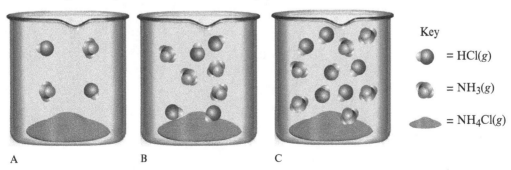

Key

● = $HCl(g)$

● = $NH_3(g)$

▲ = $NH_4Cl(g)$

A   B   C

In a third experiment involving an initial starting mass of 20.0 g of solid granular ammonium chloride in a 0.50 L evacuated rigid container, the temperature of the system was rapidly increased to 550 K. Although the student predicted the total pressure would double, the total pressure after 36 minutes was 2.2 atm, the same as in the first experiment.

e)   Based on the data and information presented, explain why the total pressure in this third experiment was the same as in the first experiment when the system achieved equilibrium.

In a fourth experiment involving an initial starting mass of 10.0 g of solid granular ammonium chloride in a 0.50 L evacuated rigid container, the temperature of the system was rapidly increased to 550 K. After 40 minutes when the system achieved equilibrium, equal small amounts of ammonia gas and HCl gas, were inserted into the system, initially raising the total pressure to 2.8 atm.

f) When the system restores itself to equilibrium, would the total pressure inside the container be greater than, less than, or equal to the total equilibrium pressure in experiment one?

g) How would you design a fifth experiment to show that the equilibrium constant will change if the temperature of the system changes? What variables would you keep constant? What variable(s) would you change?

Data Interpretation and Analysis Question Answers with Brief Explanations

a) $P_{total} = P_{NH_3} + P_{HCl} = 2.1$ atm.

b) $K_p = (P_{NH_3})(P_{HCl})$

c) $K_p = 1.2$

d) "B"

e) The concentration of a solid or the amount of a solid does not influence the equilibrium concentrations, but the solid does need to be present to maintain equilibrium.

f) The total pressure inside the container would be less than 2.8 atm.

g) Keep the initial amount of ammonium chloride the same through three different runs, each run at a different temperature. Record the total pressure for each run at equilibrium. Calculate K_p.

READING GUIDE

The material in this chapter is the focus of Unit 7 on equilibrium in the AP curriculum. Equilibrium is one of the five most pervasive processes in chemistry. The concepts of a dynamic equilibrium, equilibrium constants, and Le Châtelier's principle are concepts to master.

Fetal Hemoglobin and Equilibrium   Section 16.1

1. What does a large value of K indicate? What does a small value of K indicate?

2. For a system at equilibrium, if the concentration of reactants or products changes, what happens to the reaction?

3. Explain how oxygen gets from the mother to the fetus when the mother's and fetus's blood do not mix?*

The Concept of Dynamic Equilibrium   Section 16.2

4. What does it mean when a reaction is reversible?

5. What is a dynamic equilibrium for a chemical reaction? Does this mean the concentrations of reactants and products are equal. Explain.

6. Is the reaction still occurring at equilibrium? Explain your answer.

7. Explain what is occurring in the below reaction as it proceeds from (a) to (d). How can you tell when equilibrium is reached?

Dynamic Equilibrium

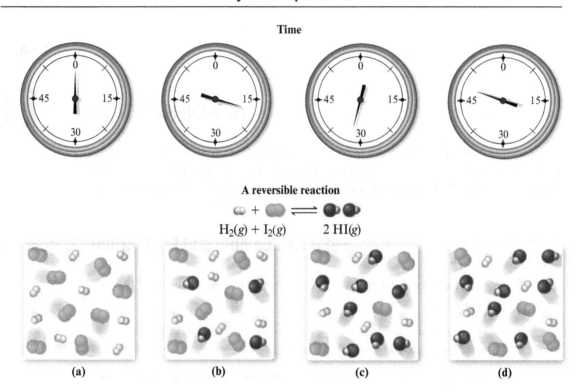

8. Identify on the graph when equilibrium is reached. Explain what data you are using to make this claim.

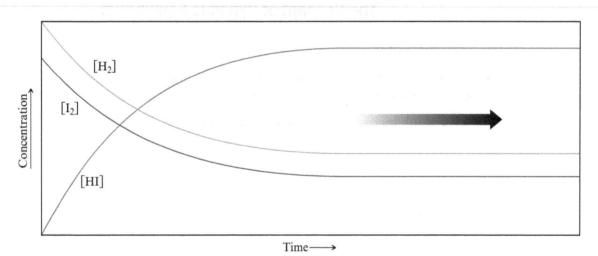

The Equilibrium Constant (*K*)   Section 16.3

9. What is an equilibrium constant? What is the law of mass action? What does it represent?

10. Explain how to write an equilibrium expression. Use the equation
$C_3H_8(g) + 5\,O_2(g) \rightleftharpoons 3\,CO_2(g) + 4\,H_2O(g)$ as an example along with your explanation.

11. What does the size of the equilibrium constant indicate about a reaction? Include $K \ll 1$, $K = 1$, and $K \gg 1$.

12. If this figure represents equilibrium, would this example have a small or large equilibrium constant? What evidence supports your claim?

$$H_2(g) + Br_2(g) \rightleftharpoons 2\,HBr(g)$$

$$K = \frac{[HBr]^2}{[H_2][Br_2]} =$$

13. If this figure represents equilibrium, would this example have a small or large equilibrium constant? What evidence supports your claim?

$$N_2(g) + O_2(g) \rightleftharpoons 2\,NO(g)$$

$$K = \frac{[NO]^2}{[N_2][O_2]} =$$

14. Explain what happens to the value of the equilibrium constant and why in each of the following situations:

The chemical equation is reversed:

The coefficients in the equation are changed:

Two or more equations are added together to get a balanced overall reaction:

Section 16.4   **Expressing the Equilibrium Constant in Terms of Pressure**

15. How is writing a pressure equilibrium expression different than writing a concentration equilibrium expression? Use the equilibrium system $H_2(g) + I_2(g) \rightleftharpoons 2\,HI(g)$ to illustrate your answer.

16. What equation is used to change K_p to K_c? Identify all variables. Does every equilibrium system have a K_p? Why or why not?

Section 16.5   **Heterogeneous Equilibria: Reactions Involving Solids and Liquids**

17. What is a heterogeneous equilibrium?

18. Why are solids and pure liquids ignored in equilibrium expressions?

A Heterogeneous Equilibrium

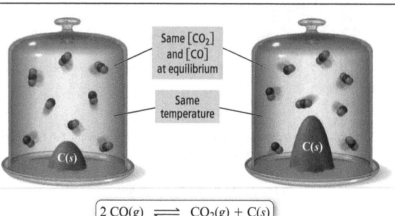

$$2\,CO(g) \rightleftharpoons CO_2(g) + C(s)$$

19. What evidence supports the claim that the above figure is an example of a heterogenous equilibrium.

Section 16.6   **Calculating the Equilibrium Constant from Measured Equilibrium Concentrations**

20. Do initial concentrations affect the value of K? Explain your answer.

21. What is an ICE table? What is it used for? What units are used for concentrations?

22. Why are coefficients important to analyze when using an ICE table?

The Reaction Quotient: Predicting the Direction of Change   Section 16.7

23. What is Q and why is it important in equilibrium systems?

24. Explain what will occur if:

 $Q > K$:

 $Q = K$:

 $Q < K$:

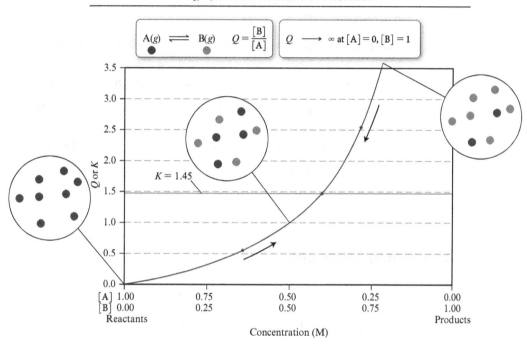

Q, K, and the Direction of a Reaction

$A(g) \rightleftharpoons B(g)$ $Q = \dfrac{[B]}{[A]}$ $Q \longrightarrow \infty$ at $[A] = 0$, $[B] = 1$

$K = 1.45$

Q or K

[A] 1.00	0.75	0.50	0.25	0.00
[B] 0.00	0.25	0.50	0.75	1.00
Reactants				Products

Concentration (M)

25. On the above figure, indicate where the following are located:
    $Q < K$, $Q = K$, and $Q > K$. Explain what evidence supports your choice.

26. What does it mean when a reaction shifts to the left? To the right? How do you know the direction of the shift?

Finding Equilibrium Concentrations   Section 16.8

27. What is the 5% rule? When is it used?

28. When does a quadratic equation need to be used when solving for an equilibrium concentration or pressure in an equilibrium system? When can the $-x$ factor be ignored, so the quadratic equation doesn't need to be solved? What factors provide evidence this can be done?

Section 16.9   **Le Châtelier's Principle: How a System at Equilibrium Responds to Disturbances**

29. What is the concept behind Le Châtelier's Principle?

30. Explain how to analyze what will happen to a chemical system at equilibrium if more of a species is added to the system. Does the phase (s, l, or g,) of the addition matter? How will an addition affect K?

31. Explain how to analyze what will happen to a chemical system at equilibrium if pressure is added to the system. What factors determine if the reaction will shift in response to the addition?

32. Explain how to analyze what will happen to a chemical system at equilibrium if the temperature of the system is increased. How will the equilibrium value change? Does it make a difference if the reaction exothermic or endothermic.

33. Explain how to analyze what will happen to a chemical system at equilibrium if the temperature of the system is decreased. Does it make a difference if the reaction exothermic or endothermic? How will the equilibrium value change?

34. How does adding a catalyst affect a system at equilibrium?

35. How does adding an inert gas affect a system at equilibrium?

Self-Assessment Answers

1. _____   2. _____   3. _____

4. _____   5. _____   6. _____

7. _____   8. _____   9. _____

10. _____   11. _____   12. _____

13. _____   14. _____   15. _____

ACIDS AND BASES

Acid and bases are covered in Unit 8 of the AP Chemistry Framework and include several of the learning objectives listed below. Included in this list are the concepts of acid–base of equilibrium.

This chapter covers the three theories of acids and bases. Each is useful for different characteristics of acid–base reactions. Of the three theories, the Brønsted-Lowry definition is the most useful and the definition you are expected to know. In the AP curriculum, identification of a Lewis acid or base is not required, although understanding the concepts will be beneficial to understanding complex ions and other concepts in the AP curriculum. Section 17.2 presents basic information that students should already know about acids and bases. The most critical sections of the chapter are:

17.3 **Definitions of Acids and Bases**

17.4 **Acid Strength and the Acid Ionization Constant (K_a)**

17.5 **Autoionization of Water and pH**

17.6 **Finding the $[H_3O^+]$ and pH of Strong and Weak Acid Solutions**

17.7 **Base Solutions**

17.8 **The Acid–Base Properties of Ions and Salts**

17.9 **Polyprotic Acids**

17.10 **Acid Strength and Molecular Structure**

Specific Learning Objectives Addressed in This Chapter:

TRA-2 A substance can change into another substance through different processes, and the change itself can be classified by the sort of processes that produced it.

TRA-2.A Identify a reaction as acid–base reaction.

TRA-2.B Identify species as Bronsted–Lowry acids, bases, and/or conjugate acid–base pairs, based on proton-transfer involving those species.

SAP-9 The chemistry of acids and bases involves reversible proton-transfer reactions, with equilibrium concentrations being related to the strength of the acids and bases involved.

SAP-9.A Calculate the values of pH and pOH, based on K_w and the concentration of all species present in a neutral solution of water.

SAP-9.B Calculate pH and pOH based on concentrations of all species in a solution of a strong acid or a strong base.

SAP-9.C Explain the relationship among pH, pOH, and concentrations of all species in a solution of a monoprotic weak acid or weak base.

SAP-9.D Explain the relationship among concentrations of major species in a mixture of weak and strong acids and bases.

SAP-9.E Explain results from the titration of a monoprotic or polyprotic acid or base solution, in relation to the properties of the solution and its components.

SAP-9.F Explain the relationship between the strength of an acid or a base and the structure of the molecule or ion.

Concepts and Vocabulary to Review:

Section 17.2   **The Nature of Acids and Bases**

Acids taste sour, can neutralize bases, turn blue litmus red, and dissolve many metals. Some common acids are hydrochloric, sulfuric, nitric, and acetic acids. Bases have a bitter taste, feel slippery, turn red litmus blue, and can neutralize acids. Some common bases are sodium hydroxide, potassium hydroxide, sodium bicarbonate, sodium carbonate, and ammonia.

Section 17.3   **Definitions of Acids and Bases**

The two main theories of acids and bases are in this section; they are the Arrhenius definition and the Brønsted-Lowry definition. The primary definition used in AP is the Brønsted-Lowry since it is more inclusive.

Arrhenius defined acids and bases by ions present and formed when dissociated in water. Acids have H^+ ions and dissociate with water to form H_3O^+ known as hydronium. The hydronium ion can be simply abbreviated as $H^+(aq)$ and is accepted in AP although it is actually the hydronium ion.

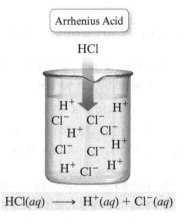

Arrhenius Acid

HCl

$$HCl(aq) \longrightarrow H^+(aq) + Cl^-(aq)$$

Figure 17.1 Arrhenius Acid   An Arrhenius acid produces H^+ ions in solution, which will interact with water molecules to form hydronium ions.

Arrhenius bases are identified by the presence of hydroxide ions (OH^-), which ionize in aqueous solutions.

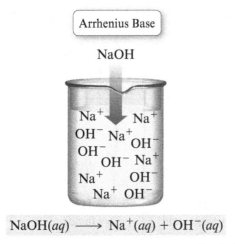

$$NaOH(aq) \longrightarrow Na^+(aq) + OH^-(aq)$$

Figure 17.2 Arrhenius Base   An Arrhenius base produces OH^- ions in solution.

Brønsted-Lowry defined acids and bases according to what occurs in chemical reactions. Acids donate protons and bases accept protons. An H^+ is a proton, so when looking at a reaction you can identify the acid as the reactant substance losing an H^+ and the base as the reactant substance gaining the H^+. This means these reactions have both an acid and a base. In the chemical equation

$$HCl(aq) + H_2O(l) \longrightarrow H_3O^+(aq) + Cl^-(aq)$$

(H^+)
(donated to)

the H^+ starts with HCl and is donated to the H_2O. HCl donated the proton and is therefore an acid, and because the water accepted the proton, it is the base. Water can also act as a acid. For instance, in the chemical equation

$$NH_3(aq) + H_2O(l) \rightleftharpoons NH_4^+(aq) + OH^-(aq)$$

(H^+)
(donated to NH_3)

the reactant ammonia molecules accepted the proton to form the ammonium ion, while the reactant water donated the proton and formed the hydroxide ion. In this case, ammonia is the base and water is the acid.

Substances such as water, which can either serve as an acid or a base depending on the situation, are called amphoteric.

In the preceding chemical equation, $NH_3(aq) + H_2O(l) \rightleftharpoons NH_4^+(aq) + OH^-(aq)$; when looking at the reverse reaction, an acid and base can also be identified. The ammonium ion is the acid donating the H^+ to the $OH,^-$ and the hydroxide is the base accepting the H^+. The acid and base in the reverse reaction are called the conjugate acid and conjugate base. Because the acid in the forward reaction forms the conjugate base and the base in the forward reaction forms the conjugate acid, these are called conjugate acid–base pairs.

In this equation, you can see the conjugate acid–base pairs are identified by tie-lines.

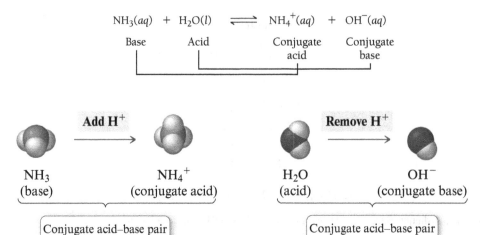

$$NH_3(aq) \ + \ H_2O(l) \ \rightleftharpoons \ NH_4^+(aq) \ + \ OH^-(aq)$$

| Base | Acid | Conjugate acid | Conjugate base |

Add H$^+$

NH$_3$
(base)

NH$_4^+$
(conjugate acid)

Conjugate acid–base pair

Remove H$^+$

H$_2$O
(acid)

OH$^-$
(conjugate base)

Conjugate acid–base pair

Figure 17.3 Conjugate Acid–Base Pairs   A conjugate acid–base pair consists of two substances related to each other by the transfer of a proton. One will be in the reactants, and it's pair will be in the products.

Section 17.4   Acid Strength and the Acid Ionization Constant (K_a)

Acids are considered weak or strong based on the amount of ionization they undergo in an aqueous solution. Strong acids will completely ionize and weak acids will not. In weak acids, the ions in the acid have a strong attraction to each other, resulting in the tendency to remain mostly as molecules, although some will ionize. Since both the forward reaction of dissociating into ions and the reverse reaction of forming ions are ongoing, this reaction will reach equilibrium.

A Weak Acid

When HF dissolves in water, only a fraction of the molecules ionize.

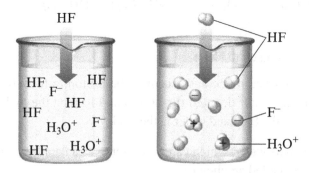

Figure 17.4 Ionization of a Weak Acid   When HF dissolves in water, only a fraction of the dissolved molecules ionize to form H$_3$O$^+$ and F$^-$. The solution contains many intact HF molecules.

For acids, this equilibrium constant is called K_a. Problems with K_a are the same as those with as K_c; they just refer to a weak acid equilibrium system. Comparing the forward to the backward reaction, we find that the less dissociation occurs in the forward reaction, the more the backward reaction is favored and the smaller the value of K_a, and therefore the weaker the acid. K_a values can be used as data to help rank the acid strength of a group of weak acids. The smaller the value, the weaker the acid.

Table 17.1 Acid Ionization Constants (K_a) for Some Monoprotic Weak Acids at 25 °C

The printed light H in the acid formula is indicated also lighter in the structural formula. Not all H's in a formula are acidic.

Acid	Formula	Structural Formula	Ionization Reaction	K_a	pK_a
Chlorous acid	$HClO_2$	H—O—Cl=O	$HClO_2(aq) + H_2O(l) \rightleftharpoons$ $H_3O^+(aq) + ClO_2^-(aq)$	1.1×10^{-2}	1.96
Nitrous acid	HNO_2	H—O—N=O	$HNO_2(aq) + H_2O(l) \rightleftharpoons$ $H_3O^+(aq) + NO_2^-(aq)$	4.6×10^{-4}	3.34
Hydrofluoric acid	HF	H—F	$HF(aq) + H_2O(l) \rightleftharpoons$ $H_3O^+(aq) + F^-(aq)$	6.8×10^{-4}	3.17
Formic acid	$HCHO_2$	H—O—C(=O)—H	$HCHO_2(aq) + H_2O(l) \rightleftharpoons$ $H_3O^+(aq) + CHO_2^-(aq)$	1.8×10^{-4}	3.74
Benzoic acid	$HC_7H_5O_2$	H—O—C(=O)—C₆H₅	$HC_7H_5O_2(aq) + H_2O(l) \rightleftharpoons$ $H_3O^+(aq) + C_7H_5O_2^-(aq)$	6.5×10^{-5}	4.19
Acetic acid	$HC_2H_3O_2$	H—O—C(=O)—CH₃	$HC_2H_3O_2(aq) + H_2O(l) \rightleftharpoons$ $H_3O^+(aq) + C_2H_3O_2^-(aq)$	1.8×10^{-5}	4.74
Hypochlorous acid	HClO	H—O—Cl	$HClO(aq) + H_2O(l) \rightleftharpoons$ $H_3O^+(aq) + ClO^-(aq)$	2.9×10^{-8}	7.54
Hydrocyanic acid	HCN	H—C≡N	$HCN(aq) + H_2O(l) \rightleftharpoons$ $H_3O^+(aq) + CN^-(aq)$	4.9×10^{-10}	9.31
Phenol	HC_6H_5O	H—O—C₆H₅	$HC_6H_5O(aq) + H_2O(l) \rightleftharpoons$ $H_3O^+(aq) + C_6H_5O^-(aq)$	1.3×10^{-10}	9.89

Comparing hydrocyanic acid and acetic acid K_a values, hydrocyanic acid is much weaker acid than the acetic acid. This indicates the bonds in hydrocyanic acid are stronger than the ones in acetic acid. The smaller the K_a value, the weaker the acid and less ionization occurs.

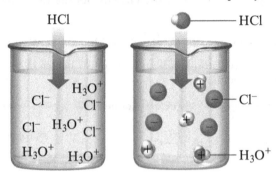

A Strong Acid

When HCl dissolves in water, it ionizes completely.

Figure 17.5 Ionization of a Strong Acid   When HCl dissolves in water, it completely ionizes to form H_3O^+ and Cl^-. The solution contains virtually no intact HCl.

If the acid is strong, the attractions between the ions are weaker than the attraction to water molecules and the acid will dissociate completely or nearly so. If the acid dissociates completely or close to completely, it is an example of a forward reaction going to completion. Strong acids such as HCl exhibit complete dissociation when they are placed in water. HCl molecules interact with water molecules to form hydronium ions and chloride ions.

$$HCl(g) + H_2O(l) \rightarrow H_3O^+(aq) + Cl^-(aq)$$

An indication of strong acid dissociation is the very large K_a values of these acids.

The six strong acids are HCl, HBr, HI, HNO_3, $HClO_4$, and H_2SO_4. Any other acid is weak. Only the removal of the first H^+ in H_2SO_4 is considered to be a strong acid as the removal of the second H^+ is not complete. Sulfuric acid is an example of a diprotic acid in that it has two protons or H^+ available to ionize. Acids with only one H^+ are called monoprotic and acids with three H^+'s are called triprotic. Phosphoric acid, H_3PO_4, is triprotic.

Section 17.5   Autoionization of Water and pH

Since water is an acid and base, two waters react to form hydronium and hydroxide. This is called the autoionization of water. The reaction is as follows.

Water acting as both an acid and a base

$$H_2O(l) + H_2O(l) \rightleftharpoons H_3O^+(aq) + OH^-(aq)$$

Acid   **Base**
(proton donor)   (proton acceptor)

Writing this reaction in an equilibrium expression results in $K_w = [H_3O^+][OH^-]$. The w represents water indicating K_w refers to the equilibrium ion product constant of water. K_w at 25 °C has a recognized value of 1.0×10^{-14}. Water is neutral because the hydronium and hydroxide concentrations are equal (1.0×10^{-7}) and neutralize each other; $[H_3O^+] = [OH^-]$. Unless otherwise stated, all acid–base reaction are at 25 °C.

In acidic solutions, the amount of hydronium increases (acid) and the hydroxide decreases (base); $[H_3O^+] > [OH^-]$. The actual amount of each can be calculated using $1.0 \times 10^{-14} = [H_3O^+][OH^-]$. Since the acid and base concentrations multiplied together equal the same number, as one value increases the other must decrease. In basic solutions, the hydroxide concentration increases, and the acid concentration decreases; $[H_3O^+] < [OH^-]$.

The pH scale is one way to measure the amount of hydronium ion in solution where the pH $= -\log[H_3O^+]$. The negative log indicates the greater amount of acid present, the LOWER the acid number will be. For instance, a hydronium concentration of 0.0010 will equal a pH of 3.00, and a concentration of 0.10 will equal a pH of 1.00. Therefore, the lower the pH is, then the more acidic the solution. Since the scale is logarithmic, the difference between concentrations of a pH of 1 and a pH of 3 is not 2 but 10^2 or a factor of 100. Another concept about pH values is the number of significant figures present. Since the value is dealing with logs, the number in the front, the mantissa, is not part of the significant figures. The significant figures are the places to the right of the decimal. A pH of 3.00 has two significant figures.

In a solution of pure water at 25 °C, the concentration of hydronium was 1.0×10^{-7}, which is a pH of 7.00. Hence, at a pH of 7.00 the solution is neutral. When the base concentration is greater than the acid concentration, the pH will be greater than 7.00.

If the base concentration is known, the hydronium concentration must be calculated before calculating a pH value. Another way is to convert first to pOH and then to pH. This requires using the following two equations: pOH $= -\log[OH^-]$ and pH $+$ pOH $= 14$. The pOH scale is just the reverse of the pH scale. The more basic the solution is, the lower the pOH is.

Scale Table

Scale	Acid	Base	Neutral
pH	< 7	> 7	7
pOH	> 7	< 7	7

The pH Scale

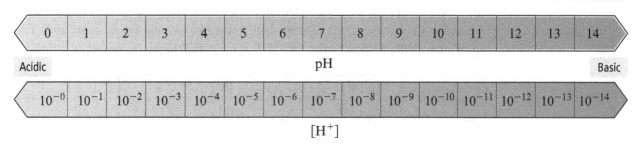

Figure 17.6 **The pH Scale**   An increase of 1 on the pH scale corresponds to a factor of 10 decrease in $[H_3O^+]$.

0.0	1.0	2.0	3.0	4.0	5.0	6.0	7.0	8.0	9.0	10.0	11.0	12.0	13.0	14.0

Acidic   pH   Basic

14.0	13.0	12.0	11.0	10.0	9.0	8.0	7.0	6.0	5.0	4.0	3.0	2.0	1.0	0.0

pOH

Figure 17.7 pH and pOH

Combining all of these equations, we can see a pattern to help students remember the steps to determining a value.

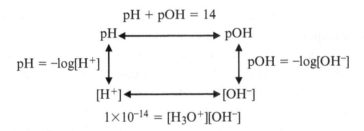

$$pH + pOH = 14$$
$$pH \longleftarrow pOH$$
$$pH = -\log[H^+] \qquad pOH = -\log[OH^-]$$
$$[H^+] \longleftarrow [OH^-]$$
$$1 \times 10^{-14} = [H_3O^+][OH^-]$$

Other values are pK_a and pK_b. In both cases, the $-\log$ is taken. For pK_a, the equation is $pK_a = -\log[K_a]$ and for pK_b, the equation is $pK_b = -\log[K_b]$. The pK_a and pK_b values are half way to equivalence. Again the scales are logarithmic and are an indication of the strength of the acid or base. For acetic acid with a K_a of 1.8×10^{-5}, $-\log[1.8 \times 10^{-5}] = 4.82$. This would be the pH of a 1.0 M solution of acetic acid.

Section 17.6   Finding the [H₃O⁺] and pH of Strong and Weak Acid Solutions

Since strong acids ionize 100%, the concentrations of the acid will equal the concentration of the hydronium ion. A 1.00 M HCl solution will have 1.00 M H^+ and 1.00 M Cl^- concentrations. For weak acids, this is not the case, and this is why it is crucial to recognize the differences between strong and weak acids. The first step is to decide if the acid is a strong or weak acid, knowing all acids cannot be treated the same in problems.

Weak acids do not fully ionize. An example is $HF \rightleftharpoons H^+ + F^-$. HF goes to equilibrium and therefore a calculation needs to be done to determine the H^+ concentration. Solving this problem will be just like solving for K_c using an ICE set up. Starting with a 1.00 M solution of HF, we see that the set up would be as follows:

	[HF]	[H⁺]	[F⁻]
I	1.00	0*	0
C	$-x$	$+x$	$+x$
E	$1.00 - x$	x	x

*There is some H^+ from the autoionization of water, but it is so small it can be ignored.

Solving is again the same as before where $K_a = \dfrac{[H^+][F^-]}{[HF]}$, which substituted

would be $K_a = \dfrac{[x][x]}{[1.00 - x]}$. The K_a values of the weak acids are in table. The K_a

of HF is 3.5×10^{-4}, therefore, $3.5 \times 10^{-4} = \dfrac{[x][x]}{[1.00 - x]}$. The $-x$ value in the de-

nominator follows the same 5% rule as before in order to be dropped and not solve
the quadratic equation; $x = 0.019$ M.

Percent ionization of an acid is calculated the same way as before and needs to be

done to assure the $-x$ value could be dropped. % ionization $= \dfrac{[H^+]}{[HA]} \times 100\%$. The

HA concentration is the initial concentration, and the H^+ is the concentration at equi-

librium (x in the ICE set up). In this case, % ionization $= \dfrac{[0.019]}{[1.00]} \times 100\%$, which

is 1.9% ionization, therefore it was fine to drop the $-x$ value.

As with all equilibrium systems, Le Châtelier's principle also applies to disturbances.
If more HF acid is added to HF $\rightleftharpoons$ H^+ + F^-, the system will respond by shifting
to the right, which increases the percent ionization.

Base Solutions   Section 17.7

Analysis of basic solutions follows the same principles as acids. Bases ionizing 100% are strong and those bases that do not ionize to this extent are
weak. Strong base equations have a single forward arrow going to completion;
$NaOH(aq) \longrightarrow Na^+(aq) + OH^-(aq)$. The strong bases include all the alkali
metal hydroxides. Strong bases can use the concentration in the pOH equation: a 1.0
M NaOH ionizes to 1.0 M Na^+ and 1.0 M OH^-, so pOH $= -\log[1.0]$; therefore, using the equation pH + pOH $= 14$, the pOH $= 0$. In the pH scale, this would be 14.

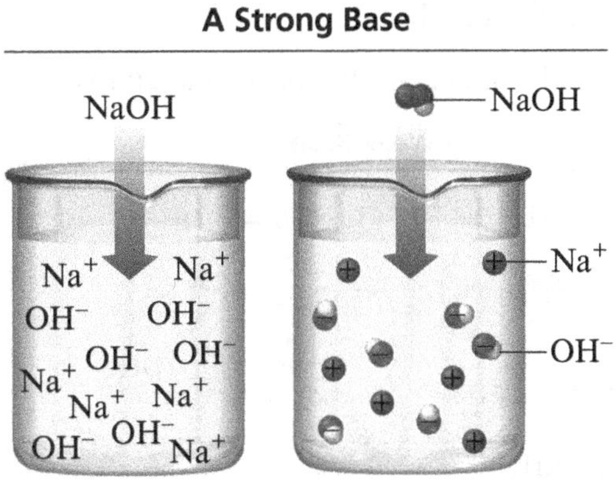

A Strong Base

Figure 17.8 Ionization of a Strong Base   When NaOH dissolves in water, it dissociates completely into
Na^+ and OH^-. The solution contains virtually no intact NaOH.

Weak bases have double arrows going to an equilibrium;

$NH_3(aq) + H_2O(l) \rightleftharpoons NH_4^+(aq) + OH^-(aq)$.

To find the concentration to use in the pOH equation, a K problem must be solved using an ICE format. Since the substance is a base, the K is a K_b.

Table 17.2 Some Common Weak Bases

Weak Base	Ionization Reaction	K_b (at 25 °C)
Carbonate ion (CO_3^{2-})*	$CO_3^{2-}(aq) + H_2O(l) \rightleftharpoons HCO_3^-(aq) + OH^-(aq)$	1.8×10^{-4}
Methylamine (CH_3NH_2)	$CH_3NH_2(aq) + H_2O(l) \rightleftharpoons CH_3NH_3^+(aq) + OH^-(aq)$	4.4×10^{-4}
Ethylamine ($C_2H_5NH_2$)	$C_2H_5NH_2(aq) + H_2O(l) \rightleftharpoons C_2H_5NH_3^+(aq) + OH^-(aq)$	5.6×10^{-4}
Ammonia (NH_3)	$NH_3(aq) + H_2O(l) \rightleftharpoons NH_4^+(aq) + OH^-(aq)$	1.76×10^{-5}
Bicarbonate ion (HCO_3^-)* (or hydrogen carbonate)	$HCO_3^-(aq) + H_2O(l) \rightleftharpoons H_2CO_3(aq) + OH^-(aq)$	2.3×10^{-8}
Pyridine (C_5H_5N)	$C_5H_5N(aq) + H_2O(l) \rightleftharpoons C_5H_5NH^+(aq) + OH^-(aq)$	1.7×10^{-9}
Aniline ($C_6H_5NH_2$)	$C_6H_5NH_2(aq) + H_2O(l) \rightleftharpoons C_6H_5NH_3^+(aq) + OH^-(aq)$	3.9×10^{-10}

*The carbonate and bicarbonate ions must occur with a positively charged ion such as Na^+ that serves to balance the charge but does not have any part in the ionization reaction. For example, it is the bicarbonate ion that makes sodium bicarbonate ($NaHCO_3$) basic. We look more closely at ionic bases in Section 17.8.

An example follows showing how to find the pH of a weak base. Using a 1.00 M solution of NH_3, we find the set up would be as follows:

	$[NH_3]$	$[NH_4^+]$	$[OH^-]$
I	1.00	0	0
C	$-x$	$+x$	$+x$
E	$1.00 - x$	x	x

$K_b = \dfrac{[NH_4^+][OH^-]}{[NH_3]}$, which substituted would be $K_b = \dfrac{[x][x]}{[1.00 - x]}$. The K_b of NH_3 is 1.76×10^{-5}. The $-x$ value in the denominator follows the same 5% rule as before in order to be dropped and not solve the quadratic equation: $x = 0.00420$ M. In this case, % ionization $= \dfrac{[0.00420]}{[1.00]} \times 100\%$, which is 0.420% ionization, showing it was fine to drop the $-x$. Le Châtelier's principle also applies to disturbances of the equilibrium.

Weak bases, like weak acids, only partially ionize and go to equilibriums in water.

A Weak Base

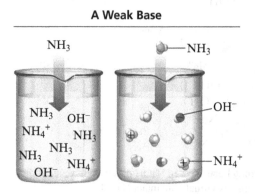

Figure 17.9 Ionization of a Weak Base   When NH_3 dissolves in water, it partially ionizes water to form NH_4^+ and OH^-. Most of the NH_3 molecules in solution remain as NH_3.

The Acid–Base Properties of Ions and Salts   Section 17.8

The anions of acids and the cations of bases combined together to form ionic compounds called salts. Remember in the Brønsted-Lowry definition there are conjugate acid–base pairs. The acid HCl donates the H^+, and the anion Cl^- is the conjugate base pair.

$$HCl(aq) + H_2O(l) \longrightarrow H_3O^+(aq) + Cl^-(aq)$$

For the base NH_3, the cation NH_4^+ is its conjugate acid pair.

$$NH_3(aq) + H_2O(l) \rightleftharpoons NH_4^+(aq) + OH^-(aq)$$

Whether or not these ions will influence the pH of the resultant solution depends on their interaction with water.

If the ions present do not have an interaction with water, the solution will remain neutral. For instance, the salt NaCl is made from the cation Na^+ of the strong base NaOH and the anion Cl^- of the strong acid HCl. Neither of these ions will undergo hydrolysis with the water and remain as ions in solution. The anions of strong acids are neutral and the cations of strong bases are neutral.

Strong acid anion: $Cl^-(aq) + H_2O(l) \longrightarrow$ no reaction and the solution remains neutral

Strong base cation: $Na^+(aq) + H_2O(l) \longrightarrow$ no reaction and the solution remains neutral

Hence, NaCl is a neutral salt. Neutral salts are formed from the anions of strong acids and the cation from strong bases. Neither ion undergoes a hydrolysis reaction. Another example of a neutral salt is KCl.

Strong acid strong base reaction: $HCl(aq) + KOH(aq) \longrightarrow H_2O(l) + KCl(aq)$

Neutral salt: $KCl(aq) \longrightarrow K^+(aq) + Cl^-(aq)$

$K^+(aq) + H_2O(l) \rightleftharpoons$ no reaction $Cl^-(aq) + H_2O(l) \rightleftharpoons$ no reaction

In contrast, anions of weak acids are weak bases and will undergo a hydrolysis reaction with water. Cations of weak bases are weak acids and will also undergo a hydrolysis reaction with water. These reactions can drive the pH to be acidic or basic. For example, the anion fluoride from the weak acid hydrofluoric acid (HF) reacts with water to form an equilibrium system with the weak hydrofluoric acid molecule and hydroxide ions. The hydroxide ions will make the pH basic.

$$F^-(aq) + H_2O(l) \rightleftharpoons HF(aq) + OH^-(aq)$$

The F^- has a strong affinity for H^+ and will remove the H^+ from the water, leaving OH^- ions behind. The table below indicates the strength of the acid and the base strength of the anion present.

Because they undergo hydrolysis with water, the cation of a weak base will affect the pH of the solution. In the example below, ammonium, which is the conjugate acid of

Acid Strength	Acid	Base	Base Strength
Strong	HCl	Cl^-	Neutral
Strong	H_2SO_4	HSO_4^-	Neutral
Strong	HNO_3	NO_3^-	Neutral
Strong	H_3O^+	H_2O	Weak
Weak	HSO_4^-	SO_4^{2-}	Weak
Weak	H_2SO_3	HSO_3^-	Weak
Weak	H_3PO_4	$H_2PO_4^-$	Weak
Weak	HF	F^-	Weak
Weak	$HC_2H_3O_2$	$C_2H_3O_2^-$	Weak
Weak	H_2CO_3	HCO_3^-	Weak
Weak	H_2S	HS^-	Weak
Weak	HSO_3^-	SO_3^{2-}	Weak
Weak	$H_2PO_4^-$	HPO_4^{2-}	Weak
Weak	HCN	CN^-	Weak
Weak	NH_4^+	NH_3	Weak
Weak	HCO_3^-	CO_3^{2-}	Weak
Weak	HPO_4^{2-}	PO_4^{3-}	Weak
Weak	H_2O	OH^-	Strong
Negligible	HS^-	S^{2-}	Strong
Negligible	OH^-	O^{2-}	Strong

Figure 17.10 Strength of Conjugate Acid–Base Pairs The stronger an acid, the weaker its conjugate base.

ammonia, reacts with water to form an equilibrium system with ammonia and hydronium ions. The hydronium ions will make the pH test acidic.

$$NH_4^+(aq) + H_2O(l) \rightleftharpoons NH_3(aq) + H_3O^+(l)$$

Knowing the cations and anions will help to determine if the salts will test acidic, basic, or neutral. As mentioned above, cations of strong bases and anions of strong acids will form a neutral salt. Examples include KCl, NaBr, and KNO_3.

Acidic salts are formed from the anion of a strong acid and the cation of a weak base due to the interaction of the cation with water such as NH_4Br.

Basic salts are formed from the anion of a weak acid and the cation of a strong base due to the interaction of the anion with water. Examples include NaF, KNO_2, and $Ca(C_2H_3O_2)_2$.

This table summarizes how to predict the pH of a salt.

Table 17.3 pH of Salt Solutions

		ANION	
		Conjugate base of strong acid	**Conjugate base of weak acid**
CATION	**Conjugate acid of weak base**	*Acidic*	*Depends on relative strengths*
	Small, highly charged metal ion	*Acidic*	*Depends on relative strengths*
	Counterion of strong base	*Neutral*	*Basic*

Another way to find the pH is to use the equation $K_aK_b = K_w$. If the K_a of the acid is known, the K_b of the conjugate base can be calculated. From the K_b, the pH can be calculated. We can also use the equation $-\log K_a + -\log K_b = 14$, which can also be written as $pK_a + pK_b = 14$.

Polyprotic Acids   Section 17.9

Polyprotic acids dissociate in several steps, each with a unique K_a. With each step, the K_a values get smaller and smaller, indicating with each successive step there is less dissociation. In other words, the majority of the H_3O^+ occurs on the first dissociation. For the most part, by calculating the concentration from the first step, the pH can be calculated since the amounts of H^+ from the additional steps are usually insignificant. The exception is with dilute sulfuric acid solutions, the actual amounts from each step need to be calculated to determine the pH.

Dissociation of a Polyprotic Acid

$$H_2C_6H_6O_6(aq) + H_2O(l) \rightleftharpoons H_3O^+(aq) + HC_6H_6O_6^-(aq)$$

$$\left[H_3O^+\right] = 2.8 \times 10^{-3} \text{ M}$$

$$HC_6H_6O_6^-(aq) + H_2O(l) \rightleftharpoons H_3O^+(aq) + C_6H_6O_6^{2-}(aq)$$

$$\left[H_3O^+\right] = 1.6 \times 10^{-12} \text{ M}$$

0.100 M $H_2C_6H_6O_6$

$$\text{Total}\left[H_3O^+\right] = 2.8 \times 10^{-3} \text{ M} + 1.6 \times 10^{-12} \text{ M}$$

$$= 2.8 \times 10^{-3} \text{ M} \qquad pH = 2.55$$

Figure 17.11 Dissociation of a Polyprotic Acid   A 0.100 M $H_2C_6H_6O_6$ solution contains an H_3O^+ concentration of 2.8×10^{-3} M from the first step. The amount of H_3O^+ contributed by the second step is only 1.6×10^{-12} M, which is insignificant compared to the amount produced by the first step.

Acid Strength and Molecular Structure   Section 17.10

Two factors affect the strength of binary acids and the ease of dissociation: the polarity of the bond and the strength of the bond in the acid. The H^+ must be δ^+ in the bond to end up being dissociated as an H^+, so the bond must be polar. In the three cases below, only the HF bond is polar with δ^+ on the H end.

H 2.2 Li 0.98 so Li is pulled toward H	H is 2.2 and C is 2.5, the difference of 0.3 indicates nonpolar bond	H 2.2 and F 4.0 indicate H is pulled toward the F
$\longleftarrow\;+$		$+\;\longrightarrow$
H—Li	H—C	H—F
Not acidic	Not acidic	Acidic

Using electronegativity values, in LiH, the H is δ^-, so this is not acidic, whereas H—C is considered to be nonpolar and so cannot be acidic. The HF is acidic.

It also makes sense that the stronger the bond, the harder it is to remove the H^+, so the less the acid dissociates, and the weaker the acid is. If bond energies are known, the stronger acid will have the smaller bond energy. In the table below, HF which is a weak acid and HCl and HBr which are both strong acids bond energies are compared. The data supports the higher the bond energy, the weaker the acid.

Acid	Bond Energy (kJ/mol)	Type of Acid
H—F	565	Weak
H—Cl	431	Strong
H—Br	364	Strong

When combining the effect of bond strength and polarity, the following trend is observed.

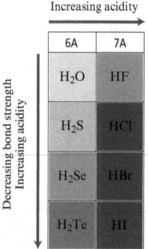

Figure 17.12 Acidity of the Group 6A and 7A Hydrides   From left to right, the hydrides become more acidic because the H—Y bond becomes more polar. From top to bottom, these hydrides become more acidic because the H—Y bond becomes weaker.

Since electronegativities increase to the right of the periodic table, the bond with hydrogen becomes more polar and the acids get stronger, and as the bond energies decrease down a column, acid strength increases.

In oxyacids, the more oxygen atoms on the acid, the more the molecule can polarize and pull the electron density away from the H − O bond, weakening the bond and allowing the H^+ to be removed more easily. This can be determined by analyzing data in the following table:

Acid	Structure	K_a
$HClO_4$	O ‖ H—O—Cl=O ‖ O	Strong
$HClO_3$	O ‖ H—O—Cl=O	1
$HClO_2$	H—O—Cl=O	1.1×10^{-2}
$HClO$	H—O—Cl	2.9×10^{-8}

Using this data, we find that the ranking of these acids from strongest to weakest is $HClO_4 > HClO_3 > HClO_2 > HClO$.

When comparing oxyacids with the same number of oxygen atoms, the electronegativity of the other atom (not the H or O) determines which is stronger. The more electronegative atom will polarize the bond more, making it easier to remove the H^+, and is therefore the stronger acid.

Acid	Electronegativity of Y	K_a
H—O—I	2.5	2.3×10^{-11}
H—O—Br	2.8	2.0×10^{-9}
H—O—Cl	3.0	2.9×10^{-8}

Using this data, we see HOCl is the strongest of these acids and HOI is the weakest.

Evaluation of data and accompanying explanations to determine the stronger or weaker acid are included in the science practices that students need to master.

Lewis Acids and Bases   Section 17.11

The Lewis theory of acids is based on donating electrons and accepting electrons. An acid is an electron acceptor and bases are electron donors. It helps to draw Lewis structures to see this relationship.

$$H^+ + :NH_3 \longrightarrow \left[H\!:\!NH_3\right]^+$$

Brønsted–Lowry model focuses on the proton   Lewis model focuses on the electron pair

In this reaction, the ammonia has a lone pair of electrons it donates to the H^+, identifying H^+ as the acid and NH_3 as the base. So why the difference? This theory allows for acid–base reactions that do not involve H^+. For instance, $AlCl_3 + NH_3$ is a Lewis acid–base reaction.

$$
\begin{array}{c}
:\!\overset{\cdots}{\underset{\cdots}{Cl}}\!:\quad H \\
| \qquad | \\
:\!\overset{\cdots}{\underset{\cdots}{Cl}}\!-\!Al + :\!N\!-\!H \\
| \qquad | \\
:\!\overset{\cdots}{\underset{\cdots}{Cl}}\!:\quad H
\end{array}
\longrightarrow
\begin{array}{c}
:\!\overset{\cdots}{\underset{\cdots}{Cl}}\!:\quad H \\
| \qquad | \\
:\!\overset{\cdots}{\underset{\cdots}{Cl}}\!-\!Al\!:\!N\!-\!H \\
| \qquad | \\
:\!\overset{\cdots}{\underset{\cdots}{Cl}}\!:\quad H
\end{array}
$$

Al has an incomplete octet with six electrons, and N has a lone pair of electrons to donate to the bond. NH_3 is acting as a base and $AlCl_3$ as an acid.

In this equation, identify the Lewis acid and the Lewis base.

Section 17.12   Acid Rain

Some gases in the atmosphere combine with water droplets in the air to form acid rain. Some of the gases are: sulfur dioxide which forms sulfuric acid, nitrogen dioxide which forms nitric acid, and carbon dioxide which forms carbonic acid, come primarily from the burning of fossil fuels. The acids formed will eat away at metals and statues as well as lower the pH of bodies of water. Many organisms, especially aquatic ones, are sensitive to the changes in pH.

Additional Practice

Self-Assessment Quiz Questions Q1, Q2, Q3, Q4, Q5, Q6, Q7, Q8, Q9, Q10, Q11, Q12, Q13, Q14, and Q15

Problems:

Review Questions 2, 4, 5, 6, 7, 8, 9, 12, 13, 14, 15, 16, 17, 18, 19, and 25

The Nature and Definitions of Acids and Bases 33, 35, and 37

Acid Strength and Ka 41 and 43

Autoionization of Water and pH 47, 48, 51, and 54

Acid Solutions 57, 66, 69, 73, and 77

Base Solutions 81, 87, 89, and 94

Acid–Base Properties of Ions and Salts 95, 96, 99, and 101

Polyprotic Acids 109 and 110

Molecular Structure and Acid Strength 117 and 119

Cumulative Problems 127, 128, 137, and 141

Conceptual Problems 157, 158, and 159

Equations to know:

$$K_a = \frac{[H_3O^+][A^-]}{[HA]}$$

$$K_w = [H_3O^+][OH^-] = 1.0 \times 10^{-14} (\text{at } 25\,°C)$$

$$pH = -\log[H_3O^+]$$

$$pOH = -\log[OH^-]$$

$$pH + pOH = 14.00$$

$$pK_a = -\log K_a$$

$$\text{Percent ionization} = \frac{\text{concentration of ionized acid}}{\text{initial concentration of acid}} \times 100\%$$

$$= \frac{[H_3O^+]_{\text{equil}}}{[HA]_{\text{init}}} \times 100\%$$

$$K_a \times K_b = K_w$$

Practice AP Test Questions

A student is given 50.0 mL 0.020 M solutions of four acids. Use the data in the following table to help answer Questions 1–5.

Acid	K_a
HF	6.8×10^{-4}
HCOOH	1.8×10^{-4}
CH_3CH_2COOH	1.8×10^{-5}
HOCl	3.0×10^{-8}

1. Which is the weakest acid?

   A) HF

   B) HCOOH

   C) CH_3CH_2COOH

   D) HOCl

2. Which 0.020 M acid solution has the highest percentage ionization?

   A) HF

   B) HCOOH

   C) CH_3CH_2COOH

   D) HOCl

3. Determine the pH of an aqueous solution of 0.020 M HOCl.

   A) 1.70

   B) 2.45

   C) 4.61

   D) 9.22

4. The following particulate diagrams are used to represent equal volumes of the acids. Which diagram does not represent any of the four acids?

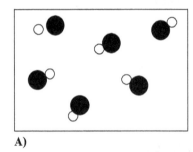

A)

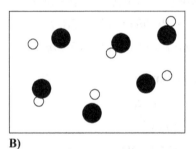

B)

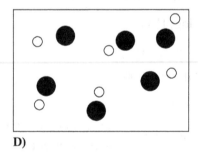

C)

D)

5. Each acid solution is titrated with 0.020 M NaOH solution until the acid is neutralized. At the equivalence point, the resultant solution from which acid will have the highest pH?

   A) HF

   B) HCOOH

   C) CH_3CH_2COOH

   D) HOCl

6. Identify the acid and conjugate-base pair in the following chemical reaction.

   $$NH_3(aq) + H_2O(l) \rightleftharpoons NH_4^+ (aq) + OH^-(aq)$$

   acid conjugate-base

   A) NH_3, OH^-

   B) H_2O, OH^-

   C) NH_3, OH^- and H_2O, NH_4^+

   D) NH_4^+ , NH_3

7. Draw the Lewis structure of each acid. Place the following acids in order of increasing acid strength.

$HClO_2$ $HClO_3$ $HClO$ $HClO_4$

A) $HClO_2 < HClO_4 < HClO < HClO_3$

B) $HClO < HClO_2 < HClO_3 < HClO_4$

C) $HClO_2 < HClO_3 < HClO_4 < HClO$

D) $HClO_4 < HClO_2 < HClO_3 < HClO$

8. Refer to you answer in Question 7. Which statement best explains your reasoning to select the trend in acid strength?

A) Chlorine is more electronegative than oxygen. Oxygen is more electronegative than hydrogen. This creates a partial positive charge on the hydrogen.

B) The partial negative charge on the oxygen in water is attracted to the partial positive charge on the hydrogen in the weakest acid resulting in more hydrogens being pulled off the acid.

C) Chlorine is the central atom in each of the Lewis structures for all of the acids. When a hydrogen is pulled off, it creates an anion that is resonance stabilized.

D) Oxygen is more electronegative than hydrogen. The more oxygen an acid has, the electron pair in the $H—O$ bond are pulled closer to the oxygen, creating a fuller partial positive charge on hydrogen and creating a weaker $H—O$ bond.

9. Calculate the hydroxide ion concentration in an aqueous solution of NaOH with a measured pH of 9.85 at 25 °C.

A) 7.1×10^{-5} M

B) 4.2×10^{-10} M

C) 8.7×10^{-10} M

D) 6.5×10^{-5} M

10. Identify the reaction that is an acid–base reaction.

A) $2\,Fe(NO_3)_3(aq) + 3\,Na_2S(aq) \longrightarrow Fe_2S_3(s) + 6\,NaNO_3(aq)$

B) $CH_3CO_2H(aq) + H_2O(l) \rightleftharpoons H_3O^+(aq) + CH_3CO_2^-(aq)$

C) $2CH_3NO_2(l) + 3/2\,O_2(g) \rightarrow 2CO_2(g) + 3H_2O(l) + N_2(g)$

D) $BaCl_2(aq) + Na_2SO_4(aq) \rightarrow 2\,NaCl(aq) + BaSO_4(s)$

1. D); 2. A); 3. C); 4. D); 5. C); 6. B); 7. B); 8. D); 9. A); 10. B)

Chapter 17 Practice AP Test Questions Answers:

Data Interpretation and Analysis Question: Comparing the Relative pH of Weak Acids

A student investigates the following research question: How does the structure of a weak acid influence the pH of a solution? The student writes the equilibrium equation for the reaction of propanoic acid with water

$$HC_3H_5O_2(aq) + H_2O(l) \rightleftharpoons C_3H_5O_2^-(aq) + H_3O^+(aq)$$

The student constructs Table 1 listing the name, chemical formula, K_a, and structure for three weak acids.

Table 1

Compound	Chemical Formula	K_a	Structure
Pyruvic acid	$HC_3H_3O_3$	2.8×10^{-3}	
Lactic acid	$HC_3H_5O_3$	1.4×10^{-4}	
Propanoic acid	$HC_3H_5O_2$	1.34×10^{-5}	

The student formulates the following rule: A weak acid containing the same number of carbon atoms, but more oxygen atoms and/or fewer hydrogen atoms compared to another weak acid, will generate a more acidic solution, when comparing solutions with the same initial concentration. In order to confirm this rule, the student prepares 0.050 M aqueous solutions of pyruvic acid, lactic acid, and propanoic acid and measures the pH of each solution. Based on the three compounds listed in Table 1, the pH measurements are in agreement with the rule.

a) Using Student #1's rule, which 0.050 M solution have will have the lowest pH? Explain.

A second student reviews the laboratory notebook of the first student and suggests they measure the pH of a 0.050 M malonic acid solution. Malonic acid is a diprotic acid.

Malonic acid	$H_2C_3H_2O_4$	$Ka_1 = 1.4 \times 10\text{-}3$ $Ka_2 = 2.0 \times 10\text{-}6$	

b) Using Student #1's rule, would the pH of a 0.050 M malonic acid solution have a pH lower, the same, or higher compared to the pH of a 0.050 M pyruvic acid solution? Explain.

c) The measured pH of 0.050 M malonic acid solution is approximately the same as the pH of a 0.050 M pyruvic acid solution. Does the rule work? Explain.

d) Formulate your own rule that will help you compare the pH of weak acid solutions having the same initial concentration.

e) Write your own research question that will help construct a series of experiments to better investigate what influences the pH of a weak acid solution.

f) Write the balanced chemical equation established when pyruvic acid is placed in water.

g) Write the equilibrium–constant expression for the equilibrium system established when pyruvic acid is placed in water.

h) Which particle representation diagram best depicts the relative number of particles present in the 0.050 M weak acid solution with the lowest pH, compared to the 0.050 M weak acid solution with the highest pH? Explain.

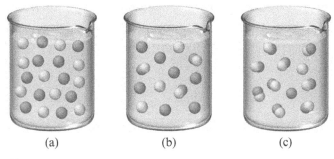

(a)   (b)   (c)

Key

● = HA   where A represents an anion in a weak acid molecule

● = H$^+$ or H$_3$O$^+$

● = A$^-$ A$^-$ represents an anion

Data Interpretation and Analysis Question Answers with Brief Explanations

a) Since pyruvic acid has more oxygen atoms and fewer hydrogen atoms than the other two acids, the rule predicts that pyruvic acid will have the lowest pH.

b) Since malonic acid has more oxygen atoms and fewer hydrogen atoms compared to pyruvic acid, the rule predicts a 0.050 M malonic acid solution will have the lower pH compared to a 0,050 M pyruvic acid solution.

c) The rule does not work since the pH of malonic acid is about the same as pyruvic acid. It is not the total number of oxygen atoms or the total number of hydrogen atoms that determines the pH of a weak acid solution.

d) New rule: The K_a of a weak acid indicates the extent to which H_3O^+ ions will form in solution, the greater the number of H_3O^+ ions, the larger the hydronium ion concentration, $[H_3O^+]$, and the lower the pH. $pH = -\log[H_3O^+]$.

e) How does the K_a of a weak acid and the initial concentration of a weak acid influence the pH of the solution?

f) $HC_3H_3O_3(aq) + H_2O(l) \rightleftharpoons C_3H_3O_3{-}(aq) + H_3O^+(aq)$.

g) $K_a = \dfrac{[C_3H_3O_3{}^-][H_3O^+]}{[HC_3H_3O_3]}$

h) The K_a of a weak acid indicates the extent to which H_3O^+ ions will form in solution, the larger the value of K_a, the greater the number of H_3O^+ ions in solution, the larger the hydronium ion concentration, $[H_3O^+]$, and the lower the pH. $pH = -\log[H_3O^+]$.

READING GUIDE

This chapter contains concepts found in Unit 8 of the AP Chemistry curriculum. Everything in the chapter except Lewis acids and bases and calculations with polyprotic acids is essential content in the AP Chemistry curriculum. Traditionally, all AP Chemistry Exams include questions pertaining to acid–base equilibria.

Heartburn Section 17.1

1. What causes heartburn?*

2. What is the main acid in the stomach?*

3. What component of saliva counteracts acid?* What is GERD?

4. What makes up proteins? DNA?

The Nature of Acids and Bases Section 17.2

5. List four characteristics of acids.

6. For each of the following acids, write their formula and list one use of each acid:

Table 17.1 Some Common Acids

Name	Formula	Occurrence/Uses
Hydrochloric acid		
Sulfuric acid		
Nitric acid		
Acetic acid		
Citric acid		
Carbonic acid		
Hydrofluoric acid		
Phosphoric acid		

7. What acid is the main component of vinegar?

8. What is a carboxylic acid? Include a formula and draw a structure or Lewis Dot Diagram in your answer.

9. List four properties of bases. What are alkaloids? Include an example in your answer.

10. For each of the following bases, write their formula and list one use of each base:

Table 17.2   Common Bases

Name	Formula	Occurrence/Uses
Sodium hydroxide		
Potassium hydroxide		
Sodium bicarbonate		
Sodium carbonate		
Ammonia		

Section 17.3   Definitions of Acids and Bases

11. What is the definition of an Arrhenius acid? Arrhenius base?

12. What is a hydronium ion and what is its formula?

13. What formula is used interchangeably with hydronium?

14. What does the term *dissociate* mean? Why is this term used with acids and bases? Include the following figures in your explanation.

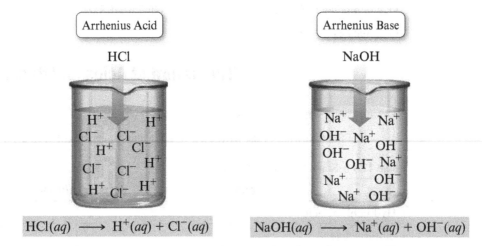

15. What are the definitions of a Brønsted–Lowry acid and base? Why must an acid and base always occur together in this theory?

16. Why are the Brønsted–Lowry definitions of acids and bases considered more useful?

17. What does the term *amphoteric* mean? Give an example of an amphoteric substance.

18. What are conjugate acid–base pairs? How can they be identified (use the figures below to help you with your answer).

19. In the following equation, identify the acid, base, conjugate acid, and conjugate base. Show tie-lines between acid–base pairs.

$$HCl(aq) + H_2O(l) \rightarrow H_3O^+(aq) + Cl^-(aq)$$

Acid Strength and the Acid Ionization Constant (K_a)   Section 17.4

20. What is the difference in the percent of dissociation between a strong acid and weak acid? Use the figures below in your answer. What types of arrows are used in chemical equations for strong acids? Weak acids?

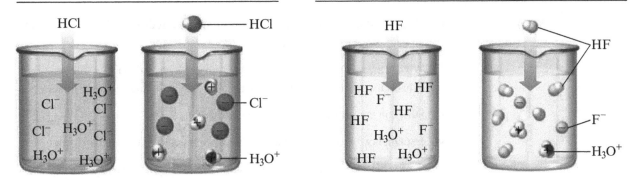

A Strong Acid   A Weak Acid

21. Define each type of acid and include an example.

    Monoprotic:

    Diprotic:

    Triprotic:

22. Name and give the formula of five strong acids.

23. Draw a picture showing what happens when the acid HBr is added to water.

24. Explain the following diagram. What characteristic indicates if an acid will be strong or weak?

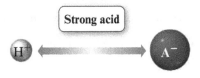

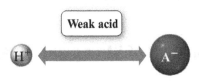

25. Name and give the formulas of five weak acids. Include a diprotic and triprotic acid in your answer.

26. How does the acid ionization constant (K_a) indicate the strength of the acid?

27. Why is water not included in K_a expressions?

28. Write the chemical equation and K_a expression for acetic acid being added to water.

Section 17.5   Autoionization of Water and pH

29. Explain what is meant when someone says water undergoes autoionization. Use an equation in your answer.

30. What is K_w? At 25 °C, what is the value of K_w? At this temperature, why is water neutral?

31. How can the concentrations of hydronium and hydroxide be calculated in an acidic or basic solution?

32. What is the relationship between hydronium and hydroxide in an acidic solution? What is the relationship between hydronium and hydroxide in a basic solution?

33. How can the pH of a solution be calculated?

34. Explain how to determine the number of significant figures in a pH value.

35. On the pH scale, what values are acidic? Neutral? Basic? Label these values on the number line below.

The pH Scale

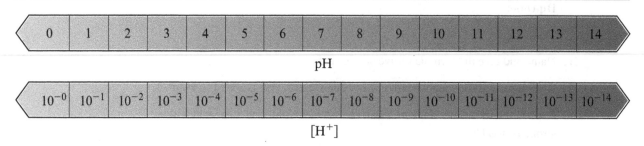

36. What factor represents the difference between a pH of 2 and 3? 2 and 5?

37. What is a pOH scale? How is pOH calculated? How is this scale different from a pH scale?

38. Which equation allows one to change from the pH scale to the pOH scale?

39. What is the concentration unit used in calculations of pH?

Section 17.6   Finding the [H₃O⁺] and pH of Strong and Weak Acid Solutions

40. How is pH calculated for a strong acid? Why is this different for a weak acid? Explain.

41. How is the percent ionization of a weak acid calculated? What is the relationship between the percent ionization of the acid and the concentration of a weak acid? Explain why you would use Le Châtelier's principle.

42. When two acids are mixed, how is the pH calculated? How is the calculation different for strong acid and strong base compared to weak acid and strong base calculations?

Base Solutions   Section 17.7

43. Use the diagrams as evidence to support your claims about the dissociation of strong and weak bases.

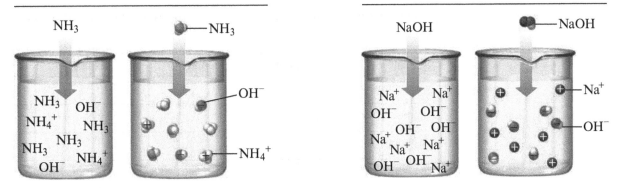

44. What metal hydroxides form strong bases? On the periodic table, where is the location of the metals forming these metal hydroxides?

45. What is K_b? What is pK_b?

46. Write the K_b expression for the reactions represented here.

$$H-\overset{\cdot\cdot}{N}\underset{|}{\overset{|}{H}}-H(aq) + H-\overset{\cdot\cdot}{\underset{\cdot\cdot}{O}}-H(l) \rightleftharpoons H-\overset{H}{\underset{|}{\overset{|}{N^+}}}-H(aq) + {}^-\overset{\cdot\cdot}{\underset{\cdot\cdot}{O}}-H$$

$$H-\overset{H}{\underset{|}{\overset{|}{C}}}\underset{H}{\overset{|}{-}}\overset{\cdot\cdot}{\underset{|}{N}}\underset{H}{\overset{|}{-}}H(aq) + H-\overset{\cdot\cdot}{\underset{\cdot\cdot}{O}}-H(l) \rightleftharpoons H-\overset{H}{\underset{|}{\overset{|}{C}}}\underset{H}{\overset{|}{-}}\overset{H}{\underset{|}{\overset{|}{N^+}}}-H(aq) + {}^-\overset{\cdot\cdot}{\underset{\cdot\cdot}{O}}-H$$

47. Explain how to calculate the pOH and $[OH^-]$ in a basic solution of a strong base and of a weak base. Why is the calculation different?

48. Which bases are in antacids?

The Acid–Base Properties of Ions and Salts   Section 17.8

49. What is a salt? List three examples of salts.

50. Which cations act as acids? Explain your answer and include an example.

51. Which anions are neutral? Which cations are neutral? Provide an example of each.

52. Which anions act as bases? Explain your answer. Include an example of each.

53. Which types of salts are neutral? List three examples. Why are these salts neutral?

54. Which types of salts are acidic? List three examples. Why are these salts acidic?

55. Which types of salts are basic? List three examples. Why are these salts basic?

56. What is the relationship between K_a and K_b?

57. What is the relationship between pK_a and pK_b?

58. Fill in the table with the pH of the different crosses of cations and anions of salts.

Salt	Cation	Anion	Example
neutral			
basic			
acidic			

Section 17.9   Polyprotic Acids

59. What are polyprotic acids? List three examples.

60. Write the dissociation equations for phosphoric acid and sulfuric acid. For each acid, identify the dissociation that contributes the most to the pH of a polyprotic acid? Why?

Section 17.10   Acid Strength and Molecular Structure

61. How does bond polarity affect acid strength in binary acids? Explain your answer. Include diagrams in your answer.

62. How does bond strength affect the strength of an acid in binary acids? Explain your answer. Why is HF a weak acid even though it has a highly polar bond?

63. Explain how bond strength and electronegativity affect the following acids:

6A	7A
H_2O	HF
H_2S	HCl
H_2Se	HBr
H_2Te	HI

64. What is an oxyacid?

65. Which factors are used to determine the strength of an oxyacid?

66. Analyze the data below and explain why the trend occurs for oxyacids.

Acid	Electronegativity of Y	K_a
H—O—I	2.5	2.3×10^{-11}
H—O—Br	2.8	2.0×10^{-9}
H—O—Cl	3.0	2.9×10^{-8}

67. Analyze the K_a values of the oxyacids and explain why the trend occurs.

Acid	K_a
$HClO_4$	Strong
$HClO_3$	1
$HClO_2$	1.1×10^{-2}
HClO	2.9×10^{-8}

Lewis Acids and Bases   Section 17.11

Note: the AP Chemistry exam will not have questions about Lewis Acids and Bases.

68. What is a Lewis acid? How is it different from an Arrhenius acid?* How is it different than a Brønsted-Lowry acid?

69. Will all Arrhenius acids be Lewis acids? Will all Lewis acids be Arrhenius acids? Explain your answers and include examples.*

70. What is a Lewis base? How is it different than an Arrhenius base?* How is it different than a Brønsted-Lowry base?

71. Will all Arrhenius bases be Lewis bases? Will all Lewis bases be Arrhenius bases? Explain your answers.*

Section 17.12 — Acid Rain

72. What is acid rain? Why is it called acid rain when rainwater is usually acidic anyway?

73. Which gases are the main contributers to acid rain? What is the source of these gases? What are the effect of acid rain?

74. Why are most of the areas in the United States affected by acid rain located on the East Coast?*

Hydrogen ion concentration as pH from measurements made at the Central Analytical Laboratory, 2010

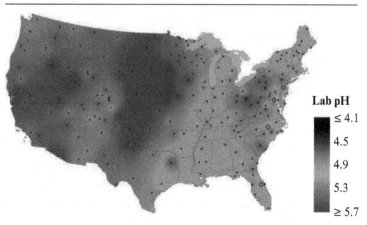

Lab pH
- ≤ 4.1
- 4.5
- 4.9
- 5.3
- ≥ 5.7

75. In general, how has the air quality changed in regards to acid rain in the last 20 years? Why?*

Self-Assessment Answers

1. _____   2. _____   3. _____

4. _____   5. _____   6. _____

7. _____   8. _____   9. _____

10. _____   11. _____   12. _____

13. _____   14. _____   15. _____

CHAPTER 18

AQUEOUS IONIC EQUILIBRIUM

This chapter contains several important sections, including those on buffers, precipitation, and acid–base titrations. Learning objectives derive from several units but come primarily from units 4, 7 and 8. Students should be able to analyze different types of titration curves, data analysis of precipitation, and data analysis of buffers. The following sections should be included in course work:

18.2 **Buffers: Solutions That Resist pH Change**

18.3 **Buffer Effectiveness: Buffer Range and Buffer Capacity**

18.4 **Titrations and pH Curves**

18.5 **Solubility Equilibria and the Solubility Product Constant**

18.6 **Precipitation**

18.7 **Qualitative Chemical Analysis**

Specific Learning Objectives Addressed in This Chapter:

TRA-2 A substance can change into another substance through different processes, and the change itself can be classified by the sort of processes that produced it.

TRA-2.A Identify a reaction as acid–base, oxidation–reduction, or precipitation.

SAP-9 The chemistry of acids and bases involves reversible proton-transfer reactions, with equilibrium concentrations being related to the strength of the acids and bases involved.

SAP-9.A Calculate the values of pH and pOH, based on K_w and the concentration of all species present in a neutral solution of water.

SAP-9.B Calculate pH and pOH based on concentrations of all species in a solution of a strong acid or a strong base.

SAP-9.C Explain the relationship among pH, pOH, and concentrations of all species in a solution of a monoprotic weak acid or weak base.

SAP-9.D Explain the relationship among concentrations of major species in a mixture of weak and strong acids and bases.

SAP-9.E Explain results from the titration of a monoprotic or polyprotic acid or base solution, in relation to the properties of the solution and its components.

SAP-10 A buffered solution resists changes to its pH when small amounts of acid or base are added.

SAP-10.A Explain the relationship between the predominant form of a weak acid or base in solution at a given pH and pK_a of the conjugate acid or the pK_b of the conjugate base.

SAP-10.B Explain the relationship between the ability of a buffer to stabilize pH and the reactions that occur when an acid or a base is added to a buffered solution.

SAP-10.C Identify the pH of a buffer solution based on the identity and concentrations of the conjugate acid–base pair used to create the buffer.

SAP-10.D Explain the relationship between the buffer capacity of a solution and the relative concentrations of the conjugate acid and conjugate base components of the solution.

TRA-6 Some reactions can occur in both forward and reverse directions, sometimes proceeding in each direction simultaneously.

TRA-6.A Explain the relationship between the occurrence of a reversible chemical or physical process, and the establishment of equilibrium, to experimental observations.

TRA-6.B Explain the relationship between the direction in which a reversible reaction proceeds and the relative rates of the forward and reverse reactions.

TRA-7 A system at equilibrium depends on the relationships between concentrations, partial pressures of chemical species, and the equilibrium constant K.

TRA-7.A Represent the reaction quotient Q_c or Q_p, for a reversible reaction, and the corresponding equilibrium expressions $K_c = Q_c$ or $K_p = Q_p$.

TRA-7.B Calculate K_c or K_p based on experimental observations of concentrations or pressures at equilibrium.

TRA-C Explain the relationship between very large or very small values of K and the relative concentrations of chemical species at equilibrium.

TRA-D Represent a multistep process with an overall equilibrium expression, using the constituent K expressions for each individual reaction.

TRA-E Identify the concentrations or partial pressures of chemical species at equilibrium based on the initial conditions and the equilibrium constant.

TRA-F Represent a system undergoing a reversible reaction with a particle model.

TRA-8 Systems at equilibrium respond to external stresses to offset the effect of the stress.

TRA-8.A Identify the response of a system at equilibrium to an external stress, using Le Châtelier's principle.

TRA-8.B Explain the relationships between Q, K, and the direction in which a reversible reaction will proceed to reach equilibrium.

SPQ-5 The dissolution of a salt is a reversible process that can be influenced by environmental factors such as pH or other dissolved ions.

SPQ-5.A Calculate the solubility of a salt based on the value of K_{sp} for the salt.

SPQ-5.B Identify the solubility of a salt, and/or the value of K_{sp} for the salt, based on the concentration of a common ion already present in solution.

SPQ-5.C Identify the qualitative effect of changes in pH on the solubility of a salt.

SPQ-5.D Explain the relationship between the solubility of a salt and changes in the enthalpy and entropy that occur in the dissolution process.

Concepts and Vocabulary to Review:

Buffers: Solutions That Resist pH Change   Section 18.2

Buffers resist changes in pH because they have in the solution components that act as both acid and base. They are composed of significant amounts of either a weak acid and its conjugate base or a weak base and its conjugate acid; therefore, it is important to know the strong and weak acids and bases. The acid component neutralizes the added base, and the base component neutralizes the added acid. When a weak acid or weak base is in solution, a certain amount of conjugate forms while reaching equilibrium. This amount is not enough to call the solution a buffer. A salt with the conjugate must be added. Acetic acid, CH_3COOH, in solution forms the conjugate actetate ion, CH_3COO^-, and hydronium, H^+, is not a buffer, but if the salt sodium acetate, $NaCH_3COO$, is added, a buffer is formed. Acidic buffers contain a weak acid and its conjugate base.

Formation of a Buffer

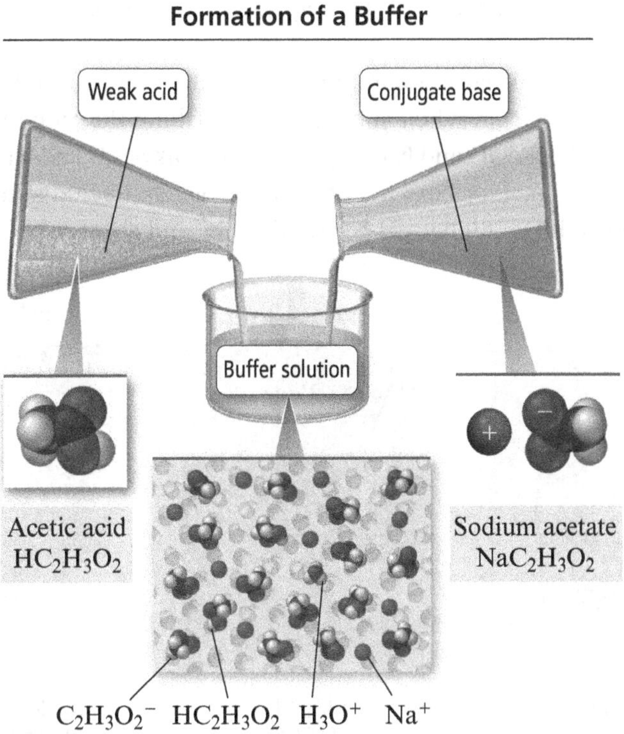

Figure 18.1 A Buffer Solution   A buffer typically consists of a weak acid (which can neutralize added base) and its conjugate base (which can neutralize added acid).

Basic buffers contain a base and it's conjugate acid.

Formation of a Buffer

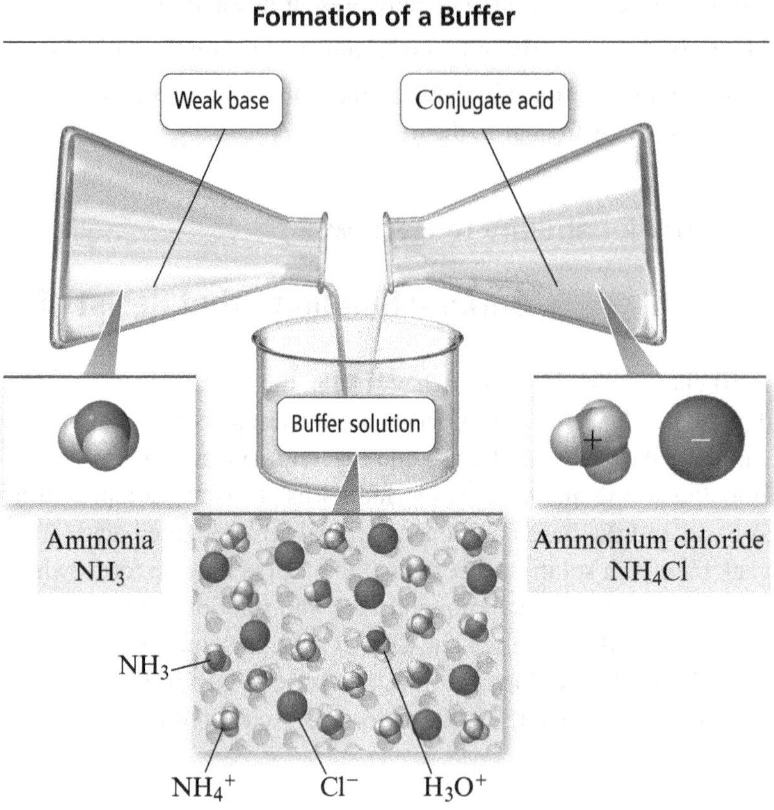

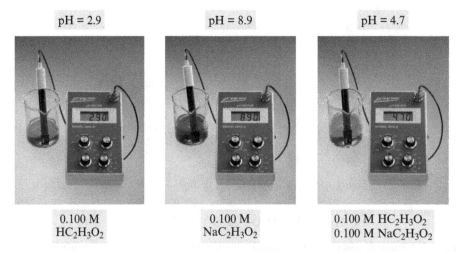

Figure 18.2 **Buffer Containing a Base**   A buffer can also consist of a weak base and its conjugate acid.

The addition of the salt with a common ion creates the common ion effect. The common ion effect occurs when substances contribute the same ion, in this case CH_3COO^- from HCH_3COO and $NaCH_3COO$. For weak acids and bases, the common ion causes the weak acid or base to not disassociate as much due to Le Châtelier's principle. The result is a higher pH for weak acids and a lower pH for weak bases.

pH = 2.9   pH = 8.9   pH = 4.7

0.100 M   0.100 M   0.100 M $HC_2H_3O_2$
$HC_2H_3O_2$ $NaC_2H_3O_2$ 0.100 M $NaC_2H_3O_2$

Figure 18.3 **The Common Ion Effect**   The pH of a 0.100 M acetic acid solution is 2.9. The pH of a 0.100 M sodium acetate solution is 8.9. The pH of a solution that is 0.100 M in acetic acid and 0.100 M in sodium acetate is 4.7. This solution contains the weak acid and its conjugate base and is a buffer.

To solve for the pH of a buffer system, the Henderson-Hasselbach equation can be used as well as an ICE table format.

The Henderson-Hasselbach equation, $pH = pK_a + \log\dfrac{[base]}{[acid]}$, is provided on the equation pages of the AP exam. Students should anticipate exam questions that assess a conceptual understanding of buffer solutions as well as calculations. Alternatively, students can use an ICE chart from an equilibrium approach to solve for concentrations and then use the pH equation to solve for the pH.

Example: Calculating the pH of a Buffer Solution Using an ICE Table Format

Calculate the pH of a buffer solution that is 0.100 M in $HC_2H_3O_2$ and 0.100 M in $NaC_2H_3O_2$.

Solution

1. Write the balanced equation for the ionization of the acid and use it as a guide to prepare an ICE table showing the given concentrations of the acid and its conjugate base as the initial concentrations. Leave room in the table for the changes in concentrations and for the equilibrium concentrations.

    $$HC_2H_3O_2(aq) + H_2O(l) \rightleftharpoons H_3O^+(aq) + C_2H_3O_2^-(aq)$$

	$[HC_2H_3O_2]$	$[H_3O^+]$	$[C_2H_3O_2^-]$
Initial	0.100	≈ 0.00	0.100
Change			
Equil			

2. Represent the change in the concentration of H_3O^+ with the variable x. Express the changes in the concentrations of the other reactants and products in terms of x.

    $$HC_2H_3O_2(aq) + H_2O(l) \rightleftharpoons H_3O^+(aq) + C_2H_3O_2^-(aq)$$

	$[HC_2H_3O_2]$	$[H_3O^+]$	$[C_2H_3O_2^-]$
Initial	0.100	≈ 0.00	0.100
Change	$-x$	$+x$	$+x$
Equil			

3. Sum each column to determine the equilibrium concentrations in terms of the initial concentrations and the variable x.

    $$HC_2H_3O_2(aq) + H_2O(l) \rightleftharpoons H_3O^+(aq) + C_2H_3O_2^-(aq)$$

	$[HC_2H_3O_2]$	$[H_3O^+]$	$[C_2H_3O_2^-]$
Initial	0.100	≈ 0.00	0.100
Change	$-x$	$+x$	$+x$
Equil	$0.100 - x$	x	$0.100 + x$

4. Substitute the expressions for the equilibrium concentrations (from step 3) into the expression for the acid ionization constant.

In most cases, you can make the approximation that *x is small*. (See Sections 16.8 and 17.6 to review the *x is small* approximation.)

$$K_a = \frac{[H_3O^+][C_2H_3O^-]}{[HC_2H_3O_2]}$$

$$= \frac{x(0.100 + x)}{0.100 - x} \qquad (x \text{ is small})$$

Substitute the value of the acid ionization constant (from Table 17.5 in the text) into the K_a expression and solve for x.

Confirm that *x is small* by calculating the ratio of x and the number it was subtracted from in the approximation. The ratio should be less than 0.05 (5%).

$$1.8 \times 10^{-5} = \frac{x(0.100)}{0.100}$$

$$x = 1.8 \times 10^{-5}$$

$$\frac{1.8 \times 10^{-5}}{0.100} \times 100\% = 0.018\%$$

Therefore the approximation is valid.

5. Determine the H_3O^+ concentration from the calculated value of x and substitute into the pH equation to find pH.

$$[H_3O^+] = x = 1.8 \times 10^{-5} \, M$$

$$pH = -\log[H_3O^+]$$

$$= -\log(1.8 \times 10^{-5})$$

$$= 4.74$$

AP students are only expected to be able to determine the initial pH of a buffer solution. Students should recognize if the ratio in the balanced equation is 1:1 and concentration of [c.base] and [acid] are equal; then the ratio of [c.base]/[acid] divides to 1. The log of 1 is 0, indicating at this set of conditions pH = pK_a. When additional acid or base is added to a buffer, a student only needs to describe what will occur after the addition using Le Châtelier's principle and how the addition will affect pH.

If the K_a of an acid is known, the K_b of the conjugate can be calculated using $K_aK_b = K_w$. Another method is to use $pK_a + pK_b = 14$.

Example: Using the Henderson–Hasselbalch Equation to Calculate the pH of a Buffer Solution Composed of a Weak Base and Its Conjugate Acid

Use the Henderson–Hasselbalch equation to calculate the pH of a buffer solution that is 0.50 M in NH_3 and 0.20 M in NH_4Cl. For ammonia, $pK_b = 4.75$.

Solution

Since K_b for NH_3 (1.76×10^{-5}) is much smaller than the initial concentrations in this problem, you can use the Henderson–Hasselbalch equation to calculate the pH of the buffer. First calculate pK_a from pK_b.

$$pK_a + pK_b = 14$$
$$pK_a = 14 - pK_b$$
$$= 14 - \log 1.76 \times 10^{-5}$$
$$= 14 - 4.75$$
$$= 9.25$$

Then substitute the given quantities into the Henderson–Hasselbalch equation and calculate pH.

$$pH = pK_a + \log \frac{[\text{base}]}{[\text{acid}]}$$
$$= 9.25 + \log \frac{0.50}{0.20}$$
$$= 9.25 + 0.40$$
$$= 9.65$$

Buffer Effectiveness: Buffer Range and Buffer Capacity   Section 18.3

A buffer cannot neutralize any more acid than there is base present, nor can it neutralize more base than there is acid present. The amount a buffer can neutralize describes the capacity of a buffer. If 0.10 moles of acid is added to a buffer containing 0.01 mole of base, the buffer capacity (0.01 mole) will be exceeded. Once exceeded, the pH will not remain stable and will become more acidic. The more moles of the buffering components present, the greater the effectiveness of the buffer will be.

The buffering range is the pH range in which the buffer is effective. The most effective range is within one pH unit plus or minus of the pK_a for an acidic buffer. For a pK_a of 4, the best buffering range is between 3 and 5. In the following titration curve notice that the pH around this point is fairly stable. A pH near the equivalence point would not work as a buffering region because the pH has a large range in this area.

To make a buffer of a certain pH, first choose the acid or base and conjugate pair with the right pH range (+1 or −1 of pK_a). For the greatest capacity, choose concentrations that are equal. The greater the concentrations, the higher the ability of the buffer to resist pH change. A solution with 2.0 M of both the weak acid and its salt has a greater capacity than a 1.0 M solution.

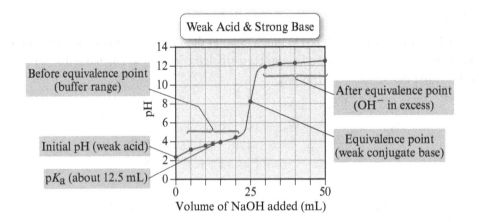

Section 18.4 Titrations and pH Curves

Titrations can be done through graphing the pH as the titration is being done and then analyzed, or an indicator can be used to determine when the titration is complete. Either way, data can be gathered to determine the concentration of the unknown.

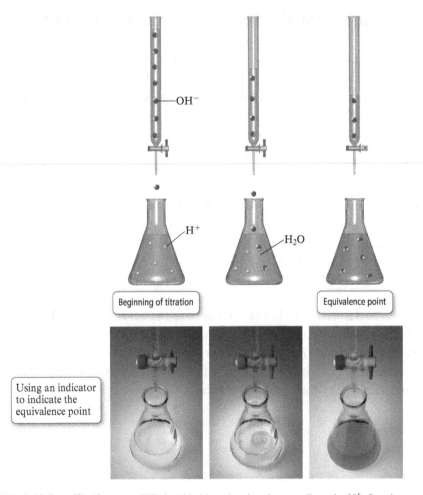

Figure 18.4 Acid–Base Titration As OH⁻ is added in a titration, it neutralizes the H⁺, forming water. At the equivalence point, the titration is complete.

When acid and base have neutralized each other, this is called the equivalence point. Since they have neutralized each other at the equivalence point, the moles of acid equal the moles of base. The indicator will visually indicate the endpoint of the titration (equivalence point) by changing color. This means the indicator must change to a different color at the approximate pH of the equivalence point. Students are not expected to know the indicator ranges except for phenolphthalein, which they should have used during lab. Students should know it is clear in acidic solutions and pink in basic solutions. (see Table 18.1).

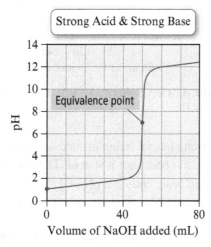

Figure 18.5 Titration Curve: Strong Acid + Strong Base   This curve represents the titration of 50.0 mL of 0.100 M HCl with 0.100 M NaOH.

When the data collected in a titration are graphed, the result is called a titration curve. A pH curve of a strong acid, strong base appears like a flattened s.

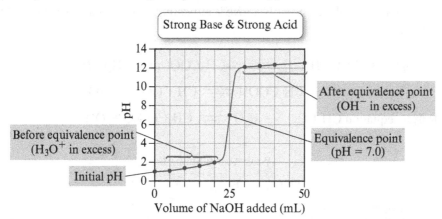

The curve has several points, identified by the components of the system. The starting pH of the acid will indicate if the acid is a weak or a strong acid. The pH at the end of the curve will indicate if the base was a weak or a strong base. In this titration curve case, the components are a strong acid due to the pH starting below 2 and a strong base finishing above a pH of 12. The pH at the equivalence point will indicate the strength of the acid and base to each other. A strong acid and strong base will reach equivalence at a pH of 7.

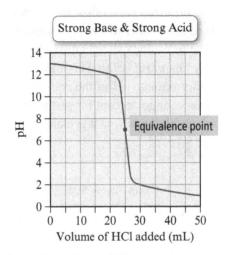

Figure 18.6 Titration Curve: Strong Base + Strong Acid   This curve represents the titration of 25.0 mL of 0.100 M NaOH with 0.100 M HCl.

In this titration curve, a strong base is being titrated with a strong acid. Students should expect titrations to start with a base, not just acid. The titration curve starts at a pH of 13, an indication of a strong base, ends at a pH of 1, an indication of a strong acid, and the equivalence point is at a pH of 7. Strong acid/strong base solutions do not buffer.

A common misconception is that equivalence will always be at a pH of 7. A strong base and a weak acid will have a basic equivalence point due to the hydrolysis of the conjugate base of the weak acid. An example would be sodium hydroxide and acetic acid. The acetate ion would undergo hydrolysis forming acetic acid and hydroxide ion driving the pH to test basic at equivalence. On the titration curve, a weak base is indicated by the pH starting above 2 and a strong base is indicated by the ending pH above 12. The equivalence point is above 7 indicating a strong base was titrated with a weak acid.

$$NaOH(aq) + CH_3COOH(aq) \rightleftharpoons NaCH_3COO(aq) + H_2O(l)$$

Net ionic equation $OH^- + CH_3COOH \rightleftharpoons CH_3COO^- + H_2O$

Hydrolysis equation $CH_3COO^- + H_2O \rightleftharpoons CH_3COOH + OH^-$

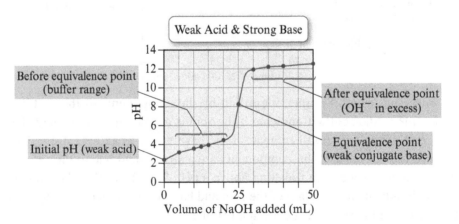

The best buffering region is near the pK_a value, which is located halfway to the equivalence point (also called the half equivalence point).

A weak base and a strong acid will have an acidic equivalence point due to the hydrolysis of the conjugate acid of the weak base. An example would be ammonia and hydrochloric acid.

$HCl(aq) + NH_3(aq) \rightleftharpoons NH_4Cl(aq)$

Net ionic equation $H^+ + NH_3 \rightleftharpoons NH_4^+$

Hydrolysis equation $NH_4^+ + H_2O \rightleftharpoons NH_3 + H^+$

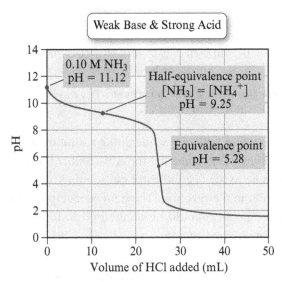

Figure 18.7 Titration Curve: Weak Base with Strong Acid   This curve represents the titration of 0.100 M NH_3 with 0.100 M HCl.

In this example, the best buffering region is near pK_b, which is halfway to equivalence. The starting pH is in the next page 12 indicating a weak base, the ending pH is below 2 indicating a strong acid and the equivalence point is below 7 indicating a strong acid was titrated with a weak base.

For polyprotic acids, the number of equivalence points usually will be equal to the number of hydrogen ions in the acid. For instance, diprotic sulfuric acid will have two equivalence points. Each dissociation reaction will have an equation and a K_a, although the majority of all $[H^+]$ contributing to the pH comes from the first dissociation.

Sulfuric acid (H_2SO_4) will have two equivalence points, and phosphoric acid (H_3PO_4) will have three.

Titration of a Polyprotic Acid

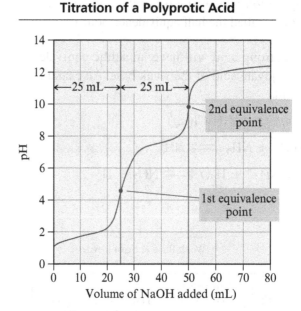

Figure 18.8 Titration Curve: Diprotic Acid with Strong Base This curve represents the titration of 25.0 mL of 0.100 M H_2SO_3 with 0.100 M NaOH.

Another way to determine an endpoint while doing a titration is by using an indicator. Indicators are themselves weak acids that turn different colors at different pH levels. Not any indicator can be used. The indicator chosen must change color in the range of the equivalence point in the reaction. The equivalence point (when moles of acid and moles of base are equal) should be located close to the endpoint (when the indicator changes color) of the titration.

Table 18.1 Ranges of Color Changes for Several Acid–Base Indicators

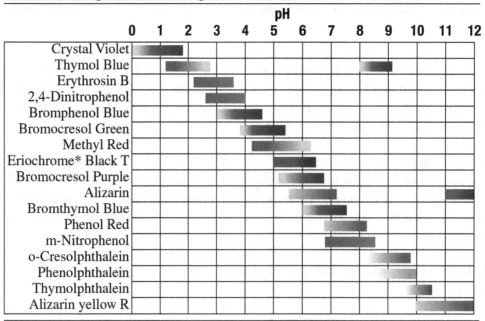

*Trademark of CIBA GEIGY CORP.

In general, try to pick an indicator with a color change within ± 1 of the endpoint pH. If a reaction reaches equivalence at a pH of 5, alizarin yellow would not be a good indicator to use, since it changes color in the pH range of 10–12, whereas methyl red would be a good indicator. If the wrong indicator is chosen, the color change will be too early or too late, giving incorrect data for calculations. You do not need to memorize this chart but rather know how to pick the correct one to use.

Solubility Equilibria and the Solubility Product Constant   Section 18.5

Another type of equilibrium is called the solubility product constant (K_{sp}). The K_{sp} is a measure of the solubility of a substance. Writing a K_{sp} expression is the same as writing other K expressions but remember water and solids are dropped. For the reaction $Ag_2S(s) + H_2O(l) \rightleftharpoons 2Ag^+(aq) + S^{2-}(aq)$, $K_{sp} = [Ag^+]^2[S^{2-}]$. The values of K_{sp} cannot be compared to determine what solution would be more insoluble, unless the species being compared have the same number of ions. Why? This is because the solving of molar solubility uses different exponents that are dependent on the stoichiometry from the balanced equation.

Table 18.2 Selected Solubility Product Constants (K_{sp}) at 25 °C

Compound	Formula	K_{sp}	Compound	Formula	K_{sp}
Barium fluoride	BaF_2	2.45×10^{-5}	Lead(II) chloride	$PbCl_2$	1.17×10^{-5}
Barium sulfate	$BaSO_4$	1.07×10^{-10}	Lead(II) bromide	$PbBr_2$	4.67×10^{-6}
Calcium carbonate	$CaCO_3$	4.96×10^{-9}	Lead(II) sulfate	$PbSO_4$	1.82×10^{-8}
Calcium fluoride	CaF_2	1.46×10^{-10}	Lead(II) sulfide*	PbS	9.04×10^{-29}
Calcium hydroxide	$Ca(OH)_2$	4.68×10^{-6}	Magnesium carbonate	$MgCO_3$	6.82×10^{-6}
Calcium sulfate	$CaSO_4$	7.10×10^{-5}	Magnesium hydroxide	$Mg(OH)_2$	2.06×10^{-13}
Copper(II) sulfide*	CuS	1.27×10^{-36}	Silver chloride	$AgCl$	1.77×10^{-10}
Iron(II) carbonate	$FeCO_3$	3.07×10^{-11}	Silver chromate	Ag_2CrO_4	1.12×10^{-12}
Iron(II) hydroxide	$Fe(OH)_2$	4.87×10^{-17}	Silver bromide	$AgBr$	5.35×10^{-13}
Iron(II) sulfide*	FeS	3.72×10^{-19}	Silver iodide	AgI	8.51×10^{-17}

*Sulfide equilibrium is of the type: $MS(s) + H_2O(l) \rightleftharpoons M^{2+}(aq) + HS^-(aq) + OH^-(aq)$

For instance, barium sulfate has two ions, Ba^{2+} and SO_4^{2-} as does lead(II) sulfate Pb^{2+} and SO_4^{2-}. Looking at the K_{sp} values in the table, barium sulfate 1.07×10^{-10} is a smaller number than lead(II) sulfate 1.82×10^{-8} and therefore will be more insoluble. In this case, solubility constants could be compared. In the next example, the number of ions are not the same and molar solubility must be calculated. To determine if silver chloride with two ions is more insoluble than calcium fluoride with three ions, the molar solubility of each would need to be calculated to answer the question. To determine the actual molar solubility will require a calculation. When two ions are present, $K_{sp} = s^2$, so the square root of the K_{sp} value indicates the molar solubility. If three ions are present, the general formula is $K_{sp} = 4s^3$. Both K_{sp} values are close to each other—1.77×10^{-10} and 1.46×10^{-10}, respectively—but the molar solubility values are not. The square root of 1.77×10^{-10} gives a molar solubility of 1.33×10^{-5} M for silver chloride, and the solving $1.46 \times 10^{-10} = 4s^3$ gives a molar solubility of 3.32×10^{-4} M for calcium fluoride. The silver chloride value is smaller and is less soluble indicating it will precipitate before the calcium fluoride. K_{sp} values are also temperature dependent. Comparing the solubilities at different temperatures can indicate if the temperature is causing a shift to the left or to the right in the equilibrium.

How molar solubility is affected by common ions and pH can be analyzed using Le Châtelier's principle. Adding a common ion to the ions on the product will cause a shift to the left and decrease solubility. Which way the reaction will shift when adding acid or base depends on the species in solution. If the solution is basic, adding acid removes base by neutralizing it, and the reaction will shift to the right (the products side) to replace the lost hydroxide ions. If more base (common ion) is added to the basic solution, the reaction will shift to the left, decreasing solubility. If the solution is acidic, adding base will increase its solubility as the base removes the hydrogen ions, causing a shift to the right to replace the lost ions. If more acid is added to an acidic solution, the reaction will shift to the left and become more insoluble due to the common ion effect. Ionic compound solubility is lower in a solution with a common ion than in pure water.

Section 18.6   Precipitation

When precipitates form, a misconception is to think ALL ions have formed the precipitate. Understanding that the solution has both precipitate and ions present at equilibrium is important. Although if the substance is very insoluble, only a few ions will be in solution and the K_{sp} value will be very small.

K_{sp} and Q are used to determine not only when precipitates form but also the concentrations of the ions still in solution. When two solutions are added together, the issue of whether a precipitate will form can also be determined by using the reaction quotient (Q). If 0.0010 M $AgNO_3$ and 0.00024 M NaCl are mixed forming AgCl, then $Q = [0.0010 \text{ M Ag}^+][0.00024 \text{ M Cl}^-]$. Q is 2.4×10^{-7} and K_{sp} is 1.77×10^{-10}. $Q > K_{sp}$ in this case. If $Q > K_{sp}$, then the solution is supersaturated, and excess will precipitate out.

Unsaturated solutions will not form a precipitate, and data analysis will show $Q < K_{sp}$. When $K_{sp} = Q$, then the solution is saturated. The maximum amount has been dissolved, and the addition of any more will form a precipitate.

$Q > K_{sp}$ precipitation will occur
$Q = K_{sp}$ saturated solution
$Q < K_{sp}$ unsaturated and precipitation will not occur

When two or more ions are in solution that will precipitate when a given ion is added, the ions can be isolated from each other. In one method, when two precipitates form when the same ion is added, the most insoluble will precipitate first. Another method is to add ions to precipitate one ion and not another. This is called selective precipitation. Adding a chloride anion will precipitate out silver, mercury, and lead cations. A common water test is to precipitate out all the lead ions by adding excess chloride ions and precipitating lead chloride. After drying and massing the precipitate, one can calculate the concentration of lead ion in the original water sample.

Qualitative Chemical Analysis   Section 18.7

Qualitative analysis is a method used to identify unknown cations in a sample. The process involves knowing solubility rules and determining which cations form precipitates with the anions added.

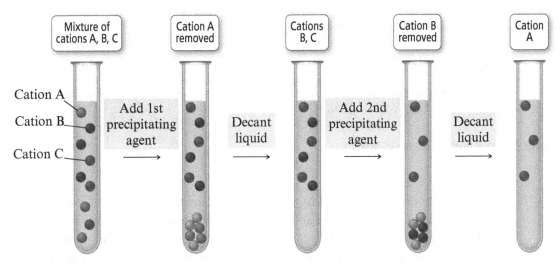

Figure 18.9 Qualitative Analysis   In qualitative analysis, specific ions are precipitated successively by the addition of appropriate reagents.

Through this process, cations can be isolated from each other and tested to see what is present. This can be seen in a qualitative analysis flowchart.

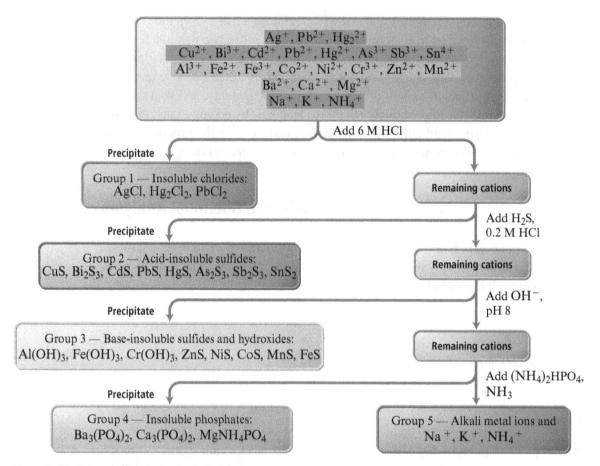

Figure 18.10 A General Qualitative Analysis Scheme

AP students are not expected to memorize the qualitative analysis flowchart but should be able to look at data and use it as evidence to make a claim about what might be in a solution. Students should do a qualitative analysis lab to understand how the flowchart helps them to identify unknowns. If a solution contained ions of silver, copper, and zinc, adding hydrochloric acid first would precipitate out the silver in the form of silver chloride. After decanting and separating the precipitate from the solution, adding hydrosulfuric acid to the solution would precipitate out copper(II) sulfide. After centrifuging and separating the precipitate and decanting off the solution, adding sodium hydroxide would precipitate zinc hydroxide.

When the only cations left in solution are alkali metals, flame tests can be used to identify the ions.

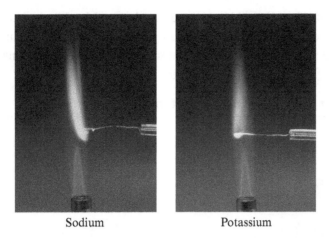

Sodium   Potassium

Figure 18.11 Flame Tests   The sodium ion produces a yellow-orange flame. The potassium ion produces a violet flame.

Complex Ion Equilibria   Section 18.8

While knowledge of, and calculations with K_f are not on the AP exam, it is important to understand K_f values are large and drive a reaction forward and how solubility is affected by complex ion formation. A silver chloride precipitate will dissolve with the addition of excess ammonia by forming the complex diammine silver ion.

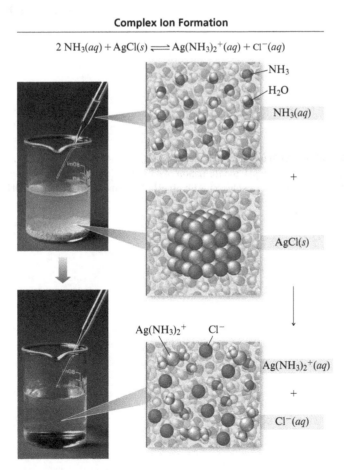

Complex Ion Formation

$$2 \, NH_3(aq) + AgCl(s) \rightleftharpoons Ag(NH_3)_2{}^+(aq) + Cl^-(aq)$$

NH$_3$
H$_2$O
NH$_3$(aq)

+

AgCl(s)

Ag(NH$_3$)$_2{}^+$ Cl$^-$

Ag(NH$_3$)$_2{}^+$(aq)

+

Cl$^-$(aq)

Figure 18.12 Complex Ion Formation   Normally insoluble AgCl is made soluble by the addition of NH$_3$, which forms a complex ion with Ag$^+$ and dissolves the AgCl.

Solubility can also be affected by the type of solution. Metal hydroxide solutions are amphoteric—they can behave as an acid or a base. For instance, aluminum hydroxide is insoluble in pH neutral solutions but in acidic and basic solutions it is soluble.

pH-Dependent Solubility of an Amphoteric Hydroxide

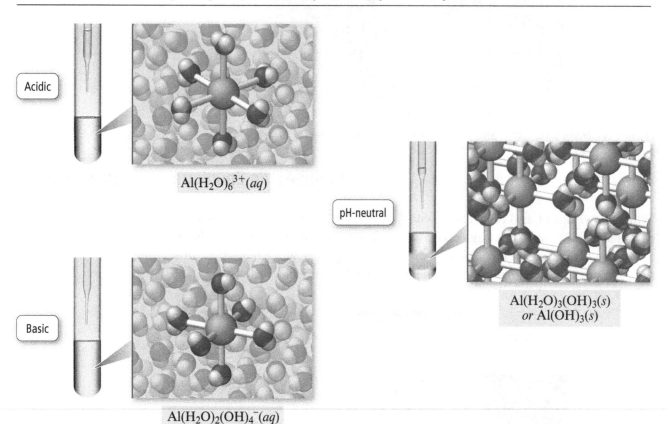

Figure 18.13 Solubility of an Amphoteric Hydroxide   Because aluminum hydroxide is amphoteric, its solubility is pH-dependent. At low pH, the formation of $Al(H_2O)_6^{3+}$ drives the dissolution. At neutral pH, insoluble $Al(OH)_3$ precipitates out of solution. At high pH, the formation of $Al(H_2O)_2(OH)_4^-$ drives the dissolution.

Additional Practice

Self-Assessment Quiz Questions Q1, Q2, Q3, Q4, Q5, Q6, Q7, Q8, Q9, Q10, Q11, Q12, Q13, Q14, and Q15

Problems:
Review Questions 2, 3, 6, 8, 9, 11, 13, 14, 17, 19, 20, and 25
The Common Ion Effect and Buffers 29, 32, 33, 36, 41, 43, 53, 57, and 59
Titrations, pH Curves, and Indicators 61, 62, 63, 64, 65, 66, 67, 68, 75, 76, 77, 78, and 81
Solubility Equilibria 85, 87, 89, 90, 92, and 94
Precipitation and Qualitative Analysis 101 and 107
Cumulative Problems 114, 116, 119, and 121
Conceptual Problems 149, 150, 151, 152, 153, and 154
Data Interpretation and Analysis 160

Equations to know:

$$pH = pK_a + \log \frac{[\text{base}]}{[\text{acid}]}$$

$$pH \text{ range} = pK_a \pm 1$$

Practice AP Test Questions

1. When two solutions, each having a volume of 50.0 mL and concentration of 0.750 M, are mixed, which resultant solution would resist a large change in pH when small amounts of a strong acid or a strong base are added?

   A) $HBr(aq)$ and $KOH(aq)$

   B) $NH_4Br(aq)$ and $NH_3(aq)$

   C) $HBr(aq)$ and $KBr(aq)$

   D) $NH_4Br(aq)$ and $KBr(aq)$

2. Calculate the pH of 40.0 mL of solution that is 0.400 M in sodium formate and 0.800 M in formic acid (HCO_2H). The K_a of formic acid is 1.77×10^{-4}.

   A) 3.45   C) 4.05

   B) 3.75   D) 4.14

3. A volume 30.0 mL of 1.0 M oxalic acid was titrated with 1.00 M NaOH. A graph of pH versus volume of NaOH added was plotted and appears below. At which point can one determine the pK_{a1} of oxalic acid?

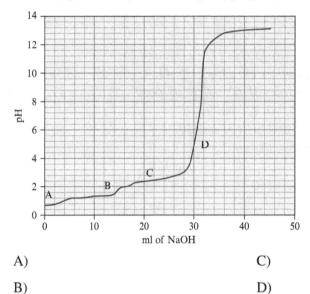

A)   C)

B)   D)

4. A 50.0 mL sample of 0.300 M nitrous acid (HNO_2) is titrated with 50.0 mL of 0.300 M KOH. Determine the pH at the equivalence point using two significant figures. The K_a of nitrous acid is 4.50×10^{-4}.

A) 3.35   C) 8.26

B) 7.00   D) 11.81

5. The following diagrams represent the molecular level of small volumes of solutions containing various amounts of nitrous acid (HNO_2) and potassium nitrite. Water molecules, potassium ions, hydroxide ions, and hydronium ions have been omitted. Which solution has the greatest buffer capacity?

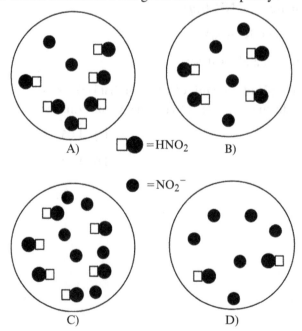

6. Determine the pH of a 0.100 M hypochlorous acid solution ($K_a = 3.5 \times 10^{-8}$). The equation for the equilibrium system established by hypochlorous acid:

$$HOCl(aq) + H_2O(l) \rightleftharpoons H_3O^+(aq) + OCl^-(aq).$$

A) 3.23

B) 3.72

C) 4.23

D) 4.72

7. Consider 50.00 mL of 0.100 M nitric acid, HNO_3 a strong acid, and 50.00 mL of 0.100 M nitrous acid, HNO_2, a weak acid ($K_a = 4.5 \times 10^{-4}$).

This means that _____.

A) an aqueous solution of HNO_2 contains equal concentrations of $H^+(aq)$ and $NO_2^-(aq)$ at equilibrium.

B) an aqueous solution of HNO_2 contains fewer OH^- ions compared to a solution of HNO_3.

C) HNO_3 dissociates 80% to $H^+(aq)$ and $NO_3^-(aq)$ when it establishes an equilibrium system with water.

D) It will take more 0.100 M NaOH to completely neutralize the HNO_3 solution compared to the HNO_2 solution.

8. Using the data in the table below displaying K_a values for some weak acids, which of the 0.100 M acid solutions will have a greater percent dissociation?

Acid	K_a
HOAc	1.8×10^{-5}
$HC_7H_5O_2$	6.3×10^{-5}
HNO_2	4.5×10^{-4}
HF	6.8×10^{-4}

A) HOAc   (CH_3COOH, acetic acid)

B) $HC_7H_5O_2$ (C_6H_5COOH, benzoic acid)

C) HNO_2

D) HF

Questions 9 and 10 use information provided in the following scenario. The plot shows two titration curves, each representing the titration of 50.00 mL of 0.100 M strong acid with 0.100 M NaOH and 0.100 M weak acid with 0.100 M NaOH.

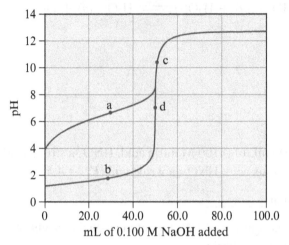

mL of 0.100 M NaOH added

9. Which point a–d represents the formation of the most amount of salt (conjugate base) one can obtain for the titration of a weak acid?

A) Point a

B) Point b

C) Point c

D) Point d

10. It takes the same volume (milliliters) of NaOH to neutralize the weak acid as it takes to neutralize the strong acid. Explain.

A) It really takes more volume to neutralize the 0.100 M strong acid compared to the 0.10 M weak acid because the strong acid has more H^+ ions in solution.

B) It takes less volume to neutralize the 0.100 M strong acid compared to the 0.10 M weak acid because more OH^- ions are needed to pull off the undissociated H^+ ions.

C) Since it takes the same volume of NaOH to neutralize the 0.10 M strong acid and the 0.10 M weak acid the resultant solution is neutalized and therefore the resultant solutions of each should be neutral and the pH should be 7.

D) The conjugate base formed from the reaction of the base and strong acid is neutral, while the conjugate base formed from the reaction of the base and weak acid is basic. This explains the difference in the pH of the solutions at the equivalence point.

1. B); 2. A); 3. B); 4. C); 5. C); 6. C); 7. A); 8. D); 9. C); 10. D)

Chapter 18 Practice AP Test Questions Answers:

Data Interpretation and Analysis Question: Buffer Solutions

A buffer solution was prepared by adding 1.00 mole of propanoic acid, CH_3CH_2COOH, and 1.00 mole of sodium propanoate, CH_3CH_2COO, Na^+ to enough water to make 250.0 mL of solution at 25 °C. The K_a value for propanoic acid is 1.34×10^{-5}. This buffer solution had a measured pH of 4.87 and established an equilibrium system as represented by the following equation:

$$HC_3H_5O_2(aq) + H_2O(l) \rightleftharpoons C_3H_5O_2^-(aq) + H_3O^+(aq)$$

Three other 250.0 mL buffer solutions, W, X, and Y, were prepared using the amounts of propanoic acid and sodium propanoate listed in Table 1.

Table 1

	Propanoic Acid	Sodium Propanoate	Initial pH	Estimated pH After the Addition of HCl
Buffer V	1.00 mol	1.00 mol	4.87	
Buffer W	0.0100 mol	0.0100 mol		
Buffer X	0.0100 mol	1.00 mol		
Buffer Y	1.00 mol	0.0100 mol		
Buffer Z			3.87	

a) Estimate whether the pH for each of the three buffer solutions. (W, X, and Y) have the same pH, a more acidic pH, or a less acidic pH compared to buffer solution V.

b) Explain how you selected the pH values for each of the three buffer solutions (W, X, and Y).

c) Sketch a particulate diagram showing the major species present in buffer solution V. Do not include the water molecules.

Figure 18.1   Buffer V

d) Which of the four buffer solutions (V, W, X, or Y) has the greatest buffer capacity? Explain.

e) Estimate the pH of each of the buffer solutions (V, W, X, and Y) after the addition and after the complete reaction of 1.0 mL of 1.00 M HCl with each of the buffer solutions. Explain.

f) Write the equation representing how the 1.0 mL of 1.00 M HCl reacts with a chemical species in buffer solution V.

g) Given the particulate diagram representing a small volume of buffer solution X before the addition of any HCl, and 0.001 second after the addition of HCl but before any reaction occurs, sketch a particulate level diagram of buffer solution X after the reaction of 1.0 mL of 1.00 M HCl with the buffer solution.

Figure 18.2   Buffer X

h) Which buffer solution can react with the most 1.0 M HCl and still maintain the identity of being a buffer?

i) How many moles of propanoic acid and how many moles of sodium propanoate would you mix to form a 250.0 mL buffer solution Z having a pH of 3.87 and a buffer capacity twice the size of buffer solution V?

Data Interpretation and Analysis Question Answers with Brief Explanations

Table 1

	Propanoic Acid	Sodium Propanoate	Initial pH	Estimated pH After the Addition of HCl
Buffer V	1.00 mol	1.00 mol	4.87	4.86
Buffer W	0.0100 mol	0.0100 mol	4.87, the same	4.86
Buffer X	0.0100 mol	1.00 mol	6.87, less acidic	6.88
Buffer Y	1.00 mol	0.0100 mol	2.87, more acidic	2.86
Buffer Z	2.00 mol	0.200 mol	3.87	

a) pH of Buffer W = ph Buffer V, pH of Buffer X > pH Buffer V. The pH Buffer Y < pH Buffer V.

b) Buffer W contains equal moles of weak acid and the sodium salt of the weak acid, pH = pK_a. Buffer X contains less moles of weak acid and compared to the sodium salt of the weak acid, pH = pK_a + log[Anion][HA]. Since the [Anion] > [HA] the log term > 1, pH Buffer X > pH Buffer V. Buffer Y contains more moles of weak acid compared to the sodium salt of the weak acid. Since the [Anion] < [HA,] the log term < 1, pH Buffer Y < pH Buffer V.

c)

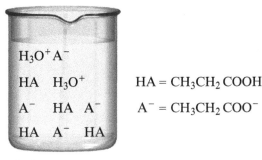

$HA = CH_3CH_2\,COOH$

$A^- = CH_3CH_2\,COO^-$

Figure 18.1   Buffer V

d) Of the four buffer solutions, Buffer V has the greatest buffer capacity since it contains the largest amount of moles of both propanoic acid and sodium propanoate compared to the other three buffer solutions.

e) Estimate the pH after the addition of HCl: Buffer V, 4.86; Buffer W, 4.86; Buffer X 6.88, Buffer Y, 2.86. Since acid is added in all cases, the acid reacts with the propanoate ion to generate propanoic acid, which makes the solution more acidic, or a lower pH.

f) $C_3H_5O_2^-(aq) + H_3O^+(aq) \rightarrow HC_3H_5O_2(aq) + H_2O(l)$

g)

h) Buffer solution C can react with the most acid since it has the most moles of the propanoate ion.

i) 2.00 mole of propanoic acid and 0.200 mole of sodium propanoate.

$$pH = pK_a + \log\{[\text{Anion}]/[\text{HA}]\}$$
$$3.87 = 4.87 + \log\{[\text{Anion}]/[\text{HA}]\}$$
$$-1.00 = \log\{[\text{Anion}]/[\text{HA}]\}$$
$$10^{-1.00} = 10\,\log^{\{[\text{Anion}]/[\text{HA}]\}}$$
$$0.100 = \{[.200]/[2.00]\}$$

READING GUIDE

The concepts in this chapter are part of Unit 7 on equilibrium. Buffer solutions and their properties, titrations and titration curves, and precipitate formation concepts are part of the AP Chemistry curriculum.

Section 18.1 ## The Danger of Antifreeze

1. What is ethylene glycol? Why are animals attracted to it? Why is this attraction a problem?

2. Explain how the blood is able to keep a stable pH. What species are used to maintain this stability?

Section 18.2 ## Buffers: Solutions that Resist pH Change

3. What is a buffer? What composes a buffer? How does the buffer work?

4. Explain what evidence in this figure below supports the claim that this is a buffer solution.

Formation of a Buffer

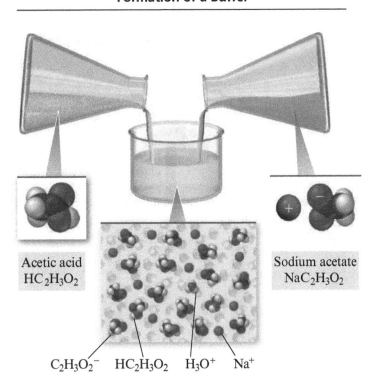

Acetic acid
$HC_2H_3O_2$

Sodium acetate
$NaC_2H_3O_2$

$C_2H_3O_2^-$ $HC_2H_3O_2$ H_3O^+ Na^+

5. How is the pH of a buffer calculated? Explain what happens to the pH when acid is added to a buffer. Explain what happens to a buffer when a base is added.

Buffer Effectiveness: Buffer Range and Buffer Capacity   Section 18.3

6. What factors determine the effectiveness of a buffer?

7. What is buffer capacity?

8. What is the range of a buffer? How is it determined? How is the highest pH of a buffer determined? How is the lowest pH of a buffer determined?

9. A buffer is most effective when which two conditions are met? Explain why.

10. How can you calculate the range over which a buffer will be most effective? What is the range of effectiveness for a buffer with a pK_a of 6?

Titrations and pH Curves   Section 18.4

11. What is the equivalence point of a titration?

12. What is a titration curve?

13. Using the curve provided, describe what evidence is provided in a titration curve.

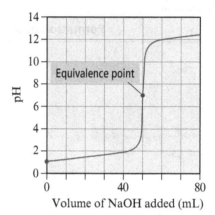

14. Describe what is occurring in the below image. What does the observation in each flask indicate?

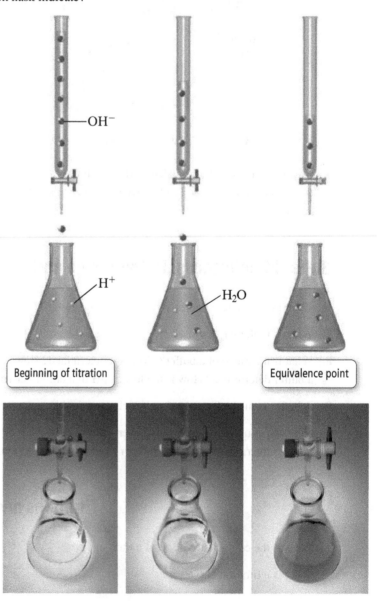

15. What does the shape of a titration curve depend on?

16. Compare and contrast these two titration curves.

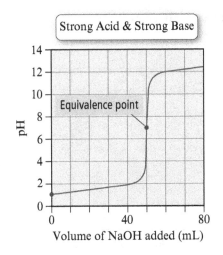

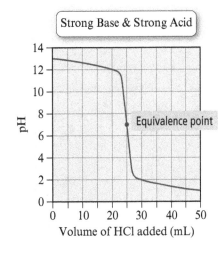

17. How does the titration curve from a titration of a weak acid and a strong base differ from a titration with a strong acid and a strong base?

18. What does the amount of base or acid added to reach the equivalence point depend on?

19. How can a titration curve be used to determine the pK_a of an acid?

20. Why is the pH of a titration of a weak acid and strong base always basic at the equivalence point?

21. Explain how this titration curve indicates a weak acid and strong base were titrated.

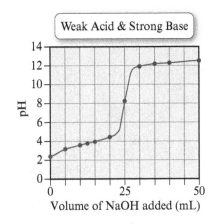

22. What features of this titration curve indicate a weak base was titrated with a strong acid?

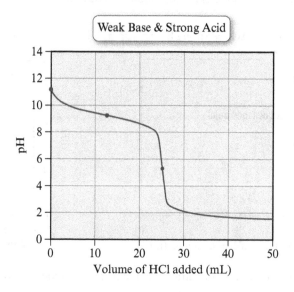

23. What features of this titration curve indicate the titration was done with a polyprotic acid?

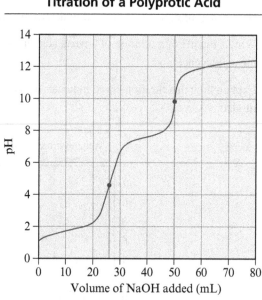

24. What does each equivalence point in a polyprotic titration represent?

Note: CALCULATIONS of each species in a polyprotic titration will not be assessed on the AP Chemistry Exam.

25. What does the endpoint of a titration indicate? What is the difference between an equivalence point and an end point of a titration? Why is it important to choose the right indicator?

26. What are indicators composed of? What must occur for an indicator to be effective?

27. What color is phenolphthalein in an acid? In a base?

28. Why must you use only a small amount of indicator?

29. List an indicator to use for each of the following changes in pH at the equivalence point:

    pH range 4–5:

    pH range 6–7:

    pH range 8–9:

Solubility Equilibria and the Solubility Product Constant   Section 18.5

30. What is K_{sp}? What does K_{sp} indicate? How do you write a K_{sp} expression?

31. What is molar solubility? What are the units of molar solubility? How is it calculated?

32. Explain why K_{sp} is not the molar solubility.

33. What ions are in hard water?

34. Why can you not compare K_{sp} values to the relative solubility between two compounds?

35. What effect do common ions have on solubility of a compound?

36. How does pH affect solubility of a compound? Use magnesium hydroxide as an example in a basic pH and in an acidic pH.

Note: Problems involving calculations of the solubility of compounds as a function of pH are not included in the AP Chemistry Curriculum.

Precipitation   Section 18.6

37. What is the difference between Q and K_{sp}? How does a common ion affect solubility?

38. What conditions are present in an unsaturated solution?

39. What conditions are present in a saturated solution?

40. What conditions are present in a supersaturated solution?

41. Explain how Q can be used to determine if two solutions poured together will precipitate.

42. Explain the process of selective precipitation.

43. How do you determine the concentrations necessary to cause precipitation?

Section 18.7   Qualitative Chemical Analysis

44. What is the difference between qualitative and quantitative analysis?

45. Explain what is occurring in this series of steps below in a qualitative analysis. What are these steps called?

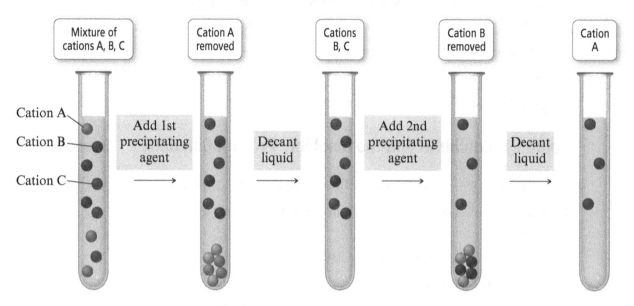

46. If HCl is added to a mixture of metal cations, what ions are not present if a precipitate does not form?

Note: Problems involving the prediction of the solubility of compounds as a function of pH are included in the AP Chemistry Curriculum. Students can expect to be assessed on the AP Chemistry Exam on their qualitative understanding of this topic.

47. On the following diagram, indicate the insoluble compounds formed and the substance added in the flowchart.

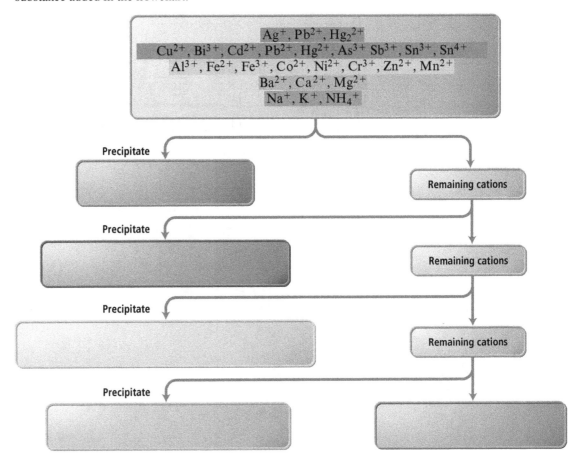

Ag^+, Pb^{2+}, Hg_2^{2+}
Cu^{2+}, Bi^{3+}, Cd^{2+}, Pb^{2+}, Hg^{2+}, As^{3+} Sb^{3+}, Sn^{3+}, Sn^{4+}
Al^{3+}, Fe^{2+}, Fe^{3+}, Co^{2+}, Ni^{2+}, Cr^{3+}, Zn^{2+}, Mn^{2+}
Ba^{2+}, Ca^{2+}, Mg^{2+}
Na^+, K^+, NH_4^+

Precipitate

Remaining cations

Precipitate

Remaining cations

Precipitate

Remaining cations

Precipitate

48. How can the presence of alkali metals be identified? What would be observed for sodium ions and potassium ions?

Complex Ion Equilibria   Section 18.8

49. Define the following terms:

    Complex ion:

    Ligand:

    Formation constant:

50. Using AgCl(s) as an example, explain how adding ammonia increases its solubility.

51. Why do the amphoteric metal hydroxides become more soluble with the addition of acid or base?

52. What are four cations that form amphoteric hydroxides?

Self-Assessment Answers

1. _____   2. _____   3. _____

4. _____   5. _____   6. _____

7. _____   8. _____   9. _____

10. _____   11. _____   12. _____

13. _____   14. _____   15. _____

FREE ENERGY AND THERMODYNAMICS

Thermodynamics is the focus of Unit 9 in the AP Chemistry Framework. Thermodynamics provides the evidence for the driving forces in processes and reactions and is crucial to be understood. There are many misconceptions about thermodynamics. One misconception revolves around spontaneity, which has to do with speed. This comes from the association with spontaneous in English, referring to something that is immediately happening. In chemistry, spontaneous occurs naturally, but it may be very slow. As a result, scientists and the AP exam use the phrase "thermodynamically favorable." Another misconception is thinking that catalysts affect spontaneity. Catalysts affect the speed of the reaction but do not contribute to whether or not the reaction will happen. Nonspontaneous reactions can only be made to happen by the addition of energy. The most important sections in the chapter are as follows:

Specific Learning Objectives Addressed in This Chapter:

ENE-4 Some chemical or physical processes cannot occur without intervention.

ENE-4.A Identify the sign and relative magnitude of the entropy change associated with chemical or physical processes.

ENE-4.B Calculate the entropy change for a chemical or physical process based on the absolute entropies of the species involved in the process.

ENE-4.C Explain whether a physical or chemical process is thermodynamically favored based on an evaluation of ΔG°.

ENE-4.D Explain, in terms of kinetics, why a thermodynamically favored reaction might not occur at a measurable rate.

ENE-5 The relationship between $\Delta G°$ and K can be used to determine favorability of a chemical or physical transformation.

ENE-5.A Explain whether a process is thermodynamically favored using the relationships among K, $\Delta G°$, and T.

ENE-5.B Explain the relationship between external sources of energy or coupled reactions and their ability to drive thermodynamically unfavorable processes.

Concepts and Vocabulary to Review:

Section 19.1   # Cold Coffee and Dead Universes

The first law of thermodynamics states that the amount of energy is constant. The tendency for energy to spread out or dissipate is the second law of thermodynamics. In energy transactions then, energy is rearranged and part of the energy is converted and lost as heat. The more steps involved in the process, the greater the heat loss.

Heating with Natural Gas

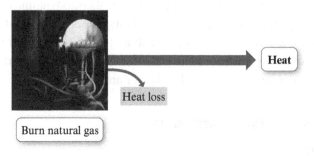

Heating with Electricity

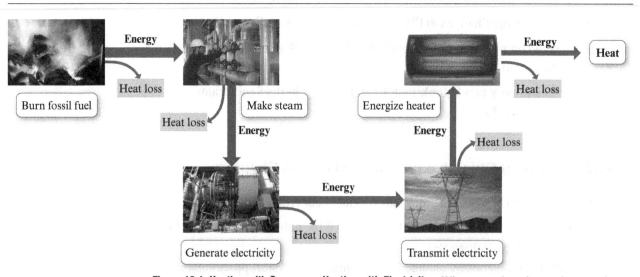

Figure 19.1 Heating with Gas versus Heating with Electricity   When natural gas heats a home, only a single energy transaction is involved, so the heat loss is minimized. When electricity is used to heat a home, a number of energy transactions are required, each of which involves some loss. The result is a much lower efficiency.

The second law of thermodynamics predicts if reactions will happen.

Spontaneous and Nonspontaneous Processes   Section 19.2

Spontaneous processes are those that occur without any outside intervention or external force. Ice spontaneously melts and becomes liquid water at 25 °C. Spontaneous does not indicate that this happens quickly, but only that it will happen. Nonspontaneous processes will not occur unless there is an outside force. In the AP Chemistry curriculum, the terms *thermodynamically favorable* and *unfavorable* are used for spontaneous and nonspontaneous, respectively. Diamonds, an allotrope of carbon, are hard and are said to "last forever," yet it is possible for diamonds to turn into graphite another allotrope of carbon. C(diamond) −C(graphite) is thermodynamically favored; however, the process is so slow that it cannot be observed in a person's lifetime. Other processes that are not favorable can be made to happen with the addition of energy such as electrolysis. It is important to remember that being thermodynamically favored does NOT indicate anything about the rate of the reaction.

Entropy and the Second Law of Thermodynamics   Section 19.3

Enthalpy does not by itself determine if a reaction will happen. If it did, all spontaneous reactions would be exothermic and release heat, but this is not the case. The other factor to be considered is entropy. Simply, entropy is the number of microstates exhibited by a system. In reactions, an increase in the number of microstates is positive entropy, and a movement to fewer microstates is negative energy. There is a decrease in the number of microstates during an endothermic process. There is an increase in the number of microstates in an exothermic process.

The second law of thermodynamics states that for any spontaneous process, the entropy of the universe increases ($\Delta S > 0$). The key part of the statement is that the

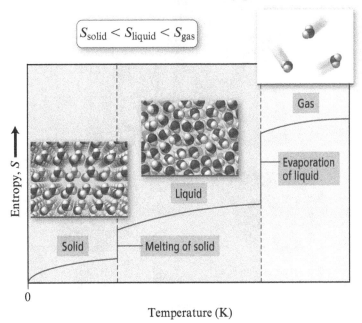

Figure 19.2 Entropy and State Change   Entropy increases when matter changes from a solid to a liquid and from a liquid to a gas.

universe is increasing. Entropy (*S*) increases with the number of energetically different (more microstates) ways to arrange a system or microstates. The greater number of possible microstates, the greater the entropy. Gas particles have the most ways since they are independent from each other compared to a solid.

Entropy, like enthalpy, is a state function. The pathway does not matter just the initial state and the final state. AP exam questions will ask you to predict from a series of reactions, which will have the greatest increase in entropy. Observing the states of each substance usually provides the answer. If solid reactants are making gases as a product, entropy has increased.

Section 19.4   Entropy Changes Associated with State Changes

Phase transitions from solid to liquid, liquid to gas, and solid to gas all have positive entropy as more random particles are present in the end. In chemical reactions, if the number of moles of gases increases during the reaction, the entropy also increases. There are spontaneous reactions that decrease in entropy, but in contrast the surroundings and universe entropy increase. The units of entropy are J/K. The change in entropy is related to the joules of energy absorbed per temperature in Kelvin of substance. A reversible process will have the opposite sign but the same magnitude of entropy. Ice melting is moving to more microstates and is positive in sign, whereas water freezing into ice is moving to fewer microstates, so the sign is negative but the magnitude of the number will be the same.

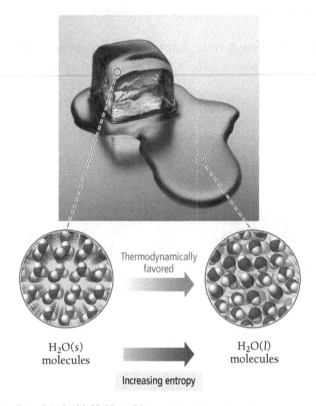

Thermodynamically
favored

$H_2O(s)$
molecules

$H_2O(l)$
molecules

Increasing entropy

Figure 19.3 Entropy Associated with Melting of Ice.   When ice melts, the arrangement of water molecules changes from organized microstates to more microstates.

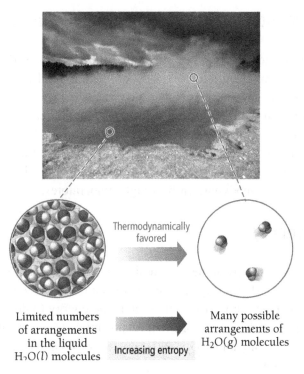

Figure 19.4 Entropy Associated with Evaporation of Water. When water evaporates, the arrangement of water molecules increases as there are more possible arrangements of molecules.

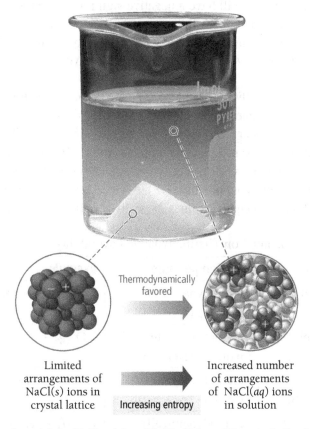

Figure 19.5 Entropy Associated with Dissolving of Salt in Water. When a salt dissolves, it leaves the limited arrangement of the crystal lattice and increases the number of microstates with ions in solution.

Section 19.5   **Heat Transfer and Changes in the Entropy of the Surroundings**

The second law of thermodynamics states that the entropy of the universe must increase. When a more structured process occurs such as ice freezing, the surroundings have gained heat. In general, exothermic processes increase the entropy of the surroundings through the dispersal of heat energy, while endothermic processes decrease the entropy of the surroundings. It is important to keep in mind that the sign of the system and surroundings will be opposite but that the magnitude will be the same. The amount of entropy change is temperature dependent. The freezing of water is not favored thermodynamically at high temperatures.

Section 19.6   **Gibbs Free Energy**

Neither enthalpy nor entropy alone can predict whether a reaction is thermodynamically favored. It is the relationship between them that is the key to this determination. For a spontaneous reaction to occur, there must be energy to do work. Gibbs free energy is the measure of this energy or chemical potential. $\Delta G > 0$ is nonspontaneous, $\Delta G = 0$ is at equilibrium, and $\Delta G < 0$ is spontaneous. Gibbs free energy is calculated from the equation

$$\Delta G = \Delta H - T\Delta S$$

All spontaneous processes will have a negative sign for ΔG, but the size of the free energy indicates how spontaneous the process will be. The more negative the number is, the more spontaneous the process will be. The equation also shows that both enthalpy (ΔH) and entropy (ΔS) are used to determine ΔG.

When ΔH is negative (exothermic) and ΔS is positive, the driving force of favorability is both factors, although one may contribute more than the other. Thinking about the equation, a negative number (ΔH) subtracting a positive value ($-T\Delta S$), no matter the temperature, will always be negative. In contrast, when ΔH is positive (endothermic) and ΔS is negative, neither is a driving force as, regardless of what the temperature is, the value always comes out positive; $(+) - (-) = (+)$. The question that arises concerns when both are negative values or positive values. When both are negative,

Table 19.1   The Effect of ΔH, ΔS, and T on Thermodynamic Favorability

ΔH	ΔS	Low Temperature	High Temperature	Example
−	+	thermodynamically favorable ($\Delta G < 0$)	thermodynamically favorable ($\Delta G < 0$)	$2\,N_2O(g) \rightarrow 2\,N_2(g) + O_2(g)$
+	−	not thermodynamically favorable ($\Delta G > 0$)	not thermodynamically favorable ($\Delta G > 0$)	$3\,O_2(g) \rightarrow 2\,O_3(g)$
−	−	thermodynamically favorable ($\Delta G < 0$)	not thermodynamically favorable ($\Delta G > 0$)	$H_2O(l) \rightarrow H_2O(s)$
+	+	not thermodynamically favorable ($\Delta G > 0$)	thermodynamically favorable ($\Delta G < 0$)	$H_2O(l) \rightarrow H_2O(g)$

then $(-) - (-) = (?)$; whether or not the final value is spontaneous depends on the size of $T\Delta S$ and is therefore temperature dependent. If the value of T is small, then the value can remain negative and the driving force is the enthalpy, but if T is large, the ΔG value will become positive. When both are positive values, then $(+) - (+) = (?)$ and again the temperature makes a difference. To be a negative ΔG value, the $T\Delta S$ must be larger than the ΔH value. The higher the temperature, the more likely the ΔG value will be negative. In this case, entropy is the driving force of the favorability. Gibbs free energy is a state function. Only the beginning and the end matter, not the steps in between.

The free energy measures the chemical potential of a spontaneous reaction. In the following diagram, the direction of the spontaneous direction can be determined.

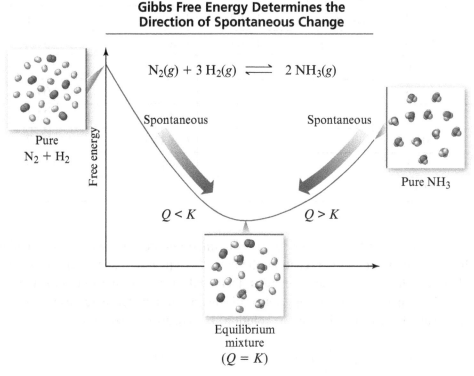

Figure 19.6 Gibbs Free Energy   Gibbs free energy is also called chemical potential because it determines the direction of spontaneous change for chemical systems.

A decrease in free energy indicates a thermodynamically favored process where $\Delta G < 0$. An increase in Gibbs free energy indicates a thermodynamically unfavored process.

Entropy Changes in Chemical Reactions: Calculating ΔS°_{rxn} Section 19.7

To calculate ΔS°_{rxn}, we need to know what the conditions are. The symbol $^\circ$ refers to standard state conditions. Standard state for a gas is a pressure of 1 atm, liquids and solids is a temperature of 25 °C, and a solution is a concentration of 1 M. Individual substance values are reported per mole of substance and are therefore called standard molar entropies ($S°$). The values are based on comparison to the third law of thermo-dynamics, saying the entropy of a perfect crystal at absolute zero is zero. Some of the considerations for entropy values are the state of matter, the allotrope present, whether or not it is in solution, molecular complexity, and molar mass. In each case, the freedom for translational motion, rotational motion, and vibrational motion affects the value.

Table 19.2 Standard Molar Entropy Values ($S°$) for Selected Substances at 298 K

Substance	$S°$(J/mol · K)	Substance	$S°$(J/mol · K)	Substance	$S°$(J/mol · K)
Gases		**Liquids**		**Solids**	
$H_2(g)$	130.7	$H_2O(l)$	70.0	$MgO(s)$	27.0
$Ar(g)$	154.8	$CH_3OH(l)$	126.8	$Fe(s)$	27.3
$CH_4(g)$	186.3	$Br_2(l)$	152.2	$Li(s)$	29.1
$H_2O(g)$	188.8	$C_6H_6(l)$	173.4	$Cu(s)$	33.2
$N_2(g)$	191.6			$Na(s)$	51.3
$NH_3(g)$	192.8			$K(s)$	64.7
$F_2(g)$	202.8			$NaCl(s)$	72.1
$O_2(g)$	205.2			$CaCO_3(s)$	91.7
$Cl_2(g)$	223.1			$FeCl_3(s)$	142.3
$C_2H_4(g)$	219.3				

Notice that the units are J/mol · K. This is important because when you calculate the standard entropy of the reaction, the balanced equation makes a difference. For allotropes, the structure chosen matters. Diamond has fewer microstates than graphite and will have a lower entropy value. Placing a salt in water increases the entropy as the salt dissolves into ions in the solution. The equation to solve is

$$\Delta S°_{rxn} = \sum n_p S°(\text{products}) - \sum n_r S°(\text{reactants})$$

This equation represents the total of standard entropies of the products which are multiplied by their coefficients minus the total of standard entropies of the reactants which are multiplied by their coefficients.

Section 19.8   Free Energy Changes in Chemical Reactions: Calculating $\Delta G°_{rxn}$

At standard conditions, free energy can be calculated by using $\Delta G°_{rxn} = \Delta H°_{rxn} - T\Delta S°_{rxn}$ or standard thermodynamic data of free energy of formation values employing $\Delta G°_{rxn} = \sum n_p \Delta G°_f(\text{products}) - \sum n_r \Delta G°_f(\text{reactants})$. $\Delta G°_f$ is the free energy of formation and represents the change in free energy when 1 mole of a compound in its standard state forms from its elements in their standard states. The $\Delta G°_f$ of elements in their standard states is zero.

Example: Calculating ΔG°_{rxn} from Standard Free Energies of Formation

Ozone in the lower atmosphere is a pollutant that can form by the following reaction involving the oxidation of unburned hydrocarbons:

$$CH_4(g) + 8\,O_2(g) \longrightarrow CO_2(g) + 2\,H_2O(g) + 4\,O_3(g)$$

Use the standard free energies of formation to determine ΔG°_{rxn} for this reaction at 25 °C.

Solution

Begin by looking up (in Appendix IIB in the textbook) the standard free energies of formation for each reactant and product. Remember that the standard free energy of formation of a pure element in its standard state is zero.

Reactant or product	ΔG°_f (in kJ/mol)
$CH_4(g)$	−50.5
$O_2(g)$	0.0
$CO_2(g)$	−394.4
$H_2O(g)$	−228.6
$O_3(g)$	163.2

Calculate ΔG°_{rxn} by substituting into the following equation.

$$
\begin{aligned}
\Delta G^\circ_{rxn} &= \sum n_p\,\Delta G^\circ_f(\text{products}) - \sum n_r\,\Delta G^\circ_f(\text{reactants}) \\
&= [\Delta G^\circ_{f,\,CO_2(g)} + 2(\Delta G^\circ_{f,\,H_2O(g)}) + 4(\Delta G^\circ_{f,\,O_3(g)})] - [\Delta G^\circ_{f,\,CH_4(g)} + 8(\Delta G^\circ_{f,\,O_2(g)})] \\
&= [-394.4\ \text{kJ/mol}_{rxn} + 2(-228.6\ \text{kJ/mol}_{rxn}) + 4(163.2\ \text{kJ/mol}_{rxn})] \\
&\quad - [-50.5\ \text{kJ/mol}_{rxn} + 8(0.0\ \text{kJ/mol}_{rxn})] \\
&= -198.8\ \text{kJ/mol}_{rxn} + 50.5\ \text{kJ/mol}_{rxn} \\
&= -148.3\ \text{kJ/mol}_{rxn}
\end{aligned}
$$

For Practice

One of the reactions that occurs within a catalytic converter in the exhaust pipe of a car is the simultaneous oxidation of carbon monoxide and reduction of NO (both of which are harmful pollutants):

$$2\,CO(g) + 2\,NO(g) \longrightarrow 2\,CO_2(g) + N_2(g)$$

Use standard free energies of formation to determine ΔG°_{rxn} for this reaction at 25 °C. Is the reaction favorable at standard conditions? ($-689.6\ \text{kJ/mol}_{rxn}$)

Manipulating Equations and Gibbs Free Energy

ΔG°_{rxn} is dependent on the balanced equation. If the equation is doubled, the ΔG°_{rxn} value doubles. What factor the equation changes by is the same factor ΔG°_{rxn} will change by. If the reaction is reversed, the free energy sign is changed. If the balanced equation is found by adding a series of reactions together (Hess's law), the ΔG°_{rxn} of each equation used can also be added together.

The energy freed during a reaction is available to do work. Therefore, the value of the free energy is the theoretical limit of the maximum possible work. In reality, part of this free energy is converted to heat, which is lost to the surroundings. For a reaction with a positive free energy value such as recharging a battery, this value becomes the minimum amount of energy needing to be added to cause the reaction to occur.

Section 19.9

Free Energy Changes for Nonstandard States: The Relationship between ΔG_{rxn}° and ΔG_{rxn}

When nonstandard conditions are used for a reaction, the free energy can still be calculated: $\Delta G_{rxn} = \Delta G_{rxn}^{\circ} + RT \ln Q$. Q is the same mass action ratio or quotient from equilibrium calculations (products over reactants each raised to the power of their coefficients), R is the gas constant with energy units 8.314 J/mol · K, and as always the temperature (T) is in Kelvin. When the reaction is at equilibrium, the value of free energy will be zero. The reaction is going both forward and in reverse with no net change. By comparing ΔG and ΔG°, one can determine at what set of conditions the reaction is more favorable.

Example: Calculating ΔG_{rxn} under Nonstandard Conditions

Consider the reaction at 298 K:

$$2\, NO(g) + O_2(g) \longrightarrow 2\, NO_2(g) \qquad \Delta G_{rxn}^{\circ} = -71.2 \text{ kJ/mol}_{rxn}$$

Calculate ΔG_{rxn} under these conditions:

$$P_{NO} = 0.100 \text{ atm}; \qquad P_{O_2} = 0.100 \text{ atm}; \qquad P_{NO_2} = 2.00 \text{ atm}$$

Is the reaction more or less favored under these conditions than under standard conditions?

Solution

Use the law of mass action to calculate Q.

$$Q = \frac{(P_{NO_2})^2}{(P_{NO})^2\, P_{O_2}} = \frac{(2.00)^2}{(0.100)^2 (0.100)} = 4.00 \times 10^3$$

Substitute Q, T, and ΔG_{rxn}° into the following equation to calculate ΔG_{rxn}. (Since the units of R include joules, write ΔG_{rxn}° in joules.)

$$
\begin{aligned}
\Delta G_{rxn} &= \Delta G_{rxn}^{\circ} + RT \ln Q \\
&= -71.2 \times 10^3 \text{ J/mol}_{rxn} + 8.314\, \frac{\text{J}}{\text{mol} \cdot \text{K}} (298 \text{ K}) \ln(4.00 \times 10^3) \\
&= -71.2 \times 10^3 \text{ J/mol}_{rxn} + 20.5 \times 10^3 \text{ J/mol}_{rxn} \\
&= -50.7 \times 10^3 \text{ J/mol}_{rxn} \\
&= -50.7 \text{ kJ/mol}_{rxn}
\end{aligned}
$$

The reaction is favored under these conditions, but less spontaneous than it would be under standard conditions (because ΔG_{rxn} is less negative than ΔG_{rxn}°).

Check

The calculated result is consistent with what you would expect based on Le Châtelier's principle; increasing the concentration of the products and decreasing the concentration of the reactants relative to standard conditions should make the reaction less spontaneous than it was under standard conditions.

For Practice

Consider the reaction at 298 K:

$$2 H_2S(g) + SO_2(g) \longrightarrow 3 S(s, \text{rhombic}) + 2 H_2O(g) \qquad \Delta G^\circ_{rxn} = -102 \text{ kJ}$$

Calculate ΔG_{rxn} under these conditions:

$$P_{H_2S} = 2.00 \text{ atm}; \quad P_{SO_2} = 1.50 \text{ atm}; \quad P_{H_2O} = 0.0100 \text{ atm}$$

Is the reaction more or less spontaneous under these conditions than under standard conditions? ($\Delta G_{rxn} = -123$ kJ, the reaction is more favorable compared to standard conditions.)

Free Energy and Equilibrium: Relating ΔG°_{rxn} to the Equilibrium Constant (K)

Section 19.10

The relationship between free energy and the equilibrium constant is shown in the equation $\Delta G^\circ_{rxn} = -RT \ln K$. Logistically, analyzing each value can indicate the sign of the other value.

The curves in the graphs on the following page show the extent of reaction based on the size of K. Notice that when $K < 1$, the bottom of the curve is on the reactant side, indicating that the reaction is not favorable in the forward direction. When $K = 1$, the reaction is at equilibrium and ΔG is 0. When $K > 1$, the bottom of the curve is on the products side, indicating that this reaction is favorable in the forward direction.

When $K < 1$, then ΔG°_{rxn} is positive. This reaction will be thermodynamically favored in the reverse direction.

When $K > 1$, then ΔG°_{rxn} is negative. This reaction is favored in the direction written and will not be thermodynamically favored in the reverse direction.

When $K = 1$, then ΔG°_{rxn} is zero. This reaction is at equilibrium under standard conditions.

Other ways to calculate K with thermodynamic data include:

$$\ln K = -\frac{\Delta H^\circ_{rxn}}{R}\left(\frac{1}{T}\right) + \frac{\Delta S^\circ_{rxn}}{R} \quad \text{and} \quad \ln \frac{K_2}{K_1} = -\frac{\Delta H^\circ_{rxn}}{R}\left(\frac{1}{T_2} - \frac{1}{T_1}\right).$$

Since ΔG°_{rxn} can be calculated from enthalpy and entropy values, the first equation is substituting the values at one temperature condition. The second equation is calculating what happens to the equilibrium constant when the reaction is carried out at two different temperatures. Analyzing data regarding what is occurring during the reaction at two temperatures should indicate if the free energy value is increasing or decreasing.

Table 19.3 Relationship between the Equilibrium Constant, K, and the Gibbs Free Energy of a System.

K value	ln K	ΔG°_{rxn}	Favorable?	Graph
$K < 1$	negative	positive	no	
$K = 1$	zero	zero	at equilibrium	
$K > 1$	positive	negative	yes	

Additional Practice

Self-Assessment Quiz Questions Q1, Q2, Q3, Q4, Q5, Q6, Q7, Q8, Q9, Q10, Q11, Q12, Q13, Q14, Q15, and Q16

Problems:
Review Questions 6, 12, 13, and 16
Entropy, the Second Law of Thermodynamics, and the Direction of Spontaneous Change 27, 28, 29, 30, 31, 36, 37, 40, and 41
Standard Entropy Changes and Gibbs Free Energy 43, 47, 51, 55, and 67
Free Energy Changes, Nonstandard Conditions, and The Equilibrium Constant 69, 71, 76, and 81
Cumulative Problems 83 and 84
Challenge Problems 104 and 107
Conceptual Problems 110, 112, 113, 114, 116, and 117
Data Interpretation and Analysis 123

Equations to know:

Standard Change in Entropy

$$\Delta S^{\circ}_{rxn} = \sum n_p S^{\circ}(\text{products}) - \sum n_r S^{\circ}(\text{reactants})$$

Change in entropy of surroundings

$$\Delta S_{surr} = \frac{-\Delta H_{sys}}{T} \text{ (constant } T, P)$$

Change in Gibbs Free Energy

$$\Delta G = \Delta H - T\Delta S$$

Methods of Calculating the Free Energy of Formation

1. $\Delta G^{\circ}_{rxn} = \Delta H^{\circ}_{rxn} - T\Delta S^{\circ}_{rxn}$

2. $\Delta G^{\circ}_{rxn} = \sum n_p \Delta G^{\circ}_f (\text{products}) - \sum n_r \Delta G^{\circ}_f (\text{reactants})$

The Relationship between ΔG°_{rxn} and ΔG_{rxn}

$$\Delta G_{rxn} = \Delta G^{\circ}_{rxn} + RT \ln Q \qquad R = 8.314 \text{ J/mol} \cdot \text{K}$$

The Relationship between ΔG°_{rxn} and K

$$\Delta G^{\circ}_{rxn} = -RT \ln K$$

Practice AP Test Questions

1. Of the following, which compound has the largest entropy? All compounds are at some high temperature, T.

   A) $H_2O(g)$

   B) $H_2S(g)$

   C) H_2Se

   D) H_2Te

2. The particulate diagram below represents a view of the sublimation process of iodine in which solid iodine becomes iodine vapor

$$I_2(s) \rightarrow I_2(g) \quad \Delta G° = 20 \text{ kJ/mol}$$

   What are the signs (+ or −) of ΔH, ΔS, and ΔG for this process at 289 K if the partial pressure of the iodine vapor is 1 mm Hg?

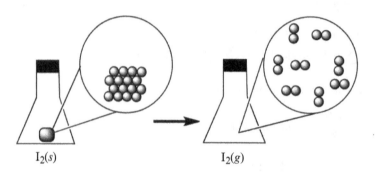

$I_2(s)$ $I_2(g)$

   A) $\Delta H = +, \Delta S = +, \Delta G = +$

   B) $\Delta H = +, \Delta S = +, \Delta G = -$

   C) $\Delta H = -, \Delta S = -, \Delta G = +$

   D) $\Delta H = -, \Delta S = -, \Delta G = -$

3. Consider the reaction: $Ag^+(aq) + Br^-(aq) \longrightarrow AgBr(s)$

Substance	$\Delta H°_f$ (kJ/mol)	$S°$ (J/mol K)
$Ag^+(aq)$	105.9	73.93
$Br^-(aq)$	−120.9	80.71
$AgBr(s)$	−100.4	107.1

   Determine the temperature (in units of C) above which the reaction is nonspontaneous.

   A) Between 50 and 125 °C

   B) Between 126 and 175 °C

C) Between 176 and 200 °C

D) Above 200 °C

4. Potassium reacts with water $2 K(s) + 2 H_2O(l) \longrightarrow 2 KOH(aq) + H_2(g)$

The temperature of the water is observed to increase as the potassium reacts with water. What occurs with the enthalpy change and the entropy change?

A) The enthalpy change is negative, and the entropy change is negative.

B) The enthalpy change is negative, and the entropy change is positive.

C) The enthalpy change is positive, and the entropy change is negative.

D) The enthalpy change is positive, and the entropy change is positive.

5. For the reaction of nitrogen gas with chlorine gas

$N_2(g) + 3 Cl_2(g) \longrightarrow 2 NCl_3(g)$ $\Delta H° = -250$ kJ and $\Delta S° = -260$ J/K

Calculate $\Delta G°$ and indicate if the equilibrium is shifted to reactants or products.

A) $\Delta G°$ is approximately -300 kJ, and the equilibrium favors the products.

B) $\Delta G°$ is approximately -300 kJ, and the equilibrium favors the reactants.

C) $\Delta G°$ is approximately -150 kJ, and the equilibrium favors the products.

D) $\Delta G°$ is approximately -150 kJ, and the equilibrium favors the reactants.

6. ΔS is positive for which one of the following reactions.

A) $C_3H_6(g) + H_2(g) \rightarrow C_3H_8(g)$

B) $4 NH_3(g) + 5 O_2(g) \rightarrow 4 NO(g) + 6 H_2O(g)$

C) $C_3H_8(g) + 5 O_2(g) \rightarrow 3 CO_2(g) + 4 H_2O(g)$

D) $N_2(g) + 3H_2(g) \rightarrow 2NH_3(g)$

Questions 7–9 pertain to the following table of thermodynamic data for chloroform.

Substance	$\Delta H°_f$ (kJ/mol)	$S°$ (J/mol K)
$CHCl_3(g)$	-103.18	295.61
$CHCl_3(l)$	-134.47	201.7

7. Complete the following sentence. The vaporization of $CHCl_3(l)$ to $CHCl_3(g)$ is

_____.

A) favorable at low temperature and unfavorable at high temperature

B) unfavorable at low temperature and favorable at high temperature

C) unfavorable at all temperatures

D) favorable at all temperatures

8. The value of $\Delta S°$ for the vaporization of chloroform at the boiling point

   $CHCl_3(l) \rightarrow CHCl_3(g)$

   is _____ J/K·mol.

   A) −93.9

   B) −62.6

   C) +93.9

   D) +144.3

9. Determine the temperature (in units of K) at which liquid chloroform reaches its boiling point and the process becomes spontaneous.

   $CHCl_3(l) \rightleftharpoons CHCl_3(g)$

   A) 273

   B) 333

   C) 552

   D) 3000

10. Consider the reaction $2SO_3(g) \rightleftharpoons 2SO_2(g) + O_2(g)$ and the relevant thermodynamic data:

Substance	$\Delta H°_f$ (kJ/mol)	$S°$ (J/mol K)	$\Delta G°_f$ (kJ/mol)
$SO_3(g)$	−395.77	256.677	−371
$SO_2(g)$	−296.84	248.21	−300.1
$O_2(g)$	0.0	205.07	0.0

The value of K for the reaction at 25 °C is _____ and state if the forward reaction is thermodynamically favorable or not.

A) 3.58×10^{-13}, thermodynamically unfavorable

B) 3.58×10^{-13}, thermodynamically favorable

C) 1.03, at equilibrium, neither favorable nor unfavorable

D) 2.77×10^{12}, thermodynamically favorable

Data Interpretation and Analysis Question: $\Delta H°$, $\Delta S°$, $\Delta G°$ for the Fermentation of Glucose

One source of ethanol for industrial use is from the fermentation of glucose by yeast in the absence of oxygen to produce ethanol and carbon dioxide according to the following chemical equation:

$$C_6H_{12}O_6(s) \xrightarrow{\text{yeast}} 2\,CH_3CH_2OH(l) + 2\,CO_2(g) \text{ at 298 K} \quad K_p = 8.9 \times 10^{39}$$

When this reaction occurs, the surroundings become warm.

Thermodynamic data for the reactant and products involved in this reaction are given in Table 1.

Table 1 Thermodynamic Functions for Select Compounds

	$\Delta H°_f$ (kJ/mol) at 298 K	$S°$(J/mol K)
$C_2H_5OH(l)$	−277.63	161
$CO_2(g)$	−393.5	213.7
$C_6H_{12}O_6(s)$	−1273.3	212.1

a) If a 1.00 kg sample of glucose (MM = 180.) reacts completely, what is the maximum mass, in units of grams, of ethanol that can be produced?

b) Determine the $\Delta H°_{rxn}$, in units of kJ, for glucose producing ethanol and carbon dioxide.

c) Is the reaction of glucose producing ethanol and carbon dioxide an endothermic or exothermic reaction? Explain.

d) Determine the heat exchanged when 1.00 kg of glucose reacts.

e) Determine the change in entropy, $\Delta S°_{rxn}$ in units of J/K, for glucose producing ethanol and carbon dioxide.

f) Calculate the value and determine the sign for the standard free energy change, $\Delta G°$, for this reaction at 298 K. Include appropriate units in your answer.

g) Is a favorable reaction dependent on the temperature of the reaction? Explain.

h) If the temperature of the reaction increases, will the equilibrium constant for this reaction increase, decrease, or remain the same?

During the fermentation of glucose, the pressure of carbon dioxide gas was measured as a function of time. The data are displayed in Graph 1 and in Table 2.

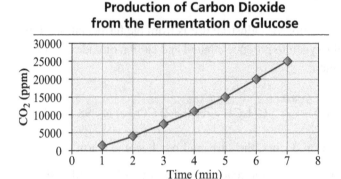

Production of Carbon Dioxide from the Fermentation of Glucose

Graph 1   Production of Carbon Dioxide from the Fermentation of Glucose.

Table 2   Pressure of Carbon Dioxide from the Fermentation of Glucose as a Function of Time

Time (min)	Pressure of Carbon Dioxide (ppm)
0	
1	1300
2	4000
3	7500
4	11000
5	15000
6	20000
7	25000

i) Is the rate of this reaction zero, first, or second order? Explain.

Data Interpretation and Analysis Question Answers with Brief Explanations

a) $1.0 \text{ kg} \times \dfrac{1000.0 \text{ g}}{1.00 \text{ kg}} \times \dfrac{1.00 \text{ mol glucose}}{180 \text{ g glucose}} \times \dfrac{2 \text{ mol ethanol}}{1 \text{ mol glucose}} \times \dfrac{46.06 \text{ g ethanol}}{1 \text{ mol ethanol}}$

$= 512 \text{ g ethanol}$

b) $\left[2 \text{ mol} \times \left(-277.63 \dfrac{\text{kJ}}{\text{mol}} \right) + 2 \text{ mol} \left(-393.5 \dfrac{\text{kJ}}{\text{mol}} \right) \right] - \left[1 \text{ mol} \times \left(-1273.3 \dfrac{\text{kJ}}{\text{mol}} \right) \right]$

$= -69.0 \text{ kJ}$

c) The reaction is exothermic. $\Delta H°$ is negative. The surroundings become warmer indicating the reaction is exporting heat.

d) $1.00 \text{ kg glucose} \times \dfrac{1000.0 \text{ g}}{1.00 \text{ kg}} \times \dfrac{1.00 \text{ mol glucose}}{180 \text{ g glucose}} \times \left(-69.0 \dfrac{\text{kJ}}{\text{mol glucose}} \right)$

$= -380 \text{ kJ}$

e) $\left[2\ \text{mol} \times \left(161\ \dfrac{\text{J}}{\text{K mol}} \right) + 2\ \text{mol} \left(213.7\ \dfrac{\text{J}}{\text{K mol}} \right) \right] - \left[1\ \text{mol} \times \left(212.1\ \dfrac{\text{kJ}}{\text{K mol}} \right) \right]$

$= +537.3\ \text{J/K}$

f) $\Delta G° = \Delta H° - T \Delta S° = -69.0\ \text{kJ/mol glucose} - (298\text{K})\ (+537.3\ \text{J/K mol})$
$= -229\ \text{kJ}$

g) Yes, this reaction is temperature dependent.

h) $\Delta H°$ is negative; when the temperature increases, the equilibrium for the reaction is shifted to the left (according to Le Châtelier's principle). This means that the equilibrium constant decreases.

i) Zero order since a graph of concentration vs time is a straight line

CHAPTER 19

READING GUIDE

The driving forces of reactions are covered in this chapter as are two major thermodynamic functions; the standard change in Gibbs Free Energy, $\Delta G°$, and the standard change in entropy, $\Delta S°$. Together $\Delta H°$ and $\Delta S°$ can be used to determine if a reaction is thermodynamically favorable. The AP Exam will not use the terms spontaneous and nonspontaneous but instead will use thermodynamically favorable and unfavorable. Unit 9 in the AP Chemistry Curriculum is about the role of energy in predicting the direction of changes in matter. Although the topics presented in this chapter are some of the more difficult topics in the AP Chemistry curriculum, every part of this chapter needs to be understood.

Section 19.1   **Nature's Heat Tax: You Can't Win and You Can't Break Even**

1. What is a *heat tax*? How does a heat tax apply to the law of conservation of energy?* Explain why it takes more energy to recharge a battery than the energy originally used by the battery.

2. Using the figures below, explain why a four-step process has a higher heat cost than a one-step process:

Heating with Natural Gas

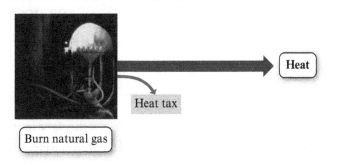

Heating with Electricity

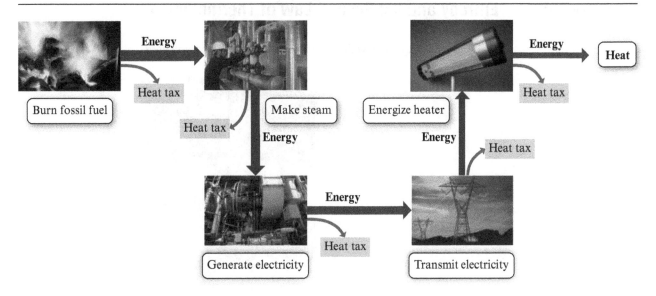

Spontaneous and Nonspontaneous Processes   Section 19.2

3. Does favorability of a reaction indicate the speed of the reaction? Explain.

4. Give an example of a thermodynamically favorable process that occurs at a very slow rate.

5. How does a catalyst affect thermodynamic favorability? Explain.

6. Can a non thermodynamically favorable reaction occur? Justify your answer.

7. Explain the difference between what thermodynamics and kinetics indicate about a reaction.

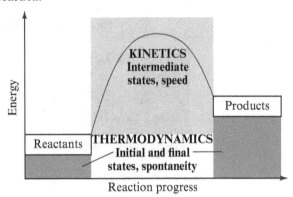

Section 19.3   Entropy and the Second Law of Thermodynamics

8. Explain how this figure represents an increase in entropy.

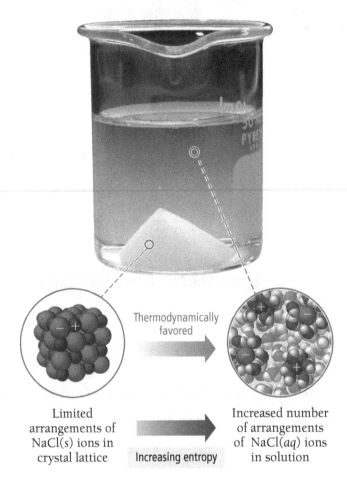

9. What is entropy? How do the number of microstates affect entropy?

10. What is the second law of thermodynamics? Explain the concept of this law in terms of energy microstates.

11. Why is entropy a state function?

12. What conditions result in entropy being a positive value? A negative value? Using the concept of entropy, explain why heat moves from an object with a higher temperature to an object with a lower temperature.

13. Explain why entropy increases as the temperature increases.

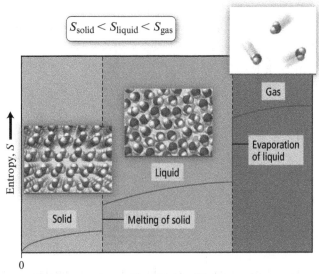

14. Identify four processes where entropy always increases? What are the units of entropy and what do they signify?

Heat Transfer and Changes in the Entropy of the Surroundings   Section 19.4

15. Explain how a process decreasing in microstates such as liquid water turning to ice be a favored process.

16. What is the relationship between an exothermic process and entropy of the surroundings? Explain.

17. What is the relationship between an endothermic process and entropy of the surroundings? Explain.

18. Why is entropy temperature dependent? Justify your answer.

Gibbs Free Energy   Section 19.5

19. What is Gibbs free energy? Write the equation for Gibbs Free Energy and explain each of the variables.

20. Explain the concept of free energy using the following diagram.

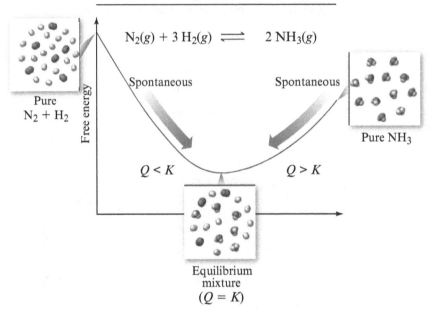

**Gibbs Free Energy Determines the
Direction of Spontaneous Change**

$$N_2(g) + 3\,H_2(g) \rightleftharpoons 2\,NH_3(g)$$

Pure
$N_2 + H_2$

Free energy

Spontaneous   Spontaneous

Pure NH_3

$Q < K$ $Q > K$

Equilibrium
mixture
$(Q = K)$

21. Why does a negative ΔG value indicate a favored process?

22. Mathematically explain the value of ΔG under each of the following conditions:

    Enthalpy positive and entropy negative:

    Enthalpy positive and entropy positive:

    Enthalpy negative and entropy positive:

    Enthalpy negative and entropy negative:

23. When entropy and Enthalpy have the same sign, why is the reaction temperature dependent?

Section 19.6   Entropy Changes in Chemical Reactions: Calculating $\Delta S°_{rxn}$

24. What are the standard states for the following:

    Gas:

    Solid:

    Solution:

25. What is the third law of thermodynamics?

26. How are standard entropy values determined? Why is entropy an extensive property?

27. What equation is used to determine the standard state entropy of a reaction? How is the change in entropy for a reaction calculated?

28. Why is it important to know the state of each substance and the allotrope used in the calculation of the standard state entropy of a reaction?

Free Energy Changes in Chemical Reactions: Calculating ΔG°_{rxn} Section 19.7

29. What is the symbol for the standard change in free energy? What does a negative value indicate about a reaction?

30. What is ΔG°_f? Explain the differences between ΔG°_f, ΔG°_{rxn} and ΔG?

31. What are three ways to calculate ΔG°_{rxn}? Include equations in your answer.

32. Explain how to calculate ΔG°_{rxn} if the reaction coefficients are tripled, if the equation is reversed, and if the reaction is found as a sum of several reactions.

33. Using a rechargeable battery as an example, explain why not all free energy is available to perform work.

34. For a reaction with a positive ΔG°_{rxn}, what is required to make the reaction occur?

Free Energy Changes for Nonstandard States: The Relationship Between ΔG°_{rxn} and ΔG_{rxn} Section 19.8

35. What is the difference between and ΔG_{rxn}? When should each value be used?

36. What equation is used to change between the two values ΔG°_{rxn} and ΔG_{rxn}? What is the mass action ratio? Why is it used in this equation?

37. What is true of ΔG_{rxn} at equilibrium? Explain how to identify equilibrium on the graph.

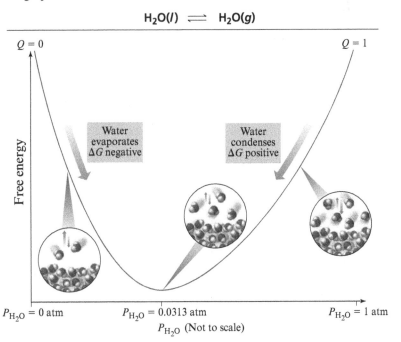

$$H_2O(l) \rightleftharpoons H_2O(g)$$

$Q = 0$ $Q = 1$

Free energy

Water evaporates ΔG negative

Water condenses ΔG positive

$P_{H_2O} = 0$ atm $P_{H_2O} = 0.0313$ atm $P_{H_2O} = 1$ atm

P_{H_2O} (Not to scale)

Section 19.9

Free Energy and Equilibrium: Relating ΔG°_{rxn} to the Equilibrium Constant (K)

38. Fill in the chart indicating the sign of each value with the condition listed. In the last column, indicate if the reaction is favored or not.

K Value	ln K	ΔG°_{rxn}	Favored?	Diagram of Free Energy and K
$K < 1$				
$K = 1$				
$K > 1$				

39. Explain how to convert from K to ΔG°_{rxn}.

40. Explain what each of the following equations are used to calculate:

$$\ln K = -\frac{\Delta H^{\circ}_{rxn}}{R}\left(\frac{1}{T}\right) + \frac{\Delta S^{\circ}_{rxn}}{R}$$

$$\ln \frac{K_2}{K_1} = -\frac{\Delta H^{\circ}_{rxn}}{R}\left(\frac{1}{T_2} - \frac{1}{T_1}\right)$$

Self-Assessment Answers

1. _____   2. _____   3. _____

4. _____   5. _____   6. _____

7. _____   8. _____   9. _____

10. _____   11. _____   12. _____

13. _____   14. _____   15. _____

ELECTROCHEMISTRY

Most students have little background in electrochemistry, and helping students acquire the vocabulary used in electrochemistry is foundational information to cover in Unit 9. Section 20.3. is a crucial section in electrochemistry for AP Chemistry. Students need to be able to determine if a reaction will be spontaneous, what positive voltage means, and how to read a standard reduction potential table. Several learning objectives are addressed from various units in the AP Curriculum.

20.2 **Balancing Oxidation–Reduction Equations**

20.3 **Voltaic (or Galvanic) Cells: Generating Electricity from Spontaneous Chemical Reactions**

20.4 **Standard Electrode Potentials**

20.5 **Cell Potential, Free Energy, and the Equilibrium Constant**

20.6 **Cell Potential and Concentration**

20.8 **Electrolysis: Driving Nonspontaneous Chemical Reactions with Electricity**

Specific Learning Objectives Addressed in This Chapter:

TRA-1 A substance that changes its properties, or that changes into a different substance, can be represented by chemical equations.

TRA-1.A Identify evidence of chemical and physical changes in matter.

TRA-1.B Represent changes in matter with a balanced chemical or net ionic equation:
- For physical changes.
- For given information about the identity of the reactants and/or products.
- For ions in a given chemical reaction.

TRA-2 A substance can change into another substance through different processes, and the change itself can be classified by the sort of processes that produced it.

TRA-2.A Identify a reaction as acid–base, *oxidation–reduction*, or precipitation.
TRA-2.C Represent a balanced redox reaction equation using half-reactions.

ENE-6 Electrical energy can be generated by chemical reactions.

ENE-6.A Explain the relationship between the physical components of an electrochemical cell and the overall operational principles of the cell.

ENE-6.B Explain whether an electrochemical cell is thermodynamically favored based on its standard cell potential and the constituent half-reactions within the cell.
ENE-6.C Explain the relationship between deviations from standard cell conditions and changes in cell potential.
ENE-6.D Calculate the amount of charge flow based on changes in the amounts of reactants and products in an electrochemical cell.

ENE-5 The relationship between $\Delta G°$ and K can be used to determine favorability of a chemical or physical transformation.

ENE-5.B Explain the relationship between external sources of energy or coupled reactions and their ability to drive thermodynamically unfavorable processes.

Concepts and Vocabulary to Review:

Section 20.2   ## Balancing Oxidation–Reduction Equations

A review from Chapter 5 on assigning oxidation numbers and identifying what is oxidized and what is reduced is important to understanding electrochemistry. From these steps, it will be easy to finish balancing the reaction.

1. Assign oxidation states to all atoms and identify what is being oxidized and what is being reduced.

2. Separate into two half-reactions. Balance each half-reaction to have the same number of each atom on both sides of the equation and the required number of electrons for the change in oxidation state. If in acidic solution, add H^+ as a reactant to the half-reaction with O atoms.

    • What is oxidized frees up electrons as a product, and what is reduced uses up the same electrons. In the half reaction, these electrons will be on the reactant side.

3. Balance the charge in both half-reactions so that, when added, the electrons will cancel.

4. Add the two half-reactions together.

When first reading this equation, if one is only looking at numbers of atoms it appears to be balanced $Al(s) + Ni^{2+}(aq) \rightarrow Al^{3+}(aq) + Ni(s)$, but the equation is not balanced due to unbalanced charge. Following the above steps to balance the equation, the steps would be as follows:

1. Looking at oxidation states, $Al = 0$, $Ni^{2+} = +2$, $Al^{3+} = +3$, $Ni = 0$; Al (0 to +3) is losing electrons and being oxidized, and Ni^{2+} (+2 to 0) is gaining electrons and is being reduced.

2. The two half reactions are $Al(s) \rightarrow Al^{3+}(aq) + 3\ e^-$ and $Ni^{2+}(aq) + 2\ e^- \rightarrow Ni(s)$. The lowest common multiple between 3 and 2 is 6.

3. $2(Al(s) \rightarrow Al^{3+}(aq) + 3\ e^-)$ and $3(Ni^{2+}(aq) + 2\ e^- \rightarrow Ni(s))$
   - $2\ Al(s) \rightarrow 2\ Al^{3+}(aq) + 6\ e^-$
   - $3\ Ni^{2+}(aq) + 6\ e^- \rightarrow 3\ Ni(s)$

4. Adding the two half-reactions together, the electrons cancel and the chemical equation is $2\ Al(s) + 3\ Ni^{2+}(aq) \rightarrow 2\ Al^{3+}(aq) + 3\ Ni(s)$

The half-reactions will be important in subsequent sections and balancing half-reactions must be a mastered skill.

Voltaic (or Galvanic) Cells: Generating Electricity from Spontaneous Chemical Reactions

Section 20.3

This section is full of vocabulary that students need to understand. While definitions will not be tested on the AP exam, students need to know what the words mean if they are to understand the questions asked. For instance, if the students are asked to identify the anode on a diagram and draw the direction of electron flow, students need to know what the anode is and provide evidence to support their claim.

A Spontaneous Redox Reaction: Zn + Cu²⁺

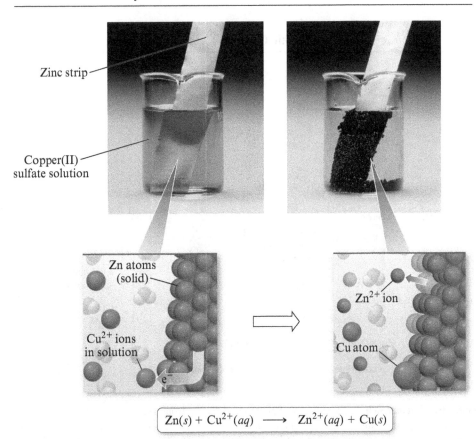

Zinc strip

Copper(II) sulfate solution

Zn atoms (solid)

Cu²⁺ ions in solution

e⁻

Zn²⁺ ion

Cu atom

$$Zn(s) + Cu^{2+}(aq) \longrightarrow Zn^{2+}(aq) + Cu(s)$$

Figure 20.1 A Thermodynamically Favored Oxidation–Reduction Reaction   When zinc is immersed in a solution containing copper ions, the zinc atoms transfer electrons to the copper ions. The zinc atoms are oxidized and dissolve in the solution. The copper ions are reduced and are deposited on the zinc electrode.

For instance, in Figure 20.1, a zinc electrode is placed in a copper(II) sulfate solution. Evidence that the copper is being reduced from Cu^{2+} to Cu is the observation of the copper coming out of the solution and plating the zinc. The color of the solution will go from the blue color of the copper(II) cation to the colorless solution of the zinc cation, also indicating that the copper was reduced and the zinc was oxidized. In every redox reaction, while one species is oxidized, another species is reduced.

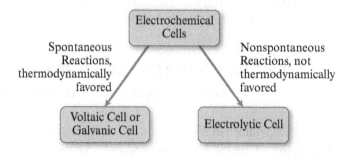

In electrochemical cells, spontaneous reactions produce electrical current during a reaction, whereas nonspontaneous reactions use electrical current to make a reaction occur.

A Voltaic Cell

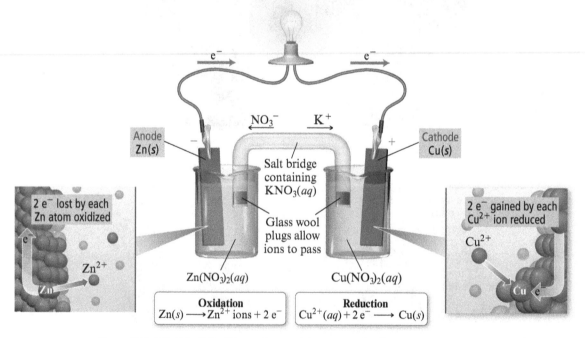

Figure 20.2 A Voltaic Cell The tendency of zinc to transfer electrons to copper results in a flow of electrons through the wire that lights the bulb. The movement of electrons from the zinc anode to the copper cathode creates a positive charge buildup at the zinc half-cell and a negative charge buildup at the copper half-cell. The flow of ions within the salt bridge neutralizes this charge buildup, allowing the reaction to continue.

In a galvanic cell, the anode is the half-cell where oxidation occurs. Oxidation frees the electrons, which bump other electrons up the electrode then bump electrons across the wire to the cathode where other electrons are used in the reduction half-cell at the cathode. It is a misconception that each electron generated at the anode travels all the way from the anode to the cathode. Instead, it is the direction of the electron flow that is from the anode to the cathode.

The anode electrode will lose mass as it converts atoms to cations. The cations enter the solution and in order to prevent a build-up of positive charge anions from the salt bridge migrate into the half-cell. To keep the cell from becoming unbalanced with respect to charge. The anions in the salt bridge will flow toward the anode. At the cathode, there will be an increase of mass as cations in solution are reduced to atoms which may deposit on the cathode. If an inert electrode is present, a gas may form and bubbling will be observed. This new gas product will account for the increase in mass, as the cations are reduced and leave the solution as gas. To neutralize the negative charge build up, cations in the salt bridge will migrate into the solution of the half-cell with the cathode. If the salt bridge dries up, the reaction will cease since the ions cannot easily migrate through a solid and the charge buildup is not being neutralized.

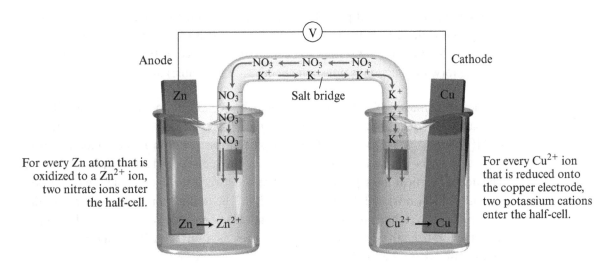

Figure 20.3 The Function of a Salt Bridge in a Zinc-Copper Voltaic Cell. If aqueous potassium nitrate is used as the solution in the salt-bridge, the K^+ ions migrate toward the cathode and the NO_3^- ions migrate toward the anode.

What causes the spontaneous reaction? For a simple galvanic cell with a zinc electrode in 1.0 M $Zn(NO_3)_2(aq)$ and a nickel electrode in $Ni(NO_3)_2(aq)$, the zinc metal is more active than the nickel metal. Zinc gives up electrons easier compared to nickel. The electrons in zinc are subjected to a slightly greater push compared to the electrons in nickel. When two metals are connected in a circuit, electrons are pushed out of the more active metal electrode, and into the wire connecting the two electrodes. Electrons flow toward the least active metal electrode. In this situation, zinc serves as the anode.

In order for zinc to have electrons pushed out of the metal and into a wire, a zinc atom in the electrode must lose two electrons; Zn^{2+} cations form and are released into the solution. We can represent this process by the following half-equation: $Zn \rightarrow Zn^{2+} + 2\,e^-$. Hence, oxidation occurs at the anode. In order for the nickel metal to receive two electrons, some of the Ni^{2+} ions in solution will each gain two electrons, $Ni^{2+} + 2\,e^- \rightarrow Ni$ at the nickel electrode. Reduction occurs at the cathode. Electrons are neither created nor destroyed in a galvanic cell. The nickel electrode has a greater tendency to be reduced compared to the zinc electrode. The electrons in the wire will flow toward the cathode. The ions in the salt bridge will migrate to balance the charge in the two compartments. Together electrons flowing in the wire and ions migrating in the aqueous solution creates an electrical current.

The difference in potential between the two cells is measured in volts. This difference in potential energy is referred to as electromotive force (emf). In a voltaic cell, this is cell potential (E_{cell}). One volt is a joule per coulomb (J/C), and one coulomb per second (C/s) is an ampere (A). If standard conditions are present, then the label will be E°_{cell} or standard emf. The conditions are 1 atm of pressure, $25\,°C$, and 1 M solutions.

When comparing the cell potentials, if the potential difference is positive, it will occur even if the difference is small. When there is a small difference, the less the tendency there is for the reaction to occur, but it will occur. If the potential is negative, the forward reaction is nonspontaneous (not favorable) and will not occur.

An electrochemical cell can be indicated with a special cell notation. For the cell with the balanced equation $2\,Al(s) + 3\,Ni^{2+}(aq) \rightarrow 2\,Al^{3+}(aq) + 3\,Ni(s)$, the notation is $Al(s)\,|\,Al^{3+}\,||\,Ni^{2+}(aq)\,|\,Ni(s)$. The first part of the notation is the anode reaction $Al \rightarrow Al^{3+} + 3\,e^-$, with a single vertical line $|$ between Al and Al^{3+}, a phase change. The double vertical lines $||$ indicate the break between the anode reaction (electrode and the ion it forms) and the cathode reaction. The double vertical can represent the salt bridge. The cathode reaction is represented last. Again a single vertical line separates the ion from the electrode it plates or uses as a surface with an inert electrode, in this case $Ni^{2+} + 2\,e^- \rightarrow Ni$.

Inert Platinum Electrode

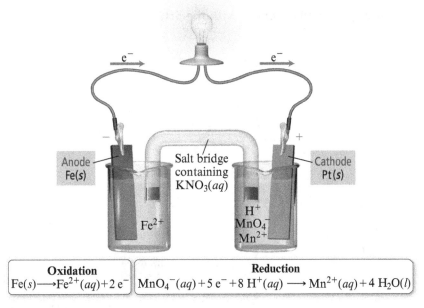

Oxidation	Reduction
$Fe(s) \longrightarrow Fe^{2+}(aq) + 2\,e^-$	$MnO_4^-(aq) + 5\,e^- + 8\,H^+(aq) \longrightarrow Mn^{2+}(aq) + 4\,H_2O(l)$

Figure 20.4 Inert Platinum Electrode   When the participants in a half-reaction are all in the aqueous phase, a conductive surface is needed for electron transfer to take place. In such cases an inert electrode of graphite or platinum is often used. In this electrochemical cell, an iron strip acts as the anode and a platinum strip acts as the cathode. Iron is oxidized at the anode, and MnO_4^- is reduced at the cathode.

The cell notation for the reaction above is

$$Fe(s)\,|\,Fe^{2+}(aq)\,||\,MnO_4^-(aq),\,H^+(aq),\,Mn^{2+}(aq)\,|\,Pt(s)$$

where Pt is the inert electrode.

Standard Electrode Potentials   Section 20.4

Electrode potentials are determined by comparing them to the standard hydrogen electrode (SHE), which is assigned a value of zero.

Standard Hydrogen Electrode (SHE)

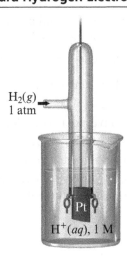

$H_2(g)$
1 atm

Pt

$H^+(aq)$, 1 M

Figure 20.5 The Standard Hydrogen Electrode   We arbitrarily assign the standard hydrogen electrode (SHE) an electrode potential of zero. All other electrode potentials are then measured relative to the SHE.

All the potentials are measured relative to the SHE.

Measuring Half-Cell Potential with the SHE

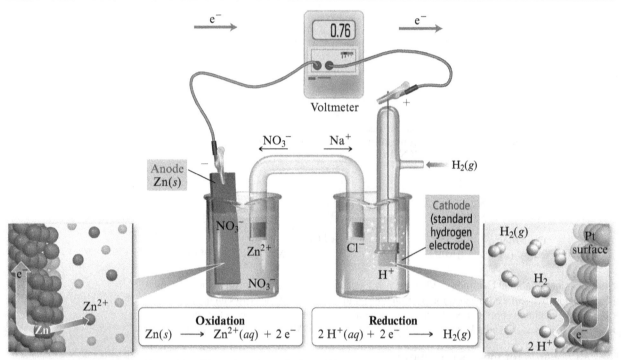

Figure 20.6 Measuring Electrode Potential Because the electrode potential of the SHE is zero, the electrode potential for the oxidation of Zn is equal to the cell potential.

The difference between the final state (cathode) and the initial state (anode) determines $E°_{cell}$.

$$E°_{cell} = E°_{cathode} - E°_{anode}$$

If the forward reaction is favorable, the value of $E°_{cell}$ is positive. A quick check needs to be done when using the standard electrode reductions potentials chart: the oxidation half-reaction at the anode (which will be written in reverse on a reductions chart) must be below the cathode half-reaction to end up being spontaneous. To determine $E°_{cell}$ for a cell with the overall reaction $Zn + Cu^{2+} \rightarrow Zn^{2+} + Cu$, first look at the two half-reactions $Zn \rightarrow Zn^{2+} + 2\,e^-$ and $Cu^{2+} + 2\,e^- \rightarrow Cu$.

As shown in Table 20.1, the oxidation reaction $Zn(s) \rightarrow Zn^{2+}(aq) + 2\,e^-$ written as a reduction is $Zn^{2+}(aq) + 2\,e^- \rightarrow Zn(s)$ and is below $Cu^{2+}(aq) + 2\,e^- \rightarrow Cu(s)$, so when calculated, this should have positive voltage and be spontaneous. Using $E°_{cell} = E°_{cathode} - E°_{anode}$; $E°_{cell} = 0.34\,V - -0.76\,V$ or $1.10\,V$. Please be aware that some chemistry textbooks reverse the order of the reduction potentials from most negative to most positive that is, listing the Li+ reaction at the top. On the AP test, students will be given the potentials needed for the problem in a small table and not the entire table.

Table 20.1   Standard Electrode Potentials at 25 °C

Reduction Half-Reaction		E_0 (V)	
Weaker reducing agent	$F_2(g) + 2\,e^-$ $\rightarrow 2\,F^-(aq)$	2.87	Stronger oxidizing agent
	$H_2O_2(aq) + 2\,H^+(aq) + 2\,e^-$ $\rightarrow 2\,H_2O(l)$	1.78	
	$PbO_2(s) + 4\,H^+(aq) + SO_4^{2-}(aq) + 2\,e^-$ $\rightarrow PbSO_4(s) + 2\,H_2O(l)$	1.69	
	$MnO_4^-(aq) + 4\,H^+(aq) + 3\,e^-$ $\rightarrow MnO_2(s) + 2\,H_2O(l)$	1.68	
	$MnO_4^-(aq) + 8\,H^+(aq) + 5\,e^-$ $\rightarrow Mn^{2+}(aq) + 4\,H_2O(l)$	1.51	
	$Au^{3+}(aq) + 3\,e^-$ $\rightarrow Au(s)$	1.50	
	$PbO_2(s) + 4\,H^+(aq) + 2\,e^-$ $\rightarrow Pb^{2+}(aq) + 2\,H_2O(l)$	1.46	
	$Cl_2(g) + 2\,e^-$ $\rightarrow 2\,Cl^-(aq)$	1.36	
	$Cr_2O_7^{2-}(aq) + 14\,H^+(aq) + 6\,e^-$ $\rightarrow 2\,Cr^{3+}(aq) + 7\,H_2O(l)$	1.33	
	$O_2(g) + 4\,H^+(aq) + 4\,e^-$ $\rightarrow 2\,H_2O(l)$	1.23	
	$MnO_2(s) + 4\,H^+(aq) + 2\,e^-$ $\rightarrow Mn^{2+}(aq) + 2\,H_2O(l)$	1.21	
	$IO_3^-(aq) + 6\,H^+(aq) + 5\,e^-$ $\rightarrow \frac{1}{2}I_2(aq) + 3\,H_2O(l)$	1.20	
	$Br_2(l) + 2\,e^-$ $\rightarrow 2\,Br^-(aq)$	1.09	
	$VO_2^+(aq) + 2\,H^+(aq) + e^-$ $\rightarrow VO^{2+}(aq) + H_2O(l)$	1.00	
	$NO_3^-(aq) + 4\,H^+(aq) + 3\,e^-$ $\rightarrow NO(g) + 2\,H_2O(l)$	0.96	
	$ClO_2(g) + e^-$ $\rightarrow ClO_2^-(aq)$	0.95	
	$Ag^+(aq) + e^-$ $\rightarrow Ag(s)$	0.80	
	$Fe^{3+}(aq) + e^-$ $\rightarrow Fe^{2+}(aq)$	0.77	
	$O_2(g) + 2\,H^+(aq) + 2\,e^-$ $\rightarrow H_2O_2(aq)$	0.70	
	$MnO_4^-(aq) + e^-$ $\rightarrow MnO_4^{2-}(aq)$	0.56	
	$I_2(s) + 2\,e^-$ $\rightarrow 2\,I^-(aq)$	0.54	
	$Cu^+(aq) + e^-$ $\rightarrow Cu(s)$	0.52	
	$O_2(g) + 2\,H_2O(l) + 4\,e^-$ $\rightarrow 4\,OH^-(aq)$	0.40	
	$Cu^{2+}(aq) + 2\,e^-$ $\rightarrow Cu(s)$	0.34	
	$SO_4^{2-}(aq) + 4\,H^+(aq) + 2\,e^-$ $\rightarrow H_2SO_3(aq) + H_2O(l)$	0.20	
	$Cu^{2+}(aq) + e^-$ $\rightarrow Cu^+(aq)$	0.16	
	$Sn^{4+}(aq) + 2\,e^-$ $\rightarrow Sn^{2+}(aq)$	0.15	
	$2\,H^+(aq) + 2\,e^-$ $\rightarrow H_2(g)$	0	
	$Fe^{3+}(aq) + 3\,e^-$ $\rightarrow Fe(s)$	−0.036	
	$Pb^{2+}(aq) + 2\,e^-$ $\rightarrow Pb(s)$	−0.13	
	$Sn^{2+}(aq) + 2\,e^-$ $\rightarrow Sn(s)$	−0.14	
	$Ni^{2+}(aq) + 2\,e^-$ $\rightarrow Ni(s)$	−0.23	
	$Cd^{2+}(aq) + 2\,e^-$ $\rightarrow Cd(s)$	−0.40	
	$Fe^{2+}(aq) + 2\,e^-$ $\rightarrow Fe(s)$	−0.45	
	$Cr^{3+}(aq) + e^-$ $\rightarrow Cr^{2+}(aq)$	−0.50	
	$Cr^{3+}(aq) + 3\,e^-$ $\rightarrow Cr(s)$	−0.73	
	$Zn^{2+}(aq) + 2\,e^-$ $\rightarrow Zn(s)$	−0.76	
	$2\,H_2O(l) + 2\,e^-$ $\rightarrow H_2(g) + 2\,OH^-(aq)$	−0.83	
	$Mn^{2+}(aq) + 2\,e^-$ $\rightarrow Mn(s)$	−1.18	
	$Al^{3+}(aq) + 3\,e^-$ $\rightarrow Al(s)$	−1.66	
	$Mg^{2+}(aq) + 2\,e^-$ $\rightarrow Mg(s)$	−2.37	
	$Na^+(aq) + e^-$ $\rightarrow Na(s)$	−2.71	
	$Ca^{2+}(aq) + 2\,e^-$ $\rightarrow Ca(s)$	−2.76	
	$Ba^{2+}(aq) + 2\,e^-$ $\rightarrow Ba(s)$	−2.90	
	$K^+(aq) + e^-$ $\rightarrow K(s)$	−2.92	Weaker oxidizing agent
Stronger reducing agent	$Li^+(aq) + e^-$ $\rightarrow Li(s)$	−3.04	

Another indicator on the table is the ability of an acid to react with a metal. Any metal below the SHE on Table 20.1 will dissolve in acid and generate hydrogen gas. In the figure below, $Zn \rightarrow Zn^{2+} + 2\,e$, while $2\,H^+ + 2\,e^- \rightarrow H_2$. $E^\circ_{cell} = 0 - (-0.76\,V)$ or $+0.76\,V$. In this case, the E° for the reaction is calculated because there is a direct transfer of electrons between the zinc and the hydrogen. Therefore, the E°_{cell} cannot be measured with a voltmeter.

$$Zn(s) + 2\,H^+(aq) \longrightarrow Zn^{2+}(aq) + H_2(g) \quad E^\circ_{rxn} = +0.76 \text{ volts}$$

Figure 20.7 Oxidation-Reduction Reaction of Zinc and Hydrochloric Acid When zinc is placed in hydrochloric acid, the transfer of electrons occurs directly between the zinc and hydronium ions.

This holds true for all but nitric acid, which will dissolve copper which is also above the SHE.

The half-reaction with the more positive electrode potential has a stronger attraction for electrons and is reduced. The half-reaction with the more negative electrode potential is oxidized. For any reaction that is thermodynamically favored, the E°_{cell} will be positive.

Section 20.5   Cell Potential, Free Energy, and the Equilibrium Constant

Several indicators are used to determine if a reaction is thermodynamically favored. These include, K, ΔG°, and E°_{cell}. The values can be converted to other values in the equations below. It is important to recognize signs: if a reaction is spontaneous, then E°_{cell} is positive, K is larger than one since products are favored, and ΔG° is negative since free energy will be available to do work. At equilibrium E°_{cell} is zero, K is one, and ΔG° is zero since both the forward and backward reactions are equally favored.

E°_{cell}	K	ΔG°	Favored?
<0	<1	>0	no
0	1	0	at equilibrium
>0	>1	<0	yes

It is important to not only understand the relationships but to also be able to do the calculations among K, $\Delta G°$, and $E°$ merging the concepts of equilibrium, electrochemistry, and thermodynamics.

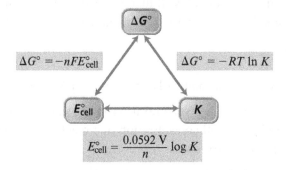

Remember the units: n is the number of moles of electrons, T is the temperature in K, R is 8.314 J/mol · K, and F is 96,485 C/mol.

Calculations among K, $\Delta G°$, and $E°$.

Calculate $\Delta G°$ for the cell $Ni(s) + 2Ag^+(aq) \rightarrow Ni^{2+}(aq) + 2Ag(s)$ $E° = 1.03$ V

$\Delta G° = -nFE°$

$\Delta G° = -2$ mol e$^-$ × 96,485 C/mol e$^-$ × 1.03 J/C

$\Delta G° = -198,759.1 = -199,000$ J or -199 kJ (note 3 significant figures from the voltage)

Since the voltage is positive, this indicates the reaction is thermodynamically favored, and the $\Delta G°$ should be a negative value.

For this reaction at 298.15 K, what is the equilibrium constant?

$\Delta G° = -RT \ln K$

$-199,000$ J $= -8.314$ J/mol·K × 298.15 K × $\ln K$

(note the use of the joules value for $\Delta G°$ since R uses joules.)

$\ln K = 80.1$

$K = 6.27 × 10^{34}$

Positive voltage favors the forward reaction so this should be a positive value.

Another solution would be to use $E°cell = (0.0592/n)\log K$

1.03 V $= (0.0592/2) \log K$

$\log K = 34.8$

$K = 6.27 × 10^{34}$

Cell Potential and Concentration   Section 20.6

In $E°_{cell}$, standard concentrations of 1.0 M are used. In concentration cells, concentrations will vary, causing voltage to change. The new voltage can be calculated using the Nernst equation, but if only asked to predict what will happen to the voltage, students can explain what will happen to voltage using Le Châtelier's principle. The difference in concentrations will drive the current flow as the cells shift to regain equilibrium. The cell with the higher concentration will decrease, while concentration of the solution in the other cell will increase. Depending on which is the anode and which is the cathode will determine if the voltage will increase or decrease.

For the reaction Zn →

- $Q = 1; E_{cell} = E°_{cell}$ at standard conditions of 1 M solutions.

- $Q < 1; E_{cell} > E°_{cell}$ The concentration in the cathode half-cell is greater than the anode half-cell concentration; the reaction will move forward and thereby increase the voltage.

- $Q = K; E_{cell} = 0$ The reaction is at equilibrium, so no net change is occurring and voltage is zero.

- $Q > 1; E_{cell} < E°_{cell}$ The anode half-cell concentration is greater than the cathode half-cell concentration, so voltage will decrease.

Concentration cells are driven by a difference in concentration. For instance, the diagram below has copper as both the anode and cathode, but the concentrations in the cells are different. The cells will try to reach the same concentrations. To do this, the more concentrated ion concentration solution must decrease by forming reducing ions at the cathode, and the dilute solution ion concentration must increase from oxidation of the anode. The electrons freed at the anode in oxidation flow toward the cathode where they cause other electrons to bump into position to take part in the reduction process.

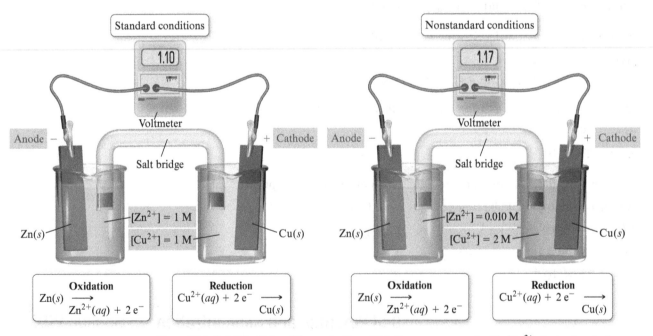

Figure 20.8 Cell Potential and Concentration This figure compares the Zn/Cu^{2+} electrochemical cell under standard and nonstandard conditions. In this case, the nonstandard conditions consist of a higher Cu^{2+} concentration ($[Cu^{2+}] > 1$ M) at the cathode and a lower Zn^{2+} concentration at the anode ($[Zn^{2+}] < 1$ M). According to Le Châtelier's principle, the forward reaction has a greater tendency to occur, resulting in a greater overall cell potential than the cell potential under standard conditions.

A Concentration Cell

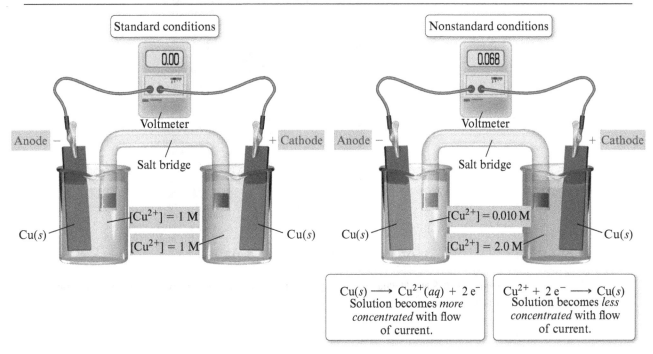

Figure 20.9 Cu/Cu⁺ Concentration Cell   If two half-cells have the same Cu^{2+} concentration, the cell potential is zero. If one half-cell has a greater Cu^{2+} concentration than the other, a spontaneous reaction occurs. In the reaction, Cu^{2+} ions in the more concentrated cell are reduced (to solid copper), while Cu^{2+} ions in the more dilute cell are formed (from solid copper). The concentration of copper ions in the two half-cells tends toward equality.

Batteries: Using Chemistry to Generate Electricity   Section 20.7

Batteries work on the same principles of the anode freeing up electrons and moving to the cathode. When the anode is used up, the battery stops. In rechargeable batteries, electricity is added to reverse the reaction back to where it can again run spontaneously in the forward direction. For different types of batteries, students should be able to identify the anode, cathode, and direction of electron flow.

Electrolysis: Driving Nonspontaneous Chemical Reactions with Electricity   Section 20.8

When reactions are nonspontaneous, energy needs to be added to cause the reaction to go in a process called electrolysis. There are many uses for this type of process, including electroplating.

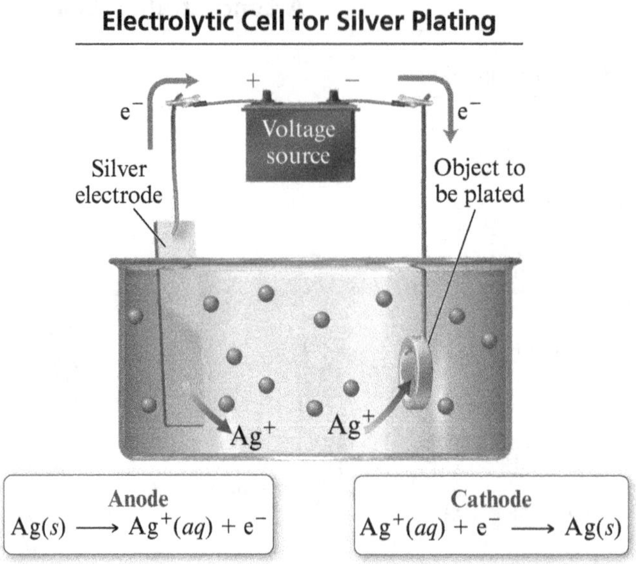

Electrolytic Cell for Silver Plating

Figure 20.10 Silver Plating   Silver can be plated from a solution of silver ions onto metallic objects in an electrolytic cell.

In this example, the energy source takes free silver ions, and plates them onto a less active metal such as gold.

Half-reaction	E°(V)
$Au^{3+} + 3e^- \rightarrow Au$	+1.50
$Ag^+ + e^- \rightarrow Ag$	+0.80
$Ni^{2+} + 2e^- \rightarrow Ni$	−0.23

$Ni(s) + 2Ag^+(aq) \rightarrow Ni^{2+}(aq) + 2Ag(s)$
$0.23 + 0.80 = E°$
$E° = 1.03 \text{ V}$

This reaction is thermodynamically favored and will not require electrolysis to occur.

$Au(s) + 3Ag^+(aq) \rightarrow Au^{3+}(aq) + 3Ag(s)$
$-1.50 + 0.80 = E°$
$E° = -0.70 \text{ V}$

This reaction is NOT thermodynamically favored and will require electrolysis to occur.

When calculating the amount of a substance that could be plated, generated, or deposited in an electrolysis reaction, the number of electrons added needs to be known. This requires knowing the current added, the time it ran, and Faraday's constant (F), which represents the energy to move 1 mole of electrons through the system. The current is measured in amperes (A), which is the number of coulombs per second.

Electrolysis of an Aqueous Salt Solution

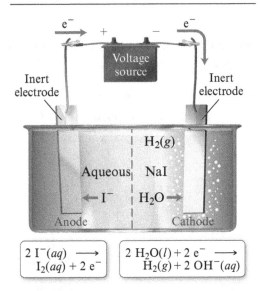

Figure 20.11 Electrolysis of Aqueous NaI In this cell, I^- is oxidized to I_2 at the anode and H_2O is reduced to H_2 at the cathode. Sodium ions are not reduced because their electrode potential is more negative than the electrode potential of water.

The Faraday constant is 96,485 coulombs (C) per mole of electrons. If 2.5 amperes ran for 20 minutes (1200 seconds), the number of electrons moving through the system would be

$$2.5 \text{ A} \times 1200 \text{ s} \times \frac{1 \text{ C}}{\text{A} \cdot \text{s}} \times \frac{1 \text{ mol e}^-}{96,485 \text{ C}} = 0.031 \text{ mol of electrons.}$$

Then, knowing the substance and the number of electrons (stoichiometry), one can make the final calculations. For instance, if the metal silver was to be plated, then $Ag^+(aq) + 1 \text{ e}^- \rightarrow Ag(s)$ and 1 mole of electrons are needed to plate 1 mole of silver. This is a ratio of 1/1. Given 0.031 mole of electrons:

$$0.031 \text{ mol e}^- \times \frac{1 \text{ mol Ag}}{1 \text{ mol e}^-} = 0.031 \text{ mol Ag.}$$

When this is multiplied by the molar mass of 196.97 g/mol, 6.1 g of silver can be plated.

These types of problems can be done as one long problem instead of in parts.

$$2.5 \text{ A} \times 1200 \text{ s} \times \frac{1 \text{ C}}{\text{A} \cdot \text{s}} \times \frac{1 \text{ mol e}^-}{96,485 \text{ C}} \times \frac{1 \text{ mol Ag}}{1 \text{ mol e}^-} \times \frac{196.97 \text{ g}}{\text{mol Ag}} = 6.1 \text{ g Ag}$$

If the cation was instead copper(II), the amount would change since $Cu^{2+}(aq) + 2 \text{ e}^- \rightarrow Cu(s)$ is a ratio of 2 electrons per mole of copper.

$$0.031 \text{ mol e}^- \times \frac{1 \text{ mol Cu}}{2 \text{ mol e}^-} = 0.016 \text{ mol Cu.}$$

These could then be converted to grams by multiplying by the molar mass of 63.55 g/mol in this case.

The problem can be done in reverse by asking how much current needs to be added to plate 2.50 grams of copper from copper(II) cations in 10.0 minutes?

$$2.50 \text{ g Cu} \times \frac{1 \text{ mol Cu}}{63.55 \text{ g}} \times \frac{2 \text{ mol e}^-}{1 \text{ mol Cu}} \times \frac{96{,}485 \text{ C}}{1 \text{ mol e}^-} \times \frac{1 \text{ A} \cdot \text{s}}{1 \text{ C}} \times \frac{x}{600 \text{ s}} = 12.7 \text{ A}$$

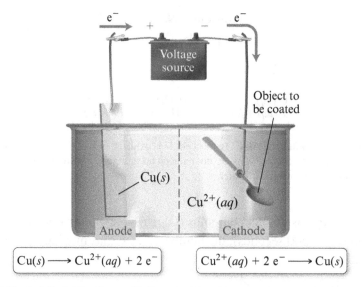

Figure 20.12 Electrolytic Cell for Copper Plating   In this cell, copper ions are plated onto other metals. It takes two moles of electrons to plate one mole of copper atoms.

Another simple example of an electrolysis process is the electrolysis of water. Here stable water will actually split into hydrogen and oxygen gas, a nonspontaneous process. See Figure 20.13.

For reactions with negative voltage, it will take the addition of this amount of voltage to cause the reaction to happen. See Figure 20.14.

When predicting the product of electrolysis reactions, it depends on if the substance is molten or in aqueous solution. If the substance is molten (a hot liquid with no water present), such as molten sodium chloride, the cation will reduce and the anion will oxidize. In this case, the sodium ion (Na^+) will form the metal Na, and chloride ion (Cl^-) will form chlorine gas (Cl_2). See Figure 20.15.

If there is a mixture of salts, then the metal ion being reduced first will be the one requiring the least amount of energy. This can be determined from a table of reduction potentials. For instance, in a mixture of calcium chloride and aluminum bromide, the $Al^{3+}(aq) + 3 \text{ e}^- \rightarrow Al(s)$ is -1.66 V which means 1.66 V needs to be added, while the $Ca^{2+}(aq) + 2 \text{ e}^- \rightarrow Ca(s)$ is -2.76 V and requires the addition of 2.76 V. The Al reaction will happen first since it requires less additional energy.

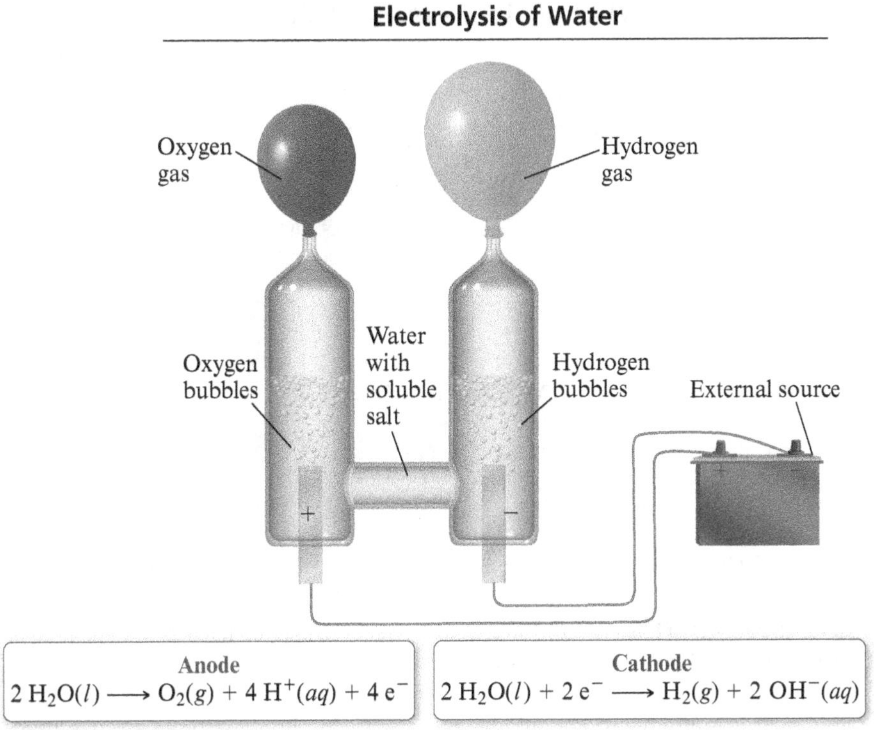

Electrolysis of Water

Oxygen gas

Hydrogen gas

Oxygen bubbles

Water with soluble salt

Hydrogen bubbles

External source

Anode	Cathode
$2 H_2O(l) \longrightarrow O_2(g) + 4 H^+(aq) + 4 e^-$	$2 H_2O(l) + 2 e^- \longrightarrow H_2(g) + 2 OH^-(aq)$

Figure 20.13 Electrolysis of Water   Electrical current can decompose water into hydrogen and oxygen gas.

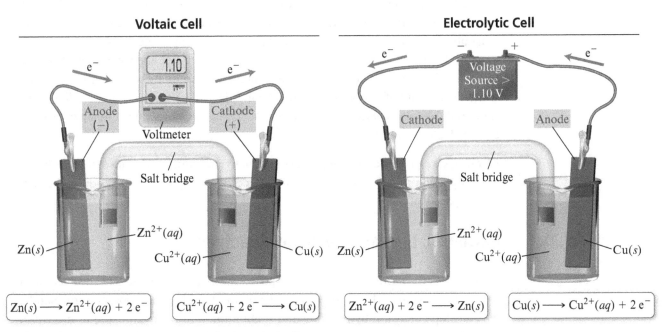

Voltaic Cell

e^-

1.10

e^-

Anode (−)

Voltmeter

Cathode (+)

Salt bridge

$Zn^{2+}(aq)$

$Cu^{2+}(aq)$

$Zn(s)$

$Cu(s)$

$Zn(s) \longrightarrow Zn^{2+}(aq) + 2 e^-$	$Cu^{2+}(aq) + 2 e^- \longrightarrow Cu(s)$

Electrolytic Cell

e^-

− +

Voltage Source > 1.10 V

e^-

Cathode

Anode

Salt bridge

$Zn^{2+}(aq)$

$Cu^{2+}(aq)$

$Zn(s)$

$Cu(s)$

$Zn^{2+}(aq) + 2 e^- \longrightarrow Zn(s)$	$Cu(s) \longrightarrow Cu^{2+}(aq) + 2 e^-$

Figure 20.14 Voltaic versus Electrolytic Cells   In a Zn/Cu^{2+} voltaic cell, the reaction proceeds in a thermodynamically favorable direction. In a Zn^{2+}/Cu electrolytic cell, electrical current drives the reaction in a thermodynamically unfavorable direction.

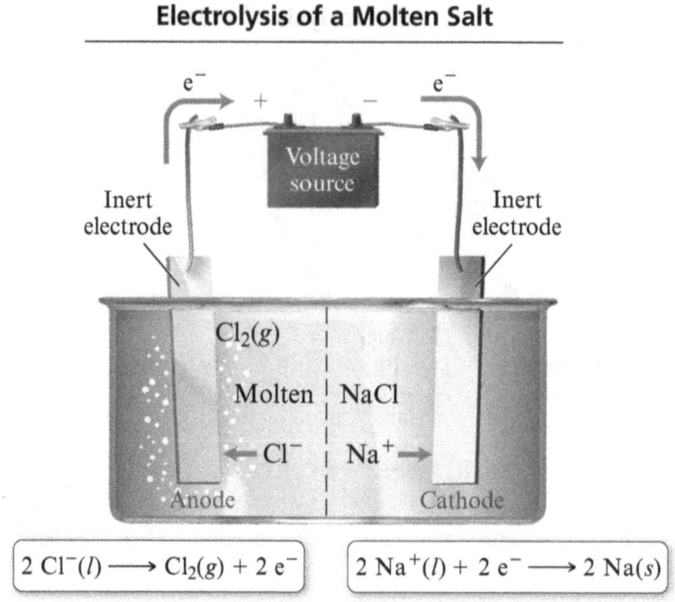

Electrolysis of a Molten Salt

$$2\ Cl^-(l) \longrightarrow Cl_2(g) + 2\ e^-$$

$$2\ Na^+(l) + 2\ e^- \longrightarrow 2\ Na(s)$$

Figure 20.15 Electrolysis of Molten NaCl   In the electrolysis of a pure molten salt, the anion (in this case Cl^-) is oxidized and the cation (in this case Na^+) is reduced.

The same is true of the anion; the one more easily oxidized will occur first. Again, simply compare voltage numbers. The chloride reaction takes more energy than the bromide reaction, so the bromide reaction will occur first.

When water is absent, in the case of the molten sodium iodide, sodium ions will be reduced and iodide ions will be oxidized. If the sodium iodide is in solution with water, this is not the case! If the substance is in a water solution, a reaction with water must also be considered. Instead, water is reduced to hydrogen gas and hydroxide ions, while the iodide is still oxidized. Why? The amount of energy needed to reduce the water ($-0.41\,V$) is less than what is needed to reduce the sodium ($-2.71\,V$), while the amount of energy to oxidize the iodide ($0.54\,V$) is less than oxidizing the water ($0.82\,V$). In general, very active metal cations are not reduced in aqueous solution in electrolysis reactions (Li^+, K^+, Na^+, Mg^{2+}, Ca^{2+}, and Al^{3+}).

Electrolysis is a very common process conducted in industry. Because of its stability, gold is plated on many exposed metal surfaces of the space shuttle and the international space station.

Section 20.9   Corrosion: Undesirable Redox Reactions

Corrosion is the oxidation of metals exposed in the environment. For instance, iron will oxidize to iron(III) oxide or rust. Knowing the electrode potential of metals, we can stop corrosion by painting and sealing the iron from exposure to moisture, electrolytes such as sodium chloride, and acids. One source of a protective layer is coating of zinc. This process is called galvanizing.

Additional Practice

Self-Assessment Quiz Questions Q1, Q2, Q3, Q4, Q5, Q6, Q7, Q8, Q9, Q10, Q11, Q12, Q13, Q14, and Q15

Problems:
Review Questions 4, 7, 12, 13, 18, 30, 31, and 36
Balancing Redox Reactions 37, 38, and 41
Voltaic Cells, Standard Potentials, and Direction of Spontaneity 43, 47 (a, b, and d), 48 (a, b, and d), 51, 53, 55, 56, 57, and 61
Cell Potential, Free Energy, and the Equilibrium Constant 65 and 72
Nonstandard Conditions and the Nernst Equation 73 and 80
Batteries, Fuel Cells, and Corrosion 88
Electrolytic Cells and Electrolysis 89, 92, 95, 99, 100, 103, and 104
Cumulative Problems 105, 106, and 117
Conceptual Problems 138, 139, 140, and 141
Data Interpretation and Analysis 147

Equations to know:

$1 \text{ A} = 1 \text{ C/s}$

$1 \text{ V} = 1 \text{ J/s}$

$2 \text{ H}^+(aq) + 2 \text{ e}^- \longrightarrow \text{H}_2(g) \quad E° = 0.00 \text{ V}$

$E°_{cell} = E°_{cathode} - E°_{anode}$

$\Delta G° = -nFE°_{cell} \qquad F = \dfrac{96{,}485 \text{ C}}{\text{mol e}^-}$

$E°_{cell} = \dfrac{0.0592 \text{ V}}{n} \log K \qquad \text{(at 25 °C)}$

$E_{cell} = E°_{cell} - \dfrac{0.0592 \text{ V}}{n} \log Q \qquad \text{(at 25 °C)}$

Practice AP Test Questions

Questions 1 and 2 pertain to the following diagrams situation: Consider Cell X and Cell Y, both operating at 25 °C and 1.0 atm pressure.

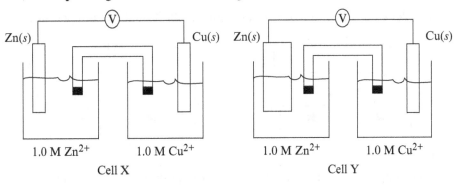

1. The $E°$ generated by Cell Y is _____ the $E°$ generated by Cell X.

    A) less than

    B) the same as

    C) greater than

    D) unknown compared to

2. Which statement is true as Cell X operates?

    A) Oxidation occurs at the copper electrode.

    B) The concentration of the Cu^{2+} ions in the Cu^{2+} solution will increase.

    C) The mass of the copper electrode will decrease.

    D) Electrons will migrate in the wire from the zinc electrode to the copper electrode.

3. An electrochemical cell Z is constructed using a silver electrode in 1.0 M silver nitrate and a copper electrode in 1.0 M copper(II) nitrate.

Half-cell reaction	$E°$
$Ag^+(aq) + e \rightarrow Ag(s)$	+0.800 V
$Cu^{2+}(aq) + 2\,e^- \rightarrow Cu(s)$	+0.340 V

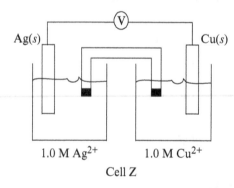

Cell Z

    A) 0.46 V   C) 1.26 V

    B) 1.14 V   D) 1.94 V

4. Consider Cell X and Cell Y, both operating at 25 °C and 1.0 atm pressure.

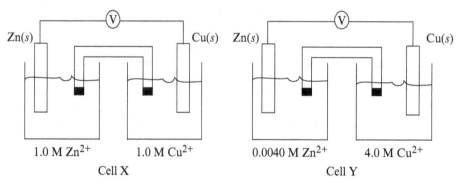

The emf, E, generated by Cell Y is _____ the emf, E, generated by Cell X.

A) less than

C) greater than

B) the same as

D) unknown compared to

Questions 5, 6, and 7 pertain to the following description and diagram. The diagram below shows an electrolytic cell in which an electric current passes through hot liquid calcium bromide, $CaBr_2(l)$, using inert electrodes.

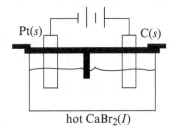

Pt(s)   C(s)

hot $CaBr_2(I)$

5. At the carbon electrode, bromide ions are oxidized.

A) True

B) False

6. The reason for my answer in 5:

A) Copper(II) ions move to the carbon electrode and accept electrons.

B) Copper(II) ions move to the carbon electrode and donate electrons.

C) Bromide ions move to the carbon electrode and accept electrons.

D) Bromide ions move to the carbon electrode and donate electrons.

7. Calculate the mass of calcium metal, in units of grams, produced by electrolysis when a current of 15.0 amps is passed through the liquid calcium bromide for 10.0 hours.

A) 0.0311 g

B) 11.2 g

C) 61.0 g

D) 112 g

8. Calculate the cell potential for the following electrochemical cell at 25 °C and determine if the reaction is thermodynamically favorable or not.

$$Mg(s) \mid Mg^{2+}(aq,\ 1.00\ M) \mid\mid Cu^{2+}(aq,\ 1.00\ M) \mid Cu(s)$$

Half-Reaction	Standard Reduction Potential (Volts)
$Cu^{2+} + 2e^- > Cu(s)$	+0.34
$Mn^{2+} + 2e^- > Mn(s)$	−1.18
$Mg^{2+} + 2e^- > Mg(s)$	−2.37

A) −2.03 V, thermodynamically unfavorable

B) +2.03 V, thermodynamically favorable

C) +2.71 V, thermodynamically favorable

D) −2.71 V, thermodynamically unfavorable

The following information pertains to Questions 9 and 10. An aqueous solution of potassium permanganate has a purple color, an aqueous solution of Mn^{2+} is colorless, and an aqueous solution of oxalic acid, $H_2C_2O_4$, is colorless. When oxalic acid is titrated with potassium permanganate, the purple color of $MnO_4^-(aq)$ fades to colorless, due to the reaction of MnO_4^- to Mn^{2+}

9. What element is being oxidized in the following redox reaction?

$MnO_4^-(aq) + H_2C_2O_4(aq) \rightarrow Mn^{2+}(aq) + CO_2(g)$

A) Mn

B) O

C) C

D) H

10. Determine the coefficients in front of $H_2C_2O_4$ and H_2O in the balanced reaction, assuming the reaction occurs in acidic solution.

$MnO_4^-(aq) + H_2C_2O_4(aq) \rightarrow Mn^{2+}(aq) + CO_2(g)$

A) $H_2C_2O_4 = 5, H_2O = 8$

B) $H_2C_2O_4 = 1, H_2O = 1$

C) $H_2C_2O_4 = 5, H_2O = 1$

D) $H_2C_2O_4 = 3, H_2O = 2$

Chapter 20 Practice AP Test Questions Answers:

1. B); 2. D); 3. A); 4. C); 5. B); 6. D); 7. D); 8. B); 9. C); 10. A)

Data Interpretation and Analysis Question: Galvanic Cells

In a laboratory experiment, a galvanic cell is constructed with a magnesium electrode immersed in 1.0 M magnesium nitrate solution and a copper electrode immersed in 1.0 M copper(II) nitrate solution. The temperature is 25 °C and the pressure is 1.00 atm. The galvanic cell is represented in the diagram below.

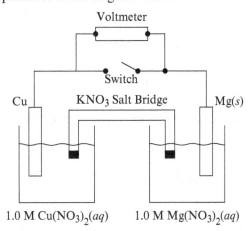

Voltmeter

Switch

Cu   KNO₃ Salt Bridge   Mg(s)

1.0 M Cu(NO₃)₂(aq)   1.0 M Mg(NO₃)₂(aq)

Table 1   lists standard electrode potentials for magnesium and copper

Half-Reaction	$E°$(V)
$Cu^{2+}(aq) + 2\ e^- \rightarrow Cu(s)$	+0.34
$Mg^{2+}(aq) + 2\ e^- \rightarrow Mg(s)$	−2.37

Before the switch is closed and the galvanic cell operates, the dry metal electrodes are weighed and the masses recorded. When the cell operates for 6.00 minutes, the voltage of the cell is recorded every 30 seconds and an ammeter inserted in the circuit shows a current of 0.120 A. At the end of the experiment, the electrodes are dried and the masses are recorded. The mass of copper electrode increased, and the mass of magnesium electrode decreased.

a) Determine $E°_{cell}$.

b) Write the chemical equation reaction representing what occurs in this galvanic cell.

c) Identify the electrode serving as the cathode. Explain.

d) Write the half-reaction that occurs at the cathode when the cell operates.

e) How does the mass of the copper electrode gain mass?

f) Sketch a particulate drawing showing what occurs at the interface of the copper electrode and the copper(II) nitrate solution.

g) Determine the mass of copper plated on the copper electrode.

h) What happens to the mass of the magnesium electrode that is being removed? Where does the mass go?

i) As the cell operates, does the measured voltage of the cell increase, decrease, or remain the same?

j) If you were to repeat this experiment,
   a. What would you do, and what data would you collect to confirm your answers to parts e and f?
   b. How would you do differently to the setup of the galvanic cell, without changing the identities of the magnesium and copper half-cells, to increase both the E_{cell}° and the current?

Data Interpretation and Analysis Question Answers with Brief Explanations

a) $E_{cell}^\circ = +0.34\ \text{V} - (-2.37\ \text{V}) = +2.71\ \text{V}$

b) $Mg(s) + Cu^{2+}(aq) \rightleftharpoons Mg^{2+}(aq) + Cu(s)$

c) Reduction occurs at the cathode. The copper electrode serves as the cathode because at the copper electrode Cu^{2+} ions are being reduced to Cu atoms.

d) $Cu^{2+}(aq) + 2\ e^- \rightleftharpoons Cu(s)$

e) Cu^{2+} ions from the copper(II) nitrate solution gain two electrons and become copper atoms attached to the copper electrode.

f) Cu(s) electrode

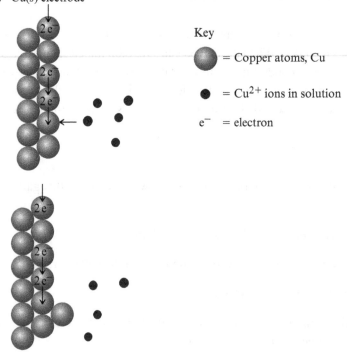

g) $0.120 \text{ A} \times 360 \text{ s} = 43.2 \text{ A} \cdot \text{s} \times \dfrac{1 \text{ C}}{1 \text{ A} \cdot \text{s}} = 43.2 \text{ C}$

$43.2 \text{ C} \times \dfrac{1 \text{ mol Cu}}{2 \text{ mol e}^-} = 2.24 \times 10^{-4} \text{ mol Cu} \times \dfrac{63.55 \text{ g}}{1 \text{ mol Cu}} = 0.0142 \text{ g Cu}$

h) The magnesium atoms on the magnesium electrode are being converted to Mg^{2+} ions. These ions enter the magnesium nitrate solution.

i) As the cell operates, the measured cell voltage decreases.

j) The initial masses of the solution should be determined before the start of the experiment, and then the mass of the solutions should be determined after the cell operates. One would need to measure the mass of the dry containers before the experiment, then fill each container with solution and weigh it again. Weigh the container and its solution after the cell operates. To increase the current, one could increase the size of the electrodes. If the concentrations of the solutions were kept at 1.0 M, increasing the size of the electrodes would not increase the E°_{cell}. Decreasing the concentration of the copper(II) nitrate solution to 0.050 M and increasing the concentration of the magnesium nitrate solution to 1.50 M will increase E°_{cell}.

READING GUIDE

Unit 9 encompasses the concepts of electrochemistry covered in this chapter. Oxidation–reduction reactions, voltaic cells, electrode potentials, cell potentials, and electrolysis are concepts important to understand. Remember the AP Exam will not use the terms spontaneous and nonspontaneous.

Section 20.1 **Lightning and Batteries**

    1. What is the most common type of fuel cell? Write the reaction that occurs in this cell.* How does a reaction generate an electrical current to produce electricity?

Section 20.2 **Balancing Oxidation–Reduction Equations**

    2. Identify the steps to balancing an oxidation–reduction reaction.

    3. Use the identified steps and balance $Al(s) + Ag^+(aq) \rightarrow Al^{3+}(aq) + Ag(s)$.

    4. What adjustments are made for a reaction done in acidic solution? Basic solution?

Section 20.3 **Voltaic (or Galvanic) Cells: Generating Electricity from Spontaneous Chemical Reactions**

    5. Vocabulary: The language of electrochemistry has several words unique to this part of chemistry. Define the following:

        Electrical current:

        Electrochemical cell:

        Voltaic cell:

        Electrolytic cell:

Half-cell:

Electrodes:

Amperes:

Volts:

Potential difference:

EMF:

Cell potential:

Standard cell potential:

Cathode:

Anode:

Salt bridge:

Note: Students need to be able to identify the cathode and anode in electrochemical cells, but are not required to label the electrodes as positive or negative.

6. Explain what is occurring in the beaker below. What evidence supports your explanation? Write a balanced net equation for the reaction.

A Thermodynamically Favored Redox Reaction: Zn + Cu^{2+}

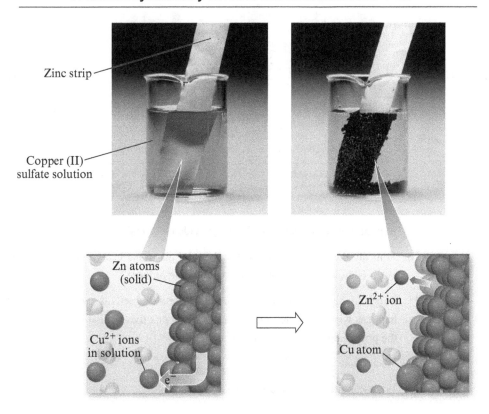

7. In the below flowchart, add where the different types of electrochemical cells should be.

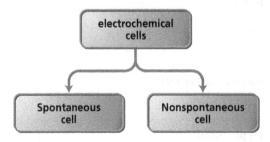

8. Label on the diagram below the following: anode, cathode, salt bridge, electrodes, half-cell. Draw arrows to show the direction of electron flow. Where does a negative charge build up occur? Where does a positive charge build up occur? What if the charge build up is not neutralized?

A Voltaic Cell

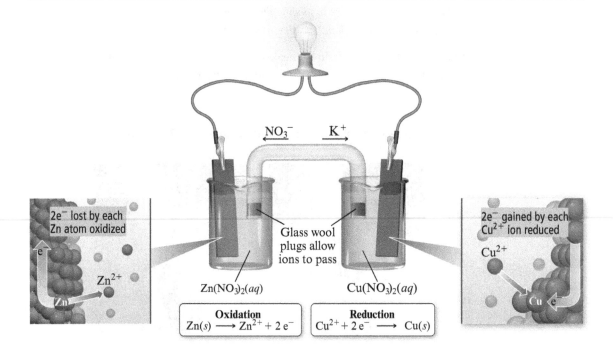

9. Explain how electrochemical cells provide electrical energy.

10. Volts are the unit used for electrical potentials. What is a volt equivalent to? What is the difference between a volt and an ampere?

11. Explain what happens when the potential between cells is zero. Why? What happens when the potential between cells is positive? What happens when the potential between cells is negative?

12. What creates current?

13. What conditions are standard for cell potential?

14. Explain what happens to the cation and anion in the salt bridge. Why? Draw an arrow on the figure showing where each migrates. Do electrons flow through the salt bridge? Explain your answer.

A Voltaic Cell

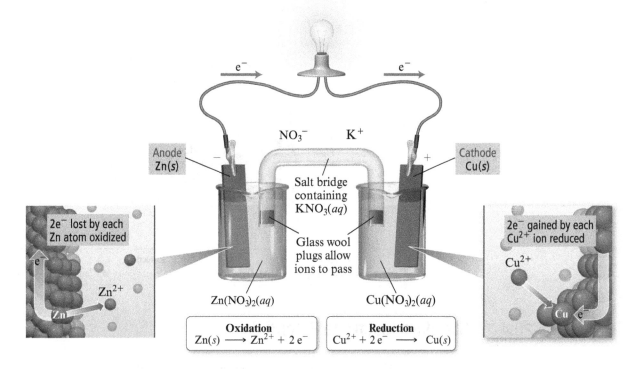

15. What does it mean "to complete the circuit"?

16. Use the following to explain what cell notation means:
$Al(s)\,|\,Al^{3+}(aq)\,|\,|\,Ag^{+}(aq)\,|\,Ag(s)$.

17. Write the cell notation for the reactions occurring in the below electrochemical cell. Why does this electrochemical cell need an inert electrode?

Inert Platinum Electrode

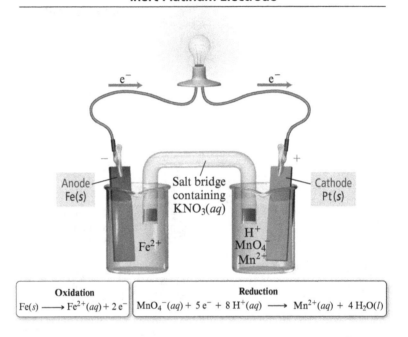

Oxidation	Reduction
$Fe(s) \longrightarrow Fe^{2+}(aq) + 2\,e^-$	$MnO_4^-(aq) + 5\,e^- + 8\,H^+(aq) \longrightarrow Mn^{2+}(aq) + 4\,H_2O(l)$

Section 20.4   Standard Electrode Potentials

18. How are standard electrode potentials determined?

19. What is the SHE and what reaction(s) occur at the SHE? Is the SHE an anode or a cathode? Explain your answer.

20. Explain what is happening in the figure below. Write the cell notation for the reaction occurring. What is the voltmeter measuring?

Measuring Half-Cell Potential with the SHE

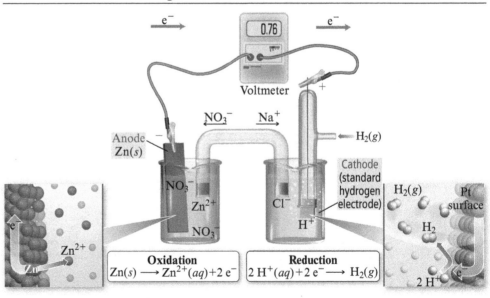

Oxidation	Reduction
$Zn(s) \longrightarrow Zn^{2+}(aq) + 2\,e^-$	$2\,H^+(aq) + 2\,e^- \longrightarrow H_2(g)$

21. What is the sign for E°_{cell} that is spontaneous? Nonspontaneous?

22. How is E°_{cell} calculated?

23. What types of potentials are the standard electrode potentials found on the table?

24. Determine the E°_{cell} for the reaction
$Al(s) + 3\,Ag^+(aq) \rightarrow Al^{3+}(aq) + 3\,Ag(s)$.

25. Explain how to use a reduction potentials table to predict, in general, if a metal will dissolve in acid. What acid is an exception? Why?

Cell Potential, Free Energy, and the Equilibrium Constant   Section 20.5

26. Fill in the following table:

E°_{cell}	K	ΔG°	Favored?
		>1	
	1		
>1			

27. What is the equation to calculate E°_{cell} from ΔG°? What does n stand for? F?

28. What is the charge in coulombs of 1 mole of electrons?

29. What is the equation to calculate E°_{cell} from K?

30. On the following diagram add the equations used to change between each of the quantities on the arrows between them:

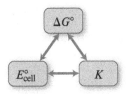

Cell Potential and Concentration   Section 20.6

31. Why doesn't a battery last forever?

32. Fill in the following table:

Concentrations	Q Compared to 1	E_{cell} Compared to E°_{cell}	Le Châtelier Explanation
Concentrations are 1 M			
Product [] > reactant []			
Reactant [] > product []			
Equilibrium []			

33. What is the Nernst equation? Use the Nernst equation to show why voltage is 0 at equilibrium, when it will be higher than standard potential, and when it will be lower than the standard potential.

34. Using the below image, explain why the voltage is higher in the second set-up when the reactions are the same:

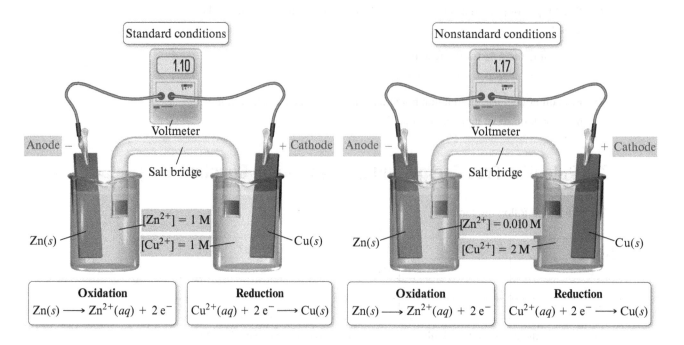

35. In a concentration cell, how can the anode and cathode be determined? Why? What evidence would support the assignment of anode and cathode as the cell runs?

36. Identify the anode and cathode. Draw an arrow of the direction of electron flow.

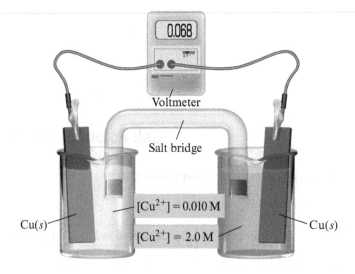

37. Explain why this concentration cell indicates zero voltage.

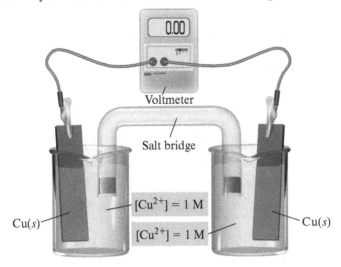

Batteries: Using Chemistry to Generate Electricity   Section 20.7

38. What are common everyday batteries called?*

39. What type of dry-cell battery has the longest "life"?*

40. Identify the anode and cathode in a dry-cell battery.*

(a)

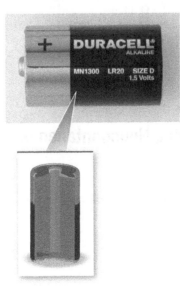

(b)

41. What types of batteries are common in cars? How can they produce 12 V when a cell only produces 2 V?*

42. What causes a lead–acid storage battery to go dead?*

43. What are three types of rechargeable batteries besides the lead–acid storage battery?*

44. Why are cadmium-based batteries such as the NiCad being replaced?*

45. What are lithium ion batteries most commonly used for? Why?*

46. Explain how a hydrogen-fuel cell works. Indicate the anode, cathode, and electron flow.*

Hydrogen–Oxygen Fuel Cell

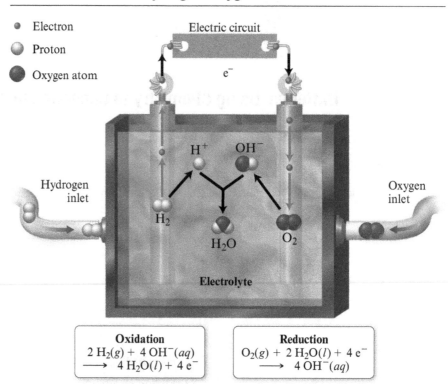

Oxidation
$$2\,H_2(g) + 4\,OH^-(aq) \longrightarrow 4\,H_2O(l) + 4\,e^-$$

Reduction
$$O_2(g) + 2\,H_2O(l) + 4\,e^- \longrightarrow 4\,OH^-(aq)$$

47. In the space shuttle program, what is generated water used for?*

Section 20.8   Electrolysis: Driving Nonspontaneous Chemical Reactions with Electricity

48. What type of reaction is electrolysis used for?

49. Using the figure below, identify and explain two differences between a voltaic cell and an electrolytic cell:

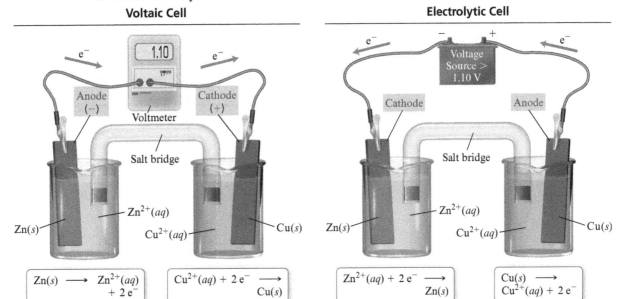

50. Explain how to predict the products of electrolysis in the following (include equations as evidence):

Molten KBr:

A mixture of NaCl and KBr:

Aqueous KCl:

51. Explain why, when current is added to pure water, no reaction occurs, but, when added to an aqueous solution, a reaction occurs.

52. How do you determine the number of moles of electrons being used in electrolysis?

53. Identify three uses of electrolysis in industry.

Corrosion: Undesirable Redox Reactions   Section 20.9

54. What is corrosion?

55. Why is aluminum metal stable?

56. Why is the oxidized coating on iron not stable?

57. What are three important components for the rusting of iron?

58. How does industry keep iron from rusting? Identify three ways.

59. What are galvanized nails?

Self-Assessment Answers

1. _____   2. _____   3. _____

4. _____   5. _____   6. _____

7. _____   8. _____   9. _____

10. _____   11. _____   12. _____

13. _____   14. _____   15. _____

RADIOACTIVITY AND NUCLEAR CHEMISTRY

Although a fascinating chapter full of discoveries that have affected our everyday lives, the AP Chemistry Framework no longer includes Nuclear Chemistry. The topics are considered to be prior knowledge for the course or are covered in a later course in chemistry. Through many experiments with radioactivity, knowledge was gained about nuclear binding energy, mass defect, and the structure of the atom. The one section pertaining to the AP exam is on kinetics since nuclear reactions are first-order reactions.

The important sections are:

    21.3 **Types of Radioactivity**

    21.6 **The Kinetics of Radioactive Decay and Radiometric Dating**

    21.8 **Converting Mass to Energy: Mass Defect and Nuclear Binding Energy**

Specific Learning Objectives Addressed in This Chapter:

SAP-1 Atoms and molecules can be identified by their electron distribution and energy.

SAP-1.A Represent the electron configuration of an element or ions of an element using the Aufbau principle:

- The atom is composed of negatively charged electrons and a positively charged nucleus that is made of protons and neutrons.

TRA-3 Some reactions happen quickly, while others happen more slowly and depend on reactant concentrations and temperature.

TRA-3.C Identify the rate law expression of a chemical reaction using data that show how the concentrations of reaction species change over time:

- Half-life is a critical parameter for first-order reactions because the half-life is constant.
- Radioactive decay processes provide an important illustration of first-order kinetics.

Concepts and Vocabulary to Review:

The Kinetics of Radioactive Decay and Radiometric Dating   Section 21.6

All radioactive decay follows first-order kinetics. Nuclear reactions therefore use the first-order integrated rate law and half-life equations. If the half-life is known, the rate constant (k) can be solved for. The units of k will be the unit of time^{-1}.

$$t_{1/2} = \frac{0.693}{k}$$

$$\ln\frac{N_t}{N_0} = -kt$$

The only difference is instead of concentrations in the integrated rate law the number of nuclides (N) is used.

Nuclides with short half-lives will have large rate constants compared to those with long half-lives and small rate constants. Looking at a graph with atoms and time, we find that when half the sample is gone one half-life has occurred.

Decay of Radon-220

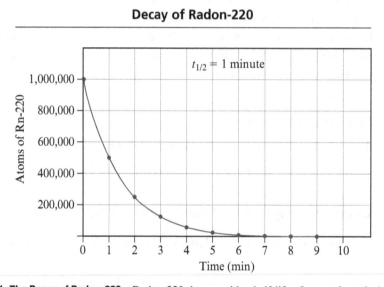

Figure 21.1 **The Decay of Radon-220**   Radon-220 decays with a half-life of approximately 1 minute.

From the graph N_0 is 1,000,000 and after 1 minute (the half-life), N_t is 500,000. Substituting and solving, k is 0.69 min^{-1}

The next half-life is when half of the remaining sample is gone. This would drop the sample to one-fourth of the original sample. Radioactive dating can be used to estimate the age of materials.

Half-Life →	1st	2nd	3rd	4th
% lost	50	75	87.5	93.75
% left	50	25	13.5	6.25
Fraction left	1/2	1/4	1/8	1/16
Fraction lost	1/2	3/4	7/8	15/16

C-14 dating can be used to date old bristlecone pine trees. The type of dating used depends on the material being sampled.

Additional Practice

Self-Assessment Quiz Questions Q5 and Q6
Problems 14, 45, 47, 106, and 115

Practice AP Test Questions

Questions 1–5 refer to the following information and graph. The decay of a 10.0 gram sample of strontium-90 is represented by plotting mass versus time in the graph below.

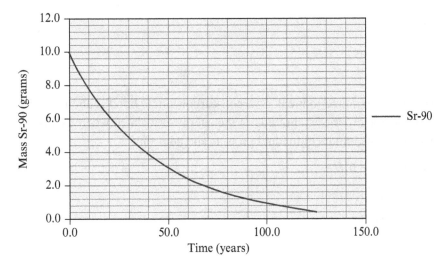

1. What is the half-life of strontium-90?

   A) 14.4 years

   B) 20.0 years

   C) 28.8 years

   D) 50.0 years

2. How much Sr-90 remains after three half-lives?

   A) 7.25 grams

   B) 5.00 grams

   C) 2.50 grams

   D) 1.25 grams

3. Strontium-90 decays to yttrium-90 by what decay process?

   A) alpha emission

   B) beta emission

   C) gamma emission

   D) electron capture or positron emission

4. Which of the following will slow down the radioactive decay process of a sample of strontium-90?

   A) lower the temperature

   B) decrease the pressure

   C) place the sample in a lead box

   D) Nothing will slow down the radioactive decay process.

5. The number of neutrons in strontium-90 is

   A) 38.

   B) 52.

   C) 76.

   D) 90.

6. The energy required to break a carbon-carbon single bond is about 350 kJ/mol. Estimate the order of magnitude of the energy associated when a carbon-12 nucleus splits into its individual protons and neutrons.

   $$^{12}_{6}C \rightarrow 6^{1}_{0}n + 6^{1}_{1}H$$

   A) 1×10^{1} kJ/mol

   B) 1×10^{4} kJ/mol

   C) 1×10^{8} kJ/mol

   D) 1×10^{12} kJ/mol

7. For the following process

   $$^{12}_{6}C \rightarrow 6^{1}_{0}n + 6^{1}_{1}H$$

   Energy is

   A) released and the process is exothermic.

   B) absorbed and the process is endothermic.

   C) released and the process is endothermic.

   D) absorbed and the process is exothermic.

8. Electromagnetic radiation having the **highest** energy is exhibited by

   A) radio.

   B) ultraviolet.

   C) gamma rays.

   D) X-rays.

9. A thin block of wood or two layers of clothing can form an effective shield against what type of radiation?

   A) Beta particles

   B) Infrared

   C) Gamma rays

   D) X-rays

10. An archeological artifact was subjected to radiocarbon dating in order to estimate its age. The wooden handle showed a carbon-14 decay rate of 13.5 counts/min per gram of carbon. Currently, living material, such as trees, exhibits a first-order rate decay of carbon-14 of 15 counts/min per gram of carbon. Carbon-14 has a half-life of about 5720 years. What is the approximate age of the wooden handle?

    A) 250 years old

    B) 350 years old

    C) 600 years old

    D) 850 years old

Chapter 21 Practice AP Test Questions Answers:

1. C); 2. D); 3. B); 4. D); 5. B); 6. D); 7. B); 8. C); 9. A); 10. D)

Data Interpretation and Analysis Question: Seaweed

Table 1 Amount of I-131 detected in samples of seaweed collected in the coastal waters of southern California.

Days	I-131 (Bq/kg)
10	25
20	28
30	27
40	28
60	280
70	140
80	70
100	35
140	25
120	25
160	300
170	150
10	25
20	28
30	27
40	28

After Japan's Fukushima Daiichi nuclear plant incident on March 12, 2011, the U.S. Environmental Protection Agency (EPA) detected an increase in levels of I-131 in the seawater in bays and in several drinking water samples in cities on California's west coast. The Fukushima Daiichi nuclear plant incident did release I-131 radiation. Iodine-131 is a short-lived radioactive element, with a half-life of 8.02 days.

Currently, I-131 is used in medicine to diagnose and treat disorders of the thyroid gland. Most large cities in southern California have hospitals treating patients with I-131. The compound is also used as a radioactive tracer in the hydraulic fracturing process associated with oil and gas extraction in California. Previous to March 2011, I-131 and other compounds used in fracking had been detected in drinking water from reservoirs and in seawater after accidental spills or unintentional releases.

The federal drinking safe water standard for Iodine-131 is an average of 3.0 pCi/L measured over several weeks.

Giant Kelp, *Macrocystis pyrifera* (commonly refereed to as seaweed), concentrates iodine in its tissues. A sample of seaweed can be collected, analyzed, and the amount of I-131 can be measured. Table 1 shows I-131 amounts measured in seaweed collected in southern California over the course of 300 days from 2013–2014, in several areas.

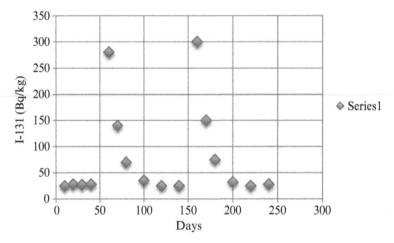

Figure 1 Amount of I-131 detected in samples of seaweed collected in the coastal waters of southern California.

a) Can the I-131 released from the Fukushima Daiichi nuclear plant be the same iodine detected in the drinking water and in the nearby seawater of southern California during collection period in the months of March–July? Explain.

b) How would you design an experiment and/or collect data to provide evidence to support or refute the claim that the I-131 released from medical facilities and/or by people being treated for thyroid conditions in southern California is the same I-131 found in drinking water from reservoirs and nearby seawater? What pattern would you expect the data collected to show?

c) How would you design an experiment and or collect data to provide evidence to support or refute the claim that the I-131 used in the hydraulic fracturing process associated with oil and that gas extraction is or is not the I-131 found in drinking water and nearby seawater of southern California? What pattern would you expect the data collected to show?

d) Do the measurements of I-313 in samples of seawater displayed in Table 1 indicate that I-131 is entering the nearby ocean water and bay areas in a continuous stream, or can the I-131 detected be considered a one-time incident from an accidental spill?

e) If the average amount of I-131 in drinking water taken from in-land reservoirs increased from 1.8 to 3.2 pCi/L from 2011 to 2016, what can be done to decrease the amount of I-131 in drinking water?

Data Interpretation and Analysis Question Answers with Brief Explanations

a) The I-131 released from the Fukushima Daiichi nuclear plant on March 12, 2011, cannot be the I-131 detected in southern California in March 2011 because I-131 has a half-life of 8.02 days. Nearly all of the I-313 from Fukushima would have decayed away.

b) One procedure is to measure the I-131 levels in seawater and in drinking water over a four-month time span. Have all of the hospitals in large cities in southern California, Los Angeles, San Diego, San Francisco area stop doing I-131 thyroid treatments for two weeks in month 2, then resume doing treatments but only half as many for two weeks, then stop treatments for two weeks in month 3. If the I-131 levels are due to hospital treatments, we would expect to see a rise and fall of I-131 levels.

c) One procedure is to monitor the I-131 levels in drinking water and in seawater for two months. At the beginning of month 3, have the fracking operations in the Los Angeles area stop using I-131 and start using a I-125 (half-life of 59 days) as the isotope tracer. For two weeks, stop all fracking operations. Then resume, fracking with the I-131 tracer. If the Iodine-131 levels drop, then increase and then if the Iodine-125 levels are zero, then increase, then decrease, the iodine amounts in the drinking water and seawater can be attributed to fracking.

d) The I-313 entering the southern California bay areas and ocean is in a continuous stream with the exception of two events.

e) In order to reduce the amount of I-131 in drinking water, freshwater aquatic plants having a propensity to absorb iodine can be grown in the drinking water in a reservoir. The plants can absorb the iodine from the water. This will reduce the I-131 amounts in the water to safe levels. Once the plants have absorbed all of the iodine they can absorb, they will be removed and replaced by fresh plants.

READING GUIDE

Nuclear chemistry is not part of the AP Chemistry curriculum, although nuclear reactions exhibit first-order kinetics half-lives. This material is important in today's world when so many current technologies and medical procedures use radioactivity. Many countries use nuclear reactors for the production of electricity.

Section 21.1

Diagnosing Appendicitis

1. What is radioactivity?

2. How can radioactive atoms detect appendicitis?

Section 21.2

The Discovery of Radioactivity

3. Explain what each of the following scientists discovered about radioactivity and what evidence supported their discovery:

   Antoine-Henri Becquerel:

   Marie Curie:

4. What is phosphorescence? What substances phosphoresce?

Section 21.3

Types of Radioactivity

5. Explain what each of the symbols in the following stand for: $_{Z}^{A}X$. What is a nuclide?

6. What are the symbols for proton, neutron, and electron?

7. Fill in the following table:

	Symbol(s)	Decay, Emission, or Capture	Composition/ Source	Effect on Mass	Effect on Proton Number	Effect on Neutron to Proton Ratio	Penetrating Power	Ionizing Power
Alpha Particle								
Beta Particle								
Gamma Ray								
Positron								
Electron								

8. What is an alpha particle similar to?

9. What must be equal for a nuclear equation to be balanced?

10. Write a balanced nuclear equation for the alpha decay of Uranium-238.

11. Explain the relationship between ionizing power and penetrating power. What particle has the highest penetrating power? Ionizing power?

12. Why is gamma radiation different from other decay methods?

13. What is a positron? What is the symbol for a positron?

The Valley of Stability: Predicting the Type of Radioactivity   Section 21.4

14. What is the strong force?

15. What determines the stability of the atom?

16. What role does the neutron play in stabilizing the nucleus? Explain.

17. Using the proton–neutron ratio, explain the valley (belt) of stability.

The Valley of Stability

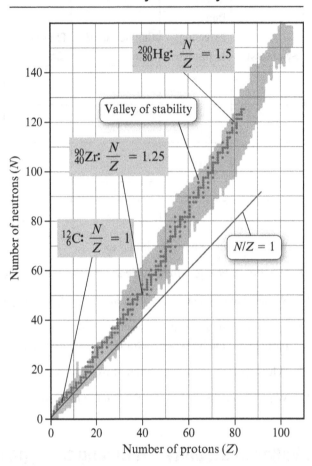

18. Using the concept of the proton–neutron ratio, explain how to predict how radioactive atoms reach stability when the ratio is high and when the ratio is low.

19. What are the magic numbers of nuclear stability? Why are these numbers important? What is a decay series? Include an example in your answer.

Section 21.5   Detecting Radioactivity

20. Explain how each of the following detect radioactivity:

    Thermoluminescent dosimeter:

    Geiger–Müller counter:

    Scintillation counter:

The Kinetics of Radioactive Decay and Radiometric Dating   Section 21.6

Note: The topics in this section could be included on an AP Chemistry Exam.

21. What is the order of kinetics for nuclear reactions?

22. What is the half-life equation for a nuclear reaction?

23. Explain how to read the half-life of this graph. What evidence in the graph supports the conclusion this exhibits is first-order kinetics?

Decay of Radon-220

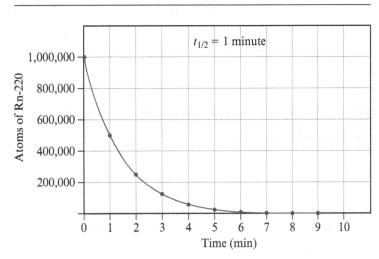

$t_{1/2} = 1$ minute

24. Write the integrated rate law for nuclear reactions. How is this different than the regular integrated rate law for first-order kinetics?

25. How is radioactive carbon used for dating? What types of substances can it date?

26. What tree is most commonly used to calibrate carbon dating? Why is it used?

27. How is uranium/lead used for dating? What types of substances can it date? What assumption is made in this type of dating?

The Discovery of Fission: The Atomic Bomb and Nuclear Power   Section 21.7

28. What experiment did Enrico Fermi undertake? What did the evidence show?

29. What scientists continued Fermi's work? What did they discover?

30. Explain the concept portrayed in this diagram:

$$^{235}_{92}U + ^{1}_{0}n \longrightarrow ^{140}_{56}Ba + ^{93}_{36}Kr + 3\,^{1}_{0}n + energy$$

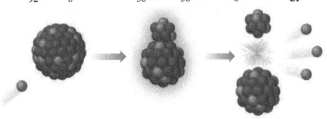

31. Explain the following concepts:

    Chain reaction:

    Critical mass:

32. What was the Manhattan Project? Why was it important?

33. How much of the world's electricity comes from nuclear power?

34. What are the benefits of nuclear power? Explain.

35. What are the problems associated with nuclear power? Explain.

36. Can a nuclear power plant produce a nuclear bomb? Explain your answer.

37. What happened at the Chernobyl and at the Fukushima Daiichi nuclear power plants? Why did each disaster happen?

Section 21.8

Converting Mass to Energy: Mass Defect and Nuclear Binding Energy

38. Explain why the mass of an atom is less than the sum of protons, neutrons, and electrons, individually. What is the name of this concept? How is this related to Einstein's in famous energy equation, $E = mc^2$?

39. What is nuclear binding energy? What does the unit MeV represent? How many joules is a MeV equal to?

40. Explain the significance of Fe-56 in the figure below:

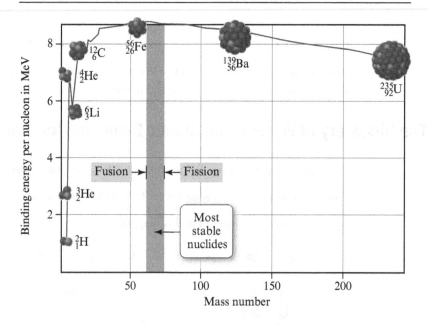

The Curve of Binding Energy

Nuclear Fusion: The Power of the Sun   Section 21.9

41. What is nuclear fusion? Can it occur on Earth? Justify your answer.

42. Write the nuclear equation for the deuterium–tritium fusion reaction. Why is nuclear fusion being researched for electrical power?

Nuclear Transmutation and Transuranium Elements   Section 21.10

43. What is transmutation?

44. Identify two machines that accelerate nuclear particles to high velocities?

45. How fast do particles go in these machines?

46. What discoveries have been made from experiments with these machines?

The Effects of Radiation on Life   Section 21.11

47. What are three effects of radiation on living things?

48. How is damage by radiation to living things measured?

49. Explain the difference among the following units: Ci, RBE, Gy, rad, and rem?

50. Identify four types of natural radiation everyone is exposed to.

Radioactivity in Medicine and Other Applications   Section 21.12

51. What is a radiotracer? How is it used? Identify three radiotracers and explain their use.

52. What is a PET scan and what can it be used for?

53. What is *irradiation* and why is it used with food?

54. How has irradiation been used to control fruitfly and mosquito populations?

Self-Assessment Answers

1. _____   2. _____

3. _____   4. _____

5. _____   6. _____

7. _____   8. _____

9. _____   10. _____

ORGANIC CHEMISTRY

Many sections of this chapter go into more detail than the AP curriculum requires. Although there are no specific learning objectives, students are expected to look at data and structures, including organic compounds, and analyze properties such as polarity, intermolecular forces, and boiling points. Many organic molecules are discussed during the year, such as weak organic acids like ethanoic (acetic) acid, where it will be helpful if the students can draw the structure, although on the AP exam students are usually given the structure. The major sections to understand are the naming systems, functional groups, and general characteristics of organic families:

Specific Learning Objectives Addressed in This Chapter:

SAP-3. Atoms or ions bond due to interactions between them, forming molecules.

SAP-3.A Explain the relationship between the type of bonding and the properties of the elements participating in the bond.

- 2. Valence electrons shared between atoms of similar electronegativity constitute a nonpolar covalent bond. For example, bonds between carbon and hydrogen are effectively nonpolar even though carbon is slightly more electronegative than hydrogen.
- 3. Valence electrons shared between atoms of unequal electronegativity constitute a polar bond.

SAP-3.B Represent the relationship between potential energy and the distance between atoms, based on factors that influence the interaction strength.

- 2. In a covalent bond, the bond length is influenced by the size of the atom's core and bond order (i.e., single double, triple). Bonds with a higher order are shorter and have larger bond energies.

SAP-5 Intermolecular Forces can explain the physical properties of a material.

SAP-5.A Explain the relationship between the chemical structures of molecules and the relative strength of their intermolecular forces when:
- The molecules are of the same chemical species.
- The molecules are of two different chemical species.

SAP-5.B Explain the relationship among the macroscopic properties of a substance, the particulate-level structure of the substance, and the interactions between these particles.

Concepts and Vocabulary to Review:

Carbon: Why It Is Unique   Section 22.2

Carbon has four valence electrons and can form four bonds. These can be all single bonds or combinations of single, double, and triple bonds. This allows for a wide variety of compounds since carbon can also bond to itself and form chains, branches, and ringed structures. The term used for carbon bonding to itself in long chains is catenation.

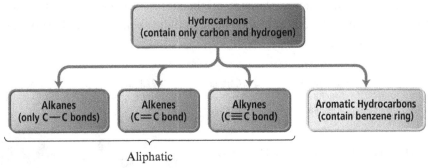

| Propane | Isobutane | Cyclohexane |

Silicon, which sits below carbon in the periodic table, does not have all these properties. Silicon is larger, making it more difficult to form double and triple bonds. Also, in the atmosphere, silicon will bond more readily to oxygen than to itself.

Hydrocarbons: Compounds Containing Only Carbon and Hydrogen   Section 22.3

Hydrocarbon compounds, which contain only carbon and hydrogen, are classified into four main groups.

Figure 22.1 Four Types of Hydrocarbons

Knowing the ending in the name is a key to knowing the type of compound bonding. Terms endings in -ane indicate single bonds between carbon atoms; -ene indicates at least one double bond is present between carbon atoms; and -yne indicates a triple bond is in the chain.

Table 22.1 Alkanes, Alkenes, Alkynes

Type of Hydrocarbon	Type of Bonds	Generic Formula*	Example
Alkanes	All single	C_nH_{2n+2}	Ethane
Alkenes	One (or more) double	C_nH_{2n}	Ethene
Alkynes	One (or more) triple	C_nH_{2n-2}	$H-C\equiv C-H$ Ethyne

*n is the number of carbon atoms. These formulas apply only to noncyclic structures containing no more than one multiple bond.

Knowing the formula of the compound alone does not indicate the structure of the compound since these compounds often branch. The same formula can have many forms (isomers) and hence different shapes, names and properties. The simplest example is butane and isobutane, which can also be called 2-methylpropane. These compounds with the same formulas but different structures are called structural isomers.

Butane

Isobutane

The same structure can be represented in different formats. The structures often seen are the full structural formulas showing all the atoms, condensed formulas showing what is located on each carbon in the chain, and the skeletal formula showing only the bonds between the carbons.

Structural formula	Condensed structural formula	Carbon skeleton formula	Ball-and-stick model	Space-filling model

Butane $CH_3-CH_2-CH_2-CH_3$

Structural formula	Condensed structural formula	Carbon skeleton formula	Ball-and-stick model	Space-filling model

Isobutane

$$H H-\overset{H}{\underset{}{C}}-H H$$
$$H-\overset{H}{\underset{H}{C}}-\overset{H}{\underset{H}{C}}-\overset{H}{\underset{H}{C}}-H$$

CH_3
$CH_3-CH-CH_3$

Structural formula	Condensed structural formula	Carbon skeleton formula	Ball-and-stick model	Space-filling model

Propene

$$H-\overset{H}{\underset{}{C}}=\overset{H}{\underset{}{C}}-\overset{H}{\underset{H}{C}}-H$$

$CH_2{=}CH-CH_3$

Propyne

$$H-C{\equiv}C-\overset{H}{\underset{H}{C}}-H$$

$CH{\equiv}C-CH_3$

One important property of some of these isomers is whether or not they are stereoisomers. There are two types of stereoisomers: geometric and optical. Geometric isomers are also called *cis-trans* isomers (see Section 22.5 for more detail). The geometric isomer will have a double bond. The chain will be continued either on the same side (up or down) or on the opposite side (up and then down or down then up).

$$\underset{H}{\overset{CH_3}{}}C{=}C\underset{H}{\overset{CH_3}{}}$$
cis-2-Butene

$$\underset{H}{\overset{CH_3}{}}C{=}C\underset{CH_3}{\overset{H}{}}$$
trans-2-Butene

In this example of *cis*-2-butene, the chain is staying on the top side of the molecule, while in *trans*-2-butene it starts up and then goes across and down.

Optical isomers (also called enantiomers) are not superimposable on each other. For instance, your hands look alike but you cannot place them on top of each other and have them look the same.

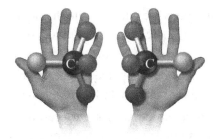

Figure 22.2 Mirror Images   The left and right hands are nonsuperimposable mirror images, just as are optical isomers.

Molecules that do this are said to be chiral. This is very important in biological organisms as many body systems and enzymes will only recognize one of the isomers.

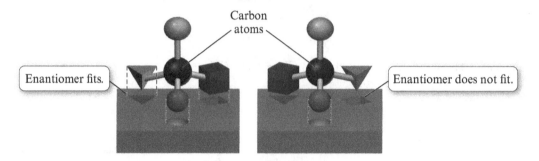

Another important characteristic of optical isomers is the way they will rotate plane polarized light. One form of the isomer will rotate plane polarized light clockwise and is called the *d* isomer (dextrorotatory), and the other will rotate this light counterclockwise and is called the *l* isomer (levorotatory). If there is an equimolar mixture of both, the light will not rotate and the mixture is called a racemic mixture. Interestingly, in the human body the recognized form of amino acids are the *l* isomers, and the carbohydrates are the *d* isomers.

Section 22.4 Alkanes: Saturated Hydrocarbons

When the carbon atoms in the chain have only single bonds between them, the compound is called an alkane. If all the other atoms are hydrogen atoms, the compound is also called a saturated hydrocarbon. The chain can be straight, branched, or ringed (cycloalkanes are not covered in the chapter and will not be addressed here, although they do exist). The straight-chained alkanes are called normal alkanes and may be designated with an *n-* in front of the name such as *n*-heptane.

Naming the alkanes requires looking at their structural formulas, knowing the prefix for the number of carbons in the chain, and the names of any branched groups called substituent groups. The simplest alkanes to name are the straight-chain hydrocarbons without branches. Only the length of chain has to be counted.

For straight-chain alkanes:

- Find the longest continuous chain and count the number of carbons in the chain. Use the prefix for this number of carbons followed by –ane.
- If any substituent groups are added, write the names of the groups in alphabetical order if there is more than one type added in front of the name.
- Number the carbons in the chain so that the groups are on the lowest numbered carbon. For each group added, put the number of the carbon it is located on in front of its name and then place a dash between the number and the name.
- If more than one of a particular group is present, also add a prefix in front of the group name such as di-(2), tri-(3), or tetra-(4). The prefix does not change the order of the substituent groups.

Table 22.2 *n*-Alkanes

n	Name	Molecular Formula C_nH_{2n+2}	Structural Formula	Condensed Structural Formula
1	Methane	CH_4		CH_4
2	Ethane	C_2H_6		CH_3CH_3
3	Propane	C_3H_8		$CH_3CH_2CH_3$
4	*n*-Butane	C_4H_{10}		$CH_3CH_2CH_2CH_3$
5	*n*-Pentane	C_5H_{12}		$CH_3CH_2CH_2CH_2CH_3$
6	*n*-Hexane	C_6H_{14}		$CH_3CH_2CH_2CH_2CH_2CH_3$
7	*n*-Heptane	C_7H_{16}		$CH_3CH_2CH_2CH_2CH_2CH_2CH_3$
8	*n*-Octane	C_8H_{18}		$CH_3CH_2CH_2CH_2CH_2CH_2CH_2CH_3$
9	*n*-Nonane	C_9H_{20}		$CH_3CH_2CH_2CH_2CH_2CH_2CH_2CH_2CH_3$
10	*n*-Decane	$C_{10}H_{22}$		$CH_3CH_2CH_2CH_2CH_2CH_2CH_2CH_2CH_2CH_3$

When the chain has branches, the groups added to the main chain are called alkyl groups if they contain only carbon and hydrogen.

Table 22.3   Common Alkyl Groups

Condensed Structural Formula	Name	Condensed Structural Formula	Name
$-CH_3$	Methyl	$\begin{array}{c}-CHCH_3\\ \mid\\ CH_3\end{array}$	Isopropyl
$-CH_2CH_3$	Ethyl	$\begin{array}{c}-CH_2CHCH_3\\ \mid\\ CH_3\end{array}$	Isobutyl
$-CH_2CH_2CH_3$	Propyl	$\begin{array}{c}-CHCH_2CH_3\\ \mid\\ CH_3\end{array}$	sec-Butyl
$-CH_2CH_2CH_2CH_3$	Butyl	$\begin{array}{c}CH_3\\ \mid\\ -CCH_3\\ \mid\\ CH_3\end{array}$	tert-Butyl

Following the steps for the branched compounds requires more of the steps since substituent groups have been added and must be accounted for in the name.

Example: Naming Alkanes

Name this alkane:

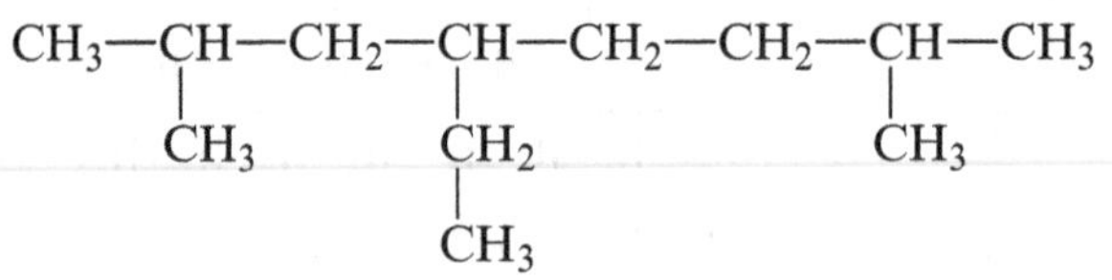

$$CH_3-CH-CH_2-CH-CH_2-CH_2-CH-CH_3$$
$$CH_3 \qquad CH_2 \qquad\qquad CH_3$$
$$CH_3$$

Solution

This compound has eight carbon atoms in its longest continuous chain.

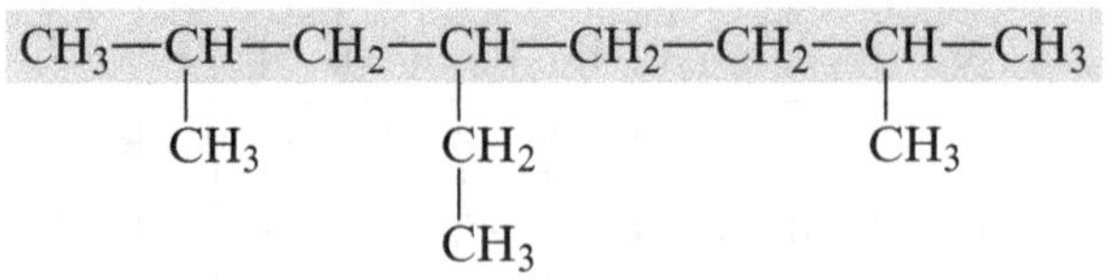

$$CH_3-CH-CH_2-CH-CH_2-CH_2-CH-CH_3$$
$$CH_3 \qquad CH_2 \qquad\qquad CH_3$$
$$CH_3$$

The correct prefix from Table 21.5 is *oct-*. The base name is octane.

This compound has one substituent named *ethyl* and two named *methyl*.

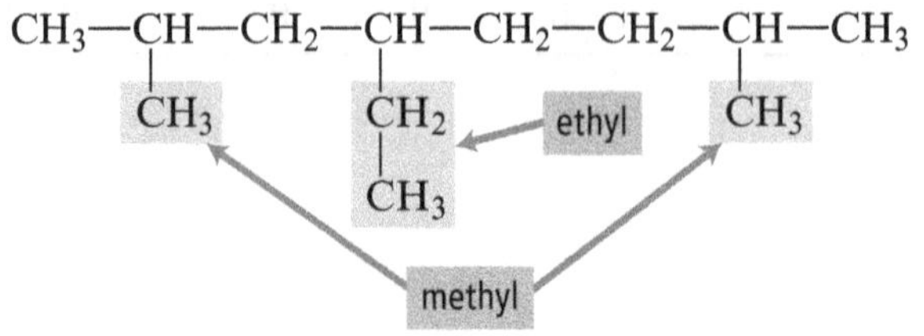

$$CH_3-CH-CH_2-CH-CH_2-CH_2-CH-CH_3$$
$$CH_3 \qquad CH_2 \qquad\qquad CH_3$$
$$CH_3$$

ethyl

methyl

Number the base chain as follows:

$$\overset{1}{CH_3}-\overset{2}{CH}-\overset{3}{CH_2}-\overset{4}{CH}-\overset{5}{CH_2}-\overset{6}{CH_2}-\overset{7}{CH}-\overset{8}{CH_3}$$
$$\qquad\quad | \qquad\qquad\; | \qquad\qquad\qquad\; |$$
$$\qquad\quad CH_3 \qquad\; CH_2 \qquad\qquad\; CH_3$$
$$\qquad\qquad\qquad\quad\; |$$
$$\qquad\qquad\qquad\quad CH_3$$

Assign the number 4 to the ethyl substituent and the numbers 2 and 7 to the two methyl substituents.

The basic form of the name of the compound is:

4-ethyl-2,7-methyloctane

List ethyl before methyl because substituents are listed in alphabetical order.

This compound has two methyl substituents; therefore, the final name of the compound is:

4-ethyl-2,7-dimethyloctane

For Practice

Name this alkane:

$$CH_3-CH_2-CH-CH_2-CH-CH_2-CH_3$$
$$\qquad\qquad\;\; | \qquad\qquad\; |$$
$$\qquad\qquad\; CH_3 \qquad\; CH_3$$

Although no questions will be "name this compound," being familiar with names can reduce "panic" when students see these types of structures of data from organic compounds.

The questions students will be expected to be able to answer are questions asking to explain trends such as the boiling points of organic compounds or to explain the different models of representation of the same compound.

Table 22.4 n-Alkane Boiling Points

n-Alkane	Boiling Point (°C)
Methane	−161.5
Ethane	−88.6
Propane	−42.1
n-Butane	−0.5
n-Pentane	36.0
n-Hexane	68.7
n-Heptane	98.5
n-Octane	125.6

Since these are all straight chain, the difference between these molecules is the amount of London dispersion force between the molecules. The dispersion forces increase as more electrons are present. In the table above, the boiling points increase as the dispersion forces increase between the molecules. The more electrons present, the greater the London Dispersion forces and therefore the greater the boiling point.

Section 22.5   Alkenes and Alkynes

Alkenes have at least one double bond, and alkynes have at least one triple bond. These compounds are unsaturated because there is a double or triple bond that can break and add additional hydrogen atoms. Take the following steps to name these types of compounds:

- Name the compound by identifying the longest chain which includes the multiple bond(s).
- Number the carbons in the chain so that the multiple bond is on the lowest numbered carbon.
- Change the ending to -ene for alkenes (double bond) and -yne for alkynes (triple bond).
- Put a number before the base name to indicate the numbered carbon the multiple bond is on. See the examples in the following tables.

Table 22.5   Alkenes

n	Name	Molecular Formula C_nH_{2n}	Structural Formula	Condensed Structural Formula
2	Ethene	C_2H_4	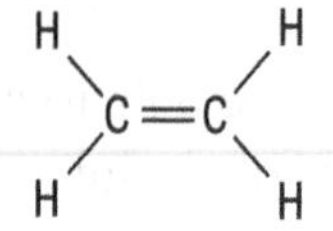	$CH_2{=}CH_2$
3	Propene	C_3H_6	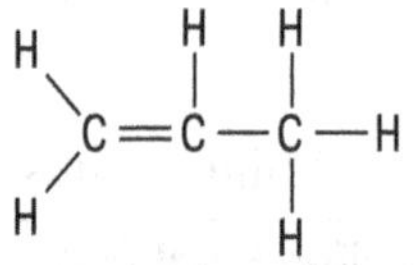	$CH_2{=}CHCH_3$
4	1-Butene*	C_4H_8	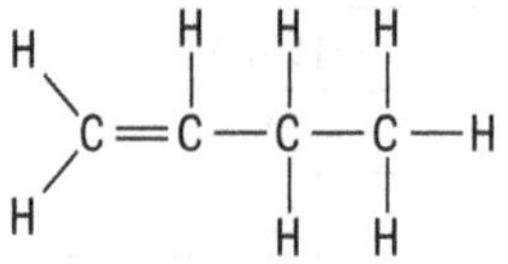	$CH_2{=}CHCH_2CH_3$
5	1-Pentene*	C_5H_{10}	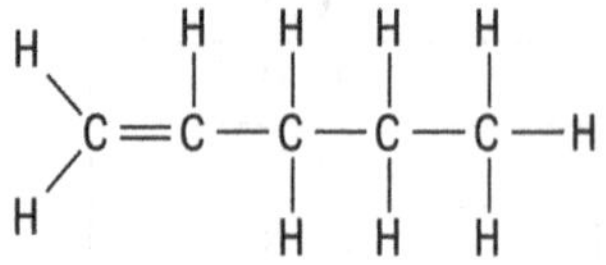	$CH_2{=}CHCH_2CH_2CH_3$
6	1-Hexene*	C_6H_{12}	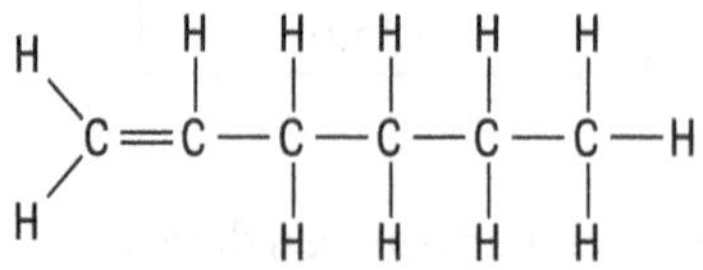	$CH_2{=}CHCH_2CH_2CH_2CH_3$

*These alkenes have one or more isomers depending on the position of the double bond. The isomers shown here have the double bond in the 1 position, meaning the first carbon–carbon bond of the chain.

Table 22.6   Alkynes

n	Name	Molecular Formula C_nH_{2n-2}	Structural Formula	Condensed Structural Formula
2	Ethyne	C_2H_2	H—C≡C—H	CH≡CH
3	Propyne	C_3H_4	H—C≡C—C(H)(H)—H	CH≡CCH₃
4	1-Butyne*	C_4H_6	H—C≡C—C(H)—C(H)—H	CH≡CCH₂CH₃
5	1-Pentyne*	C_5H_8	H—C≡C—C(H)—C(H)—C(H)—H	CH≡CCH₂CH₂CH₃
6	1-Hexyne*	C_6H_{10}	H—C≡C—C(H)—C(H)—C(H)—C(H)—H	CH≡CCH₂CH₂CH₂CH₃

*These alkynes have one or more isomers depending on the position of the triple bond. The isomers shown here have the triple bond in the 1 position, meaning the first carbon–carbon bond of the chain.

The simplest alkene is ethene, and the simplest alkyne is ethyne.

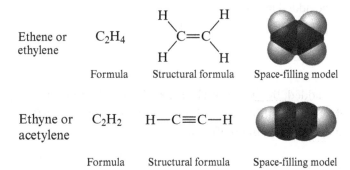

Ethene or ethylene C_2H_4

Formula   Structural formula   Space-filling model

Ethyne or acetylene C_2H_2 H—C≡C—H

Formula   Structural formula   Space-filling model

Remember that for any alkene other than ethene, the terms *cis-* and *trans-* are used to indicate if the chain goes to the same side (cis-) or across to the opposite side (trans-).

cis-2-Butene   *trans*-2-Butene

Hydrocarbon Reactions   Section 22.6

When hydrocarbons undergo complete combustion, the products are water and carbon dioxide. Students should expect to be able to balance equations, do stoichiometry problems, and do reaction analysis problems.

Section 22.7   **Aromatic Hydrocarbons**

Benzene is the base of many aromatic compounds. It has the formula C_6H_6 and has three alternating double bonds.

Benzene has two resonance structures. For simplification, the structure is written as

The delocalized electrons are indicated by the circle inside. The molecule is planar and nonpolar. These rings can be combined, and substitutions can be made for the hydrogen atoms creating new compounds. If the benzene itself is added as a functional group, it is called phenyl. There are many benzene derivative compounds.

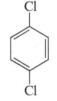

Other atoms can be substituted for hydrogens, and the name will change to reflect the location of the added atom.

Bromobenzene

If two atoms are added, the names reflect the additional atoms either by numbers or by special prefixes. Substitution on carbons 1 and 2 is the prefix *ortho-*, 1 and 3 is the prefix *meta-* and 1, and 4 is the prefix *para-*.

1,2-Dichlorobenzene   1,3-Dichlorobenzene   1,4-Dichlorobenzene

ortho-Dichlorobenzene   *meta*-Dichlorobenzene   *para*-Dichlorobenzene
           or   or   or
o-Dichlorobenzene   *m*-Dichlorobenzene   *p*-Dichlorobenzene

Benzene molecules can be added together to form other molecules such as naphthalene.

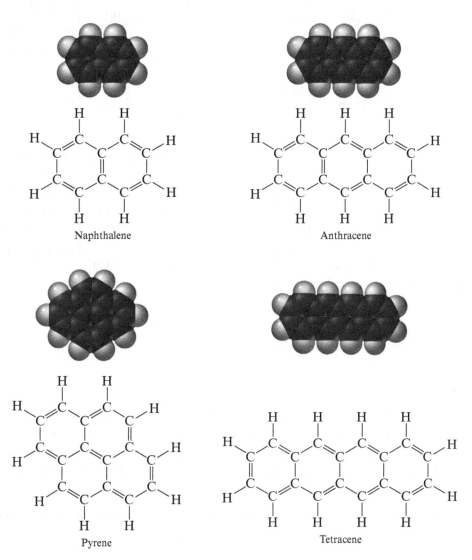

Figure 22.3 Polycyclic Aromatic Compounds   The structures of some common polycyclic aromatic compounds contain fused rings.

Functional Groups   Section 22.8–22.13

Functional groups identify families of organic compounds that have common physical properties and chemical reactivity. A functional group is an atom or group of atoms—part of a molecule that governs the chemical reactivity of that compound. We can think of a functional group as replacing one or more hydrogens from the parent hydrocarbon. Students need to be familiar with the common functional groups, should be able to draw Lewis structures for the function groups, and given a compound determine the intermolecular forces present that influence physical properties. Table 22.7 lists some of the common functional groups, their general formula, and an example of each.

Table 22.7 Some Common Functional Groups

Family	General Formula*	Condensed General Formula	Example	Name
Alcohols	R — OH	ROH	CH_3CH_2OH	Ethanol (ethyl alcohol)
Ethers	R — O — R	ROR	CH_3OCH_3	Dimethyl ether
Aldehydes	R—C—H (with O double-bonded to C)	RCHO	CH_3—C—H (with O double-bonded to C)	Ethanal (acetaldehyde)
Ketones	R—C—R (with O double-bonded to C)	RCOR	CH_3—C—CH_3 (with O double-bonded to C)	Propanone (acetone)
Carboxylic acids	R—C—OH (with O double-bonded to C)	RCOOH	CH_3—C—OH (with O double-bonded to C)	Ethanoic acid (acetic acid)
Esters	R—C—OR (with O double-bonded to C)	RCOOR	CH_3—C—OCH_3 (with O double-bonded to C)	Methyl acetate
Amines	R—N—R (with R above N)	R_3N	CH_3CH_2—N—H (with H above N)	Ethylamine

*In ethers, ketones, esters, and amines, the R groups may be the same or different.

Carboxylic Acids

In Table 22.7, the "R" represents any carbon chain. Let's focus on carboxylic acids. The R group from the parent acid forms the base name of the compound. Count the longest carbon chain containing the —COOH functional group. Form the base name by dropping the *–e* from the parent hydrocarbon and adding the ending *–oic acid*. Propane with a carboxylic acid function group is named propanoic acid.

For instance, if we start with ethane and replace the one end of the molecule with a carbonyl group, C=O, and an —OH group, the molecule now is a carboxylic acid.

Ethane

Ethanoic acid (acetic acid)

Carboxylic acid (Functional Group)

If we start with propane and replace the hydrogens on one end of the molecule with a carbonyl group and an —OH group, the molecule now is a carboxylic acid.

Propane

Propanoic acid

Carboxylic acid (Functional Group)

Both ethanoic acid and propanoic acid react with aqueous sodium hydroxide to produce a salt and water.

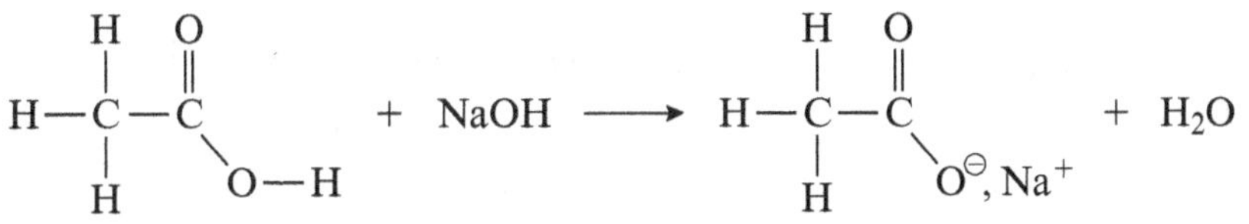

Acetic acid   Sodium hydroxide   Sodium acetate   Water

All carboxylic acids have the general formula R—COOH. Once we know the chemical behavior of a functional group, we can use this knowledge to predict the chemical behavior in other molecules containing the same functional group. The important thing to realize is the chemistry of an organic molecule is mostly determined by its functional group.

Example:

Determine the products and write a balanced chemical equation for the reaction of butanoic acid with an aqueous potassium hydroxide solution.

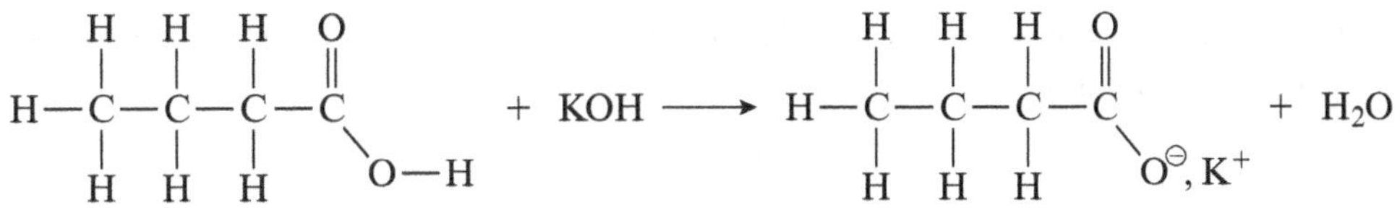

Butanoic acid   Potassium hydroxide   Potassium butanoate   Water

Most carboxylic acids are weak acids and when placed in water, the pH of the resultant solution can be determined (Section 17.6).

Alcohols

Alcohols are organic compounds containing the —OH functional group, called a hydroxyl group substituted in the parent hydrocarbon. Alcohols have the general formula R—OH.

If we start with propane and replace the hydrogens on one end of the molecule with a hydroxyl group, —OH group, the molecule now is an alcohol.

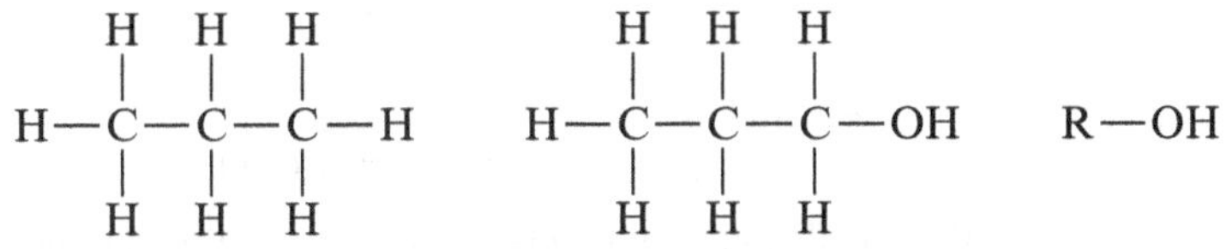

Propane   Propanol   Alcohol (Functional Group)

The —OH group in alcohols is not hydroxide group. Because the —OH group is directly attached to a carbon, the —OH group does not dissociate into hydroxide ions, and hence, it does not affect pH of the solution. Students should be able to look at the structure of a compound and determine if it is polar, will form hydrogen bonds with water, and analyze a trend of given properties. Carboxylic acids and alcohols are polar molecules and form hydrogen bonds with water.

Alcohols react with carboxylic acids, in the presence of acid, to form esters. For example, propanoic acid reacts with ethanol to form ethyl propanoate and water.

Propanoic acid   Ethanol   Ethylpropanoate   Water

This is called a condensation reaction since it produces water.

Esters

All esters have the general formula R—COO—R. The R group from the parent carboxylic acid forms the base name of the compound. Next, replace the H on the COOH with the alkyl group from the alcohol. Name the alkyl group with the ending –*yl*. Change the –*ic* on the carboxylic acid to -*ate*, and drop the word *acid*. Propanoic acid is the parent acid, when it reacts to form an ester this group is named *propanoate*. The ethanol molecule is derived from ethane, drop the *ane* and add *yl* to yield *ethyl*.

Amines

Most amines are weak bases, and when placed in water, the pH of the resultant solution can be determined (Section 17.7).

$$RNH_2(aq) + H_2O(l) \rightleftharpoons RNH_3^+(aq) + OH(aq)$$

Amines are an important class of organic compounds because they contain nitrogen and are derived from ammonia. Each nitrogen atom has a lone-pair of electrons which gives amines the basis for their chemical behavior. Amines are named according to the hydrocarbon groups attached to the nitrogen and assign the ending –*amine*. For example, if we start with ammonia and replace the one of the hydrogens with a propyl group, the molecule now is an amine.

Ammonia   Propyl group   Propyl amine   Amine
(Functional Group)

Amines react with strong acids to form salts called ammonium salts. For example, propylamine reacts with hydrochloric acid to form propylammonium chloride

$$CH_3CH_2CH_2NH_2(aq) + HCl(aq) \rightleftharpoons CH_3CH_2CH\ NH_3^+Cl^-(aq)$$

Amines react with weak acids to form amides. For example, propylamine reacts with acetic acid to form methylpropylamide and water, a condensation reaction.

$$CH_3CH_2CH_2NH_2(aq) + CH_3COOH(aq) \rightarrow CH_3CONHCH_2CH_2CH_3(aq)$$

Summary

Sections 22.8–22.13 discusses examples of each of the common organic functional groups. This material provides a good foundation for the study of organic chemistry. In recent years there has been more organic chemistry structures on the AP Chemistry exam incorporated into the multiple-choice and free-response questions.

Additional Practice

Self-Assessment Quiz Questions Q1, Q2, Q3, Q4, Q5, Q6, Q9, and Q10

Problems:
Review Questions 6, 8, 9, 10, 11, 21, and 24
Hydrocarbons 34
Alkanes 41, 43, and 45
Alkenes and Alkynes 51, 53, and 55
Aromatic Hydrocarbons 61, 63, and 67
Alcohols 71 and 72
Aldehydes and Ketones 75 and 76
Carboxylic Acids and Esters 79 and 80
Ethers 83 and 84
Amines 85 and 86
Cumulative Problems 89, 90, 91, 92, and 93

Practice AP Test Questions

Questions 1–6 refer to the following information and structure

$$H-C\equiv\overset{*}{C}-\underset{\underset{H}{|}}{\overset{\overset{H}{|}}{C}}-H$$

1. Hydrocarbons containing a carbon–carbon triple bond are called _____.

    A) alkanes   B) alkenes   C) alkynes   D) aldehydes

2. The hybridization of the carbon atom indicated by a (*) in the above structure is

    A) sp.   B) sp^2.   C) sp^3.   D) dsp^2.

3. What is the name of the compound?

    A) propane   B) propene   C) propyne   D) 1-methylethyne

4. For the structure above, identify the hybrid orbital(s) used by the carbon atom indicated by a (*) for bonding with the carbon atom in the CH_3 group.

        A)   B)   C)   D)

5. The compound represented by the structure above is not soluble in water.

   A) It is not soluble because it is less dense than water.

   B) It is not soluble because it has a higher molar mass.

   C) It is not soluble because it is a polar molecule.

   D) It is not soluble because it is a nonpolar molecule.

6. The $H-C\equiv C*$ bond angle in the structure above is:

   A) 90°

   B) 109.5°

   C) 120°

   D) 180°

7. Which one of the following molecules would be the least polar?

   A) CH_3CH_2Cl

   B) $CH_3CH_2NH_2$

   C) CH_3OCH_3

   D) $HOCH_2CH_2OH$

8. Using Lewis structures and formal charge rules, identify which of the following ions is most stable.

   $CH_3CH_2COO^-$ $CH_3CH_2^+$ $^-OOCCH_2COO^-$

   A) $^-OOCCH_2COO^-$

   B) $CH_3CH_2^+$

   C) $CH_3CH_2COO^-$

   D) All of these compounds are equally stable according to Lewis theory and formal charge rules.

9. Compare the structures of the following organic compounds and determine which sample of the liquid compound would have the highest normal boiling point.

   A) $CH_3CH_2NH_2$

   B) CH_3CH_2OH

   C) CH_3CH_2F

   D) $HOCH_2CH_2OH$

10. Compare the structures of the following organic compounds and determine which sample of the compound would be least soluble in water.

A) $CH_3CH_2NH_2$

B) CH_3CH_2I

C) CH_3CH_2OH

D) $HOCH_2CH_2OH$

Chapter 22 Practice AP Test Questions Answers:

1. C); 2. C); 3. C); 4. A); 5. D); 6. D); 7. C); 8. A); 9. D); 10. B)

Data Interpretation and Analysis Question: Mass Spectrometry

Carbon and bromine each have two major naturally occurring isotopes. The isotope, exact mass, and relative percent abundance are listed in Table 1.

Table 1

Isotope	Exact Mass (amu)	Relative Abundance
^{12}C	12.00	98.9%
^{13}C	13.00	1.1%
^{79}Br	79.00	50.5%
^{81}Br	81.00	49.5%

Mass spectrometry is an analytical technique that helps scientists identify compounds based on the exact mass of charged particles. This technique creates charged particles by removing an electron from the main structure and by fragmenting the main structure. A simplified mass spec of ethane, CH_3CH_3, is shown below. The peak at m/z 30 is $CH_3CH_3^+$ (MM = 30.0), and the m/z peak at 15 is CH_3^+. Some isotopes of ethane containing ^{13}C atoms may be too low in number for adequate display on the mass spectrum.

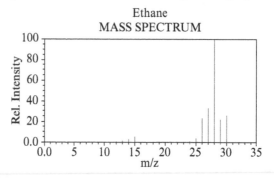

Ethane
MASS SPECTRUM

Source: NIST Chemistry WebBook (http://webbook.nist.gov/chemistry)

a) Given the mass spec of ethane, what species most likely corresponds to the m/z peak 29? What species corresponds to the m/z peak 15?

b) Draw the Lewis structure of 1-bromoethane, CH_3CH_2Br.

c) If an isotope of 1-bromoethane contained ^{79}Br, determine the exact mass of $CH_3CH_2{}^{79}Br$, assuming each of the carbons is ^{12}C.

A mass spec of 1-bromoethane is shown below.

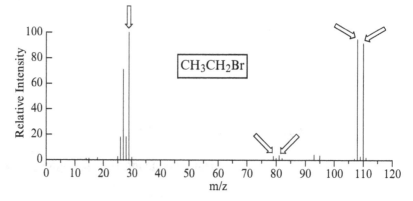

d) The peak at m/z 108 corresponds to what isotope of 1-bromoethane?

e) The peak at m/z 110 corresponds to what isotope of 1-bromoethane?

f) Using the masses listed on a periodic table, what is the molar mass of CH_3CH_2Br? Why is this mass not a major peak on the mass spectrum?

g) What are the peaks at m/z 79 and m/z 81?

h) The peak at m/z 29 is what fragment of CH_3CH_2Br?

Data Interpretation and Analysis Question Answers with Brief Explanations

a) The peak at m/z 29 could be $CH_3CH_2^+$ (MM = 29.0), with both carbons atoms being ^{12}C. The peak at m/z 15 could be CH_3^+ (MM = 15.0).

b)

H—C—C—Br with H H on top and H H on bottom

c) 108 is most likely the molar mass of $CH_3CH_2{}^{79}Br^+$, assuming each of the carbons is ^{12}C.

d) The m/z 108 peak corresponds to $CH_3CH_2{}^{79}Br^+$, assuming each of the carbons is ^{12}C.

e) The m/z 110 peak corresponds to $CH_3CH_2{}^{81}Br^+$, assuming each of the carbons is ^{12}C.

f) Using the masses on the periodic table, we find that the molar mass of CH_3CH_3Br is 108.965 amu or 109 amu. The masses listed on the periodic table are the weighted averages of all of the naturally occurring isotopes of each element. The weighted average for bromine is 79.9. No bromine atoms have an exact mass of 79.9 amu; therefore, the mass spec will not detect this mass for bromine.

g) The m/z peak at 79 is $^{79}Br^+$, and the m/z peak at 81 is $^{81}Br^+$.

h) The peak at m/z 29 is $CH_3CH_2^+$?

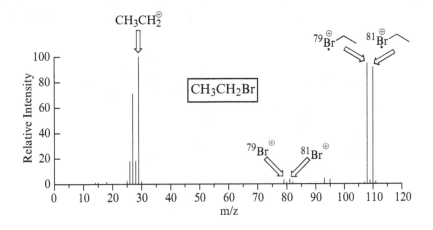

READING GUIDE

This chapter contains the basic information students need to know about organic chemistry and structures of organic compounds for the AP Chemistry Exam: Lewis structures of organic compounds, functional groups, polymers, and the basic properties of these types of compounds. Several sections in this chapter provide considerably more detail than required by the AP Chemistry curriculum. The following topics are not included on the AP Chemistry Exam chirality, enantiomers, and organic reactions such as addition and condensation reactions:

Section 22.1   Fragrances and Odors

1. Draw the condensed structure and name the compound responsible for skunk odor.*

2. What general types of compounds are studied in organic chemistry? What is common to all of the compounds?

Section 22.2   Carbon: Why It Is Unique

3. Use the following diagrams to explain the unique properties of carbon:

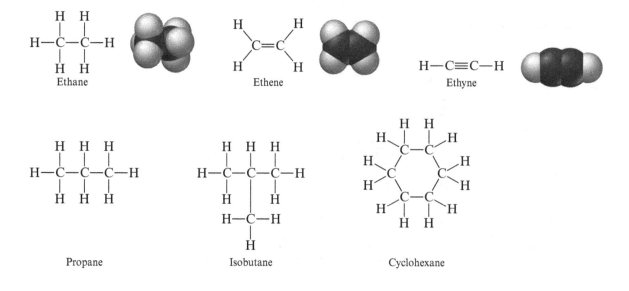

4. Explain why silicon is not as versatile as carbon.

5. Why were the experiments by Friedrich Wöhler so important for organic chemistry?*

Hydrocarbons: Compounds Containing Only Carbon and Hydrogen

Section 22.3

6. What are the types of hydrocarbons? What are the differences among them? Put their names in the following chart:

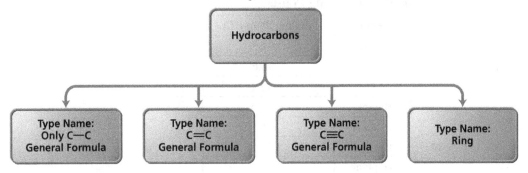

7. What is an aliphatic hydrocarbon?

8. What are structural isomers?

9. Explain the difference between structural formulas, condensed structural formulas, and carbon skeletal formulas. Why is each used?

10. Using butane and isobutane, fill in the following table:

Compound	Formula	Structural Formula	Condensed Structural Formula	Carbon Skeleton Formula
Butane				
Isobutane				

11. What are stereoisomers? Name two types and explain the difference between them.*

12. What does the term *chiral* indicate?* What is a racemic mixture?

13. What is another term for an optical isomer? What are the types of optical isomers? How do they differ from each other?*

14. Why is the type of optical isomer important in biological systems?*

Alkanes: Saturated Hydrocarbons

Section 22.4

15. What are *n*-alkanes? Why are these molecules considered saturated?

16. Fill in the following table:

Name	Formula	Structural Formula	Condensed Formula
Methane			
Ethane			
Propane			
n-butane			
n-pentane			
n-hexane			

17. Explain the reason for the trend in boiling points of the *n*-alkanes.

n-Alkane Boiling Points

n-Alkane	Boiling Point (°C)
Methane	−161.5
Ethane	−88.6
Propane	−42.1
n-Butane	−0.5
n-Pentane	36.0
n-Hexane	68.7
n-Heptane	98.5
n-Octane	125.6

18. Explain the required steps in naming alkane compounds, using the following compound to demonstrate the steps:

$$CH_3-CH-CH_2-CH-CH_2-CH_2-CH-CH_3$$

with branches: CH_3 on the second carbon; CH_2-CH_3 on the fourth carbon; CH_3 on the seventh carbon.

Section 22.5   Alkenes and Alkynes

19. Fill in the following table:

Type of Compound	Base Formula	Type of Bond	Geometry Around C in Multiple Bond
Alkene			
Alkyne			

20. Why are alkene and alkyne compounds said to be unsaturated?

21. What are the steps in naming alkene and alkyne compounds?

22. Use the steps in question 21 to name the following compounds:

$$CH_3-C=C-CH_2-CH_3$$
with CH_3 above the first C, and CH_2 below the second C, and CH_3 below the CH_2

$$CH_3-CH-CH-C\equiv CH$$
with CH_3 above the second CH (as CH_3-CH), CH_3 below the middle CH

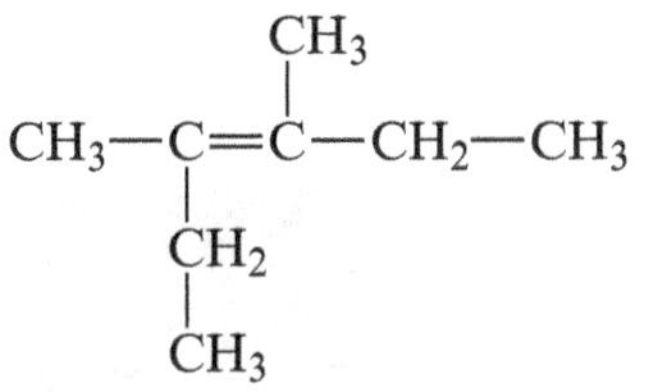

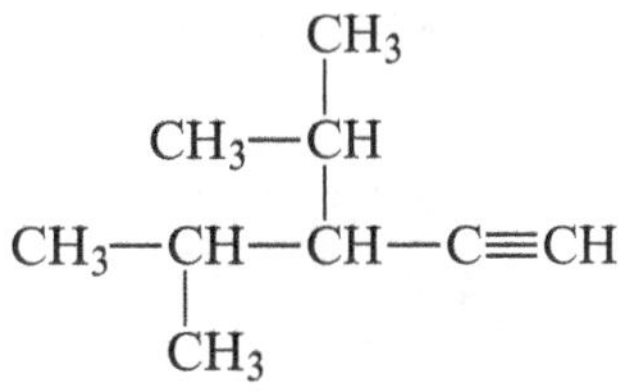

23. For the following compounds, fill in the empty columns in the below chart:

Name	Formula	Structural Formula	Condensed Formula
Ethene			
Propene			
2-butene			
Ethyne			
2-butyne			

24. What is the difference between *cis-* and *trans-* isomers in alkenes? Include a diagram in your answer.

Hydrocarbon Reactions   Section 22.6

25. What are the products of complete hydrocarbon combustion?

26. What are halogenation reactions? What is the general formula for a halogenation reaction? Explain why this is considered a substitution reaction.*

27. What occurs when alkenes and alkynes undergo addition reactions?*

28. What are hydrogenation reactions? Give an example of one.*

29. What is Markovnikov's rule? What is it used for?

Note: This topic is not included in the AP Chemistry curriculum.

Aromatic Hydrocarbons   Section 22.7

30. Draw the two resonance structures of benzene. Draw the carbon skeletal formula of benzene and explain how it represents the two resonance structures.

31. Why are benzene and its compounds called aromatics?

32. Explain how to name each of the following:*

   Monosubstituted benzenes:

   Disubstituted benzenes:

33. If benzene is the substituent, what is it called?

34. What are polycyclic aromatic compounds? Name each of the following polycyclic aromatic compounds.*

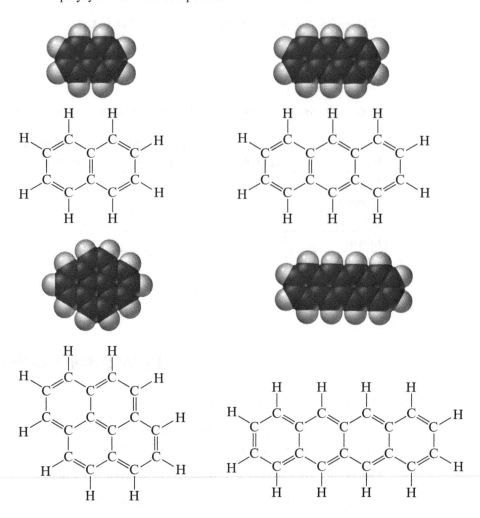

35. What type of reaction does benzene normally undergo?

Section 22.8   **Functional Groups**

36. What is a functional group? What are organic compound families?

37. Fill in the table with the general formula and an example of each family:

Some Common Functional Groups

Family	General Formula*	Condensed General Formula	Example	Name
Alcohols				
Ethers				
Aldehydes				
Ketones				
Carboxylic acids				
Esters				
Amines				

*In ethers, ketones, esters, and amines, the R groups may be the same or different.

Alcohols   Section 22.9

38. What functional group is found in alcohols?

39. Explain how to name an alcohol.

40. Identify three common alcohols and what they are used for.

41. In each of the following types of reactions, explain how alcohols react:

   Substitution:

   Dehydration:

   Oxidation:

   With active metal:

42. Indicate on the drawing below what atoms are lost or gained in the series of reactions given. Identify the direction of oxidation and explain why it is oxidation. Identify the direction of reduction and explain why it is reduction.

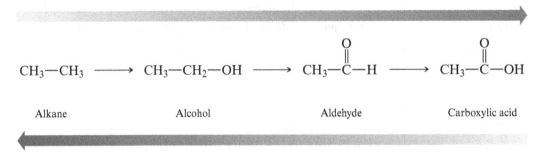

| Alkane | Alcohol | Aldehyde | Carboxylic acid |

Section 22.10   Aldehydes and Ketones

43. What is the general formula of an aldehyde?

44. What is the general formula of a ketone?

45. What is the difference between an aldehyde and a ketone if they both have the same functional group?

46. Explain how to name aldehydes and ketones.

47. Identify each of the following as an aldyhyde or ketone. Circle the functional group in each and name each compound:

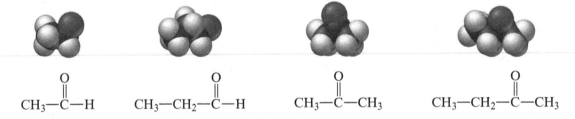

48. What is a common aldehyde? What is it found in?

49. What is the most common ketone? What is it found in?

50. How can aldehydes and ketones be formed? What is the product of a reaction when an aldehyde and ketone are reduced?

51. What are the most common reactions of aldehydes or ketones?

Section 22.11   Carboxylic Acids and Esters

52. What is the base formula of a carboxylic acid? How are these acids named?

53. Draw the condensed structural formulas of ethanoic acid and propanoic acid.

54. What is another name for ethanoic acid? What is ethanoic acid the main ingredient of?

55. What is the base formula of an ester? How are esters named?

56. What are esters best known for? Include an example in your answer.

57. Draw the structure of methyl butanoate.

58. Do carboxylic acids behave as a strong acid or a weak acid in reactions?

59. What type of compounds do carboxylic acids react with in order to form esters? Why are these called condensation reactions?

Ethers   Section 22.12

60. What are ethers?

61. What is the base format to name ethers? Explain the difference in naming ethers with the same R group and different R groups. Name each of these ethers.

CH_3-O-CH_3

$CH_3-O-CH_2-CH_3$

$CH_3-CH_2-O-CH_2-CH_3$

62. What is the most common ether and what is it used for?

Amines   Section 22.13

63. What are amines? How are amines named?

64. Draw a condensed structural formula of ethylamine.

65. Identify two properties of amines.

66. What forms when amines react with strong acids?

Self-Assessment Answers

1. _____   2. _____
3. _____   4. _____
5. _____   6. _____
7. _____   8. _____
9. _____   10. _____

BIOCHEMISTRY

This chapter focuses on compounds with biological functions. Most of this material is not in the AP curriculum but is referenced in understanding concepts in and across multiple areas of chemistry including Lewis structures, bonding, and equilibrium. The topics covered give a sound foundation for the chemistry needed in biology.

Specific Learning Objectives Addressed in This Chapter:

SAP-3 Atoms or ions bond due to interactions between them, forming molecules.

SAP-3.A Explain the relationship between the type of bonding and the properties of the elements participating in the bond.

- Valence electrons shared between atoms of similar electronegativity constitute a nonpolar covalent bond. For example, bonds between carbon and hydrogen are effectively nonpolar even though carbon is slightly more electronegative than hydrogen.

- Valence electrons shared between atoms of unequal electronegativity constitute a polar bond.

SAP-5 Intermolecular Forces can explain the physical properties of a material.

SAP-5.A Explain the relationship between the chemical structures of molecules and the relative strength of their intermolecular forces when:

- The molecules are of the same chemical species.

- The molecules are of two different chemical species.

SAP-5.B Explain the relationship among the macroscopic properties of a substance, the particulate-level structure of the substance, and the interactions between these particles.

- In large biomolecules or polymers, noncovalent interactions may occur between different molecules of different regions of the same large biomolecules. The functionality and properties of such molecules depend strongly on the shape of the molecule, which is largely dictated by noncovalent interactions.

Concepts and Vocabulary to Review:

Diabetes and the Synthesis of Human Insulin   Section 23.1

Many biological molecules are macromolecules such as DNA. They are created as the components hook together in long chains called polymers.

Lipids   Section 23.2

Lipids, which include fats and oils, are nonpolar and so they do not dissolve in water but instead dissolve in nonpolar solvents. Intermolecular dispersion forces between molecules can affect their melting points, determining whether certain fats are solids or liquids at room temperature. One type of lipid is a fatty acid. The long hydrocarbon chains make them insoluble in water. Other lipids include phospholipids, steroids, and glycolipids. An example of a steroid is cholesterol.

Carbohydrates   Section 23.3

The simplest carbohydrates are sugars. They can be recognized by the ending -ose in their name, such as glucose and sucrose. Polysaccharides are long chains of monosaccharides linked together. Examples include cellulose and starch.

Proteins and Amino Acids   Section 23.4

Proteins are polymers of amino acids linked together. Specific types of proteins are enzymes that act as catalysts. The shape of a protein is important to its function. Amino acids link together with a peptide bond. Chains of these form polypeptides.

Protein Structure   Section 23.5

A protein's structure will determine its function. Insoluble fibrous proteins are linear, and their function is primarily structural, such as collagen and keratin. Globular proteins are more complex but have polar chains toward the outside and nonpolar chains toward the inside, allowing them to dissolve in water. Hemoglobin and insulin are examples. The way the protein joins together results in primary, secondary, tertiary, and quaternary structures.

Levels of Protein Structure

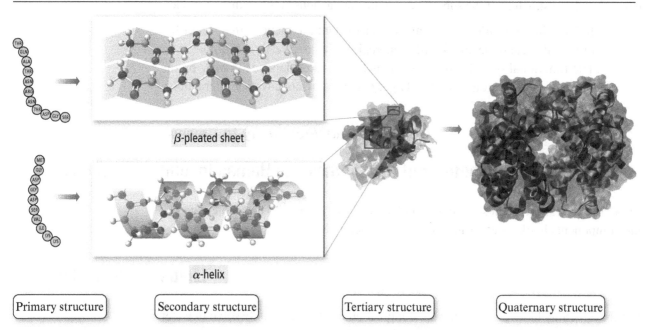

β-pleated sheet

α-helix

| Primary structure | Secondary structure | Tertiary structure | Quaternary structure |

Figure 23.1 Levels of Protein Structure   Protein structure is analyzed at four levels: primary, secondary, tertiary, and quaternary.

Section 23.6   Nucleic Acids: Blueprints for Proteins

Nucleic acids are also polymers containing a sugar, base, and a phosphate group. The bases determine which nucleic acid is present.

DNA: Basic Structure

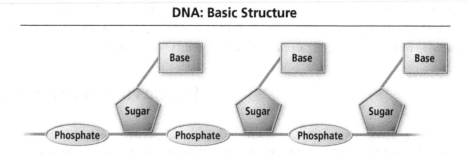

Figure 23.2 DNA Structure   DNA is composed of repeating units called nucleotides. Each nucleotide contains a sugar, a base, and a phosphate group.

In the double helix structure, the two bases are held together with a hydrogen bond. When DNA makes another copy of itself, these bonds break into two halves.

Base Pairing in DNA

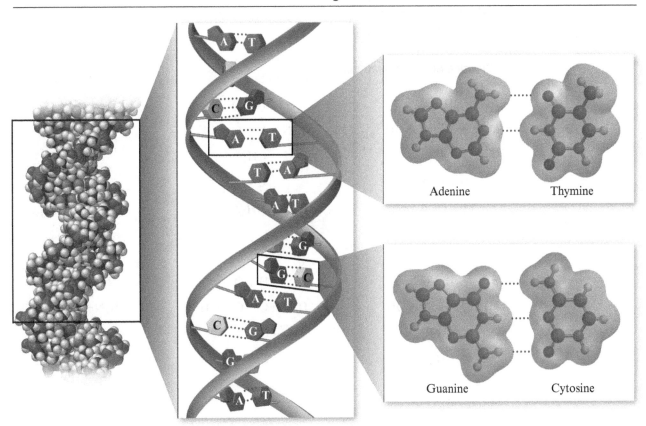

Figure 23.3 Base Pairing in DNA The bases in nucleic acids are complementary. Each pyrimidine base pairs with only one purine base (G with C, A with T) via specific hydrogen bonds that occur between the two bases.

Additional Practice

Self-Assessment Quiz Questions Q1, Q2, Q3, Q4, Q7, Q8, and Q9
Problems:
Lipids 31, 32, and 33
Carbohydrates 37

Practice AP Test Questions

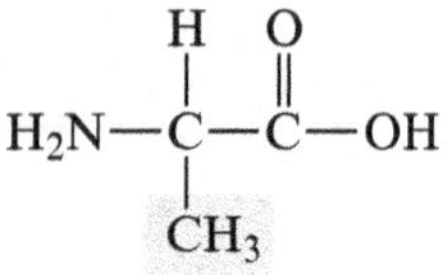

Alanine (Ala)

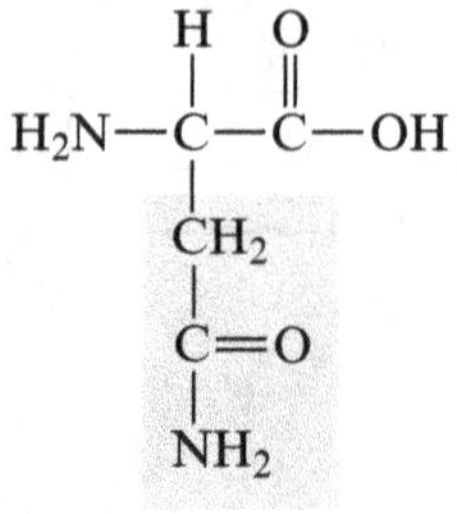

Asparagine (Asn)

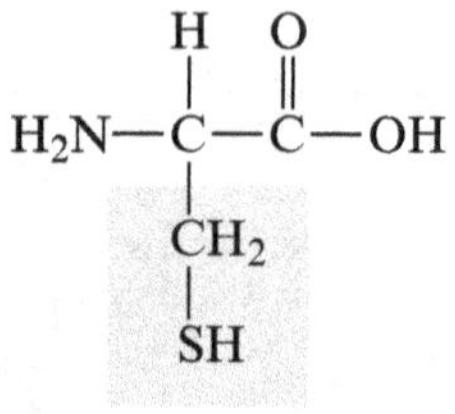

Cysteine (Cys)

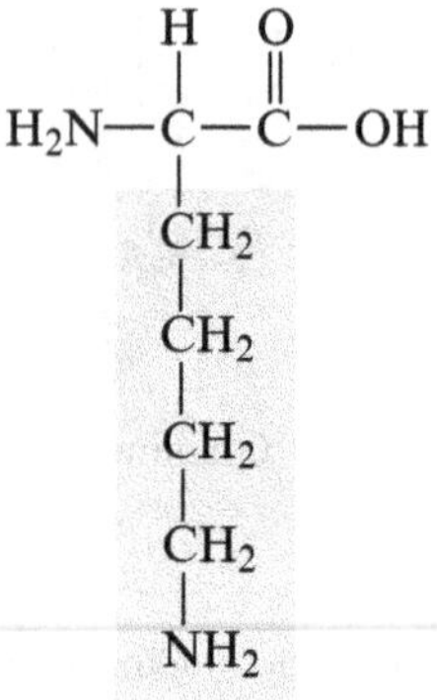

Lysine (Lys)

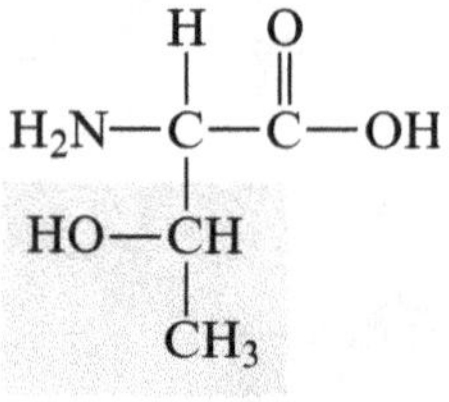

Threonine (Thr)

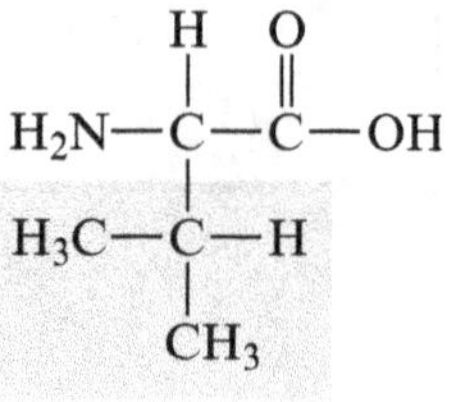

Valine (Val)

1. From the structures above, which two amino acids form the following dipeptide?

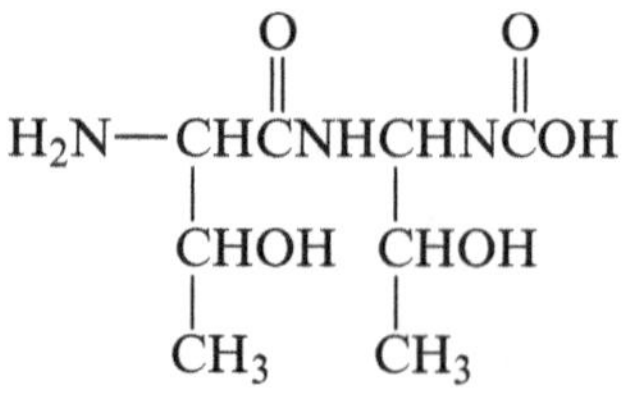

   A) lysine and alanine

   B) asparagine and threonine

   C) threonine and valine

   D) valine and cysteine

2. Amino acids have a common structure but differ from each other in their side chain or "R" group. Which one of the following amino acids contains a polar side chain?

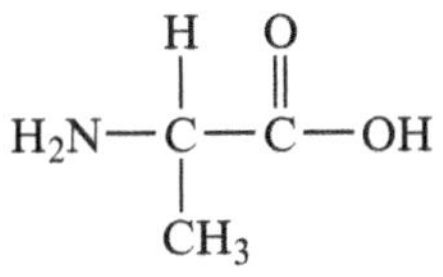

$$H_2N-\underset{\underset{CH_3}{|}}{\overset{\overset{H}{|}}{C}}-\overset{\overset{O}{||}}{C}-OH$$

Alanine (Ala)

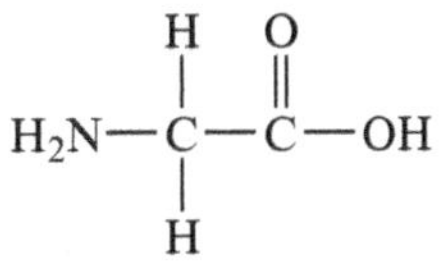

$$H_2N-\underset{\underset{H}{|}}{\overset{\overset{H}{|}}{C}}-\overset{\overset{O}{||}}{C}-OH$$

Glycine (Gly)

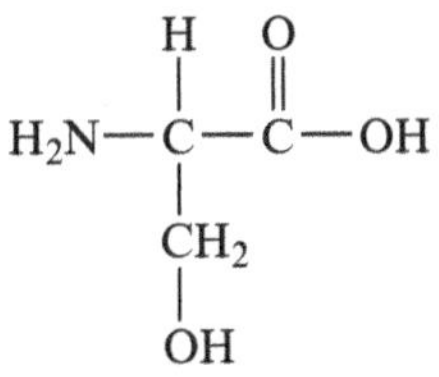

$$H_2N-\underset{\underset{\underset{OH}{|}}{CH_2}}{\overset{\overset{H}{|}}{C}}-\overset{\overset{O}{||}}{C}-OH$$

Serine (Ser)

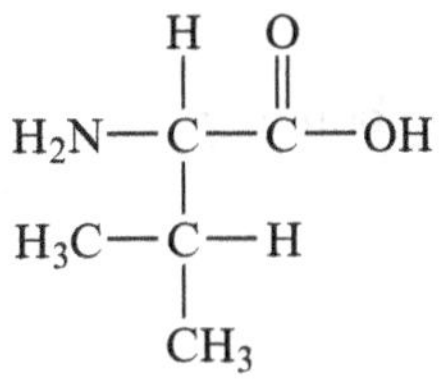

$$H_2N-\underset{\underset{\underset{CH_3}{|}}{H_3C-C-H}}{\overset{\overset{H}{|}}{C}}-\overset{\overset{O}{||}}{C}-OH$$

Valine (Val)

A) Alanine

C) Serine

B) Glycine

D) Valine

3. R represents where the following side chains are attached to an amino acid. Which is an amino acid alkaline (or basic) side chain?

A) $R-CH_2CH_3$

C) $R-CH_2CO_2H$

B) $R-CH_2CH_2OH$

D) $R-CH_2CH_2NH_2$

4. Based on the structure of its side chains, the amino acid serine can be classified as

A) acidic.

C) neutral, non-polar.

B) basic.

D) neutral, polar.

5. How many peptide bonds are present in the polypeptide shown below?

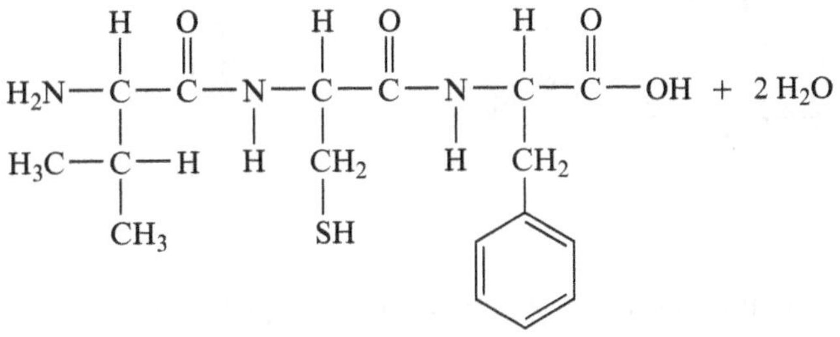

$$H_2N-\underset{\underset{\underset{CH_3}{|}}{H_3C-C-H}}{\overset{\overset{H}{|}}{C}}-\overset{\overset{O}{||}}{C}-\underset{\underset{H}{|}}{N}-\underset{\underset{\underset{SH}{|}}{CH_2}}{\overset{\overset{H}{|}}{C}}-\overset{\overset{O}{||}}{C}-\underset{\underset{H}{|}}{N}-\underset{\underset{CH_2}{|}}{\overset{\overset{H}{|}}{C}}-\overset{\overset{O}{||}}{C}-OH + 2\,H_2O$$

A) One

C) Three

B) Two

D) Four

The following structure of cytosine pertains to Questions 6 and 7.

$$N^X H_2$$

HC

HC

N^Y

N^Z

C

C

O

H

Cytosine

6. The primary force of attraction between cytosine and other cyclic amine bases in DNA is

   A) disulfide bridging bonding.

   B) ionic interactions.

   C) peptide bonding.

   D) hydrogen bonding.

7. In DNA, which nitrogen atom in cytosine participates in forming a covalent bond to a sugar?

   A) Nitrogen X

   B) Nitrogen Y

   C) Nitrogen Z

   D) Nitrogen Y and Z

8. A common pattern in the secondary structure of proteins is the β-pleated sheet structure which accounts for an extended chain and forms a zig-zag pattern as represented by the following

β-Pleated sheet protein structure

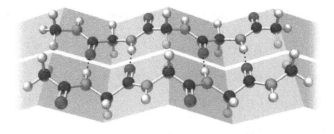

The ability of a protein to maintain this zig-zag pattern is due primarily to _____ intermolecular forces.

   A) hydrogen bonding

   B) dipole-dipole

   C) ion-dipole

   D) covalent

The following structures pertain to Questions 9 and 10. Ribose is a five-carbon sugar and can be represented by the following structure

$$
\begin{array}{c}
\overset{\displaystyle H}{}\diagdown\overset{\displaystyle O}{}\diagup \\
C \\
| \\
H-C-OH \\
| \\
H-C-OH \\
| \\
H-C-OH \\
| \\
H-C-H \\
| \\
OH
\end{array}
$$

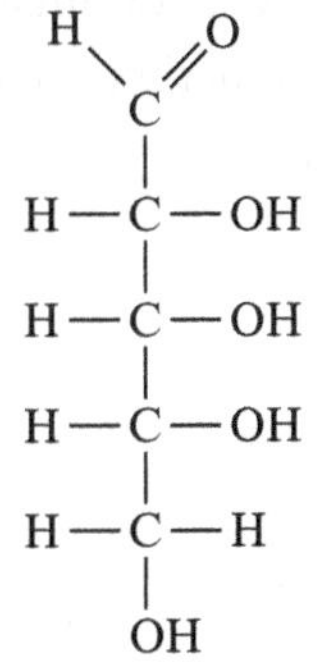

Ribose, a 5-carbon sugar

Fructose is a six-carbon sugar and can be represented by the following structure

$$
\begin{array}{c}
CH_2OH \\
| \\
C=O \\
| \\
HO-C-H \\
| \\
H-C-OH \\
| \\
H-C-OH \\
| \\
CH_2OH
\end{array}
$$

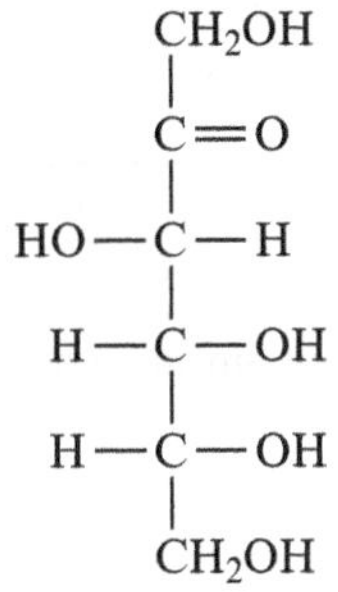

Fructose, a 6-carbon sugar

9. Ribose and fructose are carbohydrates. The term "carbohydrates" refers to a large class of polyhydroxylated _____.

   A) alcohols and carboxylic acids

   B) amines and amides

   C) aldehydes and ketones

   D) ethers and esters

10. Ribose is a monosaccharide and is also a(n)

   A) aldohexose.   C) ketohexose.

   B) aldopentose.   D) ketopentose.

1. C); 2. C); 3. D); 4. D); 5. B); 6. D); 7. B); 8. A); 9. C); 10. D)

Chapter 23 Practice AP Test Questions Answers:

Data Interpretation and Analysis Question: Enzymes

Enzymes are pH sensitive, and they have an optimal level of activity. Any changes from an optimal level will result in decreased activity. The graph below shows the activity of pepsin in comparison to that of trypsin.

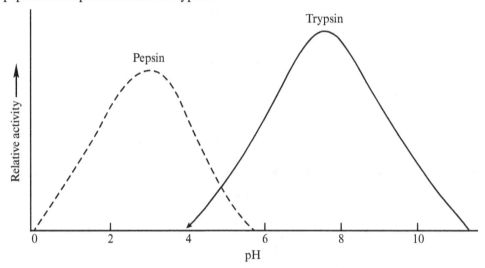

Figure 1   Shows the complex structures of pepsin and trypsin.

Pepsin

Polypeptide   Polypeptide fragments

R and R' = Leu, Phe, Trp, and Tyr (preferred); alos hydrolyzes esters

Trypsin

Polypeptide   Polypeptide fragments

R = Arg and Lys

a) What is the optimal pH for good activity for Pepsin? For Trypsin?

b) Would you find pepsin or trypsin in the stomach?

c) Will pepsin have more acidic sites or alkaline sites compared to trypsin?

d) How do enzymes speed up the rate of reaction without increasing the temperature of the reaction?

e) Could both enzymes work together effectively between the range of pH 4 and pH 6?

Data Interpretation and Analysis Question Answers with Brief Explanations

a) pH $= 3$, pH $= 7.8$

b) Pepsin because it functions best in an acidic pH. Gastric fluid is acidic.

c) Pepsin will have more acidic sites compared to trypsin.

d) Enzymes lower the activation energy by providing an alternative mechanism.

e) No, because the activity level is too low for both.

CHAPTER

23

READING GUIDE

The concepts of this chapter are part of the cross domain focus of Unit 3 of the AP Chemistry Curriculum. The cross domain focus is on biology aspects of intermolecular forces such as hydrogen bonding and understanding the structures of proteins, lipids, and carbohydrates. The AP Chemistry Exam may include questions involving the structures of compounds discussed in this chapter.

Section 23.1 Diabetes and the Synthesis of Human Insulin

1. What discovery by Sanger in 1955 changed the prognosis for diabetics? Why was this discovery such an improvement over previous methods of treatment*?
2. What were the scientists at Genentech able to do that allowed for the production of large amounts of insulin?*

Section 23.2 Lipids

3. What are the six categories of lipids?
4. Describe the solubility of lipids.
5. Draw the general structure of a fatty acid.
6. Explain the difference between saturated, monounsaturated, and polyunsaturated fatty acids.
7. Identify the structures below as saturated, monounsaturated, or polyunsaturated fatty acids.

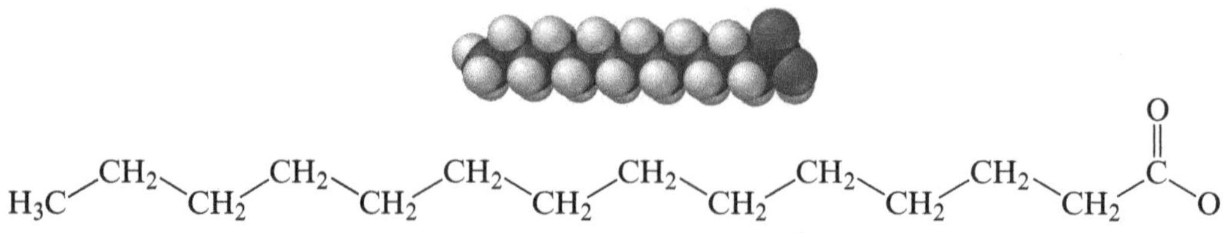

Myristic acid

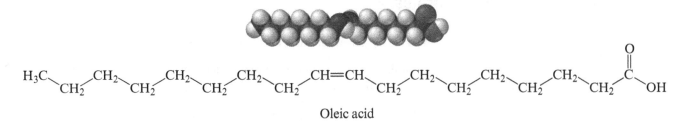

Oleic acid

8. What factors affect the melting point of fatty acids? Describe how these factors affect their melting points.

9. What are triglycerides?

10. What types of fat tend to be solid at room temperature?

11. What are three sources of unsaturated fats?

12. Identify which of the below images is a saturated fat and which is an unsaturated fat. What evidence supports your reasoning?

Tristearin

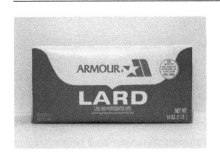

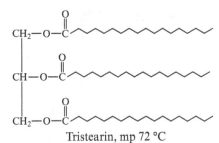

Tristearin, mp 72 °C

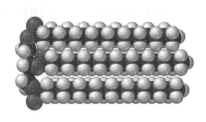

Triolein

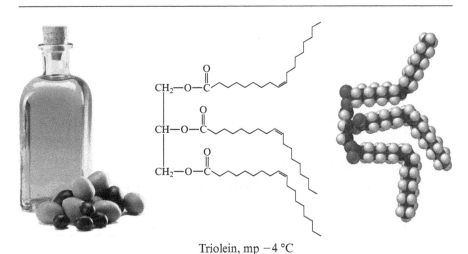

Triolein, mp −4 °C

13. What do the terms *hydrophobic* and *hydrophilic* mean? Which types of structures are hydrophobic and which are hydrophilic?

14. Can a species be both hydrophilic and hydrophobic? Explain your answer.

15. Why are phospholipids important in cell structure?

16. What are steroids? List three examples of steroids.*

Section 23.3   Carbohydrates

17. What is the general formula of a carbohydrate?

18. Draw the structure of glucose. What component of the structure allows glucose to be soluble in blood? What is glucose?

19. What is the term for simple sugars or carbohydrates? How are sugars and simple carbohydrates named?

20. What is the proper name of fruit sugar? Brain sugar? Why are fructose and glucose considered structural isomers?

21. What is a disaccharide? What process breaks up a disaccharide during digestion?

22. What are polysaccharides? What other name do they go by?

23. List three examples of polysaccharides and describe their use.

Section 23.4   Proteins and Amino Acids

24. What function do proteins have in living organisms?

25. What are enzymes?

26. What are proteins composed of?

27. Identify the main parts of the general structure of an amino acid below.

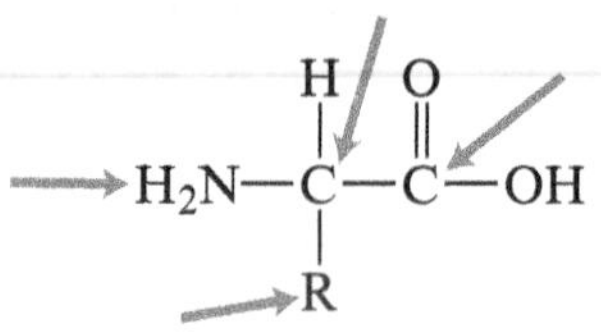

Amino acid general structure

28. Identify the primary function of each class of protein. Give an example of each.

Protein Functions

Class of Protein	Primary Function	Example
Structural proteins		
Enzymes		
Hormones		
Transport proteins		
Storage proteins		
Contractile and motile proteins		
Protective proteins		

29. Draw the structure of three common amino acids and give their names.

30. When amino acids are bonded together to form a protein, what determines the structure and function of the protein? What is the difference between L-amino acids and D-amino acids?

31. What is a zwitterion?*

32. What is a peptide bond formed of?

33. What are the differences among a dipeptide, a tripeptide, a tetrapeptide, an oligopeptide, and a polypeptide?

Protein Structure   Section 23.5

34. What aspect of a protein is crucial to determining its function? What are the two main classifications of proteins?

35. What are the characteristics of fibrous proteins? Identify two uses of fibrous proteins. What levels of protein structure do fibrous proteins lack?

36. What are the characteristics of globular proteins? Identify two uses of globular proteins.

37. Identify the levels of protein structure in the following figure:

Levels of Protein Structure

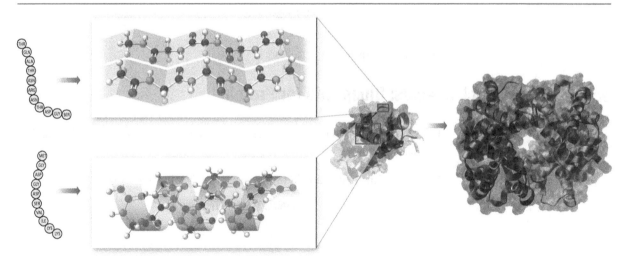

38. Explain what the main components of each of the following protein structures are:

Primary structure:

Secondary structure:

Tertiary structure:

Quaternary structure:

39. Which structure pattern includes the alpha helix? List an example of a protein with an alpha helix. What is a beta pleated structure. List an example.

40. Identify the interactions maintaining tertiary structures in proteins in the following figure:

Interactions That Maintain Tertiary Structure

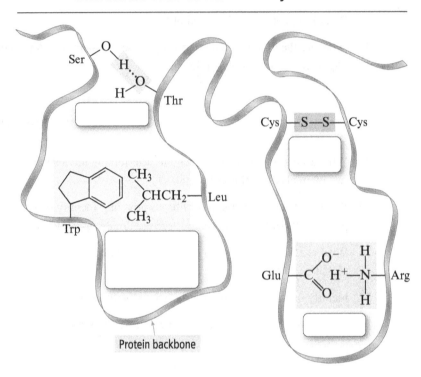

41. What is a quaternary structure?

Section 23.6   Nucleic Acids: Blueprints for Proteins

42. What are the two types of nucleic acids? Where are each one usually found inside a cell?

43. Identify the main parts in the structure of DNA in the following figure:

DNA: Basic Structure

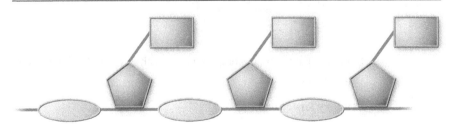

44. What are the four bases in DNA? Which of the bases are purine and which are pyrimidine and why are they given that designation?

45. What base is different in RNA?

46. What are the complementary bases?

47. Use the following figure to explain the hierarchy of genetic structure. Include an explanation of nucleotide, codon, gene, and chromosome.*

Genetic Structure

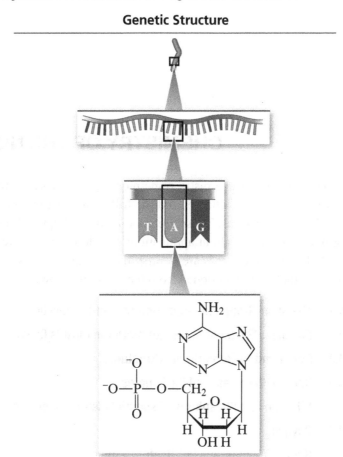

DNA Replication, the Double Helix, and Protein Synthesis   Section 23.7

48. What is the shape of DNA?

49. What process provided evidence to help scientists discover the structure of DNA?*

50. Where does protein synthesis occur in the cell?

Self-Assessment Answers

1. _____   2. _____

3. _____   4. _____

5. _____   6. _____

7. _____   8. _____

9. _____   10. _____

CHAPTER

24

CHEMISTRY OF THE NONMETALS

Students need to see how chemistry principles apply across domains in science and in their everyday life. This chapter and the following chapters give many good examples of these connections. These are good reading chapters for students in terms of background knowledge about applications and do have some review from earlier chapters. Although noble gases are nonmetals, they are not covered in this chapter. Only a few examples are mentioned from the sections below:

24.2 **The Main-Group Elements: Bonding and Properties**

24.3 **Silicates: The Most Abundant Matter in Earth's Crust**

24.4 **Boron and Its Remarkable Structures**

24.5 **Carbon, Carbides, and Carbonates**

24.6 **Nitrogen and Phosphorus: Essential Elements for Life**

24.7 **Oxygen**

24.8 **Sulfur: A Dangerous but Useful Element**

24.9 **Halogens: Reactive Elements with High Electronegativity**

Specific Learning Objectives Addressed in This Chapter:

Learning Objective 2.29 The student can create a representation of a covalent solid that shows essential characteristics of the structure and interactions present in the substance. [*See* **SP 1.1**]

Learning Objective 2.30 The student is able to explain a representation that connects properties of a covalent solid to its structural attributes and to the interactions present at the atomic level. [*See* **SP 1.1, 6.2, 7.1**]

Specific Science Practices Addressed in This Chapter:

SAP-2 The periodic table shows patterns in electronic structure and trends in atomic properties.

SAP-2.A Explain the relationship between trends in atomic properties of elements and electronic structure and periodicity.

SAP-2.B Explain the relationship between trends in the reactivity of elements and periodicity.

SAP-5 Intermolecular forces can explain the physical properties of a material.

SAP-5.A Explain the relationship between the chemical structures of molecules and the relative strength of their intermolecular forces when:

- The molecules are of the same chemical species.

- The molecules are of two different chemical species.

SAP-5.B Explain the relationship among the macroscopic properties of a substance, the particulate-level structure of the substance, and the interactions between these particles.

- In network covalent solids, the atoms are covalently bonded together in a three-dimensional network (e.g., diamond) or layers of two-dimensional networks (e.g. graphite). These are only formed from nonmetals: elemental or binary compounds of two nonmetals. Due to strong covalent interactions, covalent solids have high melting points. Three-dimensional network solids are also rigid and hard because the covalent bond angles are fixed. However, graphite is soft because adjacent layers can slide past each other relatively easily.

- Molecular solids are composed of distinct, individual units of covalently bonded molecules attracted to each other through relatively weak intermolecular forces. Molecular solids generally have a low melting point because of the relatively weak intermolecular forces present between the molecules. They do not conduct electricity because their valence electrons are tightly held within the covalent bonds and lone pairs of each constituent molecule. Molecular solids are sometimes composed of very large molecules or polymers.

Concepts and Vocabulary to Review:

The Main-Group Elements: Bonding and Properties   Section 24.2

The nonmetals, with the exception of hydrogen and helium, are filling *p* orbitals in their electron configurations. There is a huge diversity in the properties of nonmetals.

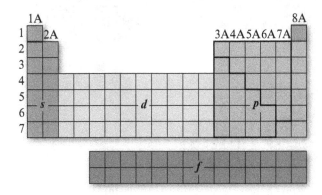

Nonmetals can form ionic bonds with metals and covalent bonds with other nonmetals. Nonmetals such as carbon and silicon can form network covalent bonds. The most electronegative elements like fluorine are nonmetals. The properties exhibited depend on the bonds and structure. Across a period, effective nuclear charge increases, which results in the smaller radii of the nonmetals. These atoms tend to form anions and are reduced in reactions.

Section 24.3   Silicates: The Most Abundant Matter in Earth's Crust

Silicon forms covalent atomic solids that have a variety of structures. Silicon is very similar to carbon and can also form chains. One important compound of silicon is SiO_2, which is tetrahedral in shape. It is called silica and is the base structure of quartz.

Section 24.4   Boron and Its Remarkable Structures

Although boron has five allotropes, it is never found alone in nature. It is always combined with oxygen. Boron is added to glass to prevent cracking. An example is Pyrex, which is used in beakers in the chemistry lab. With three valence electrons, it tends to have an incomplete octet that is sp^2 hybridized and forms a trigonal planar shape. Boron often is a Lewis acid since it needs to accept electrons to get an octet of electrons.

Section 24.5   Carbon, Carbides, and Carbonates

Carbon is the most versatile element in forming compounds. Even as an element it has several forms, including coal, graphite, and diamond. Although all are carbons, their properties vary due to their structures.

Graphite has covalent bonds in the horizontal plane but has weak interaction between the layers. This allows graphite to slide one layer over another, making it a good lubricant.

(a) Graphite   **(b)** Diamond

Figure 24.1 Network Covalent Atomic Solids   **(a)** In graphite, carbon atoms are arranged in sheets. Within each sheet, the atoms are covalently bonded to one another by a network of sigma and pi bonds. Neighboring sheets are held together by dispersion forces. **(b)** In diamond, each carbon atom forms four covalent bonds to four other carbon atoms in a tetrahedral geometry.

In contrast, diamond has covalent bonds in all four directions as each carbon is bonded to four other carbon atoms. As a result, diamond is very hard and is used in cutting tools. Carbon also has other forms such as coal, charcoal, fullerenes, and carbon black. Coal is created under pressure with decomposing plant material. It has many forms, which are named by their content. One type, bituminous coal, also contains sulfur, so that when burned it creates gases such as sulfur dioxide which when combined with water in the air forms acid rain. Carbon forms many other compounds including carbides. It can form ionic carbides and covalent carbides; in addition, it is hard and has high melting points. An example of an ionic carbide is calcium carbide, CaC_2, where carbon combines with a less electronegative metallic atom. In covalent carbides, carbon combines with another nonmetal to form compounds such as SiC. If a metal alloy such as steel has a array with space to add carbon atoms, it will form a metallic carbide; the result is a harder, less malleable metal. Soot is an amorphous form of carbon.

Carbon also combines with oxygen to form carbon dioxide, carbon monoxide, and carbonates. When carbon dioxide and water combine, the intermediate product is carbonic acid which then starts to dissociate.

$$CO_2(aq) + H_2O(l) \rightleftharpoons \underset{\text{carbonic acid}}{H_2CO_3(aq)}$$

$$H_2CO_3(aq) \rightleftharpoons H^+(aq) + \underset{\text{hydrogen carbonate}}{HCO_3^-(aq)} \rightleftharpoons 2H^+(aq) + \underset{\text{carbonate}}{CO_3^{2-}(aq)}$$

If you are asked to write an equation where some carbonic acid forms, remember that the species in the greatest concentration is the species written in the equation. For instance, if sodium carbonate combines with hydrochloric acid, the end products are aqueous sodium chloride, water, and carbon dioxide. The sodium ion and chloride ion are spectator ions in a net equation, leaving $CO_3^{2-} + H^+ \longrightarrow H_2O + CO_2$. H_2CO_3 is not the primary species. Think about the carbon dioxide in soda cans—it is a dissolved gas that comes out of solution when opened.

Nitrogen and Phosphorus: Essential Elements for Life   Section 24.6

The diatomic nitrogen gas, N_2, is the main component of the air we breathe. The strength of the triple bond in the nitrogen gas makes it very stable. With the ending configuration of $2s^2 2p^3$, nitrogen can form many compounds because it can show a variety of oxidation states, including $+2, +3, +5$, and -3.

An equilibrium reaction where Le Châtelier's principle is observed is when colorless N_2O_4 is heated to form the reddish brown NO_2.

$$N_2O_4(g) \xrightarrow{\text{heat}} 2 NO_2(g)$$

When cooled, the reaction reverts to the colorless N_2O_4. The change in color provides evidence of which part of the reaction is favored when heating and cooling.

The most important commercial nitrogen compound is the ammonia, NH_3.

Phosphorus is very similar to nitrogen, having a similar ending electron configuration. When nitrogen bonds with hydrogen, polar ammonia molecules are formed, but because phosphorus is less electronegative, when it bonds with hydrogen, the phosphine that results is not as polar as ammonia. Phosphorus also has white, red, and black allotropes. The red allotrope is used in match heads.

Section 24.7   Oxygen

With an electron configuration ending in $2s^2 2p^4$, oxygen shows a primary oxidation state of –2. Oxygen has the second highest electronegativity of all elements and is found in ionic, covalent, and network covalent compounds. To separate oxygen from the air, fractionation is used. The air is cooled until it all liquefies. Then the liquid is warmed. The other gases will vaporize before the oxygen so leaving the oxygen that can then be collected.

An allotrope of oxygen is ozone, O_3, which is a blue toxic gas with a strong odor. Ozone is used to kill bacteria especially in water purification systems. Ozone is denser than oxygen gas and, unlike oxygen gas, is diamagnetic. Ozone is naturally formed by lightening reacting with oxygen gas in the air.

Section 24.8   Sulfur: A Dangerous but Useful Element

While sulfur has the same outer electron configuration as oxygen, $s^2 p^4$, sulfur is larger owing to an additional energy level. Sulfur also forms the -2 oxidation state and has several allotropes, including a S_8 ring structure.

While H_2S, is bent in shape like water, it is less polar, as sulfur is not as electronegative as oxygen. Water also has larger bond angles than H_2S, 104.5° to 92.5°. Water forms hydrogen bonds between molecules while H_2S does not, which results in H_2S having a lower melting point than water. It is also a component of natural gas, so when it is burned it forms sulfur dioxide. When SO_2 is combined with water in the air, it forms acid rain.

Section 24.9   Halogens: Reactive Elements with High Electronegativity

All halogens are the most electronegative atoms in their period and the smallest atom in their period. Within the halogens, the atomic radius increases regularly due to the extra energy level added. All have the outer configuration of $s^2 p^5$ and show a primary oxidation state of -1. When combined with metals, the small size of fluorine and its large electronegativity result in ionic bonds with high lattice energies. Halogens can also combine with nonmetals to form covalent bonds and with other halogens to form interhalide compounds.

Additional Practice

Self-Assessment Quiz Questions Q3, Q4, Q5, Q6, Q7, Q8, Q9, and Q10

Problems:
Review Questions 4, 9, 11, and 14
Boron and Its Remarkable Structures 27
Carbon, Carbides, and Carbonates 34, 35, 37, 38, and 41
Nitrogen and Phosphorus: Essential Elements for Life 44, 45, 53, 55, and 58
Oxygen 64
Halogens 71, and 72
Cumulative Problems 79, 81, and 82
Challenge Problems 95
Conceptual Problems 100, 101, and 102

Practice AP Test Questions

1. Which element exists as a diatomic molecule at 298K?

   A) B

   B) C

   C) N

   D) Ne

2. Ozone, O_3, in the upper atmosphere is important to life on the surface of the Earth because

   A) it provides a shield against incoming X-rays and gamma rays from solar radiation.

   B) it reacts with chlorofluorocarbons to create a hole in the ozone layer.

   C) it plays a role in helping plants undergo photosynthesis.

   D) it absorbs UV solar radiation.

3. Which of the following substances is being tested as a replacement for gasoline as the fuel for medium combustion engines?

   A) NO_2

   B) CO_2

   C) H_2

   D) BF_3

4. When nonmetal oxides are placed in water, the resultant solution is _____.

   A) acidic

   B) basic

   C) amphoteric

   D) neutral

5. The major source of the element sulfur is _____.

    A) evaporation of seawater

    B) mining underground deposits of sulfur

    C) extraction from minerals containing sulfates

    D) reduction of sulfuric acid

6. The melting points of four halogens are listed in the table below. What is a reasonable explanation as to why the melting point of Iodine is the highest of the four halogens?

Element	Fluorine, F_2	Chlorine, Cl_2	Bromine, Br_2	Iodine, I_2
Melting Point (°C)	−220	−101	−7.3	113

Of the four halogens,

    A) I_2 has the highest molar mass, and therefore, it requires the greatest amount of energy to undergo a phase change.

    B) I_2 has more valence electrons, and therefore, it is more polarizable.

    C) I_2 has more total electrons, the electron cloud is easier to distort, and therefore, it is more polarizable.

    D) The melting points of the halogens increase as you go down the Periodic Table, I_2 is the furthest down.

7. Given a Periodic Table and the information about three of the alkali metals in the table below, what is a reasonable explanation as to why potassium reacts more vigorously with water compared to lithium's reactivity with water?

Alkali Metal	First Ionization Energy (kJ/mole)	$E°$ Reduction (V)	Melting Point (°C)
Li	520	−3.05	180
Na	495	−2.71	98
K	419	−2.92	63

    A) Because potassium's valence electron is further away from the nucleus compare to the other two alkali metals, it takes less energy to remove potassium's valence electron compared to lithium's valence electron; therefore, potassium reacts faster with water.

    B) Because lithium has a higher reduction potential and a smaller radius, lithium requires more energy input to get its reaction with water started and sufficient water molecules to come in contact with it compared to potassium.

    C) Because Lithium has a smaller size compared to potassium, it does not come into account with as many water molecules as does potassium.

    D) Because potassium has a lower melting point and ionization energy. The heat of reaction is sufficient to melt the solid metal. The molten metal spreads over the water and exposes a larger surface to water and thus causes a more vigorous reaction,

8. White phosphorus consists of P_4 molecules in a(n) _____ geometric structure.

   A) linear

   B) tetrahedral

   C) square planar

   D) polymer with amorphous chains

9. What is the hybridization of boron in diborane, B_2H_6?

   A) sp

   B) sp^2

   C) sp^3

   D) sigma and pi bonding

10. What is the basic building block of all silicates?

   A) $Si_2O_6^{4-}$

   B) $SiCl_4$

   C) SiO_2

   D) $SiO4^{4-}$

1. C); 2. D); 3. C); 4. B); 5. D); 6. C); 7. A); 8. B); 9. C); 10. D)

Chapter 24 Practice AP Test Questions Answers:

Data Interpretation and Analysis Question: Phosphorus and Compounds with Phosphorus

The element phosphorus has several allotropes. White phosphorus is P_4 and has a tetrahedral-like arrangement, whereas red phosphorus has a boat arrangement of four phosphorus atoms, with the two end phosphorus atoms connected to other P_4 units to form a chain as illustrated in Figure 1.

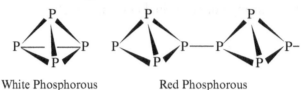

White Phosphorous   Red Phosphorous

Figure 1   Structure of white and red phosphorus.

Table 1   List some of the properties of white and red phosphorus.

	White Phosphorus	Red Phosphorus
Solubility in water	No	No
Reaction with water	No reaction	No reaction
Reaction with $O_2(g)$	Yes	No

a) Are the P-P bonds in white phosphorus and red phosphorus ionic, polar covalent, or covalent? Explain.

b) What is the hybridization of phosphorus in white phosphorus?

c) Given the structures of red and white phosphorus, suggest a reason why white phosphorus reacts with oxygen gas while red phosphorus does not react with oxygen gas.

d) Complete and balance the following equations. One product forms in each reaction, and the product is different in all reactions.

   i) $P_4(s) + 3O_2(g) \longrightarrow$ _____

   ii) $P_4(s) + 6Cl_2(g) \longrightarrow$ _____

e) P_4O_{10} forms an acidic solution when placed in water. Complete and balance the following equation:

   $P_4O_{10} + 6H_2O \longrightarrow$ _____

f) Sketch a 3-D drawing of P_4O_{10}. The oxygen atoms bonded to the phosphorus atoms in P_4O_{10} have a tetrahedral-like arrangement. All of the oxygen atoms obey the Octet Rule. No two phosphorus atoms in P_4O_{10} are bonded together.

g) P_4 and P_4O_{10} each have a tetrahedral structure feature. Does this mean the chemical bonding is the same? Explain.

h) Offer an explanation as to why P_4 does not react with water but P_4O_{10} does.

Data Interpretation and Analysis Question Answers with Brief Explanations

a) P-P bonds are covalent bonds since $\Delta EN = 0$.

b) The P-P-P bond angle is about 60°

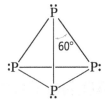

c) sp^3

d) The structure of red phosphorus is like a polymer with long chains, which makes interacting with O_2 molecules difficult. White phosphorus has individual P_4 units, which can directly interact with O_2 molecules.

e) i) $P_4O_6(s)$,   ii) $4\ PCl_3(g)$

f) $4\ H_3PO_4$

g)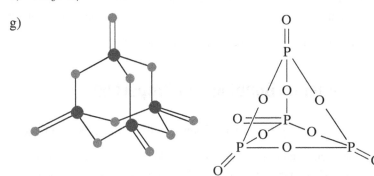

h) A comparison of P_4 and P_4O_{10}, shows that the chemical bonding is not the same. In P_4, the P atoms are using sp^3 hybrid orbitals. There are sigma bonds between each phosphorus atom. In P_4O_{10}, each phosphorus atom has three sigma bonds to three oxygen atoms and a pi bond to a fourth oxygen atom. The P atoms in P_4O_{10} cannot be using sp^3 hybrid orbitals.

i) P_4 does not react with water because each P atom in a P_4 molecule has one lone pair of electrons, which makes P_4 a Lewis base. Although water is amphoteric, it is not a strong enough Lewis acid to react with a Lewis base such as P_4. P_4O_{10} has many O-P-O bonds, making the structure easily accessible for the hydrogen atoms in the water molecules to interact.

READING GUIDE

The major topics covered in this chapter include background material on the properties of nonmetals. This is encompassed in Units 1, 2, and 3 covering the applications of the nonmetals in the AP Chemistry curriculum.

Section 24.1   **Insulated Nanowires**

1. What characteristics allow boron nitride to make nanotubes similar to carbon? What is one difference between carbon nanotubes and boron nitride nanotubes?*

2. What are some commercial uses of carbon nanotubes?*

Section 24.2   **The Main-Group Elements: Bonding and Properties**

3. All nonmetals except hydrogen and helium are filling what type of orbital?

4. Why do nonmetals tend to form anions? How does the location of the nonmetal on the periodic table affect its bonding properties? Why? Include a sketch of the periodic table in your answer.

Section 24.3   **Silicates: The Most Abundant Matter in Earth's Crust**

5. What type of compounds are silicates?

6. What is the formula and structure of quartz (silica)?

7. Fill in the following table:*

Type of Silicate Structure	Base Unit	Example
Aluminosilicates		
Orthosilicates		
Pyrosilicates		
Pyroxenes		
Amphiboles		
Phyllosilicates		

Boron and Its Remarkable Structures   Section 24.4

8. Why does boron behave as a semimetal?

9. How many allotropes does boron have?

10. What element does boron usually combine with in compounds?

11. What is Pyrex® and why is it used in making glass?

12. Draw the Lewis structure of the general formula of a boron halide. Identify the geometric shape.

13. What forms if B_2O_3 cools quickly? Why is this called an amorphous solid?

14. Fill in the table of the types of boranes:*

Type of Borane	Base Unit
Closo-boranes	
Nido-boranes	
Arachno-boranes	

Carbon, Carbides, and Carbonates   Section 24.5

15. What is amorphous carbon? Explain how the following structures affect the properties of graphite and diamond: (This question is review. You may want to refer back to section 12.6)

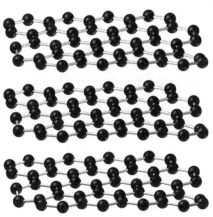 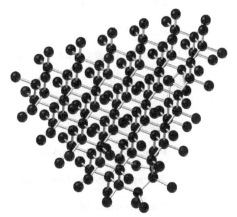

16. How is coal formed? What are the three types of coal? What are the differences among them?*

17. What are the differences among coal, coke, activated carbon, carbon black, charcoal, and soot? Include a use of each.

18. How does burning coal form acid rain? What occurs if coal is heated without air?

19. What are the three types of carbides? For each type, identify its composition, provide an example and a use.

20. What are the properties of carbon dioxide and carbon monoxide? Why are the properties so different when they are both just carbon and oxygen?

21. What property of carbon dioxide allows the oceans to act as a reservoir of carbon dioxide?

22. What are the formulas and uses of washing soda, baking soda, and baking powder?

Section 24.6   Nitrogen and Phosphorus: Essential Elements for Life

23. What are some general properties of nitrogen and phosphorus?

24. Why is nitrogen gas so stable?

25. What are the three allotropes of phosphorus? How do the properties of each type differ?

26. For each of the following nitrogen-containing compounds, identify its chemical formula, the oxidation state of the nitrogen, and provide one use:

   Ammonia

   Hydrazine

   Hydrogen azide

   Nitrogen monoxide

   Dinitrogen monoxide

   Nitric acid

27. What gases can react with water vapor in the air to form acid rain?

28. For each of the following compounds, write the chemical formula and provide a common use:

   Phosphine

   Phosphorus trichloride

   Tetraphosphorus hexaoxide

   Phosphoric acid

   Calcium phosphate

   Sodium pyrophosphate

29. What is the problem with using phosphates in detergents?

Section 24.7   Oxygen

30. What are the properties of elemental oxygen?

31. How did Joseph Priestley discover oxygen?

32. Explain how oxygen is extracted from air. Describe two other ways oxygen can be produced.

33. What is hyperbaric oxygen therapy? What is it used for?*

34. What are the three forms of oxides? Give an example of each.

35. What are the properties of ozone?

36. What are the positives and negatives of ozone use?

Sulfur: A Dangerous but Useful Element   Section 24.8

37. What are the properties of elemental sulfur? Where on Earth is elemental sulfur commonly found?

38. What is the most common allotrope of sulfur? What is its shape?

39. What sulfur compound smells like rotten eggs?

40. Compare the formulas and properties of water and hydrogen sulfide.

41. How is sulfur dioxide produced? What are some of its properties and uses?

42. How is sulfuric acid formed? What are some of its uses?

Halogens: Reactive Elements with High Electronegativity   Section 24.9

43. What are the properties of elemental fluorine? Why is fluorine the most reactive nonmetallic element?

44. Identify three compounds of fluorine and their uses.

45. What are interhalogen compounds? Give an example.

46. What are two properties of halogen oxides?

Self-Assessment Answers

1. _____   2. _____

3. _____   4. _____

5. _____   6. _____

7. _____   8. _____

9. _____   10. _____

METALS AND METALLURGY

This chapter provides background material about metals and their properties. As mentioned in Chapter 24, while very interesting material, it is not the focus of the AP curriculum. Most of the material covered was previously mentioned in other chapters. Sections that are AP material include the following:

Specific Learning Objectives Addressed in This Chapter:

SAP-2 The periodic table shows patterns in electronic structure and trends in atomic properties.

SAP-2.A Explain the relationship between trends in atomic properties of elements and electronic structure and periodicity.

SAP-2.B Explain the relationship between trends in the reactivity of elements and periodicity.

SAP-3 Atoms or ions bond due to interactions between them, forming molecules.

SAP-3.D Represent a metallic solid and/or an alloy using a model to show essential characteristics of the structure and interactions present in the substance.

- Metallic bonding can be represented as an array of positive metal ions surrounded by delocalized valence electrons.

- Interstitial alloys form between atoms of different radii, where the smaller atoms fill the interstitial spaces between the larger atoms.

- Substitutional alloys form between atoms of comparable radius, where one atom substitutes for the other in the lattice.

SAP-5 Intermolecular Forces can explain the physical properties of a material.

SAP-5.B Explain the relationship among the macroscopic properties of a substance, the particulate-level structure of the substance, and the interactions between these particles.

- Metallic solids are good conductors of electricity and heat, due to the presence of free valence electrons. They also tend to be malleable and ductile, due to the ease with which the metal cores can rearrange their structure. In an insterstitial alloy, interstitial atoms tend to make the lattice more rigid, decreasing malleability and ductility. Alloys typically retain a sea of mobile electrons and so remain conducting.

Concepts and Vocabulary to Review:

Vanadium: A Problem and an Opportunity   Section 25.1

Metallurgy includes all processes associated with mining and processes of metal production. Alloys are mixtures of metals and are very common. They are ductile and malleable.

The General Properties and Natural Distribution of Metals   Section 25.2

Properties of metals include being a good conductor of heat and electricity, hammered into sheets (malleability), and drawn into wires (ductility); they are generally silver in color. They have delocalized electrons found in an electron "sea." Properties vary, as lead is very soft, whereas chromium is very brittle. All metals form cations.

Few metals are found in their elemental form on earth, due to their reactivity. The metals found in their elemental form are called the noble metals. They include gold, platinum, silver, palladium, copper, and nickel. The highest thermal and electrical conductivity is found in copper, silver, and aluminum.

Metallurgical Processes   Section 25.3

There are many ways to separate metals. One way is through electrometallurgy. An example of this process is electrolysis, which is used to refine copper.

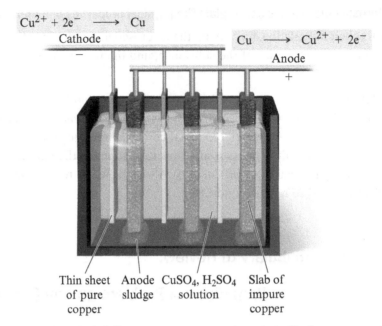

$$Cu^{2+} + 2e^- \longrightarrow Cu$$
Cathode
−

$$Cu \longrightarrow Cu^{2+} + 2e^-$$
Anode
+

Thin sheet   Anode   CuSO$_4$, H$_2$SO$_4$ Slab of
of pure   sludge   solution   impure
copper   copper

Figure 25.1 Copper Electrolysis Cell   Copper is refined by electrolysis. The impure copper is oxidized at the anode and then reduced to form pure metal on the cathode. Many precious metals collect in the sludge at the bottom of the electrolysis cell.

Section 25.4   # Metal Structures and Alloys

Alloys are metallic materials made with more than one metal. There are two types: substitutional and interstitial. In substitutional alloys, one atom of similar size is substituted for another. Nickel and copper are about the same size , 135 pm, and can easily substitute for each other.

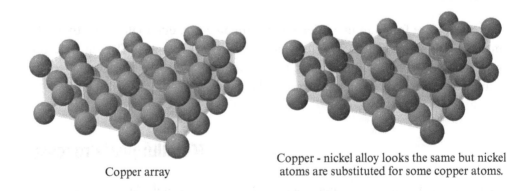

Copper array

Copper - nickel alloy looks the same but nickel atoms are substituted for some copper atoms.

In the array of atoms, because the nickel atom can substitute in for a copper atom copper-nickel alloys are quite common.

In interstitial alloys, a smaller atom fits between the atoms already present. These small atoms are often hydrogen, boron, nitrogen, or carbon. In interstitial arrays, the main array of atoms remains and the smaller atoms are added into the spaces as in figure 25.2.

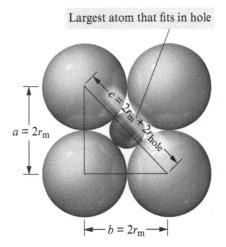

Largest atom that fits in hole

$a = 2r_m$

$c = 2r_m + 2r_{hole}$

$b = 2r_m$

Figure 25.2 A Different View of an Octahedral Hole   An octahedral hole can be viewed as the area in the middle of a square plane of atoms, with one additional atom above the hole and one additional atom below the hole, accounting for the six close atoms. The diagonal of the square is equal to the radius of the two corner atoms plus the diameter of the hole. The Pythagorean theorem relates the length of the diagonal to the lengths of the sides of the square.

Sources, Properties, and Products of Some of the 3*d* Transition Metals

Section 25.5

Titanium is stronger than steel but half as dense. It is highly resistant to corrosion because it reacts with oxygen, forming a coating on the outside of the metal. Titanium is very strong and light, so it is used in airline jet engines. White paints often include TiO_2, which was substituted for toxic PbO_2 in older paints.

Chromium is a hard, white, brittle metal, yet its compounds are colored. Colors range from anions that are orange in dichromate and yellow in chromate to compounds that are violet in chrome alum to red in chromium(II) acetate. Chromium is used in stainless steel alloys. It is also used in corrosion-resistant coatings to protect surfaces from rusting, although its use has declined owing to its toxicity.

Manganese is used to strengthen alloys when alloyed with copper, aluminum, or magnesium. Manganese can exhibit oxidation states from +2 to +7 and the purple permanganate ion, MnO_4^-, is used in oxidation–reduction reactions. It is often reduced to solid MnO_2. Cobalt, iron, and nickel are ferromagnetic. They are attracted to magnets. Their unpaired electrons align, creating a permanent magnetic field.

Copper is a low-cost, abundant metal with a reddish color that is used in electrical wires. Copper replaced lead in piping due to lead's toxicity. Bronze is an alloy of copper and tin, whereas brass is an alloy of copper and zinc.

Nickel is an unreactive metal that resists corrosion—hence its use in money. It is alloyed with steel to make the steel resistant to corrosion.

Zinc is also used in galvanizing steel. The object is dipped in zinc. The zinc coating protects the metal underneath from oxidizing. Zinc is used in solder, and zinc combined with nickel and copper makes silver brass.

Additional Practice

Self-Assessment Quiz Questions Q1, Q3, Q7, Q8, Q9, and Q10

Problems:
Review Questions 10 and 13
The General Properties and Natural Distribution of Metals 15, 16, and 18
Metallurgical Processes 28
Sources, Properties, and Products of Some of the 3d Transition Metals 47, 49, 50, and 54
Cumulative Problems 63, 64, and 68

Practice AP Test Questions

Questions 1–3 refer to the following information. Nickel sulfide is abundant in Ontario, Canada. To produce nickel metal, the nickel sulfide is roasted in air; then the product reacted with carbon monoxide to form nickel carbonyl. When the nickel carbonyl is heated, it decomposes to nickel metal

$$Ni(CO)_4(g) \rightleftharpoons Ni(s) + 4\,CO(g) \qquad \Delta S = -320\,JK^{-1}\,mol^{-1}\,\text{and}$$

$$\Delta H = -160.7\,kJ$$

	ΔG_f° (kJ/mol)
$CO(g)$	-137
$Ni(CO)_4(g)$	-587.4 kJ/mol

1. The molecular geometry of nickel carbonyl is _____.

    A) square planar

    B) trigonal pyramidal

    C) tetrahedral

    D) distorted tetrahedron

2. In order to maximize the production of nickel,

    A) increase the temperature.

    B) increase the pressure.

    C) decrease the volume.

    D) add a catalyst.

3. Assuming ΔG_f° is independent of temperature, estimate the equilibrium constant, K_p, for the reaction at 60.0 °C.

    A) less than 1.0×10^{-5}

    B) greater than 1.0×10^{-5} but less than 1

    C) greater than 1 but less than 100,000

    D) greater than 100,000

4. The process of arc-melting is used to facilitate the production of which pure metal?

A) Ag

B) Al

C) Pt

D) Ti

5. Which of the following elements is most likely to be found on Earth as an oxide?

A) Fe

B) Zn

C) Pt

D) Hg

6. The diagrams below show a representation of a metal X represented by large dark color spheres in a 4 × 4 array and an alloy of metal X with the large dark color spheres and smaller light gray spheres representing another element, Y.

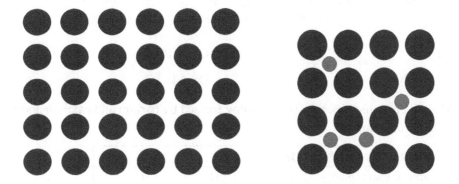

How will the properties of the alloy differ from the metal?

Compared to the metal,

A) the alloy will have a lower density and be easier to shape (malleability).

B) the alloy will have a higher density and be easier to shape (malleability).

C) the alloy will have a lower density and be more difficult to shape (malleability).

D) the alloy will have a higher density and be more difficult to shape (malleability).

7. Given the following phase diagram for a barium-calcium alloy. Determine the percentage composition and determine the melting point of the alloy at a composition that is 30% barium and 70% calcium.

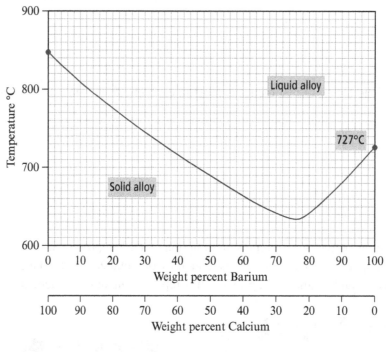

A) 848°C

B) 748°C

C) 650°C

D) 648 °C

8. Most likely, which lists the type of alloy formed by barium and calcium and by iron and calcium

Element	Ba	Ca	Fe
Atomic Radius (pm)	222	231	126

	Type of Alloy with Calcium	Type of Alloy with Iron
A)	Interstitial	Substitutional
B)	Interstitial	Interstitial
C)	Substitutional	Substitutional
D)	Substitutional	Interstitial

9. What is one way to reduce magnesium chloride to magnesium metal and chlorine gas?

A) Electrolysis of the hot liquid magnesium chloride (no water)

B) High temperature reduction with aluminum

C) Low temperature reduction with liquid nitrogen and carbon

D) Electrolysis of the hot aqueous magnesium chloride

10. What condition favors the decomposition of $Ni(CO)_4$ into Ni and CO after equilibrium is established in the system $Ni(s) + 4\,CO(g) \rightleftharpoons Ni(CO)_4(g)$ with both ΔH and ΔS having a negative sign?

A) Decrease volume

B) Increase pressure

C) Increase temperature

D) Simultaneously increase the pressure and decrease volume

Chapter 25 Practice AP Test Questions Answers:

1. C); 2. A); 3. D); 4. D); 5. A); 6. D); 7. B); 8. D); 9. A); 10. C)

Data Interpretation and Analysis Question: Alloys

When metals are heated to a high temperature, a phase change occurs and the solid metal changes its phase to a liquid. While in the liquid phase, another hot molten substance can be mixed. When cooled, different alloys can form, depending on the size of the atoms. Alloys can be classified as substitutional, interstitial, or a combination of substitutional and interstitial. Table 1 provides a listing of the atomic radius of several elements.

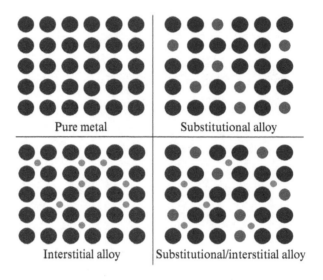

Pure metal   Substitutional alloy

Interstitial alloy   Substitutional/interstitial alloy

Table 1

Element	C	Zn	Fe	Cu	Cr
Atomic radius (pm)	70	142	126	128	128

Figure 1 provides a representation of the particulate view of atoms in a metal such as iron.

Based on the information provided in each of the following questions, decide which particulate diagram from below best represents the substance and classify the substance as a metal, nonmetal, alloy, or allotrope.

a) One type of steel is comprised of 97.9% iron and 2.1% carbon.

b) Stainless steel is comprised of 80% Fe, 18% Cr, 1% Ni, and 0.4% C.

c) Brass is comprised of 67% Cu and 33% Zn.

d) Sterling silver is comprised of 92.5% Ag and 7.5% Cu.

e) A 2016 penny, U.S. coin, is comprised of 97.5% zinc and 2.5% Cu.

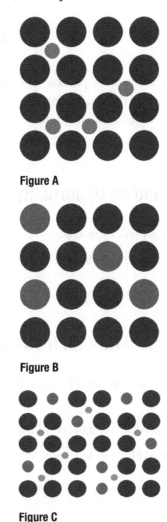

Figure A

Figure B

Figure C

Data Interpretation and Analysis Question Answers with Brief Explanations

a) Steel is an interstitial alloy, Figure A.

b) Stainless steel substitutional/interstitial combination alloy, Figure C.

c) Brass is a substitutional alloy, Figure B.

d) Sterling silver is a substitutional alloy, Figure B.

e) A 2016 penny is a substitutional alloy, Figure B.

READING GUIDE

Metals are the majority of the elements in the periodic table. Key properties of metals such as copper and zinc are covered in this chapter. The material in this chapter is primarily the focus of Units 1, 2, and 3 looking at mixtures, composition, alloys, properties, and processes of transition metals.

Section 24.1

Vanadium: A Problem and an Opportunity

1. What are three properties of vanadium?

2. Why is vanadium found in oil? Why does it need to be removed?*

3. What is metallurgy?

Section 24.2

The General Properties and Natural Distribution of Metals

4. What are three general properties of all metals? Which metals are the best thermal conductors?

5. What are thought to be the components of Earth's core?*

6. What metals occur as elements in nature? Why are they called the noble metals?

7. Explain the difference between a mineral and an ore.*

8. What are the mineral names of the following formulas?*

    PbS:

    HgS:

    ZnS:

    Fe$_2$O$_3$:

    SnO$_2$:

Metallurgical Processes   Section 25.3

9. What is extractive metallurgy? Identify three metallurgical extractive processes.*

10. What is refining metallurgy?*

11. What are two ways gangue can be separated from the desired mineral? Describe the methods shown in the following figures:*

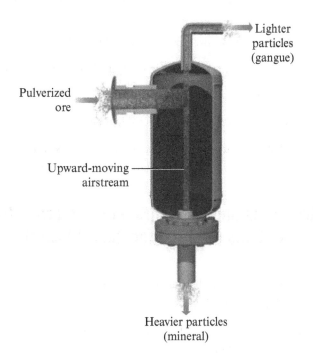

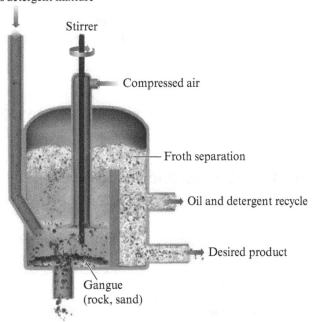

12. What is the general term for the method that uses heat to extract a metal from its mineral?*

13. Explain the differences among calcination, roasting, and smelting.*

14. What are the two main gases driven off in calcination?*

15. What are flux and slag?*

16. What is hydrometallurgy?*

17. When mining gold, what chemical was used that contaminated rivers and streams?*

18. What process is used in electrometallurgy?*

19. What metals are extracted in the Hall–Héroult process and the Bayer process?*

20. What metals are often recovered in the sludge from refining copper?*

21. What is the sintering process? Why is it used with powder metallurgy?*

22. What types of metal parts are made through powder metallurgy? What are the advantages of powder metallurgy over traditional metal casting or milling?*

Section 25.4   Metal Structures and Alloys (Be sure and read this section. It contains material for the AP Exam)

23. What is an alloy? Explain the differences among alloys, substitutional alloys, and interstitial alloys.

24. What must be true of two metal atoms to form a substitutional alloy? Give an example.

25. What characteristic of alloys causes them to have limited solubility?

26. What types of holes exist in interstitial alloys? What conditions cause each one to exist? What is the difference in their sizes?

27. How do the properties of interstitial alloys compare to the standard alloy? Explain your answer.

28. How do the properties of substitutional alloys compare to the standard alloy? Explain your answer.

Section 25.5   Sources, Properties, and Products of Some of the 3d Transition Metals

29. For each of the following metals, provide the following information: where it is found, two uses, and two properties.

    Titanium:

    Chromium:

Manganese:

Cobalt:

Copper:

Nickel:

Zinc:

30. Why is solid titanium resistant to corrosion?

31. Why are compounds containing chromium not used as often today?

32. What metals are ferromagnetic? What characteristic makes them ferromagnetic?

33. What are the components of the alloy bronze? Brass?

34. Why are water pipes now made of copper instead of lead?

35. What characteristics does nickel share with platinum and palladium?

36. What are some properties of zinc? What is galvanizing? What properties does galvanizing give steel?

Self-Assessment Answers

1. _____   2. _____

3. _____   4. _____

5. _____   6. _____

7. _____   8. _____

9. _____   10. _____

CHAPTER

26

TRANSITION METALS AND COORDINATION COMPOUNDS

This chapter goes into detail about coordination compounds and crystal field splitting. Although the details of these topics will not be tested in the AP curriculum, AP Chemistry students should know the structure of coordination compounds and that a coordination compound consists of a central metal ion bound to one or more ligands. There are other details about transition metals that provide good foundational information that students should be aware of.

26.1 **The Colors of Rubies and Emeralds**

26.2 **Properties of Transition Metals**

26.3 **Coordination Compounds**

Specific Learning Objectives Addressed in This Chapter:

SAP-1 Atoms and molecules can be identified by their electron distribution and energy.

SAP-1.A Represent the electron configuration of an element or ions of an element using the Aufbau principle.

SAP-1.B Explain the relationship between the photoelectron spectrum of an atom or ion and

- the electron configuration of the species.
- the interactions between the electrons and the nucleus.

SAP-2 The periodic table shows patterns in electronic structure and trends in atomic properties.

SAP-2.A Explain the relationship between trends in atomic properties of elements and electronic structure and periodicity.

SAP-2.B Explain the relationship between trends in the reactivity of elements and periodicity.

Concepts and Vocabulary to Review:

The Colors of Rubies and Emeralds   Section 26.1

This is background information only. The color of both rubies and emeralds is due to the chromium III ion. Rubies are red and emeralds are green, so how can this be? In both, the Cr^{3+} is replacing some of the Al^{3+} in the host crystal, but in rubies it is in Al_2O_3 while in emeralds it is $Be_3Al_2(SiO_6)$. The red of garnet and the yellow-green of peridot are both caused by Fe^{2+} substitutions, whereas the blue of turquoise is caused by Cu^{2+} substitutions in their host crystals.

Properties of Transition Metals   Section 26.2

The transition metals are adding electrons in d orbitals, have the outermost electrons in the next level of s, and have metallic bonding. Remember when looking at the following diagram, AP students are not expected to memorize the exceptions of chromium and copper, but they will be expected to explain them. The energy in $4s$ and $3d$ are very close to each other and shifting to a half-filled orbital gives additional stability.

Table 26.1   First-Row Transition Metal Orbital Occupancy

	4s	3d				
Sc	↑↓	↑				
Ti	↑↓	↑	↑			
V	↑↓	↑	↑	↑		
Cr	↑	↑	↑	↑	↑	↑
Mn	↑↓	↑	↑	↑	↑	↑
Fe	↑↓	↑↓	↑	↑	↑	↑
Co	↑↓	↑↓	↑↓	↑	↑	↑
Ni	↑↓	↑↓	↑↓	↑↓	↑	↑
Cu	↑	↑↓	↑↓	↑↓	↑↓	↑↓
Zn	↑↓	↑↓	↑↓	↑↓	↑↓	↑↓

Atomic size remains relatively the same in each period of the transition metals since the outer valence electrons remain the same for the period. This also relates to other properties such as transition metals are good conductors.

The oxidation states of the transition metals vary, but most can form a +2 ion due to the loss of the outer s electrons in the valence level. For instance, iron has a configuration of $[Ar]4s^23d^6$. The electron configuration of iron(II) is $[Ar]3d^6$, and the configuration of iron(III) is $[Ar]3d^5$.

A way to help remember to remove the outer most first is to write electron configurations by their principle quantum number. This groups all the same level together. Iron would be $1s^22s^22p^63s^23p^63d^64s^2$ or $[Ar]3d^64s^2$.

The $4s^2$ is on the end emphasizing it is removed first.

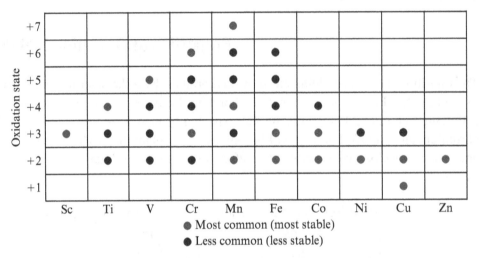

Figure 26.1 First-Row Transition Metal Oxidation States The transition metals exhibit many more oxidation states than the main-group elements. These oxidation states range from +7 to +1.

Section 26.3   Coordination Compounds

Complex ions have a central metal atom bound to one or more ligands with a coordinate covalent bond. Ligands are an electron donor that bonds with a metal atom. The ligand is a Lewis base donating the electrons, while the metal is a Lewis acid accepting the electrons.

Ligands that only donate one pair of electrons are called monodentate. The ligands are bidentate if they donate two pairs of electrons and polydentate if they donate three or more pairs of electrons. A complex ion containing a bidentate or polydentate ligand is called a chelate. Some common ligands are in the following table:

Table 26.2 Name and Formulas of Common Ligands

Ligand	Name in Complex Ion
Anions	
Bromide, Br^-	Bromo
Chloride, Cl^-	Chloro
Hydroxide, OH^-	Hydroxo
Cyanide, CN^-	Cyano
Nitrite, NO_2^-	Nitro
Oxalate, $C_2O_4^{2-}$ (ox)	Oxalato
Ethylenediaminetetraacetate $(EDTA^{4-})$	Ethylenediaminetetraacetato
Neutral molecules	
Water, H_2O	Aqua
Ammonia, NH_3	Ammine
Carbon monoxide, CO	Carbonyl
Ethylenediamine (en)	Ethylenediamine

When naming a positively charged complex ion, the ligands with a prefix for the number added are named first in alphabetical order if there is more than one type of ligand; then the central atom and the charge of the central atom follow. Complex ions are placed inside a bracket with the overall charge outside the bracket. For instance, $[Ag(NH_3)_2]^+$ is the diammine silver(I) complex. The two neutral ammonia ligands are called diammine, and the silver atom has a +1 oxidation state resulting in the overall complex having a +1 charge. The number of ligands added is called a coordination number. Usually, this number is 2, 4, or 6. Complexes with a coordination

Table 26.3 Common Geometrics of Complex Ions

Coordination Number	Shape	Model	Example
2	Linear		$[Ag(NH_3)_2]^+$
4	Square planar		$[PdCl_4]^{2-}$
4	Tetrahedral		$[Zn(NH_3)_4]^{2+}$
6	Octahedral		$[Fe(H_2O)_6]^{3+}$

number of two are linear in shape. If the coordination number is four, the shape of the complex is either tetrahedral or square planar. Those complexes with a coordination number of six will have an octahedral shape.

If the complex ion is negatively charged the complex is named differently. The ending of the metal atom is changed to -ate. Cu^+ in a complex would be cuprate(I).

Table 26.4   Names of Common Metals when Found in Anionic Complex Ions

Metal	Name in Anionic Complex
Chromium	Chromate
Cobalt	Cobaltate
Copper	Cuprate
Gold	Aurate
Iron	Ferrate
Lead	Plumbate
Manganese	Manganate
Molybdenum	Molybdate
Nickel	Nickelate
Platinum	Platinate
Silver	Argentate
Tin	Stannate
Zinc	Zincate

$[Pt(NH_3)_2Cl_4]^{2-}$ has two ammonias and four chlorines in the complex. Since ammonia is neutral and each chloro is a -1 charge, this indicates the platinum is a $+2$ charge. Alphabetically, ammine comes before chloro, so the name would be diammine tetrachloroplatinate(II).

Additional Practice

Self-Assessment Quiz Questions Q1, Q3, and Q4

Problems:
Review Questions 1, 2, and 3
Properties of Transition Metals 17 and 18
Coordination Compounds 21, 23, 25, 27, and 28
Cumulative Problems 59

Practice AP Test Questions

Questions 1, 2, and 3 pertain to the following information: Given the following substances

EDTA	$C_2O_4^-$	CN^-	$H_2NCH_2CH_2CH_2NH_2$

1. Which is a monodentate ligand?

    A) EDTA   B) $C_2O_4^{2-}$ C) CN^- D) $H_2NCH_2CH_2CH_2NH_2$

2. Which is a bidentate ligand?

    A) EDTA   B) $C_2O_4^{2-}$ C) CN^- D) $H_2NCH_2CH_2CH_2NH_2$

3. Which substance is a coordination compound and not a complex ion?

    A) $[Fe(CN)_3]$

    B) $[Pt(NH_3)_2Cl_2]$

    C) $[Fe(CN)_6]^{4-}$

    D) $PtO_2 \cdot 2H_2O$

4. Ti^{3+} has _____ electron(s) in d orbitals.

    A) 0   B) 1   C) 2   D) 3

5. Square planar complexes can be formed, with metals having a _____ electron configuration. Such species are diamagnetic.

    A) d^6 B) d^8 C) d^9 D) d^{10}

6. Which one of the following elements has the highest density?

    A) V   B) Fe   C) Ta   D) Os

7. What statement is most inconsistent with the chemistry of transition elements?

   A) When bromine, chlorine, and iodine react with the higher oxidation states of the transition elements, the stability increases.

   B) Transition metal ions with the metal in its lowest oxidation state are good reducing agents.

   C) Ions that have transition metal in their highest oxidation state tend to be good oxidizing agents.

   D) The stability of the higher oxidation states increases down a periodic group.

8. The concentration of solution containing copper(II) nitrate can be determined by analyzing the absorbance and transmission of an appropriate wavelength of visible light using a colorimeter or spectrophotometer. A colorimeter has only four available wavelengths of light. Given a "color wheel," which wavelength should be selected to the maximum absorbance of light in the $Cu^{2+}(aq)$ solution?

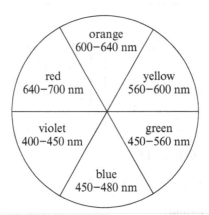

   A) 430 nm   C) 565 nm

   B) 470 nm   D) 635 nm

9. Which one of the following is a complex ion?

   A) $Cr(OH)_3$ C) $[Cr(H_2O)_6]^{3+}$

   B) CrO_4^{2-} D) $Cr_2O_7^{2-}$

10. Which metal ion is most likely to form a square planar complex ion with CN^-?

   A) Fe^{2+} C) Cu^{2+}

   B) Ni^{2+} D) Zn^{2+}

1. C); 2. D); 3. B); 4. B); 5. B) 6. D); 7. A); 8. D); 9. C); 10. B)

Chapter 26 Practice AP Test Questions Answers:

Data Interpretation and Analysis Question: Identification of a Coordination Compound

A student working in a chemistry laboratory prepares a cobalt coordination complex and determines it could be one of the following compounds:

$[Co(NH_3)_4Br_2]Br$ $[Co(NH_3)_5Br]Br_2$ $[Co(NH_3)_6]Br_3$

The students prepare 0.050 M solutions of NaCl, $BaCl_2$, $FeCl_3$ in anticipation of doing an electrical conductance experiment and measures the conductance of the solutions using a conductivity meter. The ohm is a measure of resistivity. Conductance is the inverse of resistance. All measurements of the solutions are made at 23 °C.

Aqueous Ionic Solution	Electrical conductivity, ohm^{-1}
0.050 M NaCl(aq)	100
0.050 M $BaCl_2$(aq)	200
0.050 M $FeCl_3$(aq)	300

a) Sketch a simple graph of showing the relationship between electrical conductivity and ion concentration.

b) Draw a 3D structure of any one of the cobalt coordination complexes.

c) Explain how the student can determine the identity of the cobalt coordination complex.

The student measures the electrical conductivity of the cobalt coordination complex as soon as the solution of compound is made and then again after 60.0 minutes have elapsed. The student records the following information:

	Time = 0.50 minutes	Time = 60.0 minutes
Electrical conductivity of 0.050 M solution of the coordination complex ion	191 ohm^{-1}	374 ohm^{-1}

d) Suggest an explanation for the observed results.

e) Based on the conductivity data, most likely, which coordination complex did the student prepare? Explain.

f) Write a balanced chemical equation to represent the reaction of the cobalt coordination complex with water.

Data Interpretation and Analysis Question Answers with Brief Explanations

a)

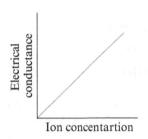

b) $[Co(NH_3)_5Br]Br_2$

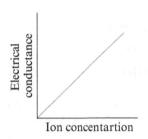

c) The student can prepare a 0.050 M solution of the complex. The student measures the conductivity of the three 0.050 M ionic solutions and the complex. Compare the conductance of the complex to the conductance of the three ionic solutions. The conductance of the $[Co(NH_3)_4Br_2]Br$ complex should be close to the conductance of NaCl since both are 1:1 cation: anion ratios. The conductance of the $[Co(NH_3)_5Br]Br_2$ complex should be close to the conductance of $BaCl_2$ since both are 1:2 cation: anion ratios. The conductance of the $[Co(NH_3)_6]Br_3$ complex should be close to the conductance of $FeCl_3$ since both are 1:3 cation: anion ratios.

d) The conductivity of the solution increases, indicating more ions are present in the solution. Water is serving as a ligand and will replace the bromide ion in the complex as a new equilibrium system is established. As more and more bromide ions enter the solution, the electrical conductivity of the solution increases.

e) $[Co(NH_3)_5Br]Br_2(aq)$ since the conductivity of this solution is similar to the conductivity of $BaCl_2(aq)$.

f) $[Co(NH_3)_5Br]Br_2(aq) + H_2O(l) \rightleftharpoons [Co(NH_3)_5\ H_2O]^{3+}(aq) + 3Br^-(aq)$

READING GUIDE

Background and entry-level information on transition metals and the complexes and compounds they form is the focus of this chapter. Students should have knowledge of the basic structures for coordination compounds, ligands, and complex ions. These types of structures have appeared on previous AP Chemistry Exams.

The Colors of Rubies and Emeralds   Section 26.1

1. In rubies and emeralds, what is the crystal in each gemstone? What element in both crystals is replaced? What ion is substituted in its place? What colors are seen in each gemstone?*

2. What is the host crystal in garnet? What ion is replaced? What ion is substituted in its place? What color is garnet?*

3. What is the host crystal in peridot? What ion is replaced? What ion is substituted in its place? What color is peridot?*

4. What is the host crystal in turquoise? What ion is replaced? What ion is substituted in its place? What color is turquoise?*

5. Identify these gemstones:*

Section 26.2   **Properties of Transition Metals**

6. What types of orbitals are transition metals in the process of filling?

7. What are three properties of transition metals?

8. When transition metals form ions, which electrons are lost first? Explain your answer.

9. Fill in the following first-row orbital diagrams of the 4th Period transition metals from [Ar].

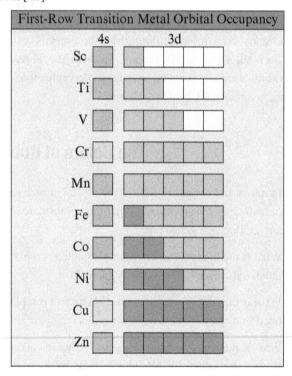

10. Use the figure below to explain how and why atomic size changes across Periods 4, 5, and 6 of the transition metals. Explain why this trend occurs.

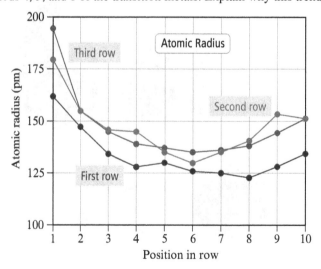

11. What is the lanthanide contraction?*

12. Use the figure below to explain how ionization energy changes across Periods 4, 5, and 6 of the transition metals. Explain why this trend occurs.

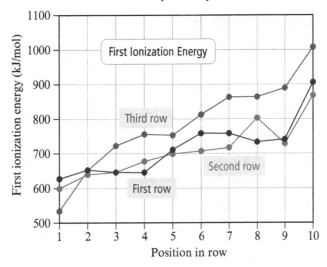

13. Use the below figure to explain the trends in electronegativity across Periods 4, 5, and 6 of the transition metals. Explain why this trend occurs.

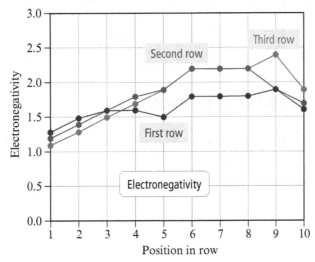

14. Fill in the following table showing the common oxidation states of the Period 4 transition metals:

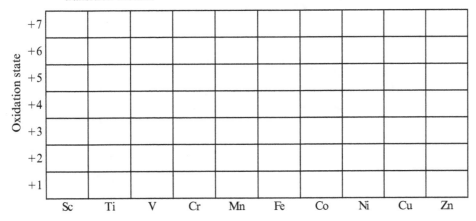

15. Explain why almost all transition metals have a 2+ oxidation state.

Section 26.3   Coordination Compounds

16. What are complex ions, ligands, and coordination compounds?

17. Explain the difference between a primary and secondary valence.*

18. What is a coordination number and how does it relate to the shape of the complex ion?

19. What is a ligand? Identify two properties of ligands. Explain the differences among monodentate, bidentate, and polydentate ligands.*

20. What is a chelating agent?

21. What are the five steps to follow when writing the name of a complex ion?

22. Name $K_3[Fe(CN)_6]$.

23. What are the molecules water and ammonia called when used as ligands?

24. If the ligand is an anion, how is the name of the anion changed to be a ligand?

25. What is EDTA?

26. How do you correctly write the formula of a complex ion?

Section 26.4   Structure and Isomerization

27. Fill in the following flowchart, identifying the types of isomers and their arrangements.

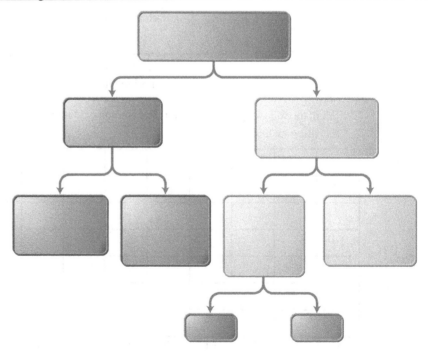

28. Explain the difference amongst coordination isomers, linkage isomers, geometric isomers, and stereoisomers?*

29. Why are these two molecules considered geometric isomers? Identify the *cis-* and the *trans-* isomer in the following diagram. Explain your reasoning.

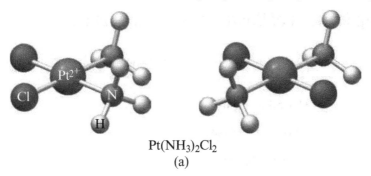

Pt(NH₃)₂Cl₂
(a)

30. What is fac-mer isomerism?*

31. What are optical isomers?*

32. Explain what chiral substances and enantiomers are.

Bonding in Coordination Compounds   Section 26.5

33. According to valence bond theory, how do coordinate covalent bonds form in transition metals?

34. What properties does crystal field theory explain that valence bond theory cannot?

35. How does the magnitude of splitting compare in strong-field complexes and weak-field complexes?

36. What color is seen in each of the following cases:

    When all visible wavelengths are absorbed?

    When no wavelengths are absorbed?

    When only some wavelengths are absorbed?

37. Explain what complimentary colors are.

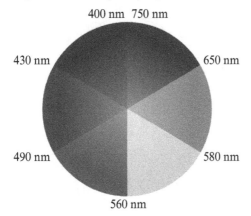

38. Explain the relationship between weak-field ligands and strong-field ligands with low-spin and high-spin complexes. How do each affect the magnetic properties of the substance?

Section 26.6

Applications of Coordination Compounds

39. Explain how coordination compounds can be used in each of the following examples:

    Chelating agents:

    Chemical analysis:

    Coloring agents:

    Biomolecules:

40. In the following table, give one biological function of each transition metal listed:

    Transition Metals and Some of Their Functions in the Human Body

Transition Metal	Biological Function
Chromium	
Manganese	
Molybdenum	
Iron	
Copper	
Zinc	

41. Draw the structures of heme and chlorophyll. How are the structures similar? How are they different?

Self-Assessment Answers

1. _____   2. _____

3. _____   4. _____

5. _____   6. _____

7. _____   8. _____

9. _____   10. _____

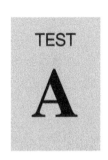
CHEMISTRY PRACTICE TEST A

Multiple-Choice Questions

Section I

(Time–90 minutes)

You may not use your calculator for Section I. You may also use a periodic table and the equation pages.

Note: For all questions, assume that the temperature is 298 K, the pressure is 1.00 atmosphere, and the solutions are aqueous unless otherwise specified.

Directions: Each of the questions or incomplete sentences in Section I are followed by four suggested answers or completions. Select the answer that is best in each case and fill in the circle on the answer sheet.

Given the following table containing information about elements, answer questions 1–3.

Element	Atomic number	Atomic mass	Ionization energy (kJ/mol)
H	1	1	1312
Li	3	6	520
C	6	12	1086
N	7	14	1402
O	8	16	1314
F	9	19	1681
Na	11	23	496

1. Which of the following statements about 1 gram of pure hydrogen gas, H_2, is correct?

    A) 1 gram of hydrogen gas has fewer atoms than 7 grams of pure nitrogen gas.

    B) 1 gram of hydrogen gas has the same number of atoms as 44 grams of pure carbon dioxide, CO_2.

    C) 1 gram of hydrogen gas has the same number of hydrogen atoms as 18 grams of water, H_2O.

    D) 1 gram of hydrogen gas has the same number of atoms as 16 grams of oxygen gas, $O_2(g)$.

2. Which of the following statements about ionization energies can be deduced?

A) Ionization energies generally increase as atomic number increases because the number of protons increase across a period.

B) Ionization energies generally increase in a period in the periodic table from left to right because the effective nuclear charge is increasing across a period.

C) Ionization energies generally decrease as atoms increase in number of electrons because the ratio of protons to electrons remains the same.

D) Ionization energies are generally similar if the number of valence electrons is the same.

3. Which statement is correct about the electron being removed when the ionization energy was measured?

A) It must be closer to the nucleus in nitrogen than for the other elements.

B) It must be further from the nucleus in carbon than for the other elements.

C) It is more strongly attracted to the nucleus as the number of protons increases.

D) Its attraction to the nucleus depends on both distance and atomic number.

Questions 4 and 5 use the following information.

The values of electron affinities for some elements are shown in the table below.

ELectron Affinities (KJ/mol)

H						He
-73						>0
Li	Be	C	N	O	F	Ne
-60	>0	-122	>0	-141	-328	>0
Na	Mg	Si	P	S	Cl	Ar
-53	>0	-134	-72	-200	-349	>0
K	Ca	Ge	As	Se	Br	Kr
-48	-2	-119	-78	-195	-325	>0
Rb	Sr	Sn	Sb	Te	I	Kr
-47	-6	-107	-103	-190	-295	>0

4. Based on the table and your knowledge of periodic properties, which elements would be expected to be found as negative ions (X^-) in compounds, and why?

A) F and Cl as they have the largest energy released when forming compounds, making the process thermodynamically favorable.

B) Ca and Sr as they have the least energy released when forming a negative ion.

C) Be, Mg, He, Ne, Ar, Kr, and Xe as they are listed as > 0 in the table.

D) Br and I as they have high energy releases, and are the largest ions.

5. Fluorine reacts with Group 1 metals and forms an anion. Potassium reacts with the halogens and forms a cation. One reason for this is

   A) a fluorine atom is larger compared to a potassium atom.
   B) fluorine has a greater ionization energy compared to potassium.
   C) fluorine has a greater electron affinity compared to potassium.
   D) at room temperature, fluorine is a diatomic gas and potassium is a solid.

Question 6 uses information in the following table.

The table below lists atomic properties of size and ionization energy across the first period.

Element	Atomic radius (pm)	First ionization Energy (kJ/mol)
Li	152	520
Be	112	899
B	85	801
C	77	1086
N	70	1402
O	73	1314
F	72	1681
Ne	70	2081

6. Which of the following best explains the data in the table?

   A) Both radius and ionization energy generally increase uniformly across the period, consistent with the shell model of atomic structure.
   B) Radius generally increases uniformly across the period, but subshells in the quantum model are needed to explain the inconsistencies in the trend of ionization energies.
   C) As the number of protons increases in the nucleus, the valence electrons are pulled closer to the nucleus. The atomic radius decreases and the force of attraction on the valence electrons increases.
   D) The values of ionization energy for N and O are out of line with the general trend predicted by the shell model because these atoms form unusually strong diatomic molecules (O_2 and N_2) and influence the measurement of ionization energy.

7. A chemist carries out a reaction to form a gaseous chemical which could have either one of the formulas drawn below.

$$\begin{array}{cc} H_3C & CH_3 \\ \diagdown \; \diagup \\ C = C \\ \diagup \quad \diagdown \\ H \quad\;\; H \end{array} \qquad \begin{array}{c} H_2C - CH_2 \\ | \qquad | \\ H_2C - CH_2 \end{array}$$

   Which of the following describes how the chemist might best find out which is the formula of the compound made?

A) Infra-red absorption spectrometry to look at vibrations of the carbon to carbon bonds.

B) Visible light absorption spectrometry to look at electronic transitions.

C) Mass spectrometry to examine the exact mass of the two compounds.

D) Gas diffusion measurements to determine the speeds of the gas molecules.

8. The concentration of bromide ion in a solution can be found by precipitating the bromide ion as silver bromide (AgBr). Assuming a complete reaction, if the amount of silver bromide collected from 500.0 mL of solution is 0.188 grams, what was the concentration, in moles per liter of bromide ion (Br^-)? The following table is given for your use:

Element	Atomic Mass
Ag	107.9
Br	79.9

A) 1.0×10^{-3} M

B) 2.0×10^{-3} M

C) 3.7×10^{-3} M

D) 2.0 M

9. The most familiar acids are compounds containing hydrogen and are classified as strong or weak. Which of the following best describes the basis for the classification of strong acid when it is dissolved in water?

A) The acid has the most H atoms in its formula to react when a base is added.

B) The maximum amount of heat is produced when the acid is dissolved in water.

C) The acid contains one of the halogen atoms (F, Cl, Br, or I) in addition to H atoms.

D) The acid transfers at least one H atom as a proton completely to water as it dissolves.

The diagram below represents the gas molecules in a sealed flask filled with methane gas at room temperature (20 °C). The boiling point of methane is −164 °C.

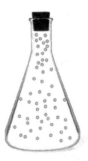

10. Which best represents the same flask when placed in a freezer at a temperature of $-20\,°C$?

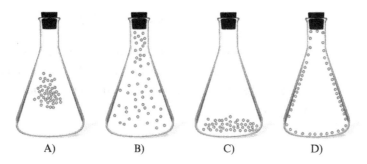

A)   B)   C)   D)

Question 11 can best be answered by referring to the following information.

The diagram below shows the results, after 4 minutes, from placing spots of three different dyes on paper strips 1 cm from the bottom of the strip and placing the paper in a small amount of solvent at the base in an enclosed container.

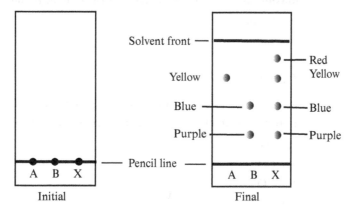

11. Which of the following best explains the results.

A) The red dye has the strongest interactions with paper and with the solvent.

B) The yellow dye has the weakest interactions with the solvent but the strongest interactions with the paper.

C) Dye X is a mixture of dye A and dye B in equivalent amounts.

D) The purple dye has the strongest interactions with paper, but the weakest with the solvent.

12. Which of the following parameters is the most useful in predicting the polarity of a bond between two atoms.

A) The relative electronegativities of the two atoms.

B) The relative atomic radius of each of the two atoms.

C) The relative ionization energies of the two atoms.

D) The relative electron affinities of the two atoms.

13. Which of the following has the correct order of bond polarity from smallest to largest of the C—X bond, where X is the atom bonded to C in each case?

A) F, O, N, C

B) N, C, F, O

C) C, N, O, F

D) O, F, C, N

14. FeO can be prepared by heating iron(II) oxalate in a vacuum. A gas mixture consisting of a mixture of carbon monoxide gas and carbon dioxide gas also forms.

$$FeC_2O_4(s) \rightleftharpoons FeO(s) + CO(g) + CO_2(g)$$

How many grams of $FeC_2O_4(s)$ (molar mass 144) are needed to produce a total volume of 2.24 L of gas at 1.00 atm and 273 K, assuming the reaction goes to completion? The gas is collected in a rigid container.

A) 1.8 g
B) 3.6 g
C) 7.2 g
D) 14 g

15. Ammonia is frequently produced by the Haber process in which nitrogen gas, N_2, and hydrogen gas, H_2, are combined to form ammonia gas, NH_3. If 2 moles of nitrogen gas and 3 moles of hydrogen gas are reacted, what is the **maximum** amount of ammonia gas that could be produced?

A) 2 mol
B) 3 mol
C) 4 mol
D) 5 mol

16. If a 22.4 L volume of a sample of gas has a density of 0.900 grams/L at 1.00 atm and 0.00 °C. Given the following gases, which could it be?

A) Ne
B) CO
C) CO_2
D) Kr

Questions 17 and 18 can be answered using the following information.

The properties of two solid substances are examined to determine their structure and suitability of forming an alloy with iron.

Substance	Radius	Electrical Conductivity of solid	Melting Point	Electrical Conductivity of liquid	Solubility in water	Hardness
X	182 pm 172 pm	not	690 °C	high	very	brittle
Y	128 pm	high	1907 °C	high	not	very hard, brittle
Fe	126 pm	high	1538 °C	high	not	soft

17. Which type of structure is most likely associated with substance X?

A) Molecular Covalent
B) Network Covalent
C) Ionic
D) Metal

18. What substance can best be mixed with iron to form an alloy and why?

    A) Substance Y because of their similar electrical conductivity in the liquid phase allows for an interstitial alloy to form.

    B) Substance Y because the radius of atoms are similar allowing a substitutional alloy to form.

    C) Substance X because of their similar electrical conductivity in the solid phase allows for an interstitial alloy to form.

    D) Substance X because the larger size of particles allowing a substitutional alloy to form.

Questions 19 and 20 use the following information.

The following diagram is a representation of a solid structure.

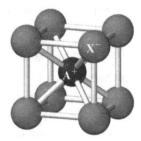

19. Which two attributes contribute most to the value of lattice energy of this solid?

    A) Electronegativity values of each of the component elements.

    B) Radius and charge of each of the component ions.

    C) Electron affinity of the anion and ionization energy of the cation.

    D) Effective nuclear charges on valence electrons of each component element.

20. Which of the following properties are most likely for this compound?

    A) soft, low melting, non-conducting as a liquid

    B) hard, high melting, conducts as a liquid

    C) hard, high melting, non-conducting as a liquid

    D) soft, low melting, conducts as a liquid

The following information is useful to help answer Question 21.

In order to measure the composition of a compound formed by reacting magnesium with oxygen gas, a student places a weighed strip of cleaned magnesium metal into a clean crucible and heats it until it burns to form a white powder. Being careful to make sure no powder is lost, the student lets the crucible cool and places it on a balance to obtain its mass. From the measured mass, the student calculates the formula of the oxide, using the known atomic masses of magnesium and oxygen.

21. What important step has the student omitted in this procedure?

    A) cutting the magnesium strip into small pieces.

    B) determining the volume of the crucible

    C) dissolving the magnesium metal in acid

    D) weighing the empty crucible.

22. A class was presented with the following list of substances and asked to order the substances according to increasing acidity.

HOOH, CH_3COOH: H_2CO_3: CH_3OCH_3; $HOOCCH_2COOH$

What feature of these molecules is most helpful to know in predicting acidity?

A) the number of —COOH functional groups
B) the total number of hydrogen atoms
C) the total number of oxygen atoms
D) the number of C—C bonds.

23. Which of the following represents a conjugate acid–base pair?

A) HNO_3; H_2SO_4 C) HCO_3^-; H_2CO_3
B) H_2O_2; H_3O^+ D) H_2SO_4; SO_4^{2-}

24. Students in a lab were investigating how much heat was given off by a "hot pack" that was triggered by snapping a small metal disk inside the pack.

Students observed the following:

i) the pack got hot
ii) its appearance changed from clear liquid to white crystals
iii) when placed in boiling water it went back to a clear liquid
iv) through all the changes, its total mass was unchanged

Based on this evidence, was the exothermic process they observed a physical or chemical change?

A) physical because no change in mass was observed
B) chemical because this involved a change in appearance
C) physical because this process can be reversed to give the original substance
D) chemical because a disk snap was needed

25. Consider a reaction that occurs by the following mechanism:

$2Cl + 2O_3 \rightarrow 2ClO + 2O_2$
$ClO + ClO \rightarrow O_2 + 2Cl$

The potential energy profile for this reaction is shown below.

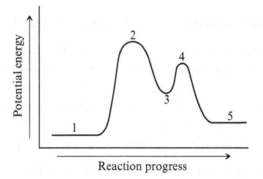

Transition states occur at which reaction stages?
A) reaction stages 1 and 5
B) reaction stages 2, 3, and 4
C) reaction stages 2 and 4
D) reaction stage 3

26. Technetium-99m is a metastable nuclear isomer of technetium-99, symbolized as $^{99m}T_c$. A hospital buys a sample of $^{99m}T_c$, a radioactive isotope used to perform kidney scans of patients. The half-life of $^{99m}T_c$ is 6.0 hours. A technician needs to determine the rate constant for $^{99m}T_c$ to ensure the patient will receive enough of the isotope to produce a good scan. Which is the correct expression for calculating the rate constant for $^{99m}T_c$ in units of min^{-1}? $\ln 2 = 0.693$.

   A) 6.0×60
   B) $6.0/60$
   C) $0.693 \times (6.0 \times 60)$
   D) $0.693/(6.0 \times 60)$

Question 27 and 28 relate to the following information.

The graph below was drawn for a reaction between chemicals X and Y to form a product Z.

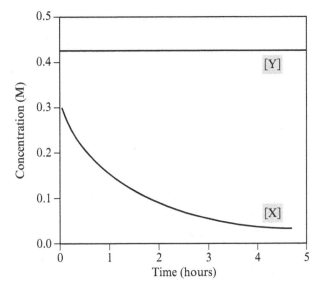

27. Assuming there are no complications, and under these conditions, what is the rate law for this reaction?

   A) Rate $= k\,[X][Y]$
   B) Rate $= k[X]$
   C) Rate $= k[Y]$
   D) Rate $= k\,[X][Y]/[Z]$

28. What is the half-life for this reaction?

   A) 0.5 hours
   B) 1 hour
   C) 2 hours
   D) 5 hours

29. In a test tube, a student placed 20 drops of 0.10 M hydrochloric acid and 2 drops of phenolphthalein solution. She then added, drop by drop, barium hydroxide solution until the solution just turned pink. 10 drops of base had been added. What was the approximate concentration of the barium hydroxide solution?

A) 0.05 M
B) 0.10 M
C) 0.20 M
D) 0.40 M

The diagram below represents energy changes for the reaction

A ⟶ B

Use this diagram in answering questions 30 and 31.

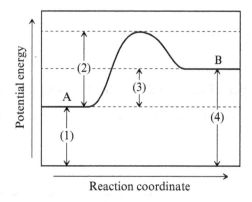

Reaction coordinate

30. If the temperature of the reaction is increased, the magnitude of which energy change will determine the rate of reaction when the temperature increases?

A) (1)
B) (2)
C) (3)
D) (4)

31. If a catalyst is added, the expected change on the diagram will be to

A) increase energy (1)
B) decrease energy (2)
C) increase energy (3)
D) decrease energy (4)

Use the following graph to help answer questions 32 and 33.

The graph shows the distribution of speeds of gas particles for four different noble gases.

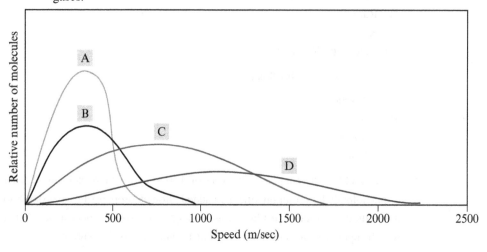

32. The plots are different for the different gases because

    A) the gases are at different temperatures
    B) speeds are directly proportional to square root of mass
    C) speeds are inversely proportional to square root of mass
    D) the kinetic energies of the gases are different

33. If the curves represented one gas at four different temperatures, which curve would represent the highest temperature?

    A) A
    B) B
    C) C
    D) D

The following information may be helpful to answer Question 34.

The gases described in this problem were confined in a cylinder with a movable piston as represented in the diagram below. Atmospheric pressure holds the piston in the cylinder. If the cylinder is heated, the piston can move and a volume change will occur.

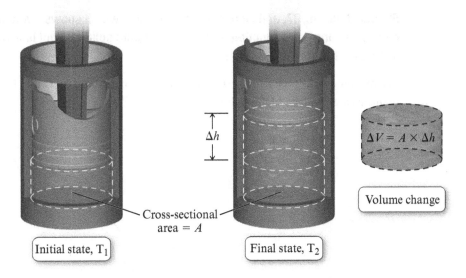

Initial state, T_1

Cross-sectional area = A

Final state, T_2

Δh

$\Delta V = A \times \Delta h$

Volume change

34. Which gas will do the greatest amount of work for a given temperature change, where $T_2 > T_1$?

    A) Xenon because it is the heaviest, so more energy transfer per collision.
    B) Helium because it is the lightest so more collisions to transfer energy.
    C) All the gases will do the same work as they have the same average kinetic energy.
    D) The actual temperature and pressure must be known before this question can be answered.

The following information relates to Question 35.

35. A 20.0 g piece of metal at a temperature of 62.0 °C was dropped into a calorimeter containing 40.0 g of water. The specific heat of water is 4.18 J/g °C. The water was stirred and its temperature was recorded over a four minute period. The data table on the next page shows the results of water:

Time (min)	Temperature (°C)
0.00	24.0
1.00	24.8
1.40	25.2
1.80	25.8
2.00	26.0
2.40	26.0
3.00	25.8
3.40	25.6

Which of the following is the most probable approximate value for the specific heat of the metal in units of J/g °C?

A) 0.148

B) 0.450

C) 0.615

D) 8.00

For Questions 36, 37, and 38 use the graph below which shows the temperature change as a function as a sample of pure solid ethanol is heated at a constant rate (50 J/minute).

The melting point of ethanol is −115 °C and the boiling point is +78 °C. The line segments are numbered I through V.

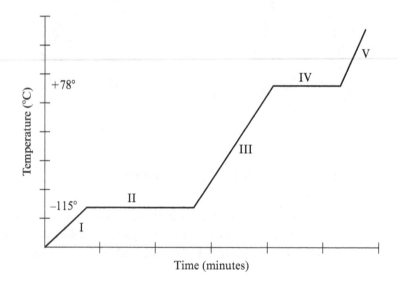

36. The slope of which line can be used, with other information, to calculate the heat capacity of solid ethanol?

A) I

B) II

C) III

D) V

37. In which region of the graph is both solid and liquid ethanol present?

   A) I
   B) II
   C) III
   D) IV

38. Which of the following can be deduced about the substance from the graph?

   A) It takes more energy to vaporize all of the liquid compared to melt all of the solid.
   B) The melting point can change as a function of the amount of substance to be heated.
   C) The heat capacity of the liquid is smaller than that of the solid.
   D) The heat of fusion is smaller than the heat of vaporization.

Use the following information to help answer questions 39 and 40.

Glucose can react with oxygen according to the following equation:

$$C_6H_{12}O_6(s) + 6O_2(g) \longrightarrow 6CO_2(g) + 6H_2O(l)$$

Standard Enthalpies of formation for three substances are given in the following table

Compound	$\Delta H^{\circ}_{formation}$ (kJ/mol)
$CO_2(g)$	−393.5
$H_2O(l)$	−285.8
$C_6H_{12}O_6(s)$(glucose)	−1273.3

39. Which of the following best explains how cells in most living system obtain energy?

   A) Glucose has strong bonds that store lots of energy. Cells use glucose to make important biochemicals.
   B) Carbon dioxide and water have stronger bonds than in glucose. Energy is released in cells when glucose is converted to CO_2 and H_2O.
   C) Glucose has stronger bonds than carbon dioxide and water, so energy is released when plants make glucose in the photosynthesis process.
   D) Oxygen, O_2, is a reactant in the conversion of glucose to carbon dioxide and water. Its heat of formation must be larger than that of glucose in order that cells can gain positive energy from this reaction.

40. Unless glucose is burned in a flame, a sample of glucose can remain stable in a bottle for a long time, but living cells can convert it to carbon dioxide and water at room temperature. Which of the following best explains how this is possible?

   A) Cells use other forms of energy, such as light, to create the activation energy needed to start the reaction.
   B) Cells contain lithium, which speeds up the reduction half-reaction compared to the sample in the bottle, where the reaction is taking place very slowly.
   C) Cells carry out the reaction in a series of small intermediate steps, each requiring only small activation energy to start them.
   D) Cells have a high oxygen concentration so the reaction goes at a faster rate. The oxygen concentration in air is lower.

The following information can be used to help answer Questions 41–45.

The following spontaneous reaction occurs when the cell represented in the diagram below operates

$$Mg(s) + 2\,Ag^+(aq) \longrightarrow 2\,Ag(s) + Mg^{2+}(aq)$$

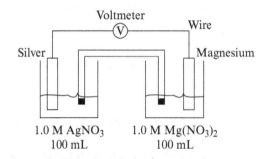

Four separate but identical electrochemical cells, W, X, Y and Z, are prepared. Cells W, X, Y, and Z all look like the diagram above,

Half-reaction	$E°$(V)
$Mg^{2+}(aq) + 2e^- \longrightarrow Mg(s)$	-2.37
$Ag^+(aq) + e^- \longrightarrow Ag(s)$	$+0.80$

41. Calculate $E°$ for cell W when it first starts to operate.

    A) -3.17 V
    B) -1.57 V
    C) $+1.57$ V
    D) $+3.17$ V

42. In cell W, the salt bridge is replaced by a magnesium wire.

    A) The voltage increases.
    B) The voltage decreases.
    C) The voltage becomes zero.
    D) No change in the voltage occurs

43. In cell X, a 50 mL sample of 2.0 M $Mg(NO_3)_2(aq)$ is added to the 1.0 M $Mg(NO_3)_2(aq)$.

    A) The voltage increases.
    B) The voltage decreases.
    C) The voltage becomes zero.
    D) No change in the voltage occurs.

44. In electrochemical cell Y, the magnesium electrode is replaced by one twice as large and the solution is 200 mL of 1.0 M $Mg(NO_3)_2(aq)$.

    A) The voltage increases.
    B) The voltage decreases.
    C) The voltage becomes zero.
    D) No change in the voltage occurs.

45. In electrochemical cell Z, a 20 mL sample of 3 M $AgNO_3(aq)$ is added to the 1.0 M $AgNO_3(aq)$ and 20 mL of deionized water are added to the 1.0 M $Mg(NO_3)_2(aq)$.

   A) The voltage increases.
   B) The voltage decreases.
   C) The voltage becomes zero.
   D) No change in the voltage occurs.

Use the following information to help answer questions 46–49.

C_4H_9Br and water react to form C_4H_9OH and two other products.

$$C_4H_9Br + 2H_2O \longrightarrow C_4H_9OH + \underline{\quad} + \underline{\quad}$$

A three-step mechanism has been proposed for this reaction.

Step 1. $C_4H_9Br \rightleftharpoons C_4H_9^+ + Br^-$	Slow
Step 2. $C_4H_9^+ + H_2O \longrightarrow C_4H_9OH_2^+$	Fast
Step 3. $C_4H_9OH_2^+ + H_2O \longrightarrow C_4H_9OH + H_3O^+$	Fast

46. Identify the intermediate(s) in the mechanism?

   A) Br^-
   B) $C_4H_9^+$
   C) $C_4H_9OH_2^+$
   D) $C_4H_9^+$ and $C_4H_9OH_2^+$

47. What is the molecularity of the rate-determining step?

   A) unimolecular
   B) bimolecular
   C) termolecular
   D) tetramolecular

48. The rate law that is consistent with the proposed mechanism is

   A) rate $= k[C_4H_9^+][Br^-]$
   B) rate $= k[C_4H_9^+][H_2O]$
   C) rate $= k[C_4H_9OH_2^+]$
   D) rate $= k[C_4H_9Br]$

49. What are the two other products in this reaction?

   A) $HBrO_4$ and HBr
   B) C_2H_5Br and C_2H_4OH
   C) Br^- and H_3O^+
   D) HBrO and $2H^+$

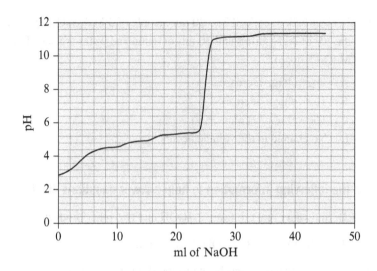

Questions 50–53 refer to the following graph and information.

The titration curve of 25.0 mL of 0.10 M weak acid, HA, with 0.10 M sodium hydroxide, NaOH, is shown in the graph below.

50. Estimate the value of acid dissociation constant K_a.

    A) 2×10^{-3}
    B) 2×10^{-5}
    C) 2×10^{-7}
    D) 2×10^{-9}

51. At the equivalence point, which of the following species has the highest concentration?

    A) HA
    B) A^-
    C) OH^-
    D) H_3O^+

52. What is the percent dissociation of the weak acid when pH = 4.74?

    A) 100%
    B) 80%
    C) 50%
    D) 10%

53. Which of the following chemical equations best represents the predominate reaction occurring as 4.0 mL of NaOH(aq) were added?

    A) $H^+(aq) + OH^-(aq) \longrightarrow H_2O(l)$
    B) $H^+(aq) + NaOH(aq) \longrightarrow H_2O(l) + Na^+(aq)$
    C) $OH^-(aq) + HA(aq) \longrightarrow H_2O(aq) + A^-(aq)$
    D) $HA(aq) + CH_3NH_2(aq) \longrightarrow A^-(aq) + CH_3NH_3^+(aq)$

Questions 54–57 refer to the following information.

A solution with initial concentrations of 0.10 M NH_3 and 1.00 M NH_4Cl is prepared. The K_b for NH_3 is 1.8×10^{-5}. The pK_b for ammonia is 4.74.

54. Estimate the pH of the resultant solution.

    A) 4.7

    B) 8.2

    C) 10.8

    D) 12.2

55. Which of the following chemical equations best represents the system at equilibrium?

    A) $NH_3(aq) + NH_4Cl(aq) \rightleftharpoons NH_3Cl^-(aq) + NH_4^+(aq)$

    B) $NH_4Cl(aq) \rightleftharpoons NH_3(aq) + HCl(aq)$

    C) $NH_4^+(aq) + Cl^-(aq) + H_2O(l) \rightleftharpoons NH_3(aq) + HClO(aq) + H^+(aq)$

    D) $NH_3(aq) + H_2O(l) \rightleftharpoons NH_4^+(aq) + OH^-(aq)$

56. Which reaction best represents predominately what happens when 0.5 mL of 0.1 M HCl(aq) is added to the resultant solution described above?

    A) $NH_4Cl(aq) + HCl(aq) \longrightarrow NH_3(aq) + 2\,HCl(aq)$

    B) $NH_3(aq) + H^+(aq) \longrightarrow NH_4^+(aq)$

    C) $OH^-(aq) + HCl(aq) \longrightarrow H_2O(l) + Cl^-(aq)$

    D) $H_2O(l) + H^+(aq) \longrightarrow H_3O^+(aq)$

57. Which statement is true for the solution described in the initial statement?

    A) The solution consists of a strong base and a weak acid.

    B) The pH solution will not change at all when a small amount of acid is added.

    C) The pH of the solution will change slightly when a small amount of acid is added.

    D) The pH of the solution will increase when 2.0 grams of solid NH_4Cl is added.

Questions 58–59 refer to the following information.

A student prepares a solution of calcium fluoride by mixing just enough solid CaF_2 in deionized water to show some solid CaF_2 remaining in the bottom of the flask. The following equation represents the system at equilibrium.

$$CaF_2(s) \overset{H_2O(l)}{\rightleftharpoons} Ca^{2+}(aq) + 2F^-(aq) \qquad K_{sp} = 4.0 \times 10^{-11}$$

58. What is the solubility product constant, K_{sp}, expression for this slightly soluble salt?

    A) $K_{sp} = \dfrac{[Ca^{2+}][F^-]^2}{[CaF_2][H_2O]}$

    B) $K_{sp} = \dfrac{[Ca^{2+}][F^-]^2}{[CaF_2]}$

    C) $K_{sp} = \dfrac{1}{[Ca^{2+}][F^-]^2}$

    D) $K_{sp} = [Ca^{2+}][F^-]^2$

The following particulate diagram represents a small volume of the saturated CaF_2 solution. Open circles represent Ca^{2+} ions, grey circles represent F^- ions and open squares represent Na^+ ions.

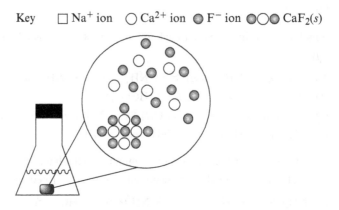

59. Which of the following particulate diagrams represent the small volume of solution after a small amount of 0.10 M sodium fluoride is added, the solution is stirred, and equilibrium is restored?

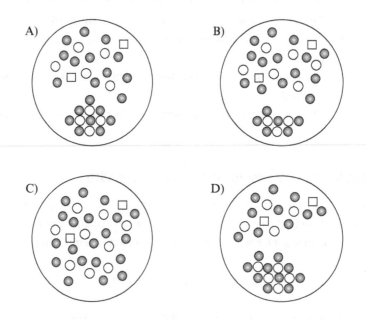

60. The following particulate drawings represent an initial state and an equilibrium state of the reaction $2Cl(g) \rightleftharpoons Cl_2(g)$. Grey spheres represent chlorine atoms. Double grey spheres represent a chlorine molecule.

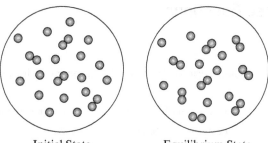

Initial State   Equilibrium State

What are the signs (+ or −) of ΔH, ΔS, and ΔG for the reaction when the system goes from the initial state to the equilibrium state?

A) $\Delta H = +, \Delta S = +, \Delta G = +$
B) $\Delta H = +, \Delta S = +, \Delta G = -$
C) $\Delta H = -, \Delta S = -, \Delta G = +$
D) $\Delta H = -, \Delta S = -, \Delta G = -$

CHEMISTRY PRACTICE TEST A

Section II　**7 Free-Response Questions**

(Time–105 minutes)

You May Use Your Calculator, Periodic Table and Equation Pages for Section II

Directions: Questions 1, 2, and 3 are long free response questions that should take a student about 20 minutes each to answer. Questions 4, 5, 6, and 7 are short free-response questions that should take a student about seven minutes each to answer. You must show all of your work, the steps involved in arriving at your answer, follow the rules for working with significant figures, and include units when appropriate to receive full credit. Your responses to these questions will be scored on the basis of the accuracy and relevance of the information displayed.

1. Students place blue crystals in a test tube and then strongly heat it. The blue crystals are observed to turn to a white powder, and a clear liquid (water) is seen at the mouth of the test tube. The liquid eventually turns to steam (water vapor) as the tube is further heated. Before and after each heating the student allows the tube to cool to room temperature and measures the mass on a sensitive balance. Students were told that the molar mass of the white powder was 159.5. The mass data are given in the table below:

Sample Information	Mass (gram)
1. Test tube empty	15.25
2. Test tube and blue crystals	20.18
3. After first heating—tube and powder	19.35
4. After second heating—tube and crystals	18.45
5. After third heating—tube + crystals	18.45

a) Calculate the mass of the blue crystals at the start of the investigation.

b) Calculate the maximum mass of water lost by the blue crystals.

c) Explain the reason the tube was heated three times.

d) Calculate the moles of water in the formula for the blue crystals in this investigation.

e) Explain why the sample and tube were allowed to cool before each weighing on the balance.

f) If the sample had not been properly cooled before weighing would this have given a larger or smaller value for the moles of water in the crystal's formula? Justify your answer.

2. Some students like to drink cranberry juice. They are very suspicious that Brand X of cranberry juice is being watered down to reduce the cost of manufacture since it has a watery taste. They have a sample bottle of a different brand that is "pure" cranberry juice.

a) Given the following apparatus, design an experiment in which the students could test their hypothesis and actually measure the amount of water that Brand X was adding. Not all the apparatus may be needed.

Provide instructions for the students, and show how they could calculate the percentage of water added to cranberry juice as a result of their measurements.

Colorimeter reading absorbance	500 mL bottle of Brand X cranberry juice
Cuvette (tubes) to fit colorimeter	150 mL bottle of "pure" cranberry juice
10, 20 and 50 mL pipets	1000 mL bottle of pure distilled water
Several 250 mL beakers	Thermometer, °C
Balance weighing up to 150 g	50 mL buret

b) When the students tried to measure pure cranberry juice in the colorimeter, the instrument showed a reading of zero as too little light was able to pass through the concentrated juice.

   What modification would need to be done to adjust for this result?

c) The students repeated the measurement three separate times with the same bottle of Brand X. For the % water added, they found 43.2%, 47.5%, and 51.1% water. What is the most likely cause of this variation? Explain what the students should do to report these results, and how they might improve their procedures.

d) How would it affect the result of the experiments if Brand X was using white grape juice that has a pale yellow color to add to the cranberry juice instead of water?

e) Would you get a higher or lower value for the amount of water you calculated that the Brand X had? Justify your conclusion.

f) How could you modify the experiment to allow for the grape juice instead of pure water?

g) Chemists use the quantity "molar absorptivity" to describe how a chemical compound absorbs light in solution. What additional information would you need to know about the "pure" cranberry juice and your colorimeter set-up to be able to calculate the "molar absorptivity" of cranberry juice?

3. Ammonium carbamate, $NH_4CO_2NH_2$, has recently been suggested as a compound to be synthesized as a way to capture CO_2 from the environment. The following table provides standard enthalpies of formation

Substance	ΔH_f° (kJ/mol)
$NH_3(g)$	-45.9
$CO_2(g)$	-393.5

a) Write the balanced equation for the formation of solid ammonium carbamate from ammonia gas and carbon dioxide gas.

b) Calculate the standard change of enthalpy of formation of solid ammonium carbamate by this reaction, given the enthalpy change for this reaction of -157.5 kJ/mol.

c) When the solid is heated it dissociates back to NH_3 and CO_2 gases. Considering the ΔH_f° value you calculated in (b) and the expected entropy change for the dissociation, predict if this reaction is thermodynamically favored in the forward direction at any temperature? Justify your answer.

d) The dissociation of solid ammonium carbamate to $CO_2(g)$ and $NH_3(g)$ is an equilibrium process. Write the expression for the equilibrium constant for the dissociation reaction.

e) Excess solid ammonium carbamate is placed in a previously evacuated sealed container at 25 °C. The total pressure in the container rises and reaches a maximum of 0.136 atm. Calculate the value of the equilibrium constant at this temperature.

f) If the temperature is increased to 50 °C and solid ammonium carbamate is still present do you expect the total pressure in the container to increase, decrease, or remain the same? Justify your answer.

4. Water, H_2O, and carbon dioxide, CO_2, are two very common substances that have 3 atoms. Yet they have very different properties as shown in the table.

Substance	Melting point	Boiling point	Dipole moment (D)
H_2O	0 °C	100 °C	1.85
CO_2	− 55.6 °C*	−78 °C	0

*at > 5 atm pressure = sublimes

a) In the boxes below draw complete Lewis dot structures for each of the two molecules.

H_2O	CO_2

b) In the boxes below draw geometric representations of each of the two molecules and label the approximate bond angles and bond types.

H_2O	CO_2

c) Using your diagrams as a guide explain how the differences in the values of the three properties for water and carbon dioxide can be explained on the basis of the atomic properties, the molecular structures and inter and intra-molecular forces. Be sure to describe BOTH substances in your answer.

5. Metals in the solid state are generally described as having bonding that can be described as an "electron sea."

a) Draw a diagram illustrating a small segment of a metal and its "electron sea."

b) In what way are the metal atoms arranged in a solid metal to help establish the electron sea and other properties?

c) Describe how conductivity can explained on the basis of the "electron sea" model of metals.

d) An engineer has formed a company to promote the use of sodium wires for high voltage electricity transmission lines since sodium has three time the electrical conductivity per gram compared to copper wire. Is sodium a good choice for this task? Explain.

6. $PV = nRT$ is a common equation known as the ideal gas equation. It can be derived by using the principles of the kinetic molecular theory (KMT) of gases.

a) What assumptions are made in KMT in order to derive the equation? The graph below shows the value of PV/RT for 1 mole of gas, which should equal 1.0 for noble gases and water as a function of changing pressure.

b) Explain why, in terms of KMT assumptions and intermolecular forces, as the pressure is increased, H_2O vapor and Xe deviate in a negative way from ideal behavior and the other gases deviate in a positive manner.

c) Explain why, in terms of KMT assumptions and intermolecular forces, as the pressure gets very high, all the gases show a positive slope (PV/RT is increasing in value).

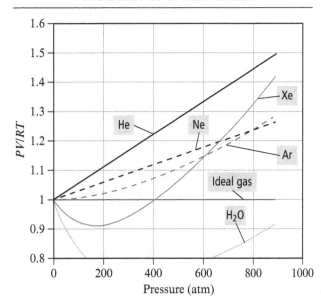

Figure 1 Real versus ideal behavior for 1 mol of an ideal gas, $PV > RT$ is equal to 1. The combined effects of the volume of gas particles and the interactions among them cause each real gas to deviate from ideal behavior in a slightly different way. These curves were calculated at a temperature of 500 K.

7. Chlorine oxide, ClO, is an intermediate species in the mechanism for the reaction of ozone with the chlorine radical in the upper atmosphere. At 25 °C, chlorine oxide decomposes to chlorine gas and oxygen gas according to the equation

$$2ClO(g) \rightarrow Cl_2(g) + O_2(g)$$

The rate of reaction of chlorine oxide was studied at 25 °C in a rigid reaction vessel, and the following data were recorded

Time (s)	[ClO] (M)
0.00	9.20090×10^{-6}
0.00100	7.56956×10^{-6}
0.00200	6.40582×10^{-6}
0.00300	5.55222×10^{-6}
0.00400	4.89936×10^{-6}
0.00500	4.38389×10^{-6}

The data were plotted in two different ways, as shown below.

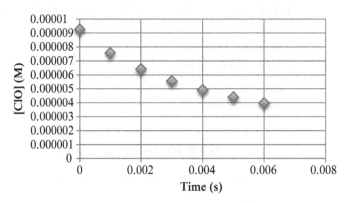

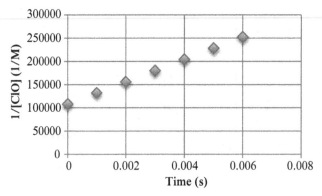

a) Before the reaction starts, assume all of the gas present is chlorine oxide. Calculate the initial pressure, in atm, of the ClO gas in the container at 25 °C.

b) Use the data provided and the data plotted in the graphs to determine the order of the reaction with respect to ClO gas.

c) What is the relationship between the rate of the reaction and the relative rate of the decomposition of ClO gas? What is the relationship between the rate of the decomposition of ClO gas and the rate of formation of oxygen gas, O_2?

d) The initial rate of the reaction is 0.00109 mol/(L s). Determine the rate constant, k, for this reaction.

CHEMISTRY PRACTICE TEST A

Section I Answer Key

60 Multiple-Choice Questions (Time–90 minutes)

Question	Key	—	Question	Key	—	Question	Key
1	D		21	D		41	D
2	B		22	A		42	C
3	D		23	C		43	B
4	A		24	C		44	D
5	C		25	C		45	A
6	C		26	D		46	D
7	A		27	B		47	A
8	B		28	B		48	D
9	D		29	B		49	C
10	B		30	B		50	B
11	D		31	B		51	C
12	A		32	C		52	C
13	C		33	D		53	C
14	C		34	D		54	B
15	A		35	B		55	D
16	A		36	A		56	B
17	C		37	B		57	C
18	B		38	C		58	D
19	B		39	B		59	D
20	D		40	C		60	D

CHEMISTRY PRACTICE TEST A

Section II Answer Key

7 Free-Response Questions (Time–105 minutes)

You may use your calculator, Periodic Table and Equation Pages for Section II

Directions: Questions 1, 2, and 3 are long free response questions that should take a student about 20 minutes each to answer. Questions 4, 5, 6, and 7 are short free-response questions that should take a student about eight minutes each to answer. You must show all of your work, the steps involved in arriving at your answer, follow the rules for working with significant figures, and include units when appropriate to receive full credit. Your responses to these questions will be scored on the basis of the accuracy and relevance of the information displayed.

1. Students place blue crystals in a test tube and then strongly heat it. The blue crystals are observed to turn to a white powder, and a clear liquid (water) is seen at the mouth of the test tube. The liquid eventually turns to steam (water vapor) as the tube is further heated. Before and after each heating the student allows the tube to cool to room temperature and measures the mass on a sensitive balance. Students were told that the molar mass of the white powder was 159.5.

   The mass data are given in the table below:

Sample Information	Mass (gram)
1. Test tube empty	15.25
2. Test tube and blue crystals	20.18
3. After first heating—tube and powder	19.35
4. After second heating—tube and crystals	18.45
5. After third heating—tube + crystals	18.45

(1 point)   a) Calculate the mass of the blue crystals at the start of the investigation.

   Mass 2 − mass 1 = 20.18 − 15.25 grams = 4.93 g

(2 points)   b) Calculate the maximum mass of water lost by the blue crystals.

   Mass 2 − mass 5 = 20.18 − 18.45 = 1.73 g

(1 point)   c) Explain the reason the tube was heated three times.

   To ensure all water is removed. (Process called drying to constant weight [mass].)

(2 points)   d) Calculate the moles of water in the formula for the blue crystals in this investigation.

   Moles of white powder = (mass 5 − mass 1)/molar mass
   = (18.45 − 15.25)/159.5 = 2.006 × 10⁻² mol
   1.73 g water = 1.73 g/(18.0 g/mole) = 9.6 × 10⁻² mol
   Ratio in formula = 9.6/2 approx = 5 moles/formula

e) Explain why the sample and tube were allowed to cool before each weighing on the balance. (2 points)

Hot objects can create an air updraft affecting the balance.

f) If the sample had not been properly cooled before weighing would this have given a larger or smaller value for the moles of water in the crystal's formula? Justify your answer. (2 points)

Larger. The air updraft would reduce the apparent mass of the dry powder increasing the moles water lost.

2. Some students like to drink cranberry juice. They are very suspicious that Brand X of cranberry juice is being watered down to reduce the cost of manufacture since it has a watery taste. They have a sample bottle of a different brand that is "pure" cranberry juice.

a) Given the following apparatus, design an experiment in which the students could test their hypothesis and actually measure the amount of water that Brand X was adding. Not all the apparatus may be needed. (2 points)

Provide instructions for the students, and show how they could calculate the percentage of water added to cranberry juice as a result of their measurements.

Colorimeter reading absorbance.	500 mL bottle of brand X cranberry juice
Cuvette (tubes) to fit colorimeter	150 mL bottle of "pure" cranberry juice
10, 20 and 50 mL pipets	1000 mL bottle of pure distilled water
Several 250 mL beakers	Thermometer, °C
Balance weighing up to 150 g	50 mL buret

Safety—wear lab coat, goggles.

Step 1. Prepare calibration standards by using pipettes to take 10 mL "pure" juice and add zero, 10, 20 and 50 mL distilled water to each. (A student could also use buret filled with pure(?) juice to add 10 mL to zero, 10, 20, and 50 mL pipetted into beakers)

Step 2. Place samples, in turn, into cuvettes. Place in colorimeter, record absorbances, plot a graph against concentration of standards.

Step 3. Add brand X juice to cuvette. Measure absorbance. Repeat with 3 different samples to get good average.

Step 4. Read values for concentration from standards plot. If less than "pure" then it has been diluted, and can calculate how much percentage.

Note it is a colorimeter, NOT a spectrophotometer, so no spectral scan or setting to wavelength is included.

b) When the students tried to measure pure cranberry juice in the colorimeter, the instrument showed a reading of zero as too little light was able to pass through the concentrated juice. (1 point)

Would your procedure take account of this problem? If not, suggest how it should be modified. Explain how your modification or your original procedure avoids this problem.

Yes and no. The diluted standards should work on scale, though further dilution might be needed (more than 10 to 60) BUT would need to dilute the brand X samples by a known amount (using same procedure as for "pure"). As long as dilution factors are accurately known, the comparison is valid.

(2 points)

c) The students repeated the measurement 3 separate times with the same bottle of Brand X. For the % water added, they found 43.2%, 47.5%, and 51.1% water. What is the most likely cause of this variation? Explain what the students should do to report these results, and how they might improve their procedures.

1. possibilities: variation from improper mixing of juice; finger prints on cuvettes scattering light; cuvette not clean before each use; or cuvettes washed with water between trials but not dried,; instrument adjustments; changes in light in room (sunlight from window, room lights on or off, etc.)

2. report mean and variation about the mean to show lack of precision.

3. control light conditions, mix juice well before experiment, clean and dry cuvettes before filling; clean cuvettes carefully on outside before placing in colorimeter. Also do repeat of both calibration standards and more than 3 measurements on brand X.

(1 point)

d) How would it affect the result of the experiments if the Brand X was using white grape juice that has a pale yellow color to add to the cranberry juice instead of water?

This will absorb light (or it would not be colored) and therefore change the result compared to the pure juice. The effect will depend on the wave-length dependence/sensitivity of the colorimeter. If students are used to using a spectrophotometer set to a specific wavelength, then they may be puzzled by this!

(1 point)

e) Would you get a higher or lower value for the amount of water you calculated that the Brand X had? Justify your conclusion.

Since the grape juice will absorb some light the brand X will appear to be more concentrated than it really is (in cranberry juice).

(2 points)

f) How could you modify the experiment to allow for the grape juice instead of pure water?

Make up standard comparisons using some "pure" white grape juice in known amounts added to the pure cranberry juice, and proceed similarly. Alternatively, if a spectrophotometer is available, scan cranberry and white grape juice to measure their absorbance spectra and choose a wavelength where the cranberry juice absorbs, but the grape juice does not.

(1 point)

g) Chemists use the quantity "molar absorptivity" to describe how a chemical compound absorbs light in solution. What additional information would you need to know about the "pure" cranberry juice and your colorimeter set-up to be able to calculate the "molar absorptivity" of cranberry juice? Explain how each piece of information you list is used in the calculation.

Would need to know (1) the molar mass of the compound in the cranberry juice that is absorbing the light; (2) the path length of light through the cuvette; (3) the absolute calibration of the read-out of the colorimeter in absorbance units.

3. Ammonium carbamate, $NH_4CO_2NH_2$, has recently been suggested as a compound to be synthesized as a way to capture CO_2 from the environment. The following table provides standard enthalpies of formation

Substance	ΔH_f° (kJ/mol)
$NH_3(g)$	-45.9
$CO_2(g)$	-393.5

a) Write the balanced equation for the formation of solid ammonium carbamate from ammonia gas and carbon dioxide gas.   (1 point)

$$2NH_3(g) + CO_2(g) \longrightarrow NH_4CO_2NH_2(s)$$

b) Calculate the standard enthalpy of formation of solid ammonium carbamate, using the reported enthalpy change for this reaction of -157.5 kJ/mol.   (2 points)

$\Delta H_{rxn}^\circ = \Sigma n_p \Delta H_f^\circ \text{(products)} - \Sigma n_r \Delta H_f^\circ \text{(reactants)}$

$\Delta H_{rxn} = \Delta H_{f\,\text{ammonium carbamate}} - ((2 \times -45.9) + (-393.5)) = -157.5$ so

$\Delta H_{f\,\text{ammonium carbamate}} = -642.8$ kJ/mol

c) When the solid is heated it dissociates back to NH_3 and CO_2 gases. Considering the ΔH_f value you calculated in (b) and the expected entropy change for the dissociation, do you predict this is a spontaneous or non-spontaneous reaction at any temperature? Justify your answer.   (2 points)

ΔS should be highly positive (solid forming 2 gases increases disorder) ΔH for decomposition is reverse of formation so is positive.

So sign of $\Delta G = \Delta H - T\Delta S$ will depend on T and magnitude of ΔS. If non-spontaneous at low T (ΔG is positive), then as $-T\Delta S$ increase with $T\Delta G$ will become negative.

d) The dissociation of solid ammonium carbamate to $CO_2(g)$ and $NH_3(g)$ is an equilibrium process. Write the expression for the equilibrium constant for the dissociation reaction.   (1 point)

$K_{eq} = ((P_{NH_3})^2 \cdot P_{CO_2})/1$

[Notes: Solid substances are not included in equilibrium constant expressions. Since partial pressures have units of atm. parenthesis "( )" are used instead of brackets "[ ]".]

e) Excess solid ammonium carbamate is placed in a previously evacuated sealed container at 25 °C. The <u>total</u> pressure in the container rises and reaches a maximum of 0.136 atm. Calculate the value of the equilibrium constant at this temperature.   2 points)

Since pure carbamate to start with, $P_{NH_3} = 2 P_{CO_2}$

Total pressure thus is

$P_{CO2} + P_{NH_3} = P + 2P = 3\,P$ so $P = 1/3 \times 0.136 = 0.0453$ atm for CO_2

And so $P_{NH_3} = 0.0907$ atm, and

$K_{eq} = (0.0907)^2 \times (0.0453) = 3.73 \times 10^{-3}$

2 points)

f) If the temperature is increased to 50 °C and solid ammonium carbamate is still present do you expect the total pressure in the container to increase, decrease, or remain the same. Justify your answer.

As the decomposition reaction is endothermic, by Le Châteliers principle, the increase in temperature will increase the forward reaction more than the reverse so more decomposition will take place and the pressure will INCREASE.

4. Water, H_2O, and carbon dioxide, CO_2, are two very common substances that have 3 atoms. Yet they have very different properties as shown in the table.

Substance	Melting point	Boiling point	Dipole moment (D)
H_2O	0 °C	100 °C	1.85
CO_2	−55.6 °C*	−78 °C	0

*at > 5 atm pressure solid carbon dioxide undergoes sublimation at temperatures above −55.6 °C.

(1 point)

a) In the boxes below draw complete Lewis dot structures for each of the two molecules.

H_2O	CO_2
H:Ö:H	:Ö::C::Ö:

(1 point)

b) In the boxes below draw geometric representations of each of the two molecules and label the approximate bond angles and bond types.

H_2O	CO_2
Single bond — :Ö: — Single bond, H H, 105.5°	Double bond — Ö=C=Ö — Double bond, 180°

(2 points)

c) Using your diagrams as a guide explain how the differences in the values of the three properties for water and carbon dioxide can be explained on the basis of the atomic properties, the molecular structures and inter and intra-molecular forces. Be sure to describe BOTH substances in your answer.

H_2O has a large dipole moment as it is not symmetrical, each O—H bond has a dipole and they do not cancel. Its boiling and melting points are high because the H atoms on 1 molecule are attracted to the oxygen on another molecule forming an additional "hydrogen bond" between the molecules. These strong intermolecular forces have to be broken for the molecules to separate in the liquid or gas, hence the high b.p and m.p. CO_2 has no NET dipole moment as the linear arrangement of the CO bonds which have dipoles cancel each other yielding no NET dipole moment. The BP and MP are low as there are no "hydrogen bonds" and only weak London Dispersion intermolecular forces between the molecules.

5. Metals in the solid state are generally described as having bonding that can be described as an "electron sea."

   a) Draw a diagram illustrating a small segment of a metal and its "electron sea." (1 point)

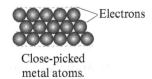

   Close-picked
   metal atoms.

   b) How are the metal atoms arranged in a solid metal to help establish the electron sea, and other properties? (1 point)

   They are close packed–fitting tightly together so electron orbital overlap can form delocalized orbitals allowing valence electrons easier motion

   c) Typical metal properties are listed as: (1 point)

      i)   Ductile—can be made into wires
      ii) Lustrous—reflecting light and having shine
      iii) Malleable—can be made into thin sheets
      iv) Conductive—have good electrical conductivity

   Describe how each of these four properties can be explained on the basis of the "electron sea" model of metals.

      i)   and (iii) Close packing means atoms can slide easily over one another hence form wires and thin sheets.
      ii) much light reflection from very even and flat surface of close-packed atoms provides luster (shine)
      iv) freer motion of electrons provides for high electrical conductivity—has small resistance to flow of electrons

   d) An engineer has formed a company to promote the use of sodium wires for high voltage electricity transmission lines since sodium has three times the electrical conductivity per gram compared to copper wires. (1 point)

      i)   Explain why sodium is such a good conductor, using the atomic properties of sodium and the electron sea model.
           Sodium is a group I element, so readily gives up an electron or shares it with other sodium atom. It is in period 2 so has a relatively small size that will pack well in a close-packed structure and will have a good electrical conductivity—low resistance to electric current.
      ii) Why would sodium NOT be a good choice for this task, despite its conductivity?

   Sodium is highly reactive with water and if any water seeped through the wire's coating, they would react violently?

6. $PV = nRT$ is a common equation known as the Ideal Gas equation. It can be derived by using the principles of the Kinetic Molecular theory (KMT) of gases

(1 point)

a) What assumptions are made in KMT in order to derive the equation?

$$P = \frac{F}{A}$$

1. Particles are negligibly small.
2. Average kinetic energy is proportional to temperature.
3. Collisions among particles are perfectly elastic.

The graph below shows the value of PV/RT for 1 mole of gas, which should equal 1.0 for noble gases and water as a function of changing pressure.

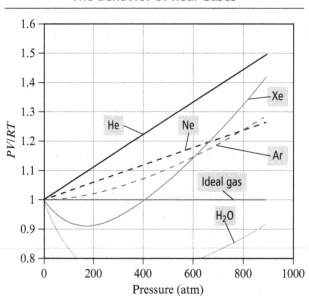

The Behavior of Real Gases

Figure 1 Real versus ideal behavior for 1 mol of an ideal gas, $PV > RT$ is equal to 1. The combined effects of the volume of gas particles and the interactions among them cause each real gas to deviate from ideal behavior in a slightly different way. These curves were calculated at a temperature of 500 K.

(1 point)

b) Explain why, in terms of KMT assumptions and intermolecular forces, as the pressure is increased, H_2O vapor and Xe deviate in a negative way from ideal behavior and the other gases deviate in a positive manner.

H_2O and Xe both exhibit higher intermolecular forces between particles. Hydrogen bonding between water molecules creates strong IMFs. Xenon's large electron cloud makes it polarizable and this allows for a large number of and stronger LDFs between xenon atoms creating a strong IMF. This effect starts at quite low pressures to "stick the particles together" so they begin to form liquid clusters and more inelastic collisions so fewer particles are behaving as ideal gases, lowering the pressure and hence giving a negative deviation. The other gases have weaker IMFs but exhibit only positive deviation because of the volume of the particles (assumption [1] above is not valid).

c) Explain why, in terms of KMT assumptions and intermolecular forces, as the pressure get very high, all the gases are showing a positive slope (*PV/RT* is increasing in value). (1 point)

All gases have real volume that results in them being less compressible at very high pressures than the ideal gas equation predicts. Assumption 1 is not valid.

7. Chlorine oxide, ClO, is an intermediate species in the mechanism for the reaction of ozone with the chlorine radical in the upper atmosphere. At 25 °C, chlorine oxide decomposes to chorine gas and oxygen gas according to the equation $2ClO(g) \rightarrow Cl_2(g) + O_2(g)$

Assume a 1.00 L container, $n = 9.200 \times 10^{-6}$ moles,

$T = 298$ K

$P = nRT/V = (9.200 \times 10^{-6}$ moles $\times R \times 298$ K$)/1.00$ L

a) $P = 2.24 \times 10^{-4}$ atm (1 point)

b) Because the graph of 1/[ClO] versus time is linear, the reaction is second order. (1 point)

c) *Rate of reaction* $= -\dfrac{1}{2} \times \dfrac{\Delta[ClO]}{\Delta t} = \dfrac{[O_2]}{\Delta t}$ (1 point)

The rate of decomposition of ClO gas is twice as fast as the rate of reaction.

The rate of decomposition of ClO gas is twice as fast as the rate of formation or rate of formation is half the rate of the loss of ClO of oxygen gas.

$1/4.899 \times 10^{-6}$ M $= k(0.00400$ s$) + 1/9.2009 \times 10^{-6}$ M

d) $k = 1.29 \times 10^{-7}$ M^{-1} s^{-1} (1 point)

CHEMISTRY PRACTICE TEST B

Multiple-Choice Questions

(Time–105 minutes)

You May Not Use Your Calculator for Section I. You may use the periodic table and equation pages.

Note: For all questions, assume that the temperature is 298 K, the pressure is 1.00 atmosphere, and the solutions are aqueous unless otherwise specified.

Directions: Each of the questions or incomplete sentences in Section I are followed by four suggested answers or complete the sentence format. Select the answer that is best in each case and fill in the circle on the answer sheet.

1. Each of the following equations represents a system at equilibrium. In which of the following reactions will a decrease in volume shift the reaction toward the reactants (toward the left)?

   A) $2NO(g) \rightleftharpoons N_2(g) + O_2(g)$

   B) $2NO(g) + O_2(g) \rightleftharpoons 2NO_2(g)$

   C) $2C_2H_4(g) + 2H_2O(g) \rightleftharpoons 2C_2H_6(g) + O_2(g)$

   D) $SO_2(s) + \frac{1}{2}O_2(g) \rightleftharpoons SO_3(g)$

2. A 1.0 molar solution of which of the following salts has the highest pH?

   A) $NaNO_3$

   B) NH_4Cl

   C) Na_2CO_3

   D) $NaHSO_4$

3. The equilibrium constant for the reaction represented by the following equation is greater than 1.0

   $$H_2PO_4^- + HBO_3^{2-} \rightleftharpoons HPO_4^{2-} + H_2BO_3^-$$

Acid	K_{a1}
H_3PO_4	7.1×10^{-3}
H_3BO_3	5.8×10^{-10}

Which of the following gives the correct relative strengths of the acids and bases in the reaction in terms of a Bronsted-Lowry definition of acids and bases?

	Acids		Bases
(A)	$H_2PO_4^- > H_2BO_3^-$	and	$HBO_3^{2-} > HPO_4^{2-}$
(B)	$H_2BO_3^- > H_2PO_4^-$	and	$HBO_3^{2-} > HPO_4^{2-}$
(C)	$H_2PO_4^- > H_2BO_3^-$	and	$HPO_4^{2-} > HBO_3^{2-}$
(D)	$H_2BO_3^- > H_2PO_4^-$	and	$HPO_4^{2-} > HBO_3^{2-}$

4. Potassium iodide, KI, is an ionic solid. It dissolves in water with an enthalpy of solution that is endothermic. Which of the following best describes the solution process for this system?

   A) The value of lattice energy for the ionic solid is more positive (endothermic) than the absolute value of the hydration energy, and the entropy change of the solution process is positive.

   B) The enthalpy of the solution process is positive and the entropy change of the solution process is negative.

   C) The enthalpy required to separate the solute particles is smaller than the heat required to separate the solvent molecules plus the heat released when the water molecules hydrate the cation and anion, and the entropy change of the solution process is negative.

   D) The enthalpy required to separate the solute particles is greater than the heat required to separate the solvent molecules plus the heat released when the water molecules hydrate the cation and anion, and the entropy change of the solution process is positive.

5. A solution is prepared to be initially 0.5 M in NaCl and 1 M in HCl. Which statement best describes this solution?

   A) a solution with a pH less than 7 that is not a buffer solution
   B) a buffer solution with a pH between 4 and 7
   C) a buffer solution with a pH between 7 and 10
   D) a solution with a pH greater than 7 that is not a buffer solution

6. Acetic acid is a monoprotic acid, with $K_a = 1.8 \times 10^{-5}$. A solution is prepared to be initially 0.5 M in CH_3COOH and 1 M in CH_3COONa. Which statement best describes this solution?

   A) a solution with a pH less than 7 that is not a buffer solution
   B) a buffer solution with a pH between 4 and 7
   C) a buffer solution with a pH between 7 and 10
   D) a solution with a pH greater than 7 that is not a buffer solution

Questions 7–12 pertain to the following information.

Iron and oxygen can combine to form three compounds. Iron(II) oxide, also informally called iron monoxide, is one of the compounds formed. It is a black-colored powder with the chemical formula FeO. The ratio of the mass of iron to mass of oxygen is 3.50 : 1.00. The ratio of the mass of iron to the mass of oxygen for another iron oxide, Fe_xO_y, is 2.62 : 1.00. The table below lists the mass of iron and oxygen in one mole of FeO.

	FeO	Fe_xO_y
Mass of Fe	55.85 g	?
Mass of O	16.00 g	?
mass Fe : mass O	3.50 : 1.00	2.62 : 1.00

7. What is the formula for Fe_xO_y?

    A) FeO_2

    B) Fe_2O_3

    C) Fe_3O_4

    D) Fe_4O_5

8. In the following particulate diagrams a triangle represents an iron atom, a shaded circle represents an oxygen atom and an open circle represents a sulfur atom. When forming Fe_xO_y compounds, which diagrams represent the law of multiple proportions?

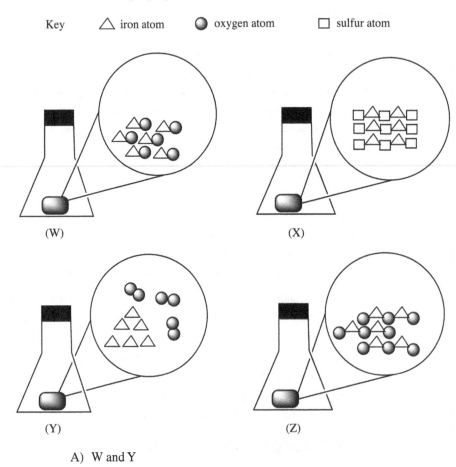

Key   △ iron atom   ● oxygen atom   □ sulfur atom

(W)   (X)

(Y)   (Z)

    A) W and Y

    B) X and Z

    C) W and Z

    D) W, Y, and Z

9. A student analyzes three samples of compounds containing only iron and oxygen. The results are shown in the table below.

	Sample X	Sample Y	Sample Z
Mass Fe	7.00 g	7.00 g	14.00 g
Mass O	2.00 g	3.00 g	4.00 g

Which sample(s) is FeO?

A) X

B) Y

C) X and Y

D) X and Z

10. Compare 10.0 gram samples of the following iron oxides. Which compound contains the most iron?

Compound	FeO	FeO$_2$	Fe$_2$O$_3$	Fe$_3$O$_4$
Molar Mass	72	88	160	232

A) FeO

B) FeO$_2$

C) Fe$_2$O$_3$

D) Fe$_3$O$_4$

11. What is the average mass, in grams, of one atom of iron?

A) less than 1.0×10^{-23} g

B) greater than 1.0×10^{-23} g but less than 1.0×10^{-20} g

C) greater than 0.01 g but less than 100 g

D) greater than 100 g

12. Estimate the number of grams of FeCl$_2$ (molar mass 127) that can form when 10.0 g of FeO (molar mass 72) reacts with excess hydrochloric acid.

$$FeO + 2HCl \longrightarrow FeCl_2 + H_2O$$

A) 5.7

B) 18

C) 25

D) 35

13. The crystal structure of iron(II) oxalate, FeC$_2$O$_4(s)$, consists of chains of oxalate-bridged iron atoms, capped by water molecules.

● Oxygen atom   ● Carbon atom   ▰ Iron atom   ○ Hydrogen atom

The geometry around the iron atoms can best be described as

A) square planar

B) trigonal bipyramidal

C) distorted tetrahedron

D) octahedral

The following information is useful for Question 14.

FeO can be prepared by heating iron(II) oxalate in a vacuum. A gas mixture consisting of carbon monoxide gas and carbon dioxide gas also forms.

$$FeC_2O_4(s) \rightleftharpoons FeO(s) + CO(g) + CO_2(g)$$

14. How many grams of $FeC_2O_4(s)$ (molar mass 144) are needed to produce a total volume of 2.24 L of gas at 1.00 atm and 273 K, assuming the reaction goes to completion? The gas mixture is collected in a rigid container.

    A) 1.8 g
    B) 3.6 g
    C) 7.2 g
    D) 14.4 g

15. A car tire containing 4.0 liters of air has a measured pressure of 2.0 atmospheres at a temperature of 20.0 °C before the car is driven. When the car has been driven at high speed, the tire temperature is measured to be 50.0 °C. Assuming the volume of the tire is constant at 4.0 liters, which equation correctly estimates the pressure in atmospheres in the tire at 50.0 °C?

    A) $P = 0.82 \times 4.0 \times (50.0 - 20.0)$
    B) $P = 2.0 \times 323 / 293$
    C) $P = 4.0 \times 293 / 323$
    D) $P = 2.0 \times 50.0 / 20.0$

Questions 16–19 use the following information.

In a sealed container in the presence of O_2 gas, CO_2 gas can establish an equilibrium with CO gas.

$$2CO(g) + O_2(g) \rightleftharpoons 2CO_2(g) \qquad \Delta H° = -500 \text{ kJ/mol rxn}$$

16. The partial pressure of $CO(g)$ can be increased by

    A) lowering the temperature and increasing the pressure
    B) increasing the temperature and the pressure
    C) increasing the temperature and lowering the pressure
    D) lowering the temperature and lowering the pressure

17. The partial pressure of $CO(g)$ can be increased by adding the following and waiting for equilibrium to be restored

    A) $NaOH(s)$ to remove $CO_2(g)$
    B) $CO_2(s)$
    C) $O_2(s)$
    D) $FeO(s)$ to form $FeC_2O_4(s)$

18. How much heat is released or absorbed when 0.500 mol of carbon monoxide gas reacts with oxygen gas to form carbon dioxide gas?

    A) 250 kJ is released
    B) 125 kJ is released
    C) 125 kJ is absorbed
    D) 250 kJ is absorbed

19. If ΔH_f° for CO_2 is $-400.$ kJ/mol, estimate ΔH_f° for CO?

   A) $+150.0$ kJ/mol
   B) -150.0 kJ/mol
   C) $+100.0$ kJ/mol
   D) -100.0 kJ/mol

20. Which of the following is the principal reason for the great difference in properties of carbon dioxide, CO_2, and silicon dioxide, SiO_2?

   A) carbon atoms have a smaller mass than silicon atoms
   B) carbon is in the first row of the periodic table, silicon is in the second row
   C) carbon atoms have four bonding (valence) electrons, silicon has twelve
   D) carbon readily forms double bonds with oxygen, silicon does not

21. What is the d orbital-filling diagram for the Fe^{3+} ion?

   $\underline{\uparrow\downarrow}$ $\underline{\uparrow\downarrow}$ $\underline{\uparrow}$ $\underline{\quad}$ $\underline{\quad}$ $\underline{\uparrow\downarrow}$ $\underline{\uparrow}$ $\underline{\uparrow}$ $\underline{\uparrow}$ $\underline{\quad}$
            (A)   (B)

   $\underline{\uparrow}$ $\underline{\uparrow}$ $\underline{\uparrow}$ $\underline{\uparrow}$ $\underline{\uparrow}$ $\underline{\uparrow\downarrow}$ $\underline{\quad}$ $\underline{\uparrow\downarrow}$ $\underline{\quad}$ $\underline{\uparrow}$
            (C)   (D)

22. Oxalate ions can readily react with $Fe^{3+}(aq)$ ions to form iron(III) oxalate ions.

   $$Fe^{3+}(aq) + 3\,C_2O_4^{2-}(aq) \rightleftharpoons [Fe(C_2O_4)_3]^{3-}(aq) \qquad K_c = 1.67 \times 10^{20} \text{ at 25 °C}$$

   If 0.0100 M Fe^{3+} is mixed with 1.00 M oxalate ion, estimate the concentration of $Fe^{3+}(aq)$ ions at equilibrium.

   A) less than 1.0×10^{-18} M
   B) between 1.0×10^{-15} M and 1.0×10^{-8} M
   C) between 1.0×10^{-8} M and 1.0×10^{-3} M
   D) greater than 1.0×10^{-3} M

23. A solution is prepared by mixing the following:

   10 mL of 0.100 M HCl
   10 mL of 0.100 M H_2SO_4
   10 mL of 0.200 M NaOH
   70 mL of pure water

   In the following table which column correctly identifies the concentrations of the species present?

Species	A $[X]$, M	B $[X]$, M	C $[X]$, M	D $[X]$, M
H^+ (pH)	3	2	1	2
Cl^-	0.1	0.01	0.01	0.01
SO_4^{2-}	0.1	0.2	0.02	0.01
Na^+	0.2	0.1	0.02	0.02

A) Column A
B) Column B
C) Column C
D) Column D

24. Given the following table containing information about some of the elements, which of the following statements is true?

Element	Atomic radius (pm)	First ionization energy (kJ/mol)
Li	152	520
Be	112	899
B	85	801
C	77	1086
N	70	1402
O	73	1314
F	72	1681
Ne	70	2081

A) Both radius and ionization energy generally increase uniformly across the period, consistent with the shell model of atomic structure.
B) Radius generally increases uniformly, but subshells in the quantum model are needed to explain the inconsistencies in the trend of ionization energies.
C) The trends in radius generally decrease and ionization energy generally increase. Both are as expected based on the nuclear model where atomic electrons are increasingly attracted as the nuclear charge increases.
D) The values of ionization energy for N and O are out of line with the general trend predicted by the shell model because these atoms form unusually strong diatomic molecules (O_2 and N_2) and influence the measurement of ionization energy.

25. Determine the standard cell potential ($E°$) for the voltaic cell based on the following reaction.

$$2Cr(s) + 3Fe^{2+}(aq) \rightarrow 3\,Fe(s) + 2Cr^{3+}(aq)$$

Reduction Half-Reaction	$E°$
$Fe^{2+}(aq) + 2e^- \rightarrow Fe(s)$	-0.44 V
$Cr^{3+}(aq) + 3e^- \rightarrow Cr(s)$	-0.74 V

A) -0.16 V
B) $+0.30$ V
C) $+0.83$ V
D) $+2.80$ V

26. In the above electrochemical cell, _____ serves as the anode.

A) Cr
B) Fe
C) Fe^{2+}
D) Cr^{3+}

Use the following information to help answer questions 27 and 28.

Carbon tetrachloride can be formed from the reaction of chlorine gas and $CHCl_3$.

$$CHCl_3(g) + Cl_2(g) \longrightarrow CCl_4(g) + HCl(g)$$

A proposed mechanism for the formation of carbon tetrachloride is

Step 1. $Cl_2(g) \rightleftharpoons 2Cl(g)$

Step 2. $Cl(g) + CHCl_3(g) \longrightarrow HCl(g) + CCl_3(g)$ Slow Step (Rate Determining)

Step 3. $Cl(g) + CCl_3(g) \longrightarrow CCl_4(g)$

27. Identify one or more species serving an an intermediate.

   A) $[Cl_2]$
   B) $[Cl]$
   C) $[CCl_3]$
   D) [Cl] and $[CCl_3]$

28. Given the following particulate diagram of the relative initial amounts of reactants, and the rate law,
    rate = k[CHCl$_3$][Cl$_2$]$^{1/2}$,
    identify the particulate diagram representing the initial conditions, which would have the fastest initial reaction.

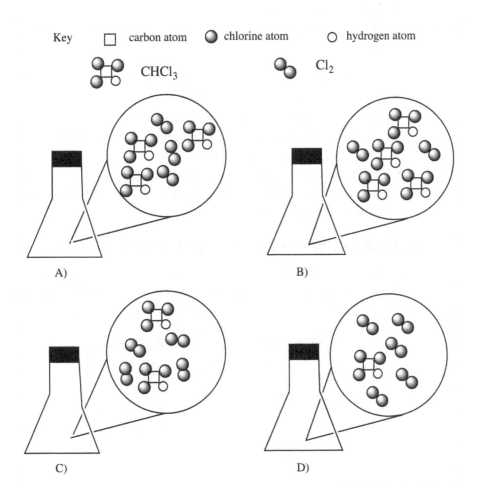

Questions 29 through 32 pertain to the following information.

Hydrogen peroxide solution decomposes to oxygen gas and water vapor. As the solution is observed to get warmer, the faster the decomposition occurs.

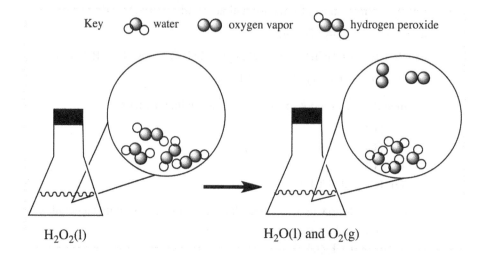

Key   water   oxygen vapor   hydrogen peroxide

$H_2O_2(l)$ $H_2O(l)$ and $O_2(g)$

29. What are the signs (+ or −) of ΔH, ΔS, and ΔG for this process?

  A) $\Delta H = +, \Delta S = +, \Delta G = +$
  B) $\Delta H = -, \Delta S = +, \Delta G = -$
  C) $\Delta H = -, \Delta S = -, \Delta G = +$
  D) $\Delta H = +, \Delta S = -, \Delta G = -$

30. How will the tendency of the decomposition of hydrogen peroxide to proceed or not proceed vary with temperature? The reaction is

  A) thermodynamically favored at all temperatures
  B) thermodynamically favored at high temperatures and thermodynamically unfavorable at low temperatures
  C) thermodynamically unfavorable at all temperatures
  D) thermodynamically unfavorable at high temperatures and thermodynamically favored at low temperatures

Use the following information to help answer Questions 31 and 32.

A student measured the volume of oxygen gas collected as 1.00 L of hydrogen peroxide decomposed, in the presence of a small amount of $KMnO_4$, as a function of time. The gas was collected at 25.00 °C and 1.00 atm of pressure.

Time, seconds	$O_2(g)$ collected, mL
0.00	0.00
45.0	2.00
90.0	4.00
135.0	6.00

31. Estimate the average rate of disappearance of hydrogen peroxide in units of M/s in the first 45 seconds.

    A) less than 1.0×10^{-6} M/s
    B) greater than 1.0×10^{-6} M/s but less than 1.0×10^{-5}
    C) greater than 1.0×10^{-5} M/s but less than 1.0×10^{-4}
    D) greater than 1.0×10^{-4} M/s but less than 1.0×10^{-3}

32. In a separate experiment, a student started with an initial concentration of 0.800 M hydrogen peroxide and determined the concentration to be 0.100 M after 54.0 minutes. Estimate the half-life for the first-order reaction in units of minutes.

    A) 6.8
    B) 14
    C) 18
    D) 28

33. The VSEPR model predicts the H-O-O bond angle in hydrogen peroxide to be

    A) greater than 60° but less than 90°
    B) less than 109.5° but greater than 90°
    C) greater than 109.5° but less than 110°
    D) less than 120° but greater than 110°

34. Using the table of average bond energies below, estimate the ΔH for the following reaction.

$$H-C\equiv C-H(g) + H-I(g) \longrightarrow \begin{matrix} H & & H \\ \diagdown & & \diagup \\ & C=C & \\ \diagup & & \diagdown \\ H & & I \end{matrix}$$

Bond	C≡C	C=C	H—I	C—I	C—H
D (kJ/mol)	839	614	299	240	413

    A) −931
    B) −506
    C) −129
    D) +129

35. A sample of gas in a 22.4 L flask has a density of 1.963 grams/L at 1.00 atm and 0.00 °C. Given the following gases, which could it be?

    A) Ne
    B) CO
    C) CO_2
    D) Kr

The diagram below represents a ratio of a mixture of gases at the molecule level in a small volume of gas in a sealed container. Oxygen molecules are represented by two joined open circles, helium atoms by grey spheres, and neon atoms by black spheres.

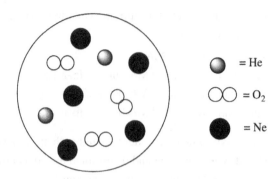

36. If the total pressure of the gases in the sealed container is 450.0 mm Hg, what is the partial pressure of neon?

    A) 45.0 mm Hg
    B) 90.0 mm Hg
    C) 135 mm Hg
    D) 225 mm Hg

37. What volume of HCl gas reacts completely with excess zinc metal to produce 2.46 L of H_2 gas at 2.00 atm and 400.0 K?

    A) 1.23 L
    B) 2.46 L
    C) 4.92 L
    D) 7.38 L

38. If 1.00 mole HBr and HF gases are allowed to effuse through a small hole under identical conditions of pressure and temperature how will the rate of effusion of HF gas compare to HBr gas?

    A) twice as fast
    B) twice as slow
    C) four times as fast
    D) four times as slow

39. Which covalent single bond is most polar?

Element	H	C	N	O
Electronegativity	2.1	2.5	3.0	3.5

    A) N—H
    B) O—H
    C) O—C
    D) O—N

40. Which of the following compounds is polar?

    A) $BeCl_2$
    B) CBr_4
    C) NF_3
    D) $AlCl_3$

41. Comparing the three bonds C—N, C=N, and C≡N, how does the C—N bond compare to the other two in terms of bond strength and bond length?

   A) strongest shortest
   B) strongest longest
   C) weakest shortest
   D) weakest longest

42. The total number of π bonds in the H—CH=CH—C≡C—C≡N molecule is

   A) 3   C) 5
   B) 4   D) 6

43. Which phrase best describes resonance forms of a molecule or ion?

   A) one always corresponds to the observed structure
   B) all the resonance structures are observed in various proportions
   C) the observed structure is an mean of the resonance forms
   D) the same atoms need not be bonded to each other in all resonance forms

44. Figure X represents an electron energy level diagram for the conduction bands and valence bands in a conductor such as copper. Which energy level diagrams represents the electron population when silicon is doped with gallium?

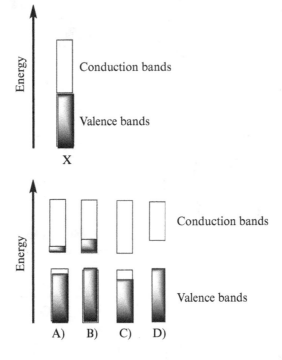

45. How many seconds are required to produce 8.00 g of aluminum metal (At. Wt. = 26.98) from the electrolysis of hot liquid $AlCl_3$ with an electrical current of 24.0 amps (A) using two electrodes?

   A) 27.0   C) 3570 s
   B) 1190 s   D) 96500 s

46. Which equation can be classified as an acid–base reaction?

    A) $HI(aq) + CsOH(aq) \rightarrow CsI(aq) + H_2O(l)$

    B) $Na_2S(aq) + 2\,AgNO_3(aq) \rightarrow 2\,NaNO_3(aq) + Ag2S(s)$

    C) $Ca(s) + 2\,H_2O(l) \rightarrow Ca(OH)_2(aq) + H_2(g)$

    D) $BCl_3(g) + 3\,H_2O(l) \rightarrow 3\,HCl(aq) + B(OH)_3(aq)$

47. Which particulate diagram below corresponds to the result of mixing aqueous calcium sulfide and aqueous sodium carbonate?

Solubility Rules:

Insoluble compounds contain . . .	Except . . .
Sulfide (S^{2-}) ions	those with alkali metal ions, Mg^{2+}, Ca^{2+}, Sr^{2+}, Ba^{2+} metal ions or NH_4^+
Carbonate (CO_3^{2}) ions	those with alkali metal ions or NH_4^+

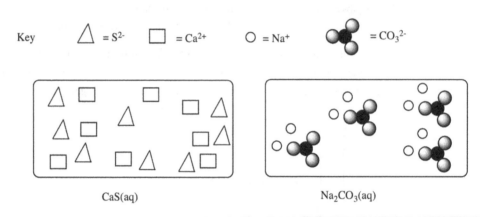

CaS(aq) Na_2CO_3(aq)

After mixing the two solutions

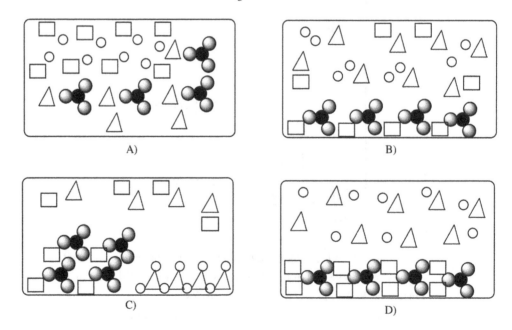

A)   B)

C)   D)

48. Which of the descriptions below correctly matches the structure type with its underlying explanation?

    A) molecular covalent: interconnected three-dimensional bonds
    B) network covalent: alternating lattice throughout solid
    C) ionic: individual molecular units within solid
    D) metal: delocalized electrons throughout solid

49. A small amount of table salt, NaCl(s), is stirred and completely dissolved in 50.0 mL water. What term best describes the resultant solution?

    A) homogeneous mixture   C) compound
    B) heterogeneous mixture   D) pure substance

Diagram (1) represents a 1.0 mL solution of particles at a given concentration. This solution is then diluted to 5.0 mL as represented in Diagram (2). 1.0 mL of this dilute solution was then transferred to each of other boxes.

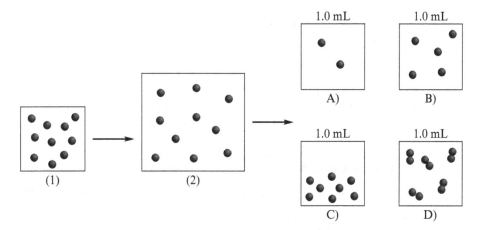

50. Which of the diagrams above represents a particle level representation of a 1.0 mL sample of the diluted solution?

    A) A   C) C
    B) B   D) D

Question 51. Hard water contains more minerals than soft water. Soft water generates foam more readily than hard water.

The diagram below shows the results of five test tubes, initially each containing different water samples, that had 5 drops of soap solution added and then shaken for 30 seconds. In the diagram the shaded area represents foam.

Test Tube Water Content	Tube
Tap water	1
Tap water + salt	2
Sea water	3
Tap water + sodium carbonate	4
Distilled water	5

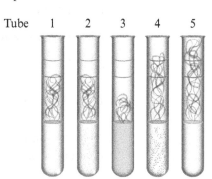

51. Which can be concluded from the results of this experiment?

    A) Sea water is softer than tap water.
    B) Sodium carbonate softens tap water.
    C) Salt softens tap water.
    D) Distilled water is harder than tap water.

Question 52–54 pertain to the following situation.

When 75.0 mL of 0.100 M $Na_2CO_3(aq)$ and 25.0 mL of 0.200 M $AgNO_3(aq)$ solutions are mixed together in a calorimeter, a white precipitate forms. The initial temperature of both solutions is 25.0 °C. The final temperature is 30.0 °C. Assume the final volume is 100.0 mL, the density of the solution is 1.08 g/mL, the reaction occurs under constant pressure, and the specific heat of the resultant solution is 4.18 J/g °C.

Solubility Rules:

Soluble Compounds contain . . .	except . . .
Alkali metals $(Li^+, Na^+, K^+, Rb^+, Cs^+)$ and NH_4^+	–
Nitrate (NO_3^-), acetate $(C_2H_3O_2^-)$	–
Halides (Cl^-, Br^-, I^-) ions	Halides of Ag^+, Hg_2^{2+}, Pb^{2+}
Sulfate (SO_4^{2-}) ions	Sulfates of $Ag^+, Ca^{2+}, Sr^{2+}, Ba^{2+}, Pb^{2+}$
Insoluble compounds contain . . .	**except . . .**
Carbonate (CO_3^{2-}), phosphate (PO_4^{3-}), sulfide (S^{2-}) ions	those with alkali metal ions or NH_4^+
Hydroxide (OH^-) ions	those with alkali metal ions or NH_4^+ or Ba^{2+}

52. Which of the following represents a complete and balanced equation for the reaction described above?

    $$\_\_Na_2CO_3(aq) + \_\_AgNO_3(aq) \longrightarrow _____ + _____$$

    Be sure to select the correct phases, i.e., (s), (l), (g), (aq), given for the products

    A) $Na_2CO_3(aq) + AgNO_3(aq) \longrightarrow Ag_2CO_3(s) + NaNO_3(aq)$
    B) $2\,Na_2CO_3(aq) + 2\,AgNO_3(aq) \longrightarrow 2\,AgCO_3(s) + 2\,Na_2NO_3(aq)$
    C) $Na_2CO_3(aq) + 2\,AgNO_3(aq) \longrightarrow Ag_2CO_3(aq) + 2\,NaNO_3(s)$
    D) $Na_2CO_3(aq) + 2\,AgNO_3(aq) \longrightarrow Ag_2CO_3(s) + 2\,NaNO_3(aq)$

53. What is the net **ionic equation** for the reaction that occurs?

    A) $Na^+(aq) + CO_3^{2-}(aq) + Ag^+(aq) + NO_3^-(aq) \longrightarrow Ag^+(s) + CO_3^{2-}(s) + Na^+(aq) + NO_3^-(aq)$

    B) $Na^+(aq) + CO_3^{2-}(aq) + 2Ag^+(aq) + 2NO_3^-(aq) \longrightarrow 2Ag^+(s) + CO_3^{2-}(s) + 2Na^+(aq) + 2NO_3^-(aq)$

    C) $CO_3^{2-}(aq) + 2Ag^+(aq) \longrightarrow Ag_2CO_3(s)$

    D) $CO_3^{2-}(aq) + Ag^+(aq) \longrightarrow AgCO_3(s)$

54. Which of the following statements is the most appropriate to determine the indicated quantity? In the following equations, q represents heat, n, represents number of moles, c represents the specific heat, and ΔT represents the change in temperature.

A) For ΔH, $\Delta H_{rxn} = q/n$ where Na_2CO_3 is the limiting reagent.
B) For ΔH_{rxn}, $\Delta H_{rxn} = q/n$ where q is determined by $q_{lost} + q_{gain} = 0$.
C) For q, $q = $ mass $\times$ c $\times$ ΔT, the mass can be determined by calculating the mass of the water and ignoring the mass of Na_2CO_3 and the mass of $AgNO_3$.
D) For q, $q = $ mass $\times$ c $\times$ ΔT, the mass can be determined by calculating the mass of Na_2CO_3 and mass of $AgNO_3$ and ignoring the mass of the water.

55. Given 0.10 M solutions of the acids listed in the table below, which acid has the lowest pH?

Acid	K_a
CH_3CHOOH	1.8×10^{-5}
HCOOH	1.8×10^{-4}
HClO	3.0×10^{-8}
HF	6.8×10^{-4}

A) CH_3CHOOH
B) HCOOH
C) HClO
D) HF

Question 56 pertains to the following information.

In an air bag, solid sodium azide, $NaN_3(s)$, decomposes to form sodium metal, $Na(s)$, and nitrogen gas, $N_2(g)$. The heat of reaction is -57 kJ/mol. A sensor that detects a crash sets off a small detonator to start the decomposition.

56. Which of the following best describes the reaction?

A) There is a large decrease in temperature so the bag gets cold.
B) There is a large increase in entropy in the reaction.
C) The reaction is non-spontaneous because it has to be started by a detonator.
D) The equilibrium constant value for this reaction must be close to 1.0.

The answers to Questions 57–60 depend upon the following information.

In a student lab, three colorless solutions were added in turn to four white powders. The student observations were recorded in the following table:

Powder	Dilute HCl	Pure Water	Dilute NH$_3$
A	none	none	none
B	bubbles, powder dissolves	none	none
C	dissolves	dissolves	dissolves
D	forms very cloudy white mixture	dissolves	forms cloudy brown mixture

Note: NONE means observed no change at all

Answer the following questions:

57. Powder A could be which of the following substances?

   A) sodium chloride
   B) calcium carbonate
   C) sugar
   D) barium sulfate

58. The reaction observed with powder B and dilute HCl could most likely be represented by which of the following equations?

   A) $CaCO_3 + 2HCl \longrightarrow Ca^{2+} + 2Cl^- + H_2O + CO_2$
   B) $NaCl + 2HCl \longrightarrow Na^+ + 3Cl^- + H_2$
   C) $2AgNO_3 + 4HCl \longrightarrow 2Ag^+ + 4Cl^- + 2O_2 + 2H_2O + N_2$
   D) $BaSO_4 + 2HCl \longrightarrow Ba^{2+} + 2Cl^- + H_2O + SO_3$

59. If two of the white powders are among the pairs listed below, which two are unable to be distinguished by the tests the student performed?

   A) sodium chloride, silver nitrate
   B) calcium carbonate, barium sulfate
   C) silver nitrate, barium sulfate
   D) sodium chloride, sugar

60. For the two powders that cannot be distinguished by the tests the student performed, which additional test could be done to help distinguish between the two powders?

   A) conductivity of aqueous solution
   B) boiling point of solution in dilute hydrochloric acid
   C) reaction when the two powders are mixed together in water
   D) spectrometry with visible light of aqueous solution

CHEMISTRY PRACTICE TEST B

7 Free-Response Questions   Section II

(Time–90 minutes)

You May Use Your Calculator, periodic table, and equation pages for Section II

Directions: Questions 1, 2, and 3 are long free-response questions that should take a student about 20 minutes each to answer. Questions 4, 5, 6, and 7 are short constructed-response questions that should take a student about seven minutes each to answer. You must show all of your work, the steps involved in arriving at your answer, follow the rules for working with significant figures, and include units when appropriate to receive full credit. Your responses to these questions will be scored on the basis of the accuracy and relevance of the information displayed.

1. ^{12}C and ^{13}C are the stable isotopes of carbon present in sufficient quantities to be readily detected. Hydrogen has three naturally occurring isotopes ^{1}H to ^{3}H. ^{3}H, known as tritium, is present in only trace amounts and is not easily detected. The following information about the mass and percent abundance of the naturally occurring stable isotopes of carbon and hydrogen are given in the table below.

Isotope	Mass (amu)	% Abundance	Isotope	Mass (amu)	% Abundance
^{12}C	12.0000	98.83	^{1}H	1.0078	99.99
^{13}C	13.0034	1.070	^{2}H	2.0141	0.0100

  a) Calculate the atomic weight (in units of amu) of carbon.

  b) Sketch a diagram for a mass spectrum of carbon.

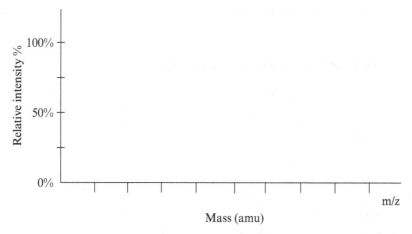

The chemical formula for acetylene (or ethyne –IUPAC nomenclature) is C_2H_2. The Lewis diagram for acetylene is

$$H-C\equiv C-H$$

c) How many **different stable isotopes** of the acetylene (ethyne) molecule (C_2H_2) exist? How many **stable isotopes** of the acetylene (ethyne) molecule (C_2H_2) have identical masses? Justify your answer and include either a diagram or a written explanation.

d) Which stable isotopes of acetylene are the **least abundant** and the **most abundant** in nature? Explain.

e) An abbreviated diagram of a mass spectrum for the isotopes of acetylene is given below. Most likely, which isotope of acetylene is the highest peak $(m/z = 26)$ due to?

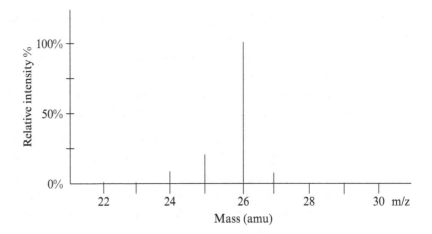

2. Two students performed an acid–base titration experiment in order to determine the concentration solution of NaOH(aq) using oxalic acid as a primary standard. The students followed most of the proper procedures for doing a titration.

Each student went to a balance and obtained a known mass of solid oxalic acid. The students recorded their mass of oxalic acid in their notebooks, placed the oxalic acid in water and proceeded to titrate the sodium hydroxide solution. Both student placed their data on the board and did their calculations.

Data–Titration of NaOH (aq) with Oxalic Acid, $H_2C_2O_4$

	Student A	Student B	Additional Trial (if needed)
Mass of solid oxalic acid	0.982 g	0.764 g	0.853 g
Final buret reading NaOH(aq)	28.35 mL	23.13 mL	
Initial buret reading NaOH(aq)	0.35 mL	1.34 mL	
Volume of NaOH solution used in the titration	28.00 mL	21.79 mL	

Each student calculated the molarity of the sodium hydroxide solution as 0.779 M and decided they did not need to do a second trial since their results were the same. When they reported their molarity to the instructor, the instructor informed the students the data on the board was correct, but their molarity was wrong.

   a) Write a balanced chemical equation for the reaction of oxalic acid with sodium hydroxide.

   b) The students used 90.0 g/mol as the molar mass of oxalic acid. Use this value to determine how the students calculated the number of moles of oxalic acid present that were completely neutralized by the base.

   c) Show how the students calculated their molarity of the sodium hydroxide.

   d) The instructor reminded the students to carefully read the label on the reagent bottle of oxalic acid and to record the important Material Safety Data Sheet (MSDS) information for oxalic acid in their notebook. If the true value of the molarity of the sodium hydroxide solution is 0.557 M. What error did the students make? What two things should the students do to improve their experiment?

Material Safety Data Sheet (MSDS)	
MSDS Name	Oxalic acid, dihydrate, reagent ACS
Catalog Numbers:	AC423150000, AC423150010
Synonyms:	Ethanedioic acid dihydrate
For information in North America, call:	800-XXXX-01
For emergencies in the US call:	800-YYYY-02

Section 2—Composition, Information on Ingredients

CAS#	Chemical Name	Percent
144-62-7	Oxalic acid, anhydrous	0.5
6153-56-6	Oxalic acid dihydrate	99.5

   e) The instructor asked the students to do an additional titration using their 0.853 g sample of oxalic acid. What volume of sodium hydroxide should the students expect to use in the titration?

3. A student is given the task of determining the identity of four unknown 1.0 M solutions each made with a salt. The solutions are labeled W through Z. The salts in no particular order are

NaCl   NaHCOO $NaCH_3COO$ NH_4Cl

The following table of acid and based dissociation constants is available.

Formula	Acid or base dissociation constants at 25 °C
CH_3COOH	$K_a = 1.8 \times 10^{-5}$
HCOOH	$K_a = 1.8 \times 10^{-4}$
HCl	$K_a = $ very large
NH_3	$K_b = 1.8 \times 10^{-5}$

Formula	Acid or base dissociation constants at 25 °C
NaOH	K_b = very large
H_2O	$K_w = 1.008 \times 10^{-14}$ at 25 °C $K_w = 0.681 \times 10^{-14}$ at 20 °C

Upon entering the lab room, the student put on safety goggles, went to the lab bench, standardized the pH meter using a pH = 7 buffer, used a graduate cylinder to measure 30.0 mL samples of each unknown salt solution, and measured the pH of each salt solution. The student recorded the following information in a lab notebook.

Unknown solution	Measured pH	Identity
W	5.96	
X	7.16	
Y	8.60	
Z	6.86	

a) Identify the salt used to make solutions W and Y and place your answer in the table above.

b) For solutions W and Y, write a balanced chemical equation showing what occurs when the salt interacts with water and establishes an equilibrium, and has a pH.

Salt W

Salt Y

c) For solutions W and Y, calculate the pH expected for the solution.

Solution W

Solution Y

d) Solutions X and Z, are hard to distinguish by pH alone, since the pH of both solution are close. Describe what additional tests can be done to help identify the salts used to make solutions X and Z. Explain.

e) Discuss one ways the student could have improved the procedure in order to obtain more accurate results.

f) Explain how each of the following could lead to an error in the measurement or the calculation of pH. Explain if the measurement or calculation would be higher, lower, or no change.

  i) The deionized water used to make all of the solutions was prepared one week prior to doing the experiment. The bottle was left on a shelf exposed to sunlight and the cap to the bottle of the deionized water was not used, exposing the water to carbon dioxide in the air.

  ii) The student uses the following chemical equation for the sodium acetate solution to determine the concentration of H_3O^+ ions in solution and uses this value to calculate pH.

$$CH_3COO^-(aq) + H_2O(l) \rightleftharpoons CH_2COO^{2-}(aq) + H_3O^+(aq)$$

4. A simulated photoelectron spectrum of an element in the ground state is represented below.

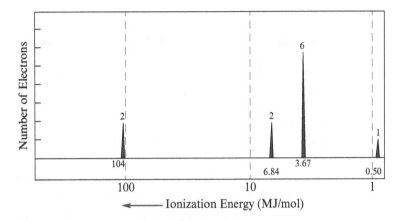

a) Based on the spectrum
   i) write the ground-state electron configuration of the element.
   ii) identify the element.
b) Calculate the wavelength, in units of nm, of electromagnetic radiation needed to remove an electron from the valence shell of an atom of the element.

5. When oxygen gains two electrons it forms the oxide ion, O^{2-}. When sulfur gains two electrons it forms the sulfide ion, S^{2-}. The electron affinity values for an atom of oxygen gas and an atom of sulfur gas are listed below.

Group 16
O
-141 kJ/mol
S
-200 kJ/mol

a) Write the equation representing the electron affinity process for an oxygen atom in the gas phase. Is this process exothermic or endothermic? Explain.
b) ΔH for the second electron affinity to go from O^- to O^{2-} is endothermic. Explain incorporating how Coulombic interactions and or electron configuration play a role in this process.

6. Nitrogen and oxygen can combine to form nitrogen dioxide, NO_2, the nitronium ion, NO_2^+, or the nitrite ion, NO_2^-.

For each of the following:
a) Draw a Lewis structure and include any resonance structures when appropriate.
b) Name the molecular geometry, and arrange in order of increasing bond angle the O—N—O bond angle about the central nitrogen atom for each species. Justify your choice of bond angle.
   i) NO_2
   ii) NO_2^+
   iii) NO_2^-

7. The change in entropy of vaporization, ΔS_{vap}, of a compound can be calculated knowing the boiling point and the change in enthalpy of vaporization of that compound.

Compound	Name	BP (°C)	ΔH_{vap} (kJ/mol)	ΔS_{vap} (J/mol K)
$C_4H_{10}O$	Diethly ether	34.6	26.5	86.1
C_2H_6O	Acetone	56.1	29.1	88.4
C_6H_6	Benzene	79.8	30.8	87.3
C_2H_5OH	Ethanol	77.8	38.6	?
H_2O	Water	100.0	40.7	?

a) Calculate the values of ΔS_{vap} for ethanol and water. Compare the calculated values for ethanol and water with the other compounds. Do ethanol and water have ΔS_{vap} values larger or smaller compared to the ΔS_{vap} values of the first three compounds?

b) Are the results of your calculation consistent with what you expect taking into account intermolecular forces and the energy involved in the vaporization process? Explain why or why not.

CHEMISTRY PRACTICE TEST B

Section I Answer Key

60 Multiple-Choice Questions (Time–90 minutes)

Question	Key	—	Question	Key	—	Question	Key	
1	D		21	C		41	D	
2	C		22	B		42	C	
3	A		23	D		43	C	
4	A		24	C		44	C	
5	A		25	B		45	C	
6	B		26	A		46	A	
7	C		27	D		47	B	
8	C		28	B		48	D	
9	D		29	B		49	A	
10	A		30	A		50	A	
11	B		31	B		51	B	
12	B		32	C		52	D	
13	D		33	B		53	C	
14	C		34	C		54	B	
15	B		35	C		55	D	
16	C		36	D		56	B	
17	B		37	C		57	D	
18	B		38	A		58	A	
19	B		39	B		59	D	
20	D		40	C		60	A	

CHEMISTRY PRACTICE TEST B

Section II Answer Key

7 Free-Response Questions (Time–105 minutes)

You May Use Your Calculator for Section II

Directions: Questions 1, 2, and 3 are long free response questions that should take a student about 20 minutes each to answer. Questions 4, 5, 6, and 7 are short constructed-response questions that should take a student about seven minutes each to answer. You must show all of your work, the steps involved in arriving at your answer, follow the rules for working with significant figures, and include units when appropriate to receive full credit. Your responses to these questions will be scored on the basis of the accuracy and relevance of the information displayed.

1. Carbon has fifteen known isotopes, from ^8C to ^{15}C. ^{12}C and ^{13}C are the only stable isotopes present in sufficient quantities to be readily detected. Hydrogen has three naturally occurring isotopes ^1H to ^3H. ^3H, known as tritium, is present in only trace amounts and is not easily detected. The following information about the mass and percent abundance of the naturally occurring stable isotopes of carbon and hydrogen are given in the table below.

Isotope	Mass (amu)	% Abundance	Isotope	Mass (amu)	% Abundance
^{12}C	12.0000	98.83	^1H	1.0078	99.99
^{13}C	13.0034	1.070	^2H	2.0141	0.0100

(2 points)   a) Calculate the atomic weight (in units of amu) of carbon.

12.00 amu (four significant figures)

(2 points)   b) Sketch a diagram for a mass spectrum of carbon.

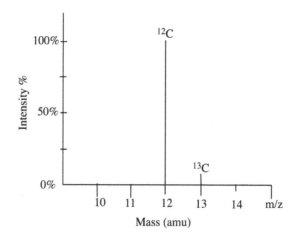

The chemical formula for acetylene (or ethyne –IUPAC nomenclature) is C_2H_2. The Lewis diagram for acetylene is

$$H-C\equiv C-H$$

c) How many **different stable isotopes** of the acetylene (ethyne) molecule   (2 points)
(C_2H_2) exist? How many **stable isotopes** of the acetylene (ethyne) molecule (C_2H_2) have identical masses? Justify your answer and include either a diagram or a written explanation.

10 possible isotopes. For convenience the mass # are indicated leaving out element symbols.

1-12-12-1 26	1-12-13-1 27	1-13-13-1 28
1-12-12-2 27	1-12-13-2 28	1-13-13-2 29
2-12-12-2 28	2-12-13-1 28	2-13-13-2 30
	2-12-13-2 29	

Four isotopes have a mass of 28, two have a mass of 27, two have a mass of 29.

d) Which stable isotopes of acetylene are the **least abundant** and the **most abundant** in nature? Explain.   (2 points)

$^1H—^{12}C≡^{12}C—^1H$ most abundant due to 98.8% carbon-12 and 99.9% hydrogen-1

$^2H—^{13}C≡^{13}C—^2H$ least abundant due to only 1% carbon-13 and 0.1% hydrogen-2

e) An abbreviated diagram of a mass spectrum for the isotopes of acetylene is given below. Most likely, which isotope of acetylene is the highest peak $(m/z = 26)$ due to?   (2 points)

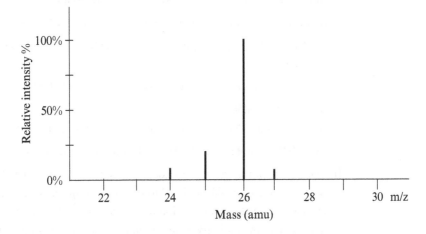

$^1H—^{12}C≡^{12}C—^1H$ mass $= 26$ and it is the most abundant

2. Two students performed an acid–base titration experiment in order to determine the concentration solution of $NaOH(aq)$ using oxalic acid as a primary standard. The students followed most of the proper procedures for doing a titration.

Each student went to a balance and obtained a known mass of solid oxalic acid. The students recorded their mass of oxalic acid in their notebooks, placed the oxalic acid in water, and proceeded to titrate the sodium hydroxide solution. Both student placed their data on the board and did their calculations.

Data–Titration of NaOH(aq) with Oxalic Acid, $H_2C_2O_4$

	Student A	Student B	Additional Trial (if needed)
Mass of solid oxalic acid	0.982 g	0.764 g	0.853 g
Final buret reading NaOH(aq)	28.35 mL	23.13 mL	
Initial buret reading NaOH(aq)	0.35 mL	1.34 mL	
Volume of NaOH solution used in the titration	28.00 mL	21.79 mL	

Each student calculated the molarity of the sodium hydroxide solution as 0.779 M and decided they did not need to do a second trial since their results were the same. When they reported their molarity to the instructor, the instructor informed the students the data on the board was correct, but their molarity was wrong.

(2 points)   a) Write a completed balanced molecular chemical equation for the reaction of oxalic acid with sodium hydroxide.

$$H_2C_2O_4 + 2NaOH \longrightarrow Na_2C_2O_4 + 2\,H_2O$$

(2 points)   b) The students used 90.0 g/mol as the molar mass of oxalic acid. Use this value to determine how the students calculated the number of moles of oxalic acid present that were completely neutralized by the base.

Student A 0.982 g $(1\ mole\ /\ 90.0\ g) = 0.0109$ mole
Student B 0.764 g $(1\ mole\ /\ 90.0\ g) = 0.00849$ mole

(2 points)   c) Show how the students calculated their molarity of the sodium hydroxide.

Student A 0.0109 mole acid $\times$ $(2\ mole\ NaOH\ /\ 1\ mole\ acid) = 0.0218$ mol NaOH

$M = 0.0218\ mol\ NaOH/0.02800\ L\ solution = 0.779\ M$

Student B 0.00850 mole
acid $\times$ $(2\ mole\ NaOH\ /\ 1\ mole\ acid) = 0.0170$ mol NaOH

$M = 0.0170\ mol\ NaOH\ /\ 0.02179\ L\ solution = 0.780\ M$

(2 points)   d) The instructor reminded the students to carefully read the label on the reagent bottle of oxalic acid and to record the important Material Safety Data Sheet (MSDS) information for oxalic acid in their notebook. If the true value of the molarity of the sodium hydroxide solution is 0.557 M, what error did the students make? What two things should the students do to improve their experiment?

Material Safety Data Sheet (MSDS)	
MSDS Name	Oxalic acid, dihydrate, reagent ACS
Catalog Numbers:	AC423150000, AC423150010
Synonyms:	Ethanedioic acid dihydrate
For information in North America, call:	800-XXXX-01
For emergencies in the US call:	800-YYYY-02

Section 2—Composition, Information on Ingredients

CAS#	Chemical Name	Percent
144-62-7	Oxalic acid, anhydrous	0.5
6153-56-6	Oxalic acid dihydrate	99.5

The students did not take into account the solid acid was a "dihydrate" and contained water. The students used an incorrect molar mass for the oxalic acid. To improve the experiment the students should use the correct molar mass and do three additional titrations.

e) The instructor asked the students to do an additional titration using their 0.853 g sample of oxalic acid. What volume of sodium hydroxide should the students expect to use in the titration?   (2 points)

23.40 mL

3. A student is given the task of determining the identity of four unknown 1.0 M solutions each made with a salt. The solutions are labeled W through Z. The salts in no particular order are

NaCl   NaHCOO   NaCH$_3$COO   NH$_4$Cl

The following solid salts and solutions are available.

pH = 4 buffer solution   pH = 7 buffer solution   pH = 9 buffer solution

1.0 M CH$_3$COOH(aq) 1.0 M HCOOH   1.0 M NH$_3$

1.0 M HCl   1.0 M NaOH   KCH$_3$COO(s)

NH$_4$I(s) KCl(s) KHCOO(s)

The following table of acid and based dissociation constants is available.

Formula	Acid or base dissociation constants at 25 °C
CH$_3$COOH	$K_a = 1.8 \times 10^{-5}$
HCOOH	$K_a = 1.8 \times 10^{-4}$
HCl	K_a = very large
NH$_3$	$K_b = 1.8 \times 10^{-5}$
NaOH	K_b = very large
H$_2$O	$K_w = 1.008 \times 10^{-14}$ at 25 °C $K_w = 0.681 \times 10^{-14}$ at 20 °C

Upon entering the lab room, the student put on safety goggles, went to the lab bench, standardized the pH meter using a pH = 7 buffer, used a graduate cylinder to measure 30.0 mL samples of each unknown salt solution, and measured the pH of each salt solution. The student recorded the following information in a lab notebook.

Unknown solution	Measured pH	Identity
W	5.96	NH_4Cl
X	7.16	NaCl
Y	8.60	CH_3COONa
Z	6.86	HCOONa

(2 points)

a) Identify the salt used to make solutions W and Y and place your answer in the table above.

W is acidic, which corresponds to $NH_4Cl(aq)$

Y is basic which corresponds to $CH_3COONa(aq)$ (see equations below)

(2 points)

b) For solutions W and Y, write a balanced chemical equation showing what occurs when the salt interacts with water, establishes equilibrium, and has a pH.

Salt W $NH_4^+ (aq) + H_2O(l) \rightleftharpoons NH_3(aq) + H_3O^+ (aq)$

Salt Y $CH_3COO^- (aq) + H_2O(l) \rightleftharpoons CH_3COOH(aq) + OH^- (aq)$

(2 points)

c) For solutions W and Y, calculate the pH expected for the solution. Please tell the students if you are using the 1.0 M cited at the top of the page, or the 0.1 M listed in the materials.

Solution W pH = 4.63

Solution Y pH = 9.37

(1 point)

d) Solutions X and Z, are hard to distinguish by pH alone. Describe what additional tests can be done to help identify the salts used to make solutions X and Z. Explain.

To 20 drops of each solution add 10 drops of 1.0 M HCOOH. The resultant solution with the HCOONa will produce a buffer and the pH will not change when some HCl is added to it. The NaCl solution with 1.0 M HCOOH will not form a buffer and the pH will change when HCl is added to this solution.

(1 point)

e) Discuss one ways the student could have improved the procedure in order to obtain more accurate results.

Test the solutions with a second calibrated pH meter, this time using a pH = 5 buffer for acidic solutions and a pH = 9 buffer for alkaline solutions.

Boil the deionized water used to make the solutions to expel carbon dioxide. Carbon dioxide dissolved in water will lower the pH.

f) Explain how each of the following could lead to an error in the measurement or the calculation of pH. Explain if the measurement or calculation would be higher, lower, or no change.

   i) The deionized water used to make all of the solutions was prepared one week prior to doing the experiment. The bottle was left on a shelf exposed to sunlight and the cap to the bottle of the deionized water was not used, exposing the water to carbon dioxide in the air.   (1 point)

   The deionized water will have a lower pH than expected due to dissolved carbon dioxide reacting with a bit of the water to give carbonic acid. If the solution is warmer than 25 °C, all of the pH measurements will be higher compared to the calculated pH because the K_w is more than 1.0×10^{-14} at temperatures higher than 25 °C.

   ii) The student uses the following chemical equation for the sodium acetate solution to determine the concentration of H_3O^+ ions in solution and uses this value to calculate pH.   (1 point)

$$CH_3COO^-\,(aq) + H_2O(l) \rightleftharpoons CH_2COO^{2-}\,(aq) + H_3O^+\,(aq)$$

The student will calculate an acidic pH when the solution is alkaline.

4. a) i. $1s^2 2s^2 2p^6 3s^1$ ii. Sodium   (2 points)

   b) 480 nm   (2 points)

5. When oxygen gains two electrons it forms the oxide ion, O^{2-}. When sulfur gains two electrons it forms the sulfide ion, S^{2-}. The electron affinity values for an atom of oxygen gas and an atom of sulfur gas are listed below.

Group 16
O
−141 kJ/mol
S
−200 kJ/mol

a) Write the equation representing the electron affinity process for an oxygen atom in the gas phase. Is this process exothermic or endothermic? Explain.   (2 points)

$O + e^- \longrightarrow O^- \; E_A = -141$ kJ/mol. The E_A process is exothermic since it involves adding an electron.

b) ΔH for the second electron affinity to go from O^- to O^{2-} is endothermic. Explain how incorporating Coulombic interaction and/or electron configuration play a role in this process.   (2 points)

Since the ratio of electrons to protons is already greater than one (9:8) in an O^- anion, adding another electron requires an input of energy to overcome the electron-electron repulsion forces.

6. Nitrogen and oxygen can combine to form nitrogen dioxide, NO_2, the nitronium ion NO_2^+ or the nitrite ion NO_2^-.

For each of the following:

(2 points)
    a) Draw a Lewis structure and include any resonance structures when appropriate.

(2 points)
    b) Name the molecular geometry, and arrange in order of increasing O—N—O bond angle about the central nitrogen atom for each species. Justify your choice of bond angle.

       i) NO_2

       ii) NO_2^+

       iii) NO_2^-

NO_2^+ has two regions of electron density around the central atom. It is an AX_2E_0 system. The bond angle is 180°. Adding one electron to achieve the NO_2 molecule adds one electron to the nitrogen atom. There are three regions of electron density around the nitrogen atom, however, the one electron is not strong enough to repel the electron in the bond so the bond angle is about 134°. Adding another electron to achieve the NO_2^- ion, creates three full regions of electron density around the nitrogen atom. The nitrite ion has a bond angle of 115°. Note, students can arrange the structures in order of increasing bond angle or students can estimate the bond angles: for NO_2 they might say "less than 180, but more than 120" or for nitrite "less than 120, but more than 90."

7. The change in entropy of vaporization, ΔS_{vap}, of a compound is the increase in entropy upon vaporization of a liquid. The value of ΔS_{vap} of a compound can be calculated from the boiling point and the change in enthalpy of vaporization of the compound.

Compound	Name	BP (°C)	ΔH_{vap} (kJ/mol)	ΔS_{vap} (J/mol K)
$C_4H_{10}O$	Diethly ether	34.6	26.5	86.1
C_2H_6O	Acetone	56.1	29.1	88.4
C_6H_6	Benzene	79.8	30.8	87.3
C_2H_5OH	Ethanol	77.8	38.6	110
H_2O	Water	100.0	40.7	109

a) Calculate the values of ΔS_{vap} for ethanol and water. Compare the calcu-   (2 points)
lated values for ethanol and water with the other compounds. Do ethanol
and water have ΔS_{vap} values larger or smaller compared to the ΔS_{vap}
values of the first three compounds?

ΔS_{vap} for ethanol $=$ 110 J/mol K ΔS_{vap} for water $=$ 110 J/mol K

Ethanol and water have ΔS_{vap} larger compared to the other compounds
listed on the Table.

b) Are the results of your calculation consistent with what you expect   (2 points)
taking into account intermolecular forces and the energy involved in
the vaporization process? Explain why or why not.

The ΔS_{vap} of ethanol and water are larger compared to the other compounds because hydrogen bonding in the liquid phase decreases the
entropy in the liquid. Strong hydrogen bonding causes the molecules to
"stick" together, therefore, there is less movement of molecules. When
the molecules in the liquid have enough energy to escape as a gas, the
gas particles are far enough away where hydrogen bonding does not occur
as frequently. Furthermore, the gas particles are moving much faster,
therefore there is a good deal more entropy. Thus the change in entropy
from the liquid phase to the gas phase is large. The results are consistent
with the calculations.

How to Calculate your score after Test B

To determine your score:

MC number correct _____ $\times$ 0.8333 $=$ _____

FR Q. 1 Number of points_____ $\times$ 1.0869 $=$ _____

FR Q. 2 Number of points_____ $\times$ 1.0869 $=$ _____

FR Q. 3 Number of points_____ $\times$ 1.0869 $=$ _____

FR Q. 4 Number of points_____ $\times$ 1.0869 $=$ _____

FR Q. 5 Number of points_____ $\times$ 1.0869 $=$ _____

FR Q. 6 Number of points_____ $\times$ 1.0869 $=$ _____

FR Q. 7 Number of points_____ $\times$ 1.0869 $=$ _____

TOTAL POINTS $=$ _____

Approximate AP Score:

80–100 $=$ 5

70–79 $=$ 4

55–69 $=$ 3

35–54 $=$ 2

0–34 $=$ 1

CREDITS

Cover "Motorized Molecules Drill Through Cells" Rice University News and Media, August 30, 2017.

Chapter 01 Page 003: Lavoisier, Antoine. Elementary Treatise of Chemistry. Trans. Robert Kerr. Paris: Chez Cuchet, 1789. Reprinted Bruxelles: Cultures et Civilisations, 1965. Print. Page 003: Oneo/Fotolia. Page 006: Al Messerschmidt/WireImage/Getty Images. Page 006: DenisLarkin/Getty Images. Page 006: YinYang/iStock/Getty Images. Page 006: Sezeryadigar/Getty Images. Page 009: Charles D. Winters/Science Source. Page 009: Clark Brennan/Alamy. Page 009: Renn Valo.

Chapter 02 Page 027: Richard Megna/Fundamental Photographs. Page 029: Edward Neville da Costa Andrade/Peter Smith Pub Inc. Page 031: Charles D. Winters/Science Source. Page 031: Charles D. Winters/Science Source. Page 031: Clive Streeter/Getty Images. Page 037: Lead Air Quality, 1990–2014 from National Trends in Lead Levels. Published by United States Environmental Protection Agency. Page 037: From Environmental Health Perspectives, Vol. 118, Issue 8, pp. 1195–1201, 2009 and Air Quality Criteria for Lead. I., U.S. EPA, 1986.

Chapter 03 Page 048: Richard Megna/Fundamental Photographs. Page 048: Charles Falco/Science. Page 048: Charles D. Winters/Science Source. Page 054: Richard Megna/Fundamental Photographs. Page 054: Richard Megna/Fundamental Photographs.

Chapter 05 Page 96: Clive Streeter/Getty Images.

Chapter 06 Page 128: Propene Mass Spectrum from National Institute of Standards and Technology. Published by U.S. Secretary of Commerce.

Chapter 08 Page 160: Poznyakov/Shutterstock. Page 160: Sierra Pacific Innovations Corporation. Page 162: Richard Megna/Fundamental Photographs. Page 162: Wabash Instrument Corp./Fundamental Photographs. Page 171: Fig 1, Ion Time-of-flight Mass/charge Spectra of Xenon Taken at a Photon Energy of 93 eV (93 eV/photon) and Different Pulse Irradiance Levels from Photoelectric Effect at Ultra-high Intensities by A. A. Sorokin, S.V. Bobashev, T. Feigl, K.Tiedtke, H. Wabnitz and M. Ritcher. Copyright © 2007 by American Physical Society.

Chapter 09 Page 191: Charles D. Winters/Science Source. Page 191: Charles D. Winters/Science Source. Page 191: Charles D. Winters/Science Source. Page 191: Dennis S.K. Collection. Page 191: Dorling Kindersley/Getty Images. Page 191: Enricoros. Page 191: Harry Taylor/Getty Images. Page 191: Jumk. de Webprojects. Page 191: Manamana/Shutterstock. Page 191: PjrStudio/Alamy Stock Photo. Page 191: Richard Megna/Fundamental Photographs. Page 191: Ted Kinsman/Science Source.

Chapter 10 Page 210: Richard Megna/Fundamental Photographs. Page 210: Richard Megna/Fundamental Photographs.

Chapter 11 Page 244: Kip Peticolas/Fundamental Photographs. Page 255: Figure 2: Photochromism of Azobenzene Derivatives and Energetic Profile for the Switching Process from Recent Advances Towards Azobenzene-based Lightdriven Real-time Information-transmitting Materials by Jaume Garcia-Amoros and Dolores Velasco. Copyright 2012 by Jaume Garcia-Amoros and Dolores Velasco.

Chapter 12 Page 273: Andrei Kuzmik/Shutterstock. Page 274: Richard Megna/Fundamental Photographs. Page 275: Maridav/Fotolia. Page 278: Reika/Shutterstock. Page 280: krutar/Shutterstock. Page 280: taffpixture/Shutterstock. Page 280: Can Balcioglu/Shutterstock.

Chapter 13 Page 296: Omikron/Science Source. Page 298: Yurakp/Fotolia. Page 298: Andrew Syred/Science Source. Page 298: Mirka Moksha/Shutterstock. Page 298: Showcake/Fotolia. Page 298: yurakp/Fotolia. Page 299: Dorling Kindersley, Ltd.

Chapter 14 Page 320: Richard Megna/Fundamental Photographs. Page 320: Richard Megna/Fundamental Photographs. Page 320: Richard Megna/Fundamental Photographs. Page 322: Spencer Hopkins/iStock/Getty Images. Page 322: Eric Gevaert/Shutterstock. Page 322: Nanjan/iStock/Getty Images. Page 322: CostinT/iStock/Getty Images. Page 322-B Alicat/Getty Images. Page 322: Kip Peticolas/Fundamental Photographs.

Chapter 16 Page 384: Richard Megna/Fundamental Photographs. Page 384: Richard Megna/Fundamental Photographs.

Chapter 17 Page 426: Hydrogen ion Concentration as pH from Measurements made at the Central Analytical Laboratory, 205, National Atmospheric Deposition Program, National Trends Network, Retrieved from http://nadp.slh.wisc.edu/maplib/pdf/2015/pH_2015.pdf.

Chapter 18 Page 430: Richard Megna/Fundamental Photographs. Page 430: Richard Megna/Fundamental Photographs. Page 430: Richard Megna/Fundamental Photographs. Page 434: Richard Megna/Fundamental Photographs. Page 434: Richard Megna/Fundamental Photographs. Page 434: Richard Megna/Fundamental Photographs. Page 443: Jerry Mason/Science Source. Page 443: Jerry Mason/Science Source. Page 443: Richard Megna/Fundamental Photographs. Page 443: Richard Megna/Fundamental Photographs.

Chapter 19 Page 462: Arthur S. Aubry/Getty Images. Page 462: Zurijeta/Shutterstock. Page 462: Getty Images. Page 462: Martin Green/Fotolia. Page 462: A.G.Siemens. Page 462: Scott T. Baxter/Getty Images. Page 482: Richard Megna/Fundamental Photographs. Page 464: Pulse/Getty Images. Page 465: paradoxdes/Fotolia. Page 465: Richard Megna/Fundamental Photographs.

Chapter 20 Page 489: Richard Megna/Fundamental Photographs. Page 489: Richard Megna/Fundamental Photographs. Page 496: Richard Megna/Fundamental Photographs. Page 519: Dorling Kindersley, Ltd.

Chapter 23 Page 575: Pearson Education, Inc. Page 575: David Murray/Dorling Kindersley, Ltd.

Chapter 24 Page 582: Dorling Kindersley, Ltd.

Chapter 26 Page 617: Dorling Kindersley Ltd. Page 617: Dorling Kindersley Limited. Page 617: Harry Taylor/Dorling Kindersley Ltd. Page 617: Harry Taylor/Dorling Kindersley Ltd. Page 617: Asya Babushkina/Shutterstock.